Universitext

Universitext

Universitext is a series of textbooks that presents material from a wide variety of mathematical disciplines at master's level and beyond. The books, often well class-tested by their author, may have an informal, personal, even experimental approach to their subject matter. Some of the most successful and established books in the series have evolved through several editions, always following the evolution of teaching curricula, into very polished texts.

Thus as research topics trickle down into graduate-level teaching, first textbooks written for new, cutting-edge courses may make their way into *Universitext*.

For further volumes:
www.springer.com/series/223

Françoise Demengel · Gilbert Demengel

Functional Spaces for the Theory of Elliptic Partial Differential Equations

Translated by Reinie Erné

 Springer

Françoise Demengel
Département de Mathématiques
Université de Cergy-Pontoise
Cergy-Pontoise Cedex, France

Gilbert Demengel
Paris Cedex 13, France

Translator
Reinie Erné
Leiden, The Netherlands

Translation from the French language edition:
Espaces fonctionnels: Utilisation dans la résolution des équations aux dérivées partielles
by Françoise Demengel & Gilbert Demengel
EDP Sciences ISBN 978-2-7598-0698-0
Copyright © 2007 EDP Sciences, CNRS Editions, France.
http://www.edpsciences.org/
http://www.cnrseditions.fr/
All Rights Reserved

ISSN 0172-5939   e-ISSN 2191-6675
Universitext
ISBN 978-1-4471-2806-9   e-ISBN 978-1-4471-2807-6
DOI 10.1007/978-1-4471-2807-6
Springer London Dordrecht Heidelberg New York

British Library Cataloguing in Publication Data
A catalogue record for this book is available from the British Library

Library of Congress Control Number: 2012931004

Mathematics Subject Classification: 35J05, 35J15, 35J25, 35J40, 35J55, 35J70, 42A85, 42C05, 46F05, 46F10, 46E27, 46E30, 46E35, 49R50

Printed on acid-free paper

Springer is part of Springer Science+Business Media (www.springer.com)

Preface

The aim of this work is to present a tool for students interested in partial differential equations, both those working toward a Master's degree in pure or applied mathematics and those with PhD research in this field. It gathers results from functional analysis that make it easier to understand the nature and properties of the functions occurring in these equations, as well as the constraints they must obey to qualify as solutions. We present modern resolution methods for a class of such problems and interpret the solutions we obtain by studying their regularity.

Let us recall that the domain in which we study a partial differential equation is an open subset Ω of $\mathbb{R}^N$. The equation is a relation that an unknown function u and its partial derivatives (cf. the preliminary chapter) must satisfy. Moreover, we impose certain conditions on the function u and possibly on some of its derivatives (see the Dirichlet and Neumann problems in the preliminary chapter), namely that they equal given functions on the boundary $\partial \Omega$ of the open set under consideration. These relations are called *boundary conditions*.

Looking for such a function is the aim of a so-called *boundary problem*. We find many examples of these in physics.

If we consider the derivatives in the usual sense in the interior of the open set, classical analysis proves to be ineffective for solving such problems, as can be illustrated with examples. Indeed, the *solutions* obtained in these examples sometimes do not belong to the spaces of differentiable functions in the classical sense because of their *irregularity*. Moreover, we can find examples in physics where the right-hand side f of the given equation has discontinuities.

Let us consider the simple example in $\mathbb{R}$ of the differential equation

$$y'' + y' + y = f,$$

where f is discontinuous at the point $t = 0$. Any solution cannot be $\mathcal{C}^2$ on $\mathbb{R}$. We can, however, look for a solution of class $\mathcal{C}^1$ with derivative y'' almost everywhere, or such that y'' is a derivative of y' in the sense of distributions. Assuming that f is even more irregular, but can be considered as a distribution that we denote by $[f]$, we are led to look for solutions that are distributions $[u]$. In this case, for every infinitely differentiable function φ with compact support in $\mathbb{R}$, we have $\langle [u], \varphi'' - \varphi' + \varphi \rangle = \langle [f], \varphi \rangle$. These solutions, which we can also consider when f is regular, are also called weak solutions of the equation.

All of this leads, by replacing the usual differentiability with that in the sense of distributions, to the concept of weak solutions for general PDEs and leads us to study certain spaces of functions whose distributional derivatives can be identified with summable pth power functions. We therefore study Sobolev spaces $W^{m,p}(\Omega)$, which are normed and complete, so that the classical theorems from functional analysis apply to them.

When there are boundary conditions, the functions in these spaces need to be extended to the boundary of Ω, since they are only defined in its interior. The existence of such extensions depends *a priori* on the regularity of the boundary. We therefore in particular study the space $W^{m,p}(\Omega)$ when the boundary of the open set Ω is a manifold that is either differentiable or piecewise differentiable. This allows us to give, for the functions in these spaces, an interpretation of the boundary conditions that is in accordance with physics.

Consequently, in many situations, the great flexibility of differentiation in the sense of distributions leads us to state limit problems under equivalent forms that are better suited to establishing existence and uniqueness theorems.

Of course, the results we obtain necessitate preliminaries. These concern the functional spaces that we can use, in particular, normed spaces, completeness, density, and the generalization of the notion of function and integration. The aim of Chapter 1 is to describe these.

Contents of this Book

Chapter 1 is titled *Notions from Topology and Functional Analysis*. In it, we first recall the definition of topological vector spaces, including the important example of normed spaces, and in particular Banach spaces. We state the Baire theorem, the open image theorem, the Banach–Steinhaus theorem and the Hahn–Banach theorem. After defining continuous linear maps, we introduce dual topology on a normed space. To illustrate the different types of convergence of sequences of functions that are most common, which are less strict than (for example) uniform convergence, we introduce weak topologies on a space and on its dual. We also define reflexive spaces, in particular Hilbert spaces, and uniform convex spaces, whose properties we use in many examples in this book. We study the space of continuous functions on an open subset of $\mathbb{R}^N$ before recalling the definitions of distribution spaces, their topologies and the operators that we define on them, as well as convergence properties of sequences. The chapter concludes with the spaces $L^p(\Omega)$, their completion and reflexivity, and the density of the regular functions.

This last part of the chapter thus forms an introduction to the Sobolev spaces that we study in later chapters.

Chapter 2 concerns these *Sobolev spaces*, which give a suitable functional setting for most of the elliptic limit problems (cf. the preliminary chapter) from physics. An important part of this chapter deals with Sobolev embedding theorems. We first present the notion of the differentiation of functions in the weak, or generalized sense, that is, differentiation in the sense of distributions. After introducing the spaces L^p, this allows us to define the Sobolev spaces $W^{m,p}(\Omega)$. The properties of $L^p(\Omega)$ lead to density results for the regular functions in the spaces $W^{m,p}(\Omega)$. The most important result of the chapter is the Sobolev embedding theorem, which gives the inclusion of the elements of $W^{m,p}(\Omega)$ in $L^q(\Omega)$ for $q > p$, or in spaces of continuous Lipschitz or Hölder functions. Some of these embeddings are compact. These compactness results, which hold for bounded open sets, form a key argument for showing the existence of solutions of coercive minimization problems (cf. Chapter 5). In the second part of the chapter, we study possible extensions of functions in $W^{m,p}(\Omega)$ to elements of $W^{m,p}(\mathbb{R}^N)$, for which we need regularity conditions on the boundary $\partial\Omega$. At this point, we define the Lipschitz open sets and the open sets of class $\mathcal{C}^m$. The chapter concludes with a trace theorem that allows us, on such open sets, to extend $u \in W^{1,p}(\Omega)$ to the boundary, giving a function in $L^p(\partial\Omega)$. This generalizes the restriction to $\partial\Omega$ for functions that are in principle only defined in the open set Ω. This theorem is very useful when stating boundary conditions for a limit problem.

Chapter 3 deals with the image of the trace map on $W^{1,p}(\Omega)$ when the open set is regular. This is our first example of a fractional Sobolev space, namely $W^{1-1/p,p}(\partial\Omega)$. The chapter also contains Green's formulas and embedding theorems. These can be deduced from the embedding results on Sobolev spaces with integer exponents that they generalize.

Chapter 4 deals with more general fractional spaces $W^{s,p}(\Omega)$ (for s a noninteger real number). It also contains embedding and compact embedding results.

In Chapter 5, we use all the theory presented up to now to prove the existence of solutions of elliptic PDEs. There are, however, two exceptions, namely minimal surfaces and linear elasticity in the case of small deformations. For the first, the theoretical justifications from functions of a measure are given in the following chapter. The second necessitates the use of Korn's inequalities, which form the main subject of Chapter 7. In many situations, the existence theorems concerning these elliptic PDEs result from rewriting these limit problems in a variational form. The solutions then appear as functions minimizing a convex and coercive functional. Next, we study the regularity of the solutions of some of these problems, using for example approximations of the derivative by finite difference or *a priori* estimation methods. We conclude the chapter with properties characterizing these PDEs, namely the maximum principle in its weak form followed by its strong form.

In Chapter 6, we study spaces related to the Sobolev spaces, in particular the space of distributions whose derivative tensor, which is symmetric and is also called the *deformation tensor*, is in $L^p(\Omega)$ for $p \in [1, \infty[$. We also study the case $p = 1$ and the spaces where the deformation is a bounded measure. In particular, we give embedding theorems analogous to those for the classical Sobolev spaces, as well as existence results for a trace on the boundary when the open set is sufficiently regular. We conclude with a section devoted to functions of a measure.

In the setting of harmonic analysis, the results of Chapter 7 lead up to a proof of Korn's inequalities in $W^{1,p}$.

We conclude the book with an appendix concerning the regularity of the solutions of the p-Laplacian problems. As a complement to Chapter 5, we establish more technical results that we obtain using *a priori* estimation methods.

Organization of the Book

Each chapter is followed by a number of exercises. In most cases we give hints for the solution. The level of the exercises varies. Some of them, indicated with a [*], offer additional details to a result given in the chapter, an application of the results with explicit computations to illustrate them, or a different proof for such a result. Other exercises, indicated with a [**], offer complements to a given subject. In some cases, the results are presented in dimension $N = 1$ or $N = 2$, where the nature of the problems and the specifics of the proposed methods can be highlighted. In these small dimensions, the methods may lead to explicit computations that can help the reader better understand the notions that are being studied.

Françoise Demengel and Gilbert Demengel

Paris, 16 September 2011

Contents

Preliminaries on Ellipticity

General Definitions

Though the following definitions can be given for complex-valued functions, we will restrict ourselves to real-valued functions.

Definition 0.1. A differential operator of order m in N variables is a map $\mathcal{A}$ that sends an m times continuously differentiable function f on an open subset Ω of $\mathbb{R}^N$ to a function $\mathcal{A}f$ on Ω, with the help of a function F:

$$\mathcal{A}f(x) = F\big(f(x), \partial_i f(x), \ldots, \partial^m_{x_1^{\alpha_1} \ldots x_N^{\alpha_N}} f(x), x\big).$$

The operator $\mathcal{A}$ is called *linear* if the function F is a polynomial of degree one with respect to each derivative D^α, where α, the order of the derivative, is an N-tuple of integers $\alpha_1, \alpha_2, \ldots, \alpha_N$ with sum $|\alpha| = \sum_1^N \alpha_i \leqslant m$. In other words,

$$\mathcal{A}f(x) = \sum_{|\alpha| \leqslant m} c_\alpha(x)(D^\alpha f)(x) + c_0'(x).$$

The functions c_α and c_0' are called the coefficients of the operator $\mathcal{A}$.

A partial differential equation is an equality $\mathcal{A}f = 0$. It is called a *linear* PDE if the operator $\mathcal{A}$ is linear, and a homogeneous linear PDE if, moreover, $c_0' = 0$. An equation is called *quasi-linear* if

$$\mathcal{A}f(x) = \sum_{|\alpha| \leqslant m} c_\alpha(x, u, \ldots, D^\beta u)D^\alpha u + c_0'(x, u),$$

where the N-tuples β satisfy $|\beta| \leqslant |\alpha| - 1$.

Definition 0.2. A solution of a partial differential equation on an open subset $\Omega' \subset \Omega$ is a function f that is sufficiently differentiable on Ω', such that $\forall x \in \Omega'$, $\mathcal{A}f(x) = 0$.

In this book we will in particular be interested in second-order linear partial differential equations. Such an equation can be written as

$$(E) \qquad \sum_{1 \leqslant j \leqslant k \leqslant N} c_{j,k}(x)\partial^2_{j,k}f(x) + \sum_{1}^{N} c_i(x)\partial_i f(x) = g(x),$$

where $g = -c'_0$ is called the second member of the equation. We say that a second-order partial differential equation has constant coefficients if the functions $c_{j,k}$ and c_i are constants.

To the linear equation (E) we associate, for every $x \in \Omega$, the quadratic polynomial $P(E)_x$ in N variables $\{X_i\}$ whose coefficients are these functions, that is,

$$P(E)_x(X_1, X_2, \ldots, X_N) = \sum_{1 \leqslant j \leqslant k \leqslant N} c_{j,k}(x)X_j X_k + \sum_{1}^{N} c_i(x)X_i.$$

Let $P(E)_x^{(2)}$ be the homogeneous part of degree 2 of this polynomial, that is,

$$P(E)_x^{(2)}(X) = \sum_{1 \leqslant j \leqslant k \leqslant N} c_{j,k}(x)X_j X_k.$$

Definition 0.3. Given a linear equation of degree 2, we consider the real symmetric square matrix $C(x)$ of order N with the $c_{j,k}(x)$ as coefficients. The homogeneous part defined above can then be written as follows using the column vector $[X]$ consisting of the N variables X_j: $P(E)_x^{(2)}(X) = {}^t[X]C(x)[X]$.

We call a PDE *elliptic at the point* $x \in \Omega$ if the eigenvalues of the matrix $C(x)$ (which in this case are real) are either all negative or all positive.

By changing the sign of the two sides of the equation, we can reduce to the case that the matrix $C(x)$ is positive definite.

For Ω connected, if $x \mapsto C(x)$ is continuous on Ω and the kernel of $C(x)$ is 0 for every $x \in \Omega$, we say that the PDE is *elliptic* on Ω. After, if necessary, changing the signs of the two sides of the equation, this corresponds to saying that the matrix $C(x)$ is always positive definite.

Let $\lambda_m(x)$ and $\lambda_M(x)$ be the minimal and maximal eigenvalues of $C(x)$, where $\lambda_m(x) > 0$. We call the PDE *strictly elliptic* if there exists a real number $\lambda_0 > 0$ such that $\forall x \in \Omega$, $\lambda_m(x) \geqslant \lambda_0$.

Finally, the PDE is called *uniformly elliptic* on Ω if, moreover, the function $x \mapsto \lambda_M(x)/\lambda_m(x)$ is bounded on Ω.

When the coefficients $c_{j,k}$ are constants, *strictly elliptic* and *uniformly elliptic* are equivalent.

Note that these definitions only concern the homogeneous part of degree 2 of (E). To limit the influence of the homogeneous part of degree 1, we sometimes add conditions on the coefficients $c_i(x)$, for example that $x \mapsto |c_i(x)|/\lambda_m(x)$ is bounded in Ω.

Example 0.4. The second-order equation in one variable $y'' + a(x)y' + b(x)y = g(x)$ is an elliptic equation.

In the case of two variables, an equation of the type

$$a\partial^2_{xx}f(x,y) + 2b\partial^2_{xy}f(x,y) + c\partial^2_{yy}f(x,y) + (\alpha\partial_x f + \beta\partial_y f)(x,y) = g(x,y),$$

with $a > 0$ is elliptic if and only if $b^2 - ac < 0$. This is the case for the Laplace operator, where $a = c = 1$ and $b = 0$.

The more general Laplace operator in N variables, which can be written as $\Delta f = \sum_1^N \partial^2_{x_j} f$, is clearly also elliptic.

By contrast, the equations that occur in wave theory, for example

$$\frac{\partial^2 u}{\partial x^2} - \frac{\partial^2 u}{\partial y^2} = f$$

in dimension 2, are not elliptic.

The equation with variable coefficients

$$x^2 \frac{\partial^2 u}{\partial x^2} + y^2 \frac{\partial^2 u}{\partial y^2} = f(x,y)$$

is elliptic only on open subsets that do not meet either of the coordinate axes.

Limit Problems

Let us state the best-known problems governed by PDEs. We take the Laplace operator as a model operator in all our examples, but the Dirichlet, Neumann and Newton problems can also be considered for other elliptic operators.

Dirichlet Problems. In the case of the Laplacian, these problems consist in solving the equation

$$\Delta u = f, \quad u|_{\partial\Omega} = g,$$

which, when $f = 0$, $N = 2$ and g is continuous, reduces to determining a harmonic function that coincides with g on the boundary.

By extension, in dimension N, the problem can be stated as follows. For an open subset $\Omega \subset \mathbb{R}^N$ with boundary Γ, given f on Ω and g on Γ, find a twice differentiable function u on Ω such that

$$\Delta u = f \quad \text{on } \Omega \quad \text{and} \quad u|_\Gamma = g.$$

Keeping the operator Δ but modifying the conditions on the boundary by, more particularly, introducing the normal derivative on the boundary $\partial\Omega$ leads to other problems.

Neumann Problems. Let Ω be a bounded open set with a regular boundary, for example with a continuously differentiable boundary, on which we can therefore define a normal vector $\overrightarrow{n}$. Given a function f on Ω and a function g on Γ, we are looking for a function u such that

$$\Delta u = f \quad \text{on } \Omega, \quad \text{and, on } \Gamma: \quad \partial_{\overrightarrow{n}} u = g.$$

Newton Problems. Let Ω be an open set with regular boundary Γ. Given a function f on Ω and two functions g and h on Γ, we are looking for a function u such that

$$\Delta u = f \quad \text{on } \Omega, \quad \text{and, on } \Gamma: \quad \partial_{\overrightarrow{n}} u + hu = g.$$

We can generalize these problems without repeating the previous definitions. For example, by replacing the operator Δ by its square as an operator, that is, $\Delta^2 = \Delta \circ \Delta$, we find the following.

Problems Involving the Bi-Laplacian Δ^2. Given a function f on Ω and functions g_1 and g_2 on Γ, we are looking for a function u such that

$$\Delta^2 u = f \quad \text{on } \Omega, \quad \text{and, on } \Gamma: \quad u = g_1 \quad \text{and} \quad \partial_{\overrightarrow{n}} u = g_2.$$

We can also define problems for the operator Δ^2 with limit conditions comparable to those of the Neumann problem, as well as analogous problems where we replace the operator Δ^2 by the operator $u \mapsto \Delta^2 u + u$.

Another way to generalize the problems is by introducing *quasi-linear* equations. Let us give some examples.

p-Laplacian Problems. This is an example of a nonlinear, quasi-linear equation. Let p be a real number with $1 < p < +\infty$. We are looking for a function u such that

$$\text{div}(|\nabla u|^{p-2}\nabla u) = f \quad \text{on } \Omega \quad \text{and} \quad u|_{\partial\Omega} = 0.$$

This is a *divergence* form. Writing it this way facilitates the application of resolution methods. Let us show that it is indeed quasi-linear. By expanding the operator on the left-hand side of the equation as in the product rule for the divergence of a scalar times a vector, we obtain the following expression:

$$|\nabla u|^{p-2}\Delta u + \nabla u \cdot \nabla(|\nabla u|^{p-2}).$$

In the first instance, this is a formal expression that holds, for example, when $p > 2$ or at points where the gradient is different from zero. Using the formula $\nabla(|\nabla u|^{p-2}) = (p-2)|\nabla u|^{p-4}\nabla u \nabla \nabla u$ and the definition of the gradient of a vector, we can then write the equation in its quasi-linear form:

$$|\nabla u|^{p-4}\left(|\nabla u|^2 \partial_{ii} u + (p-2)\partial_{ij} u \partial_i u \partial_j u\right) = f.$$

Minimal Surface Problems. We are once more dealing with a quasi-linear equation, which can be seen as an extension of the previous one for $p \to 1$. We are now looking for a function u such that

$$\mathrm{div}\Big(\frac{\nabla u}{\sqrt{1 + |\nabla u|^2}}\Big) = f \quad \text{on } \Omega \quad \text{and} \quad u|_{\partial\Omega} = g.$$

Its quasi-linear form is as follows:

$$\Big((1 + |\nabla u|^2)\partial_{ii}u - \partial_{ij}u\partial_i u\partial_j u\Big)(1 + |\nabla u|^2)^{-3/2} = f.$$

Example (of a nonlinear, quasi-linear equation). The following is an example to which we will be able to apply the results of this book. For $p > 1$ and a real number $\lambda > 0$, we have

$$\Delta u = \lambda |u|^{p-2}u \quad \text{on } \Omega \quad \text{and} \quad u|_{\partial\Omega} = 0.$$

Let us conclude this preliminary chapter by specifying the limitations of this book.

Equations that Are not Treated

Non-divergence Type Nonlinear Functions. This category includes a whole class of partial differential equations for which the concept of weak solutions cannot be used and consequently needs to be replaced by that of *viscosity solutions*. This holds in dimension $N \geqslant 2$ for

$$|\nabla u|^\alpha \Delta u = f,$$

where α is a real number > -1. We will not deal with this type of equation in this book. Note, however, that for divergence equations such as the p-Laplacian above, the notions of viscosity solutions and weak solutions coincide thanks to regularity results. For this subject, the reader can consult the work of Ishii [39], Ishii-Lions [40] and Guy Barles [3], as well as the more recent work of Busca Esteban Quaas [11] and Birindelli-Demengel [7].

Hyperbolic Equations. These are not treated using the methods presented in this course. Note that, in general, hyperbolic equations have the disadvantage of having "too many" solutions. One of the best-known hyperbolic equations is the Burgers equation $u\partial_x u = f$. Only the *entropic* solutions in the sense of Oleinik are considered physical solutions, as they are stable under certain perturbations. These are also the solutions obtained as limits of solutions of equations via elliptic regularizations. We will not consider these equations. The reader can consult the work of Oleinik, Serre, etc.

Parabolic Equations. Finally, many evolution equations are parabolic. Let us state the best-known linear ones. The heat equations can be written as

$$\partial_t u - \Delta u = f,$$

with not only limit conditions but also initial conditions, that is, conditions on the solution u at $t = 0$.

The Korteweg–De Vries problem is governed by the linear equation

$$\partial_t u - u_{3x} = f$$

on $\mathbb{R}^+ \times \mathbb{R}$ plus an initial condition. Such equations can be generalized to nonlinear equations such as the Korteweg–De Vries–Burgers equation

$$u_t - u_{3x} + u\partial_x u = f.$$

1

Notions from Topology and Functional Analysis

In this chapter we recall results from functional analysis, in particular in Banach spaces. Most results are only stated. The reader can find the proofs (for example the proof of the Hahn–Banach theorem) in publications specializing in functional analysis.

The techniques used to solve elliptic partial differential equations very frequently use the notion of compactness in the spaces L^p, or, more generally, the notion of reflexive space. We therefore devote a number of pages to reflexivity. In particular, we recall the compactness for the weak topology of bounded subsets in a reflexive space and the relation between the spaces L^p and $L^{p'}$ when p and p' satisfy $p \in [1, +\infty]$, $p' \in [1, +\infty]$, and $1/p + 1/p' = 1$. We also mention results on distributions.

1.1 Topological Vector Spaces

Let X be a vector space over $\mathbb{K}$ ($\mathbb{R}$ or $\mathbb{C}$). The convex, balanced or absorbing subsets of X play an important role in defining a topology on X that is compatible with its algebraic structure.

Definition 1.1. Let X be a vector space over $\mathbb{K}$ and let $A \subset X$.

- The subset A is called balanced if $\forall \lambda \in \mathbb{K}$, $|\lambda| \leqslant 1 \Rightarrow \lambda A \subset A$.
- It is called absorbing if

$$\forall x \in X,\ \exists r > 0,\ \forall \lambda \in \mathbb{K},\quad |\lambda| \leqslant r \Longrightarrow \lambda x \in A.$$

Definition 1.2 (Topological vector spaces, abbreviated as TVS). These are vector spaces over $\mathbb{K}$ (where $\mathbb{K}$ is either $\mathbb{R}$ or $\mathbb{C}$) endowed with a topology for which scalar multiplication and addition are continuous.

F. Demengel, G. Demengel, *Functional Spaces for the Theory of Elliptic Partial Differential Equations*, Universitext,
DOI 10.1007/978-1-4471-2807-6_1,
© Springer-Verlag London Limited 2012

A normed space is an example of a TVS whose topology is easy to study.

Definition 1.3 (Norm on a $\mathbb{K}$-vector space X). Let X be a vector space over the field $\mathbb{K}$. A norm on X is a function f from X to $\mathbb{R}^+$ satisfying the following conditions:

$$\forall x \in X, \qquad\qquad f(x) = 0 \iff x = 0$$
$$\forall c \in \mathbb{K},\ \forall x \in X, \qquad f(cx) = |c| f(x)$$
$$\forall (x,y) \in X^2, \qquad\qquad f(x+y) \leqslant f(x) + f(y)$$

A vector space endowed with a norm is called a *normed space*.

To a given norm we associate the distance function d defined by $d(x_1, x_2) = \|x_1 - x_2\|$; thus a normed space X is a metric space. It can be easily verified that scalar multiplication and addition are continuous for the topology associated with the norm. A normed space is therefore a TVS. Note that in such a space, the family $\{\mathcal{B}_{0,r}\}_{r>0}$ of open balls with center 0_X forms a fundamental system of convex neighborhoods of 0_X. That is, every neighborhood of 0_X contains an element of $\{\mathcal{B}_{0,r}\}$. By translation, this property holds at every point of X.

More generally, we say that a TVS is *locally convex* if every point of the space admits a fundamental system of convex neighborhoods (see also Proposition 1.5).

Remark 1.4. If in the previous definition we leave out the first (separating) axiom, the function f satisfying the remaining conditions is called a *seminorm*. A space endowed with a seminorm is still a TVS. It is locally convex but not Hausdorff.

Because of the importance of these spaces in functional analysis, we will present their topology in detail, first by describing a fundamental system of neighborhoods of the origin and then by providing a family of seminorms generating the topology.

Proposition 1.5. *Let $\mathcal{B}$ be a family of subsets of a $\mathbb{K}$-vector space X satisfying the following conditions:*

(1) *The family $\mathcal{B}$ is a filter base, that is, it does not contain the empty set, and*
$$\forall (A, B) \in \mathcal{B}^2,\ \exists C \in \mathcal{B}, \quad C \subset A \cap B.$$

(2) *Every subset in $\mathcal{B}$ is convex, balanced, and absorbing.*
(3) $\forall A \in \mathcal{B},\ \forall r > 0,\ \exists B \in \mathcal{B}, \quad B \subset rA.$

The family $\mathcal{B}$ is then a fundamental system of neighborhoods of 0_X for a locally convex TVS topology on X. In this topology, V is a neighborhood of $x \in X$ if there exists a $U \in \mathcal{B}$ such that $x + U \subset V$.

Proposition 1.6 (seminorms generating a locally convex TVS topology). *Let $\{\eta_\lambda\}_{\lambda \in \Lambda}$ be a family of seminorms on a $\mathbb{K}$-vector space X. Let us assume that it is separating and directed, that is, that*

(1) *For every $x \in X$, there exists a $\lambda \in \Lambda$ such that $\eta_\lambda(x) \neq 0$.*
(2) *For every pair $(\lambda_1, \lambda_2) \in (\Lambda)^2$, the functions η_{λ_1} and η_{λ_2} are bounded in the family, that is,*

$$\exists \lambda \in \Lambda, \quad \eta_\lambda \geqslant \eta_{\lambda_1} \ and \ \eta_\lambda \geqslant \eta_{\lambda_2}.$$

The set of all closed balls $\{B_{\lambda,r}\}$ associated with the seminorms in the family, defined by $B_{\lambda,r} = \{x \in X \mid \eta_\lambda(x) \leqslant r\}$, then forms a fundamental system of neighborhoods of 0_X for a locally convex Hausdorff TVS topology on X.

We can easily show that this family of balls satisfies the conditions of Proposition 1.5 and that the topology is Hausdorff, since for nonzero x_0 and λ such that $\eta_\lambda(x_0) \neq 0$, the closed ball $B_{\lambda,r}$ with $r = \eta_\lambda(x_0)/2$ does not contain x_0.

Example 1.7 (of locally convex spaces). Let us define a structure of locally convex space on the space $X = \mathcal{E}^k(]a, b[)$ of $\mathcal{C}^k$ functions on the open interval $]a, b[$ in $\mathbb{R}$. We will generalize this example later on, replacing the interval by an open subset Ω of $\mathbb{R}^N$.

Let us define as follows a function $\eta_{m,K}$ depending on an integer $m \leqslant k$ and on a compact subset K of $\mathbb{R}$ contained in $]a, b[$:

$$\eta_{m,K}(f) = \sup_{\substack{x \in K \\ 0 \leqslant \alpha \leqslant m}} \left| \frac{d^\alpha f}{dx^\alpha}(x) \right|.$$

This is a seminorm for every pair (m, K). We have thus defined a family of seminorms on X. This family, endowed with the order on real-valued functions, is directed and separating. Indeed, for any pairs (K_1, K_2) and (m_1, m_2), the functions η_{m_1, K_1} and η_{m_2, K_2} have an upper bound in the family, namely $\eta_{m,K}$ with $K = K_1 \cup K_2$ and $m = \max(m_1, m_2)$.

Moreover, for every nonzero function f on X, there exist m and K such that $\eta_{m,K}(f) \neq 0$.

The previous proposition now implies that the set $\mathcal{B}$ of closed unit balls associated with these seminorms is a fundamental system of neighborhoods of 0_X for a locally convex Hausdorff space topology on X.

Note that, in general, the topology on an arbitrary locally convex space can be defined in terms of a family of seminorms (see [75]).

1.1.1 Baire Property and Applications

Baire Spaces.

Definition 1.8. A topological space E is called a *Baire space* if it satisfies one of the following equivalent properties:

(1) For every countable family $\{U_n\}_{n\in\mathbb{N}}$ of dense open subsets of E, that is, $\overline{U_n} = E$, the intersection $\bigcap_{n\in\mathbb{N}} U_n$ is dense in E.
(2) For every countable family $\{F_n\}_{n\in\mathbb{N}}$ of closed subsets of E with empty interior, the union $\bigcup_{n\in\mathbb{N}} F_n$ has empty interior in E.

Theorem 1.9. *Let X be a Banach space, that is, a complete normed space; then X is a Baire space.*

The proof of this theorem can be found in the exercises, with hints (see also [76]). It has many important applications, in particular concerning continuous linear functions.

1.1.2 Continuous Linear Maps between Normed Spaces

From here on, all topological vector spaces will have the same base field $\mathbb{K}$. Let us recall the characterization of the continuity of a linear map, which will lead to the definition of the norm of such a map.

The continuity at every point of a linear map f from the normed space X to the normed space Y follows from its continuity at the point $x = 0$, which can be expressed by one of the two following equivalent properties:

(1) There exists an $M \geqslant 0$ such that

$$\forall x \in X, \quad \|x\|_X \leqslant 1 \implies \|f(x)\|_Y \leqslant M.$$

(2) There exists an $M \geqslant 0$ such that

$$\forall x \in X, \quad \|f(x)\|_Y \leqslant M\|x\|_X.$$

Note that, by linearity, the upper bound of $\|f(x)\|_Y$ on the unit ball in X equals the upper bound on the unit sphere $\{\|x\|_X = 1\}$. We will use this characterization to construct a norm on the space of continuous linear maps.

Definition 1.10. Given topological vector spaces X and Y, we denote by $\mathcal{L}(X,Y)$ the space of continuous linear maps from X to Y. When X and Y are normed spaces and $L \in \mathcal{L}(X,Y)$, we let

$$\|L\|_{\mathcal{L}(X,Y)} = \sup_{\substack{x \in X \\ \|x\|_X = 1}} \|L(x)\|_Y.$$

The map $L \mapsto \|L\|_{\mathcal{L}(X,Y)}$ is a norm, called the operator norm, which endows $\mathcal{L}(X,Y)$ with a natural normed space topology.

Proposition 1.11. *If X is a normed space and Y is a Banach space, then $\mathcal{L}(X,Y)$ endowed with the previous topology is a Banach space.*

A proof can be found in Exercise 1.1 at the end of this chapter.

In particular, the proposition is true for $Y = \mathbb{K}$ considered as a vector space over itself with the topology induced by the absolute value. This property is used later on in this chapter.

When X and Y are both finite dimensional, the space $\mathcal{L}(X,Y)$ is finite dimensional and coincides with the space of linear maps from X to Y with the canonical topology of a finite dimensional vector space. When X and Y are both infinite dimensional, this is no longer true.

Theorem 1.12 (open mapping theorem). *Let T be a surjective continuous linear map from a Banach space X to a Banach space Y; then the image of an open subset of X is an open subset of Y.*

Proof of Theorem 1.12.

We will follow the arguments of [76]. We begin by showing that for a neighborhood U of 0 in X, there exists a neighborhood V of 0 in Y such that

$$V \subset \overline{T(U)}.$$

Indeed, for $B(0,r) \subset U$ and $W = B(0,r/2)$, we have $X = \bigcup_{n \in \mathbb{N}^*} (nW)$, and therefore $T(X) = Y = \bigcup_{n \in \mathbb{N}^*} T(nW)$. Since the Banach space Y is covered by a countable family of closed subsets $\overline{T(nW)}$, the Baire property tells us that one of these closed subsets, say $\overline{T(n_0 W)}$, has nonempty interior. There consequently exists an open subset V_1 of Y such that $V_1 \subset \overline{T(n_0 W)}$. Since a homothety in Y is continuous, the closed subset $\overline{T(W)}$ contains the set $\frac{1}{n_0} V_1$, which is also an open subset of Y. Let y_0 be such that $B(y_0, \delta) \subset \overline{T(W)}$; then $B(0,\delta) \subset \overline{T(W)} - y_0 \subset \overline{T(W)} + \overline{T(W)} \subset \overline{T(U)}$. The neighborhood $V = B(y_0, \delta)$ of 0 satisfies the property stated above.

Let us now prove the theorem.

For the sake of simplicity, we let X_ε and Y_ε denote the open unit balls of radius ε with center 0 in X and Y, respectively. Let $\varepsilon_i = \varepsilon/2^i$, and let $\{\eta_i\}$ be a sequence of positive real numbers such that $Y_{\eta_i} \subset \overline{T(X_{\varepsilon_i})}$. We may, and do, assume that this sequence converges to 0.

Let $y \in Y_{\eta_0}$. Since $y \in \overline{T(X_{\varepsilon_0})}$, we can choose an $x_0 \in X_{\varepsilon_0}$ such that

$$\|y - Tx_0\| \leq \eta_1.$$

Since $y - Tx_0 \in Y_{\eta_1}$, there exists an $x_1 \in X_{\varepsilon_1}$ such that

$$\|y - Tx_0 - Tx_1\| \leqslant \eta_2.$$

By induction, we construct a sequence $x_n \in X_{\varepsilon_n}$ such that

$$\left\| y - \sum_{j \leqslant n} Tx_j \right\| \leqslant \eta_n.$$

The inequalities $\|x_j\|_X \leqslant \varepsilon/2^j$ imply that $\sum_h^k \|x_j\|_X \leqslant \varepsilon/2^{h-1}$. It follows that $\{\sum_{j \leqslant n} x_j\}$ is a Cauchy sequence. Since X is a Banach space, this sequence converges to an element x of X, which satisfies

$$\|x\|_X \leqslant \sum_j \|x_j\|_X \leqslant 2\varepsilon.$$

Moreover, we have $Tx = y$. Finally, as y is an arbitrary element of Y_{η_0}, we conclude that the image under T of the ball of radius 2ε with center 0 contains the ball of radius η_0 with center 0 in Y. It follows that the image of an open set under the map T is open. $\square$

Theorem 1.13 (Banach–Steinhaus). *Let $\{u_n\}$ be a sequence of continuous linear maps from a Banach space X to a normed space Y.*

If, for every x in X, the sequence $\{u_n(x)\}$ converges in Y, then there exists a constant C such that

$$\forall n \in \mathbb{N}, \quad \|u_n\|_{\mathcal{L}(X,Y)} \leqslant C.$$

Proof of Theorem 1.13 (cf. [76]).
    The pointwise convergence given in the statement of the theorem implies the existence of a limit $u(x)$ for every x. The map u from X to Y is linear. By replacing u_n by $u_n - u$, we reduce to the case that for every x, $u_n(x) \to 0$.
    Consequently, given $\varepsilon > 0$, there exists for every $x \in X$ an N such that for every $n > N$, $\|u_n(x)\|_X \leqslant \varepsilon$. In other words, if $B'(0, \varepsilon)$ denotes a closed ball in X, then we have

$$X = \bigcup_{N \in \mathbb{N}} \bigcap_{n \geqslant N} u_n^{-1}(B'(0, \varepsilon)).$$

For every N, the set $F_N = \bigcap_{n > N} u_n^{-1}(B'(0, \varepsilon))$ is closed, as it is the intersection of closed sets, by the continuity of u_n for every n. Since X is complete, and therefore a Baire space, there exists an N_0 such that F_{N_0} has nonempty interior. Let x_0 and δ be such that

$$B(x_0, \delta) \subset \bigcap_{n \geqslant N_0} u_n^{-1}(B'(0, \varepsilon));$$

then $\forall n \geqslant N_0$,

$$B(0, \delta) \subset u_n^{-1}(B'(0, 2\varepsilon)),$$

and for every $n \geqslant N_0$,

$$\sup_{y \in B(0,1)} \|u_n(y)\| \leqslant \frac{2\varepsilon}{\delta}.$$

The result follows. □

Remark 1.14. Under the hypotheses of the theorem, the linear limit map $u = \lim_{n \to +\infty} u_n$ is continuous.

Indeed, the continuity of u_n implies that

$$\forall x \in X, \quad \|u_n(x)\|_Y \leqslant \|u_n\|_{\mathcal{L}(X,Y)} \|x\|_X \leqslant C\|x\|_X.$$

The continuity of the norm $\|\cdot\|_Y$ allows us to deduce the inequality $\|u(x)\| \leqslant C\|x\|_X$ characterizing the continuity of u when taking the limit of the left-hand side.

Example 1.15 (of an application of the Banach–Steinhaus theorem). Let $\{\lambda_n\}$ be a sequence of complex numbers such that for every summable sequence $\{x_n\}$, the sequence $\sum_0^{+\infty} \lambda_n x_n$ converges. Let us show that in this case, $\sup_{n \in \mathbb{N}} |\lambda_n| < +\infty$.

Let $X = \ell^1$ be the space of summable complex sequences $x = \{x_n\}$. Endowed with the norm $\|x\| = \sum_0^{+\infty} |x_n|$, this is a Banach space (cf. Exercise 1.3). Let u_p be the linear map from X to $\mathbb{R}$ defined by $u_p(x) = \sum_0^p \lambda_n x_n$. It is continuous because

$$|u_p(x)| \leqslant \left[\sup_{0 \leqslant n \leqslant p} |\lambda_n| \right] \sum_0^p |x_n| \leqslant \left[\sup_{0 \leqslant n \leqslant p} |\lambda_n| \right] \|x\|_1.$$

This inequality also proves that $\|u_p\|_{\mathcal{L}(\ell^1, \mathbb{C})} = \sup_{0 \leqslant n \leqslant p} |\lambda_n|$. Indeed, if this bound is achieved at n_0, defining x by $x_n = \delta_{n_0}^n$ leads to the equality $\|u_p\| = \sup_{0 \leqslant n \leqslant p} |\lambda_n|$. By assumption, the sequence $\{u_p(x)\}$ converges for every x; hence, by the Banach–Steinhaus theorem, the sequence of norms $\|u_p\|_{\mathcal{L}(\ell^1, \mathbb{C})}$ is bounded, which shows that $\sup_{n \in \mathbb{N}} |\lambda_n| < +\infty$.

The converse of this property is clearly true. Moreover, starting with this characterization, we can prove that $\mathcal{L}(\ell^1, \mathbb{C}) = \ell^\infty$, the space of bounded complex sequences.

Remark 1.16. It is not in general true that, under the hypotheses of the theorem, the sequence $\{u_n\}$ converges to u in $\mathcal{L}(X, Y)$ (cf. Exercise 1.6).

1.2 Linear Functionals, Topological Dual, Weak Topology

1.2.1 Topological Dual of a TVS, Hahn–Banach Theorem

Definition 1.17 (topological dual). A continuous linear functional on a $\mathbb{K}$-topological vector space X is a linear map from X to $\mathbb{K}$ that is continuous for the topologies on X and on $\mathbb{K}$. We let X' denote the vector space consisting of these functionals.

When X is finite dimensional, it is clear that X' coincides with the algebraic dual space and that X' has the same dimension as X. We can see this by taking a basis $\{e_i\}$ of X and associating with it the dual basis consisting of the linear functionals e_i^* defined by $e_i^*(e_j) = \delta_i^j$.

When X is a finite dimensional normed space, its dual is also finite dimensional. This follows, for example, from the analytic version of the Hahn–Banach theorem that we will state below without proof. On the same occasion, we will give the geometric version of the theorem. It will not only allow us to prove certain theorems in this chapter, but will also be a key argument in the theory of convex functions that we will develop in Chapter 6.

Theorem 1.18 (Hahn–Banach). *Let X be a vector space over $\mathbb{K}$, let M be a linear subspace of X and let p be a seminorm on X. Let m' be a linear functional on M such that $|m'(x)| \leqslant p(x)$ for every x in M; then there exists a linear functional x' on X such that*

$$\forall\, m \in M, \quad x'(m) = m'(m) \quad and \quad \forall\, x \in X, \quad |x'(x)| \leqslant p(x).$$

In particular, if X is a normed space and the seminorm is $\|\cdot\|_X$, then every continuous linear functional m' on the subspace M endowed with this norm can be extended to a linear functional on X that is continuous for this same norm.

The reader can find a proof in [76]. For an arbitrary TVS, the *geometric* version of the theorem is as follows.

Theorem 1.19 (Hahn–Banach (geometric version)). *Let X be a TVS over $\mathbb{K}$. Let C be a nonempty convex open subset of X and let M be a linear subspace of X that does not meet C; then there exists a hyperplane H, that is, a subspace of X of codimension 1, that is closed, does not contain M, and does not meet C.*

The following property at least partially explains the relation between the two versions of the theorem.

Proposition 1.20. *In a TVS X over $\mathbb{K}$, a hyperplane H defined by $H = \{x \in X \mid f(x) = \alpha\}$ for a linear functional f on X and a scalar $\alpha \in \mathbb{K}$ is closed if and only if the functional f is continuous on X.*

1.2.2 A Normed Space and its Dual; Topologies on These Spaces

Norm Topologies.

Definition 1.21. Let X be a normed space over $\mathbb{K}$. We denote the space $\mathcal{L}(X, \mathbb{K})$ by X' and call it the topological dual of X. It is the set of continuous linear functionals on X, that is, the set of linear functionals f on X such that

$$\exists K > 0, \ \forall x \in X, \quad |f(x)| \leqslant K \|x\|_X.$$

There exists a natural norm on X' defined by

$$\|f\|_{X'} = \sup_{\substack{x \in X \\ \|x\|_X \leqslant 1}} |f(x)|.$$

Using our previous study of the space $\mathcal{L}(X, Y)$, we note that X' endowed with the norm $\|\cdot\|_{X'}$ is a Banach space (whether or not X is). The topology induced by the norm on X is called the *norm topology on X*. The topology on X' induced by the norm defined above is called the *norm topology on X'*.

Let us state two consequences of the Hahn–Banach theorem for this norm. One of these shows that the dual X' is not reduced to $\{0\}$.

Proposition 1.22.

(1) *If $x \in X$, $x \neq 0$, then there exists an element $x' \in X'$ such that $\|x'\|_{X'} = 1$ and $\langle x', x \rangle = \|x\|_X$.*
(2) *The norm on X can be defined by $\|x\|_X = \sup_{\|x'\| \leqslant 1} |\langle x', x \rangle|$.*

Thanks to the duality of X and its dual X', we can define weaker (or coarser) topologies than the norm topologies, where the open subspaces for the new topologies will also be open subspaces for the norm topology.

Weak Topology on X. For every $x' \in X'$, the function $x \mapsto |\langle x', x \rangle|$ is a seminorm. Let $\mathcal{F}'$ be the set of finite subsets of X'. For $F' \in \mathcal{F}'$, set

$$\forall x \in X, \quad \eta_{F'}(x) = \sup_{x' \in F'} |\langle x', x \rangle|.$$

These functions form a family of seminorms on X. Let us verify the conditions of Proposition 1.6 (see also Exercise 1.5):

- The family is directed; indeed, if we set $F' = F_1' \cup F_2'$, we have the inequality $\eta_{F'} \geqslant \eta_{F_i'}$ for $i \in \{1, 2\}$.

- The family is separating; indeed, if $x_0 \in X$ is nonzero, then Proposition 1.5 gives the existence of an $x' \in X'$ such that $\eta_{\{x'\}}(x_0) = |\langle x_0, x' \rangle| \neq 0$.

This family of seminorms therefore defines a topology of locally compact Hausdorff vector space on X, which we will denote by $\sigma(X, X')$. This is called the *weak topology on* X. If, for any element $x_0 \in X$, any finite subset F' of X' and any real $\varepsilon > 0$ we set

$$B_{x_0, F', \varepsilon} = \{x \in X \mid \forall\, x' \in F',\ |\langle x', x - x_0 \rangle| < \varepsilon\},$$

then the family $\mathcal{B}$ of such subsets of X forms a basis for the weak topology on X (cf. Exercise 1.5).

We note that a set $B_{x_0, F', \varepsilon}$ is a finite intersection of inverse images of open subsets of $\mathbb{R}$ under the continuous maps x' from the normed space X to $\mathbb{K}$. Every open subset of X for the weak topology is therefore an open subset of the normed space X. In other words, the norm topology is finer that the weak topology.

Weak-star Topology on X'. In an analogous manner, we consider the following family of seminorms indexed by the finite subsets of X:

$$\forall\, x' \in X', \quad \eta_F(x') = \sup_{x \in F} |\langle x', x \rangle|.$$

By a similar reasoning to the one given above, this family is directed. Moreover, if $x' \neq 0$, that is, the linear form x' is nonzero, there exists an $x_0 \in X$ such that $\eta_{\{x_0\}}(x') \neq 0$; hence the family is separating.

If for any $x_0' \in X'$, any finite subset F of X, and any $\varepsilon > 0$ we define

$$B'_{x_0', F, \varepsilon} = \{x' \in X' \mid \forall\, x \in F,\ |\langle x' - x_0', x \rangle| < \varepsilon\},$$

then the set $\mathcal{B}'$ of such subsets of X' is a basis for a topology of locally compact Hausdorff vector space on X', denote by $\sigma(X', X)$ and called the *weak-star topology on* X'. It is weaker than the norm topology on X'.

Note that the normed space X' has a topological dual, denoted by X'', which endows it with a third topology, the weak topology $\sigma(X', X'')$.

Also note that the norm topologies can be defined in an analogous manner by replacing the finite subsets by bounded subsets of X' or X.

Weak Convergence. We can use the previous definitions to characterize weak convergence for sequences.

Definition 1.23. Let X be a TVS.

A sequence $(u_n)_n \in X^{\mathbb{N}}$ converges to u in X with respect to the weak topology (or converges weakly) if

$$\forall\, f \in X', \quad \langle f, u_n - u \rangle \longrightarrow 0.$$

A sequence $(f_n)_n \in (X')^{\mathbb{N}}$ converges to $f \in X'$ with respect to the weak-star topology if

$$\forall x \in X, \quad \langle f_n - f, x \rangle \longrightarrow 0.$$

Continuity for the Weak Topology.

Proposition 1.24. *The linear functionals on X that are continuous for the norm topology and those continuous for the weak topology coincide.*

Proof.

It is clear that a linear functional that is continuous for the weak topology is also continuous for the norm topology. Conversely, let B_ε be a ball with center 0 in $\mathbb{K}$. The inverse image of this neighborhood under $f \in X'$ is

$$B_{\{f\},\varepsilon} = \{x \in X \mid |\langle f, x \rangle| < \varepsilon\},$$

which is a neighborhood of 0 for the weak topology. It follows that f is also continuous for the weak topology.   □

Compactness. An important result concerning the weak-star topology is the weak-star compactness of the closed unit ball in X'. We will give a weaker statement that holds when X is separable, that is, when X has a countable dense subset. In this case, the closed unit ball in X' is weakly sequentially compact. We choose to give the result in this particular case for two reasons. First, all spaces used in this book are separable and weakly sequentially compactness suffices in the applications. Second, the proof of the general result uses the Tichonoff theorem ([76]), which we find too abstract to be included in this course.

Let us recall a number of definitions and properties before stating the result.

Definition 1.25 (compactness).

- A subset A of a Hausdorff topological space is called compact if every open cover of A has a finite subcover.
- A subset A of a normed space X is called precompact if its completion is compact for the topology on X.
- A subset A of a normed space X is called relatively compact if its closure is compact.
- A subset A of a normed space X is called weakly sequentially compact if every sequence of points of A admits a subsequence that converges weakly in A.

Proposition 1.26. *Compact, precompact, and relatively compact subsets have the following properties:*

- *A compact set in a metric space X is closed and bounded, but the converse is false unless X is finite dimensional.*
- *A subset of a metric space E is precompact if and only if for every $\varepsilon > 0$, it admits a cover by a finite number of open balls of radius ε.*
- *The closure of a precompact set is compact.*
- *In a normed space, saying that A is compact is equivalent to saying that every sequence of points of A admits a subsequence that converges in X to an element of A.*
- *A precompact set in a Banach space is relatively compact.*

We leave the proof of this proposition to the reader.

Proposition 1.27. *Let X be a separable normed space and let B' be the closed unit ball in its dual X'; then B' is sequentially compact for the weak-star topology.*

Proof.

Let $\{f_n\}_{n\in\mathbb{N}}$ be a sequence of linear functionals in B'. For the proof, we fix a countable dense subset $\{x_i\}_{i\in\mathbb{N}}$ of X. The sequence $f_n(x_i)$ is then bounded for every i. By the diagonal method, we can extract a subsequence from f_n, which we will also denote by f_n, such that $(f_n(x_i))_n$ converges to l_i. Let us show that for every $x \in X$, the sequence $f_n(x)$ converges, proving the convergence of the sequence $\{f_n\}$ for the weak-star topology.

Let $\varepsilon > 0$ and $x \in X$; then there exists an x_j in the dense subset such that $\|x - x_j\|_X \leqslant \varepsilon$. Once we fix this element, there exists an integer N such that $\forall n \geqslant N,\ |f_n(x_j) - l_j| \leqslant \varepsilon$. Consequently, as the f_n are in the unit ball in X', we have the following inequality for $n \geqslant N$ and $m \geqslant N$:

$$|f_n(x) - f_m(x)| \leqslant |f_n(x) - f_n(x_j)| + |f_n(x_j) - l_j|$$
$$+ |l_j - f_m(x_j)| + |f_m(x_j) - f_m(x)| \leqslant 4\varepsilon.$$

The above plus the completeness of X' show that the sequence $\{f_n(x)\}$ converges in X' to an element that we will denote by $f(x)$. It remains to show that $f \in B'$.

Let us show that f is linear. In order to do this, let us fix x_1 and x_2 in X. We consider three subsets of the dense subset, namely sequences $\{x_j^{(1)}\}$, $\{x_j^{(2)}\}$ and $\{y_j\}$ that converge in X to x_1, x_2 and $x_1 + x_2$, respectively. By the equicontinuity of the f_n, we have

$$|f_n(x_j^{(1)}) + f_n(x_j^{(2)}) - f_n(y_j)| \leqslant \|x_j^{(1)} + x_j^{(2)} - y_j\|_X.$$

The right-hand side tends to 0. Consequently,

$$\lim f_n(y_j) = \lim(f_n(x_j^{(1)}) + f_n(x_j^{(2)})) = f(x_1) + f(x_2).$$

Repeating this method for λx, we obtain the linearity of f.

It is continuous because if we take the limit of the continuity inequality $\forall x \in X, |f_n(x)| \leqslant \|x\|_X$, we find

$$\forall x \in X, \quad |f(x)| \leqslant \|x\|_X.$$

Since this last inequality shows that $\|f\|_{X'} \leqslant 1$, we have $f \in B'$, completing the proof.   □

1.2.3 Second Dual Space, Reflexive Spaces

Definition 1.28. Let X be a normed space and let X' be its dual, which is also a normed space, and even a Banach space; then the space of continuous linear functionals on X', $(X')'$, which we also denote by X'', is also a Banach space. We call it the bidual space of X.

Let us show that there is a continuous injection from X into X''. Let $x \in X$. The map f_x that sends x' to $\langle x', x \rangle$ is clearly a continuous linear functional on X'. We can therefore define the map J from X to $(X')'$ by sending x to the linear functional f_x. This map is injective but not surjective except in special cases, namely the case of the reflexive spaces studied below.

Indeed, the image of J is exactly the set of linear functionals on X' that are continuous for the weak-star topology on X'. More precisely, we have the following theorem.

Theorem 1.29. *Let X be a normed space and let X' be its dual. A linear functional f on X' is continuous for the weak-star topology on X' if and only if it has the following property:*

$$\exists x \in X, \ \forall x' \in X', \quad f(x') = \langle x', x \rangle.$$

Proof.

Let $x \in X$; then f_x is continuous for the weak-star topology. Indeed, given $\varepsilon > 0$, the inverse image of the interval $\{|t| < \varepsilon\}$ in $\mathbb{R}$ under f_x contains the set

$$B_{0,\{x\}\varepsilon} = \{x' \mid |\langle x', x \rangle| < \varepsilon\}.$$

This set is a neighborhood of 0 (cf. Subsection 1.2.2) for the weak-star topology. Consequently, f_x is continuous for this topology.

Let f be a linear functional that is continuous for the weak-star topology on X'; then the set of $x' \in X'$ such that $|f(x')| < 1$ is a neighborhood of 0. Therefore, there exist a real number $\delta > 0$ and a finite number of elements x_i of X such that if $x' \in X'$ satisfies $|\langle x', x_i \rangle| < \delta$ for every i, then $|f(x')| < 1$.

It follows that there exist a $\delta > 0$ and a finite number of x_i, $1 \leqslant i \leqslant n$, such that for every $x' \in X'$,

$$|f(x')| \leqslant \frac{1}{\delta} \sup_i |\langle x', x_i \rangle|.$$

In particular, if $\langle x', x_i \rangle = 0$ for every i, then $f(x') = 0$. Consequently, the linear functional f on X' vanishes on the intersection of the kernels of the linear functionals f_{x_i}. By the algebraic lemma 1.30 below, there exist complex numbers α_i, $1 \leqslant i \leqslant n$, such that $f = \sum_i \alpha_i f_{x_i}$. The vector $x = \sum_i \alpha_i x_i$ therefore satisfies $f = f_x$, completing the proof. $\qquad\square$

Lemma 1.30. *Let X be a vector space. Let f be a linear functional on X that vanishes on the intersection of the kernels of n linear functionals f_i; then f is a linear combination of the f_i.*

Proof of Lemma 1.30.

We may assume that the f_i are linearly independent. Indeed, if this is not the case, there exists a $p < n$ such that, after permuting the elements of the family if necessary, the linearly independent subfamily $\{f_1, \ldots, f_p\}$ generates the same space. In this case, $\bigcap_{1 \leqslant i \leqslant p} \operatorname{Ker} f_i \subset \operatorname{Ker} f_j$ for every $j \geqslant p + 1$ and therefore $\bigcap_{1 \leqslant i \leqslant n} \operatorname{Ker} f_i = \bigcap_{1 \leqslant i \leqslant p} \operatorname{Ker} f_i$. Supposing that the lemma has been proved for linearly independent functionals, there exist λ_i such that

$$f = \sum_{1 \leqslant i \leqslant p} \lambda_i f_i,$$

so that f is a linear combination of the f_i with $i \leqslant n$.

Let us therefore assume that the f_i are linearly independent. There then exist vectors $x_j \in X$ such that

$$f_i(x_j) = \delta_i^j.$$

For every $x \in X$, we write

$$x = \sum_{1 \leqslant i \leqslant n} f_i(x) x_i + z;$$

then $z \in \bigcap_{1 \leqslant j \leqslant n} \operatorname{Ker} f_j$, so that $f(z) = 0$, and therefore

$$f(x) = \sum_{1 \leqslant j \leqslant n} f_j(x) f(x_j).$$

It follows that

$$f = \sum_{1 \leqslant j \leqslant n} f(x_j) f_j,$$

which concludes the proof. $\qquad\square$

Recall that we denote by J the injection from X into X'' that sends x to f_x, as defined in Subsection 1.2.3.

Definition 1.31. A normed space X is called reflexive if the map J is surjective, that is, if every linear functional on X' that is continuous for the norm topology is also continuous for the weak-star topology of X'.

Note that a reflexive space must be a Banach space, since it can be identified with the dual of a normed space.

Theorem 1.32. *The closed unit ball of a reflexive separable space X is weakly sequentially compact.*

Proof of Theorem 1.32.
We will use Proposition 1.27 and the following proposition.

Proposition 1.33. *Let X be a normed space with separable dual; then X is also separable.*

Proof of Proposition 1.33.
Let $\{x'_n\}_n$ be a dense subset of the unit sphere in X'. It suffices to show the existence of a countable dense subset of the unit sphere in X. Let $\{x_n\}$ be such that $\|x_n\|_X = 1$ and $x'_n(x_n) \geqslant 1/2$. Let M be the vector space generated by the x_n. We want to prove that the subspace of M consisting of the linear combinations with rational coefficients, which is countable, is dense in X. We will prove this by contradiction. Let us therefore suppose that $M \neq X$, and let $x \in X - M$. By the Hahn–Banach theorem, there exists a functional x'_0 with $\|x'_0\|_{X'} = 1$ such that $x'_0(x) \neq 0$ and $x'_0(x_n) = 0$ for every n. Consequently, for every n,

$$\langle x'_n - x'_0, x_n \rangle \geqslant \frac{1}{2},$$

which contradicts the assumption that $\{x'_n\}$ is dense.   □

The Hilbert spaces defined in the following subsection and the spaces L^p with $p \in]1, +\infty[$ are examples of reflexive spaces. The reflexivity of the space L^p follows from its uniform convexity. For Hilbert spaces, the reasoning is much more elementary.

Remark 1.34. Theorem 1.32 shows that the space $L^1(\Omega)$ is not reflexive. By way of example, consider $L^1(]-1, 1[)$ and the sequence

$$u_n = \begin{cases} n & \text{on } [-1/2n, 1/2n], \\ 0 & \text{otherwise.} \end{cases}$$

The sequence u_n is contained in the unit sphere in $L^1(]-1, 1[)$. Suppose that u_n converges weakly to u in L^1. If φ is continuous and bounded, then $\int_{-1}^{1} u_n \varphi$ converges to $\varphi(0)$, so that $u = \delta_0$, which is not an element of L^1.

1.2.4 Hilbert Spaces

Definition 1.35. For a vector space X over $\mathbb{C}$, a Hermitian inner product $(.,.)$ is a map from $X \times X$ to $\mathbb{C}$ with the following properties:

$$\forall (x, y) \in X \times X \qquad (x, y) = \overline{(y, x)}$$
$$\forall (x, y, z) \in X^3 \qquad (z, ax + by) = a(z, x) + b(z, y)$$
$$\forall (a, b) \in \mathbb{C}^2 \qquad (x, x) \geqslant 0$$
$$\forall x \in X \qquad (x, x) = 0 \iff x = 0$$

We can associate a norm with the Hermitian inner product, called the *inner product norm*, as follows:

$$(1.36) \qquad \|x\| = (x, x)^{1/2}.$$

A vector space X endowed with such a norm is called an inner product space, or pre-Hilbert space. If it is, moreover, complete for the inner product norm, then we call it a *Hilbert space*. A normed space is an inner product space if and only if the norm satisfies the following parallelogram law:

$$(1.37) \qquad \|x + y\|^2 + \|x - y\|^2 = 2(\|x\|^2 + \|y\|^2)$$

Theorem 1.38 (Riesz representation theorem). *Let X be a Hilbert space with inner product $(\cdot, \cdot)$. A linear map f from X to $\mathbb{C}$ belongs to X' if and only if*

$$\exists x \in X, \ \forall y \in X, \quad f(y) = (x, y).$$

The element x is then unique and the map that sends f to x is an isometry from X to its dual X', that is,

$$\|f\|_{X'} = \|x\|_X.$$

The reflexivity of X follows. Other important properties of inner product spaces follow from the Hilbert projection theorem, in particular the construction of orthonormal bases and the theory of Fourier series.

1.2.5 Uniformly Convex Spaces

Definition 1.39. A TVS X is called uniformly convex if

$$\forall \varepsilon > 0, \ \exists \delta(\varepsilon) > 0, \ \forall (x, y) \in X^2, \quad \|x\| = \|y\| = 1 \text{ and } \|x - y\| \geqslant \varepsilon$$
$$\implies \left\| \frac{x + y}{2} \right\| \leqslant 1 - \delta(\varepsilon).$$

Theorem 1.40. *A uniformly convex space is reflexive.*

(1) Inner product spaces are uniformly convex, as easily follows from the parallelogram law.

(2) The spaces L^p with $p \in]1, +\infty[$ are uniformly convex (cf. the proof in [1]).

For the proof of Theorem 1.40, we need Helly's theorem, which is a consequence of the Hahn–Banach theorem.

Theorem 1.41 (Helly). *Let f_i, $1 \leqslant i \leqslant n$ be linear functionals on X. Let $\gamma > 0$ and α_i, $1 \leqslant i \leqslant n$, be n complex numbers. A necessary and sufficient condition for the existence, for every $\varepsilon > 0$, of an element $x_\varepsilon \in X$ such that for every $i \in [1, n]$,*

$$f_i(x_\varepsilon) = \alpha_i, \quad \text{with} \quad \|x_\varepsilon\|_X \leqslant \gamma + \varepsilon$$

is that, for every n-tuple $(\beta_i) \in \mathbb{R}^n$, we have

$$\left| \sum_{1 \leqslant i \leqslant n} \beta_i \alpha_i \right| \leqslant \gamma \left\| \sum_{1 \leqslant i \leqslant n} \beta_i f_i \right\|_{X'}.$$

Proof of Helly's theorem.

Let us show that the condition is necessary. If $f_i(x_\varepsilon) = \alpha_i$ for every i with $\|x_\varepsilon\| \leqslant \gamma + \varepsilon$, then for every $\beta_i \in \mathbb{R}^n$, we have

$$\left| \sum_{1 \leqslant i \leqslant n} \beta_i \alpha_i \right| = \left| \sum_{1 \leqslant i \leqslant n} \beta_i f_i(x_\varepsilon) \right| \leqslant \|x_\varepsilon\| \left\| \sum_i \beta_i f_i \right\|_{X'}.$$

The result follows from the arbitrariness of ε.

Let us show that the condition is sufficient. We may assume that the f_i are linearly independent. Indeed, if this is not the case, let $f_1, f_2, \ldots, f_p$ with $p \leqslant n$ be a linearly independent generating subset of the family $\{f_i\}$.

Let us assume that the result has been proved for linearly independent functionals. We have n complex numbers α_i. Taking $\beta_i = 0$ for all $i \geqslant p + 1$, we have

$$\left| \sum_{1 \leqslant i \leqslant p} \beta_i \alpha_i \right| \leqslant \gamma \left\| \sum_{1 \leqslant i \leqslant p} \beta_i f_i \right\|_{X'},$$

whence, for every $\varepsilon > 0$, there exists an x_ε such that

$$\|x_\varepsilon\|_X \leqslant \gamma + \varepsilon \quad \text{and} \quad \forall i \leqslant p, \ f_i(x_\varepsilon) = \alpha_i.$$

We need to verify that these equalities also hold for $i \geqslant p + 1$. For this, note that if $f_{p+1} = \sum_{1 \leqslant i \leqslant p} \gamma_i f_i$, then by taking $\beta_{p+1} = -1$ and $\beta_i = \gamma_i$ for $i \leqslant p$, we have the inequality

$$\left| \sum_{1 \leqslant i \leqslant p+1} \beta_i \alpha_i \right| \leqslant \gamma \left\| \sum_{1 \leqslant i \leqslant p+1} \beta_i f_i \right\|_{X'}.$$

This implies that

$$\sum_{1 \leqslant i \leqslant p+1} \beta_i \alpha_i = 0.$$

Consequently, we have

$$\alpha_{p+1} = \sum_i \gamma_i f_i(x_\varepsilon) = f_{p+1}(x_\varepsilon).$$

We can repeat this for every f_i with $i \geqslant p+1$. In conclusion, we have shown the result if we can prove that it holds for linearly independent f_i.

Let us now suppose that the f_i are linearly independent. The map φ from X to $\mathbb{R}^p$ defined by $\varphi(x) = (f_1(x), \ldots, f_p(x))$ is therefore a continuous surjective linear map. In particular, if $S_\varepsilon = \{x \in X \mid \|x\|_X \leqslant \gamma + \varepsilon\}$, then the image of S_ε is a convex subset of $\mathbb{R}^p$ whose interior contains 0.

Let us suppose that $\vec{\alpha} = (\alpha_i)_{1 \leqslant i \leqslant p}$ does not belong to $\varphi(S_\varepsilon)$. By Theorem 1.19, there exists a hyperplane that separates the convex set $\varphi(S_\varepsilon)$ from the point with coordinates α_i. In other words, there exist β_i, $i \leqslant p$, such that

$$\sum_i \beta_i \alpha_i \geqslant \sup_{x \in S_\varepsilon} \beta_i f_i(x).$$

Since the right-hand side equals $(\gamma + \varepsilon)(\|\sum_i \beta_i f_i\|_{X'})$, we have a contradiction. $\qquad \square$

Proof of Theorem 1.40.

Let $x'' \in X''$ be an element of norm 1. By the definition of the norm, for every n there exists an f_n of norm 1 in X' such that

$$x''(f_n) \geqslant 1 - \frac{1}{n}.$$

Let $\alpha_i = x''(f_i)$ for $i \leqslant n$. For any n-tuple of real numbers β_i, we have

$$\left| \sum_1^n \beta_i \alpha_i \right| = \left| \sum_1^n \beta_i x''(f_i) \right| \leqslant \|x''\|_{X''} \left\| \sum_1^n \beta_i f_i \right\|_{X'}.$$

Consequently, by Helly's theorem applied with $\varepsilon = 1/n$, there exists an $x_n \in X$ such that for every $i \leqslant n$,

$$\|x_n\|_X \leqslant 1 + \frac{1}{n} \quad \text{and} \quad f_i(x_n) = \alpha_i = x''(f_i).$$

Note that the sequence $\|x_n\|_X$ tends to 1; indeed, setting $i = n$ gives

$$1 - \frac{1}{n} \leqslant x''(f_n) = f_n(x_n) \leqslant \|f_n\|_{X'} \|x_n\|_X \leqslant 1 + \frac{1}{n}.$$

We will use the uniform convexity to show that (x_n) is a Cauchy sequence. If this is not the case, then for every $\varepsilon > 0$ there exist sequences $n_k < m_k < n_{k+1} < \cdots$ with

$$\|x_{n_k} - x_{m_k}\| \geqslant \varepsilon.$$

Since X is uniformly convex, there exists a $\delta(\varepsilon) > 0$ such that

$$\|x_{n_k} + x_{m_k}\| \leqslant 2(1 - \delta(\varepsilon)).$$

Consequently, as $m_k > n_k$,

$$f_{n_k}(x_{n_k}) = f_{n_k}(x_{m_k}) = x''(f_{n_k}),$$

whence

$$2\left(1 - \frac{1}{n_k}\right) \leqslant f_{n_k}(x_{n_k}) + f_{n_k}(x_{m_k}) \leqslant \|x_{n_k} + x_{m_k}\| \leqslant 2(1 - \delta(\varepsilon)).$$

Taking k to $+\infty$ leads to a contradiction.

The sequence x_n therefore converges to a point x_0. By taking the limit, we have

$$\|x_0\| = 1 \quad \text{and} \quad \forall i, \quad f_i(x_0) = x''(f_i).$$

Let us show that x_0 is unique. Suppose that $y_0 \in X$, $y_0 \neq x_0$, satisfies the same equalities. Since X is uniformly convex, $\|x_0 + y_0\| < 2$. Moreover,

$$\|x_0 + y_0\|_X \geqslant f_i(x_0 + y_0) = 2x''(f_i) \geqslant 2\left(1 - \frac{1}{i}\right),$$

which leads to a contradiction when we let i tend to infinity.

Let $f_0 \in X'$. We must show that

$$f_0(x_0) = x''(f_0).$$

By the previous reasoning, there exists a $z_0 \in X$ such that

$$\|z_0\|_X = 1 \quad \text{and} \quad \forall i, \quad f_i(z_0) = x''(f_i).$$

In particular, the uniqueness tells us that $z_0 = x_0$, completing the proof of the theorem. $\square$

We will admit that the spaces L^p and ℓ^p are uniformly convex for $p > 1$, $p < \infty$, without giving a proof. The proof uses Clarkson's inequalities, which the reader can find in [23] and [1].

1.3 The Space of Continuous Functions on an Open Subset of $\mathbb{R}^N$

Definition 1.42. Let X and Y be two normed spaces. We say that X is embedded in Y if there exists a continuous injection i from X to Y, that is, an injection i and a constant $C > 0$ such that

$$(1.43) \qquad \forall\, x \in X, \quad \|i(x)\|_Y \leqslant C\|x\|_X.$$

We denote the embedding by

$$X \hookrightarrow Y.$$

We call the embedding compact if the operator i is compact, that is, if it maps a bounded subset of X to a relatively compact subset of Y. We denote the compact embedding by

$$(1.44) \qquad X \hookrightarrow_c Y.$$

Definition 1.45. Let Ω be an open subset of $\mathbb{R}^N$. For any nonnegative integer m, let $\mathcal{C}^m(\Omega)$ be the space of continuous functions whose partial derivatives up to order m are continuous on Ω. Let

$$(1.46) \qquad \mathcal{C}^\infty(\Omega) = \bigcap_{m \in \mathbb{N}} \mathcal{C}^m(\Omega),$$

and let $\mathcal{C}_c^\infty(\Omega)$ or $\mathcal{D}(\Omega)$ denote the space of $\mathcal{C}^\infty(\Omega)$ functions with compact support in Ω.

Since Ω is open, the continuous functions on Ω are not necessarily bounded. The following defines a useful and important subspace of $\mathcal{C}^m(\Omega)$.

Definition 1.47. For an open subset Ω of $\mathbb{R}^N$, let $\mathcal{C}_b^m(\Omega)$ be the subset of $\mathcal{C}^m(\Omega)$ consisting of the functions whose partial derivatives of order $\leqslant m$ are bounded and uniformly continuous on Ω. By endowing this subspace with the norm

$$(1.48) \qquad \|\varphi\|_{\mathcal{C}_b^m(\Omega)} = \sup_{|\alpha| \leqslant m} \sup_{x \in \Omega} |D^\alpha \varphi(x)|,$$

we obtain a Banach space.

Note that when Ω is a bounded open subset, any function on this space, as well as all its partial derivatives, admits a continuous extension to $\overline{\Omega}$. The space $\mathcal{C}_b^m(\Omega)$ is therefore identical to $\mathcal{C}^m(\overline{\Omega})$. Consider the following important subspace of $\mathcal{C}_b^m(\Omega)$.

Definition 1.49. For $0 < \lambda \leqslant 1$, $\mathcal{C}_b^{0,\lambda}(\Omega)$ denotes the space of Hölder continuous functions of order λ on Ω, defined as follows:

$$\mathcal{C}_b^{0,\lambda}(\Omega) = \left\{ \varphi \in \mathcal{C}_b(\Omega) \mid \exists C > 0, \, \forall (x,y) \in \Omega^2, \, |\varphi(x) - \varphi(y)| \leqslant C|x-y|^\lambda \right\}.$$

When $\lambda = 1$, these are called the Lipschitz continuous functions. More generally, we define $\mathcal{C}_b^{m,\lambda}(\Omega)$ to be the subset of $\mathcal{C}_b^m(\Omega)$ of functions φ such that

$$\exists C > 0, \, \forall \alpha, \, |\alpha| = m, \, \forall (x,y) \in \Omega^2, \quad |D^\alpha \varphi(x) - D^\alpha \varphi(y)| \leqslant C|x-y|^\lambda.$$

Endowed with the norms

$$(1.50) \quad \|\varphi\|_{m,\lambda} = \|\varphi\|_{\mathcal{C}_b^m(\Omega)} + \sup_{|\alpha|=m} \sup_{\{(x,y)\in(\Omega)^2 \mid x \neq y\}} \frac{|D^\alpha\varphi(x) - D^\alpha\varphi(y)|}{|x-y|^\lambda},$$

these are Banach spaces. Moreover, we have

$$\forall (\nu, \lambda), \quad 0 < \nu < \lambda < 1 \implies \mathcal{C}_b^{m,\lambda}(\Omega) \hookrightarrow \mathcal{C}_b^{m,\nu}(\Omega) \hookrightarrow \mathcal{C}_b^m(\Omega),$$

where the inclusions are strict.

Definition 1.51. An algebra $\mathcal{A}$ endowed with a norm is called a normed algebra if multiplication is continuous for the norm.

Example 1.52. The space $\mathcal{C}_b(\Omega)$ of continuous bounded functions on Ω, where Ω is an open subset of $\mathbb{R}^N$, is a normed algebra.

Definition 1.53. Let $\mathcal{A}$ be an algebra. A subalgebra $\mathcal{A}'$ of $\mathcal{A}$ is a vector subspace that is stable for scalar multiplication.

Theorem 1.54 (Stone–Weierstrass). *Let K be a compact subset of $\mathbb{R}^N$. Let $\mathcal{A}$ be a subalgebra of $\mathcal{C}(K, \mathbb{C})$ satisfying*

(1) $\forall \Phi, \, \Phi \in \mathcal{A} \Rightarrow \overline{\Phi} \in \mathcal{A}$ *($\mathcal{A}$ is self-adjoint).*
(2) $\forall (x,y) \in K, \, x \neq y, \, \exists \Phi \in \mathcal{A}, \, \Phi(x) \neq \Phi(y)$ *($\mathcal{A}$ separates points).*
(3) $\forall a \in \mathbb{C}$, *the function $x \mapsto a$ belongs to $\mathcal{A}$ ($\mathcal{A}$ contains the constant functions).*

Then $\mathcal{A}$ is dense in $\mathcal{C}(K, \mathbb{C})$.

An example of such an algebra is the algebra of polynomials in N variables on K whose complex coefficients have rational real and imaginary parts. In particular, this shows that $\mathcal{C}(K)$ is separable.

Proof of the Stone–Weierstrass Theorem.
Using the first property, we reduce to the case of a real algebra, where the function we wish to approximate is real. We admit without proof the

Weierstrass theorem, which allows us to uniformly approximate any continuous function on a compact space by a sequence of polynomials. Let $f \in \mathcal{A}$.
This function is uniformly bounded. Let $M = \sup |f|$. Since the function
$t \mapsto |t|$ is continuous on the compact set $[-M, M]$, there exists a sequence of
polynomials $\{P_n\}$ such that

$$\forall t \in [-M, M], \quad \||t| - P_n(t)|_\infty \leqslant \frac{1}{n}.$$

By composing functions, we deduce the inequalities

$$\forall s \in K, \quad \||f(s)| - P_n(f(s))| \leqslant \frac{1}{n}.$$

Since $\mathcal{A}$ is an algebra, $P_n(f) \in \mathcal{A}$. Consequently, $|f| \in \overline{\mathcal{A}}$. It follows from the
equalities

$$\sup(f, g) = \frac{f + g}{2} + \frac{|f - g|}{2} \quad \text{and} \quad \inf(f, g) = \frac{f + g}{2} - \frac{|f - g|}{2}$$

that if f and g belong to $\mathcal{A}$, then the functions $\sup(f, g)$ and $\inf(f, g)$ belong
to the closure $\overline{\mathcal{A}}$.

Next, let $h \in \mathcal{C}(K, \mathbb{R})$, $\varepsilon > 0$, and let s and t be two points of K. By the
separating hypothesis, there exists an $f \in \mathcal{A}$ such that $f(s) \neq f(t)$. Let

$$g = \frac{h(s)}{f(s) - f(t)}(f - f(t)) + \frac{h(t)}{f(t) - f(s)}(f - f(s)).$$

The function g equals h at the two points s and t. Since the space $\mathcal{A}$ contains
the constant functions, it follows that $g \in \mathcal{A}$. We denote this function by $g_{s,t}$.
Since $(g_{s,t} - h)(s) = 0$, the continuity of these functions implies the existence,
for every point s of K, of an open neighborhood $U(s)$ of s such that

$$\forall u \in U(s), \quad g_{s,t}(u) \geqslant h(u) - \varepsilon.$$

Since the $U(s)$ cover the compact space K when we let s vary in K, we can
find a finite number p of such points, say $(s_i)_{1 \leqslant i \leqslant p}$, such that

$$K \subset \bigcup_{1 \leqslant i \leqslant p} U(s_i).$$

Keeping t fixed, we now define $g_t = \sup_{1 \leqslant i \leqslant p} g_{s_i, t}$. By the above, as $\mathcal{A}$ is an
algebra, $g_t \in \overline{\mathcal{A}}$. For any $u \in K$, there exists an s_i such that $u \in U(s_i)$. We
thus have: $\forall u \in U(s_i), \quad g_t(u) \geqslant g_{s_i, t}(u) \geqslant h(u) - \varepsilon$, whence

$$(*) \qquad\qquad \forall u \in K, \quad g_t(u) \geqslant h(u) - \varepsilon.$$

Moreover, as $g_{s_i,t}(t) = h(t)$, we have $g_t(t) = h(t)$. It follows from the continuity at t that there exists an open neighborhood $V(t)$ of t such that $\forall u \in V(t)$, $g_t(u) \leqslant h(u) + \varepsilon$. Extracting a finite subcover $V(t_j)$ from the family of open subsets $V(t)$, we let $g = \inf g_{t_j}$. By $(*)$, we have

$(**)$ $$\forall u \in K, \quad g(u) \geqslant h(u) - \varepsilon.$$

Finally, we note that $|g - h| \leqslant \varepsilon$; indeed, for every j, we have $g_{t_j} \leqslant h + \varepsilon$. Given $u \in K$, there exists an integer j such that $u \in V(t_j)$; hence

$(***)$ $$g(u) \leqslant g_{t_j}(u) \leqslant h(u) + \varepsilon.$$

The result follows from $(**)$ and $(***)$. We have, in fact, shown the following property:

$$\forall h \in \mathcal{C}(K),\ \exists g \in \overline{\mathcal{A}}, \quad \|g - h\|_{\mathcal{C}(K)} = \sup_{u \in K} |g(u) - h(u)| \leqslant \varepsilon. \qquad \square$$

Theorem 1.55 (Ascoli–Arzelà). *Let Ω be a bounded domain in $\mathbb{R}^N$. A subset K of $\mathcal{C}(\overline{\Omega})$ is precompact in $\mathcal{C}(\overline{\Omega})$ if and only if*

(1) There exists an $M > 0$ such that $\forall \Phi \in K$, $\forall x \in \Omega$, $|\phi(x)| \leqslant M$.
(2) $\forall \varepsilon > 0$, $\exists \delta > 0$, $\forall \phi \in K$, $\forall (x,y) \in \Omega$, $|x - y| < \delta \Rightarrow |\phi(x) - \phi(y)| < \varepsilon$.

A proof of Theorem 1.55 can be found in [28], as well as a proof of the following proposition, whose second statement is a corollary of it.

Proposition 1.56. *In an open subset Ω of $\mathbb{R}^N$, we have the following embeddings :*

(1.57) $$\forall m \in \mathbb{N}, \quad \mathcal{C}^{m+1}(\overline{\Omega}) \hookrightarrow \mathcal{C}^m(\overline{\Omega})$$
(1.58) $$\forall (\lambda, \mu) \in \mathbb{R}^2, \quad 0 < \nu < \lambda \leqslant 1 \implies \mathcal{C}^{m,\lambda}(\Omega) \hookrightarrow \mathcal{C}^{m,\nu}(\Omega)$$

If Ω is bounded, then the second embedding is compact. The first is compact if, moreover, Ω is convex, or if, more generally, there exists an integer K such that any two of its points can be joined by a piecewise linear curve consisting of at most K segments in Ω.

1.4 Distributions on an Open Subset of $\mathbb{R}^N$

1.4.1 Spaces of Regular Functions on an Open Set Ω

Let Ω be an open subset of $\mathbb{R}^N$.

Definitions and Algebraic Structure. For any $k \in \overline{\mathbb{N}}$, we denote by $\mathcal{E}^k(\Omega)$ the set of $\mathcal{C}^k$ functions on Ω. For any compact subset K of $\mathbb{R}^N$ contained in Ω, we denote by $\mathcal{D}_K^k(\Omega)$ the set of $\mathcal{C}^k$ functions f on Ω with $\mathrm{supp}(f) \subset K$.

The set of functions f in $\mathcal{E}^k$ such that $\mathrm{supp}(f)$ is a compact subset of Ω is denoted by $\mathcal{D}^k(\Omega)$. We therefore have

$$\mathcal{D}^k(\Omega) = \bigcup_{K,\ \mathrm{compact}\ \subset \Omega} \mathcal{D}_K^k(\Omega).$$

The set of infinitely differentiable functions on Ω with compact support in Ω, which we denote by $\mathcal{D}(\Omega)$, or sometimes $\mathcal{C}_c^\infty(\Omega)$, is a special case since $\mathcal{D}(\Omega) = \mathcal{D}^\infty(\Omega)$.

It is clear that these definitions give vector spaces over $\mathbb{C}$.

Information Concerning the Topologies. In what follows, the differentiation indices will be N-tuples $\alpha = (\alpha_1, \alpha_2, \ldots, \alpha_N)$, where α_i is the order of the partial derivative in the variable x_i and the total order of the derivative is denoted by $|\alpha| = \sum_i \alpha_i$. We will use the following shortened notation:

$$D^\alpha(f) = \frac{\partial^{|\alpha|} f}{\partial x_1^{\alpha_1} \cdots \partial x_N^{\alpha_N}}.$$

Let us fix a nonnegative integer k. For any $\varphi \in \mathcal{E}^k(\Omega)$, integer $m \leqslant k$, and compact subset K of Ω, we let

$$\eta_{m,K}(\varphi) = \sup_{|\alpha| \leqslant m} \sup_{x \in K} \left| D^\alpha \varphi(x) \right|.$$

For any pair (m, K), this gives a seminorm on $\mathcal{E}^k(\Omega)$. The family of such seminorms is directed and separating (cf. Example 1.7).

It follows, as has already been stated in Proposition 1.6, that the family $\mathcal{B}$ of closed balls $B_{m,K}(r) = \{f \mid \eta_{m,K}(f) \leqslant r\}$ associated with these seminorms is a fundamental system of neighborhoods at the origin for a topology of locally compact Hausdorff space. By translation, we deduce a fundamental system of neighborhoods at any arbitrary element φ_0.

Note that in this locally compact space, the seminorms defined above are continuous.

Countable Family of Bases of Neighborhoods. Let us consider an increasing sequence of relatively compact open subsets $\{\Omega_j\}$ of Ω such that $\overline{\Omega_j} \subset \Omega_{j+1}$ and $\Omega = \bigcup \Omega_j$. The reader can easily show the existence of such a sequence.

If we set $K_j = \overline{\Omega_j}$, then the family of seminorms $\{\eta_{m,K_j}\}$ is a basis of (continuous) seminorms in the locally compact space $\mathcal{E}^k(\Omega)$. In other words, the closed balls associated with this family of seminorms also form a fundamental system of neighborhoods of 0 in $\mathcal{E}^k(\Omega)$.

Consequently, we can say that the space contains a *countable fundamental system of neighborhoods of* 0. Moreover, if $\{U_n\}$ is such a countable fundamental system, then setting $V_n = \bigcap_{m \leqslant n} U_m$ gives a fundamental system of decreasing neighborhoods of 0. We endow $\mathcal{D}_K^k(\Omega)$ with the induced topology. The same construction can be used for the space $\mathcal{E}^\infty(\Omega)$.

Let us now consider the space $\mathcal{D}^k(\Omega)$ for $k \leqslant +\infty$. Using the open cover above, $\mathcal{D}^k(\Omega)$ can be seen as the union of an increasing sequence of vector subspaces, namely the $\mathcal{D}_{K_j}^k(\Omega)$ with $\overline{\Omega_j} = K_j$.

Next, consider the set $\mathcal{B}$ of absorbing and balanced (cf. Definition 1.1) convex subsets B of $\mathcal{D}^k(\Omega)$ such that

$$\forall j \in \mathbb{N}, \quad B \cap \mathcal{D}_{K_j}^k(\Omega) \text{ is a neighborhood of 0 in } \mathcal{D}_{K_j}^k(\Omega).$$

We use without proof (cf. Exercise 1.4) that $\mathcal{B}$ is a fundamental system of neighborhoods of 0 for a topology of locally compact Hausdorff space, and that this topology is independent of the Ω_j. Moreover, for any compact subset K, the topology on $\mathcal{D}_K^k(\Omega)$ is induced by this topology.

In the remainder of this book, we will call this topology the *natural topology on* $\mathcal{D}^k(\Omega)$.

We will also admit without proof the following characterization of a neighborhood of 0 in a space $\mathcal{D}^k(\Omega)$, which still holds when we replace k by ∞.

Proposition 1.59. *A convex subset U of $\mathcal{D}^k(\Omega)$ is a neighborhood of 0 for the natural topology on $\mathcal{D}^k(\Omega)$ if and only if, for every K_j, the intersection $U \cap \mathcal{D}_{K_j}^k(\Omega)$ is a neighborhood of 0 for the topology on $\mathcal{D}_{K_j}^k(\Omega)$.*

Bounded Subsets and Convergent Sequences in the Locally Convex Space $\mathcal{D}^k(\Omega)$. In the space $X = \mathcal{D}^k(\Omega)$ endowed with the topology associated with an increasing sequence of locally convex subspaces, we can characterize the bounded subsets and convergent sequences using a consequence of the *Dieudonné–Schwartz theorem*. Let us state part of this theorem, which will be useful when we study distributions.

Proposition 1.60 (Dieudonné–Schwartz). *For fixed $k \leqslant \infty$, we endow $\mathcal{D}^k(\Omega)$ with its natural topology of locally compact space.*

(1) *A subset B of $\mathcal{D}^k(\Omega)$ is bounded if and only if there exists a compact subset K of Ω such that*

$$\forall \varphi \in B, \ \text{supp}(\varphi) \subset K \quad and \quad \forall m \leqslant k, \ \sup_{\varphi \in B} \eta_{m,K}(\varphi) < +\infty.$$

(2) *A sequence $\{\varphi_n\}$ converges to 0 in $\mathcal{D}^k(\Omega)$ if and only if there exists a compact subset K of Ω such that $\forall n$, $\text{supp}(\varphi_n) \subset K$ and*

$$\forall (\alpha) \in (\mathbb{N})^N, \quad |\alpha| \leqslant k \Longrightarrow \{D^\alpha \varphi_n\} \longrightarrow 0 \text{ uniformly on } K.$$

1.4.2 Regularization of Functions, Applications

In many problems we wish to approximate a locally summable function by a C^∞ function. Classically, we use the convolution with what we call a *regularizing sequence (or family)* $\{\rho_\varepsilon\}$.

Construction of $\{\rho_\varepsilon\}$. Let ρ be a function in $\mathcal{D}(\mathbb{R}^N)$ with positive values such that $\rho(x) = 0$ for $|x| \geqslant 1$ and $\int_{\mathbb{R}^N} \rho(x)dx = 1$. We can, for example, take

$$\rho(x) = \begin{cases} k \exp\left(-\dfrac{1}{1-|x|^2}\right) & \text{if } |x| < 1, \\ 0 & \text{if } |x| > 1, \end{cases}$$

with k such that $\int_{\mathbb{R}^N} \rho(x)dx = 1$. We then define ρ_ε by setting

(1.61) $$\rho_\varepsilon(x) = \varepsilon^{-N}\rho(x/\varepsilon).$$

By taking, for example, $\varepsilon = 1/j$, we obtain a so-called *regularizing* sequence.

Convolution with Summable f with Compact Support. Let f be such a function on $\mathbb{R}^N$. Let $v = f \star \rho_\varepsilon$ be the function defined by

$$\forall x \in \mathbb{R}^N, \quad v(x) = \int_{\mathbb{R}^N} f(t)\rho_\varepsilon(x-t)dt = \int_{\mathbb{R}^N} f(x-t)\rho_\varepsilon(t)dt.$$

Take x in the complement of $\text{supp}(f) + \overline{B(0,\varepsilon)}$; then for any t in the support of f, we have $|x - t| > \varepsilon$, whence $v(x) = 0$. The support of the convolution $v = f \star \rho_\varepsilon$ is therefore contained in $\text{supp}(f) + \overline{B(0,\varepsilon)}$.

Moreover, if x_0 belongs to this neighborhood, we can apply the Lebesgue differentiation theorem, which allows us to take derivatives of arbitrary order with respect to x under the integral sign. Consequently,

$$\forall \alpha \in \mathbb{N}^N, \quad D^\alpha(f \star \rho_\varepsilon) = f \star D^\alpha(\rho_\varepsilon).$$

We conclude that $f \star \rho_\varepsilon \in \mathcal{D}(\mathbb{R}^N)$.

By assuming that the support of f is included in the open set Ω, there exists an ε sufficiently small that $\text{supp}(f) + \overline{B(0,\varepsilon)} \subset \Omega$. Since any element of $\mathcal{D}(\Omega)$ extended by 0 outside of Ω is clearly a $\mathcal{D}(\mathbb{R}^N)$ function with support in Ω, it follows that $f \star \rho_\varepsilon \in \mathcal{D}(\Omega)$.

Convolution with a C^k Function f with Compact Support. Let us take $k = 0$. For a continuous function u, consider $d_\delta(x) = u \star \rho_\delta(x) - u(x)$. Using the integral of ρ_δ, which equals 1, we can write

$$|d_\delta(x)| = \left| \int_{\mathbb{R}^N} u(x-t)\rho_\delta(t)dt - \int_{\mathbb{R}^N} u(x)\rho_\delta(t)dt \right|$$

$$\leqslant \int_{\mathbb{R}^N} |u(x-t) - u(x)|\rho_\delta(t)dt.$$

The function u is uniformly continuous on the compact set $K = \operatorname{supp}(u) + \overline{B}(0,1)$. Therefore, there exists a $\delta > 0$ such that $|t| < \delta \Rightarrow |u(x-t)-u(x)| \leqslant \varepsilon$. Consequently, $\|d_\delta\|_\infty \leqslant \varepsilon \int_{\mathbb{R}^N} \rho_\delta(t)dt = \varepsilon$.

For $k = 1$ we will use the property that the derivative of a convolution equals the convolution of either of the functions with the derivative of the other. The reasoning remains the same for all values of k by induction, and we can conclude that $\eta_{m,K}(u\star\rho_\delta - u) \to 0$. Summarizing, we have the following result.

Proposition 1.62. *Let f be a summable function on Ω with compact support in Ω; then for ε small enough, the convolution $f \star \rho_\varepsilon$ is an element of $\mathcal{D}(\Omega)$.*

If for every nonnegative integer k, f belongs to $\mathcal{D}^k(\Omega)$, then when $\varepsilon \to 0$, the family $\{f \star \rho_\varepsilon\}$ tends to f in the locally compact space $\mathcal{D}^k(\Omega)$.

In particular, for any $k \in \mathbb{N}$, $\mathcal{D}(\Omega)$ is dense when considered as a subspace of $\mathcal{D}^k(\Omega)$.

We will use these properties of regularizing sequences again when studying the spaces $L^p(\Omega)$ (Section 1.5).

1.4.3 Continuous Linear Functionals on These Spaces; Distributions

Definition 1.63. A distribution on Ω is a linear functional on $\mathcal{D}(\Omega)$ that is continuous for the natural locally convex topology.

For $k \in \mathbb{N}$, a distribution on Ω of order at most k is a linear functional on $\mathcal{D}(\Omega)$ that is continuous for the natural locally convex topology of $\mathcal{D}^k(\Omega)$.

A distribution has order exactly $k \geqslant 1$ if it cannot be extended to a linear functional that is continuous on $\mathcal{D}^{k-1}(\Omega)$.

We denote the corresponding spaces of continuous linear functionals by $\mathcal{D}'(\Omega)$ and $\mathcal{D}'^k(\Omega)$. They are the duals of $\mathcal{D}(\Omega)$ and $\mathcal{D}^k(\Omega)$.

Continuity Condition for a Linear Functional. We begin by stating (cf. Exercise 1.24) a necessary and sufficient condition for the continuity of a linear functional that uses the fundamental system of neighborhoods of 0 defined using the family of seminorms $\{\eta_\lambda\}$ that generate the topology of a locally convex space X.

Proposition 1.64. *A linear functional T on X is continuous if and only if*

$$\exists \lambda, \ \exists M > 0, \ \forall x \in X, \quad |T(x)| \leqslant M\eta_\lambda(x).$$

The importance of the existence of countable fundamental systems of neighborhoods in locally convex spaces is clear in the following two propositions. The second one characterizes distributions.

Proposition 1.65. *Let T be a linear functional on one of the spaces $\mathcal{E}^k(\Omega)$, $\mathcal{E}^k_K(\Omega)$; then T is continuous if and only it is sequentially continuous, that is,*

$$\{x_n\} \longrightarrow 0 \implies \{T(x_n)\} \longrightarrow 0.$$

Proof.

Let $\{V_n\}$ be a countable fundamental system of decreasing neighborhoods of 0 in $X = \mathcal{E}^k(\Omega)$ (cf. Subsection 1.4.1). Let us assume that the linear functional T on this space is sequentially continuous but not continuous. There then exists an open disc D with center 0 in $\mathbb{C}$ such that $T^{-1}(D)$ does not contain any element V_n of the fundamental system. Let C be the complement of $T^{-1}(D)$ in X. Let us then take a sequence $\{x_n\}$ in X such that $x_n \in V_n \cap C$. This sequence tends to 0 in X while for any n, $T(x_n) \notin D$. Consequently, T is not sequentially continuous, contradicting the assumption. $\qquad\square$

Let us now consider the continuity of the linear functionals on $X = \mathcal{D}^k(\Omega)$. By the definition of the locally convex topology on $X = \mathcal{D}^k(\Omega)$, where $k \leqslant +\infty$, a linear functional T on X is continuous if and only if its restrictions T_j to the subspaces $X_j = \mathcal{D}^k_{K_j}(\Omega)$ are continuous.

Indeed, if T is continuous on X and D is an open disc with center 0 in $\mathbb{C}$, then the convex set $T^{-1}(D)$ is a neighborhood of 0 in X. By the definition of the topology on X, $(T_j)^{-1}(D) = T^{-1}(D) \cap X_j$ is then a neighborhood of 0 in X_j, giving the continuity of T_j. The equality above proves the converse. Summarizing, we find the following characterization of distributions, or rather of distributions of order $\leqslant k$.

Proposition 1.66. *Let T be a linear functional on $X_k = \mathcal{D}^k(\Omega)$, where $k \in \mathbb{N} \cup \{+\infty\}$. The following three properties are equivalent:*

(1) *The linear functional T is continuous on X_k.*
(2) *The linear functional T is sequentially continuous on X_k.*
(3) *For any compact $K \subset \Omega$, the restriction of T to the space $\mathcal{D}^k_K(\Omega)$ is continuous. In other words, there exist a $C > 0$ and an integer $m \leqslant k$ ($m \in \mathbb{N}$ in the case $X_\infty = \mathcal{D}(\Omega)$) such that*

$$\forall \varphi \in X_k, \quad |\langle T, \varphi \rangle| \leqslant C\eta_{m,K}(\varphi).$$

Proof.

The proof of the equivalence of (1) and (2) is analogous to that of Proposition 1.65. Above, we expressed their equivalence to the continuity of the restrictions to the spaces $\mathcal{D}^k_{K_i}(\Omega)$. The fact that every compact subset is included in some K_j and the characterization given in Proposition 1.64 give the equivalence with (3). $\qquad\square$

Remark 1.67. To apply the condition of sequential continuity, we must not forget the condition that the sequences of $\mathcal{D}(\Omega)$ converge to 0, established in the Dieudonné–Schwartz theorem 1.60.

1.4.4 Examples

We leave it to the reader to show the (sequential) continuity of the linear functionals considered below.

Example 1.68 (distribution associated with a function). Let f be a locally summable function on Ω. We associate with it a distribution, called regular, and denoted by T_f or $[f]$, as follows:

$$\varphi \in \mathcal{D}(\Omega), \quad \langle T_f, \varphi \rangle = \int_\Omega f(x)\varphi(x)dx.$$

Example 1.69 (Dirac distribution). We define the Dirac distribution at $a \in \mathbb{R}^N$ by

$$\varphi \in \mathcal{D}(\mathbb{R}^N), \quad \langle \delta_a, \varphi \rangle = \varphi(a).$$

There is no function f such that $\delta_a = [f]$. Consequently, this distribution is called singular. It has order $\leqslant 0$.

Example 1.70 (*principal value* distribution). In the case $N = 1$, we define the principal value of $1/x$ by

$$\varphi \in \mathcal{D}(\mathbb{R}), \quad \langle \text{Vp}(1/x), \varphi \rangle = \lim_{\varepsilon \to 0} \int_{|x| \geqslant \varepsilon} \frac{\varphi(x)}{x} dx.$$

We can also write

$$\lim_{\varepsilon \to 0} \int_{|x| \geqslant \varepsilon} \frac{\varphi(x)}{x} dx = \int_\mathbb{R} \frac{\varphi(x) - \varphi(-x)}{x} dx.$$

We can show the continuity of $\text{Vp}(1/x)$ using the mean value theorem. The order of this distribution is finite and $\leqslant 1$.

Example 1.71 (*Hadamard finite part* distribution). Let $N \geqslant 1$. The function $x \mapsto f(x) = 1/|x|^N$ is not locally summable on $\mathbb{R}^N$. We define the distribution $T = \text{Pf}(1/|x|^N)$ by setting:

$$\forall \varphi \in \mathcal{D}(\mathbb{R}^N), \quad \langle \text{Pf}(1/|x|^N), \varphi \rangle = \lim_{\varepsilon \to 0} \left[\int_{|x| \geqslant \varepsilon} \frac{\varphi(x)}{|x|^N} dx + \omega_{N-1}\varphi(0)\ln(\varepsilon) \right],$$

where ω_{N-1} is the area of the unit sphere in $\mathbb{R}^N$. We can show that the order of the distribution is $\leqslant 1$.

Likewise, we define the Hadamard finite part distribution of $1/|x|^{N+1}$, which will play an important role in the study of the *Riesz transforms* (cf. Chapter 7). It is the distribution that maps $\varphi \in \mathcal{D}(\mathbb{R}^N)$ to the number

$$\left\langle \mathrm{Pf}(1/|x|^{N+1}), \varphi \right\rangle = \lim_{\varepsilon \to 0} \left[\int_{|x| \geqslant \varepsilon} \frac{\varphi(x)}{|x|^{N+1}} \, dx - \omega_{N-1} \frac{\varphi(0)}{\varepsilon} \right].$$

1.4.5 Topologies on the Space of Distributions $\mathcal{D}'(\Omega)$

As is the case for normed spaces, we can put many topologies of locally convex space on the dual $\mathcal{D}'$. More particularly, we define the norm topology and weak topology on this dual using seminorms.

Weak Topology on $\mathcal{D}'$. To an arbitrary finite subset F of $\mathcal{D}(\Omega)$, we associate the seminorm

$$\forall T \in \mathcal{D}'(\Omega), \quad p_F(T) = \sup_{\varphi \in F} |\langle T, \varphi \rangle|.$$

We can easily see that this defines a directed and separating family of seminorms on $\mathcal{D}'(\Omega)$. We can therefore apply Proposition 1.6. It follows that the family of closed balls associated with the p_F forms a fundamental system of neighborhoods of 0 for a topology of locally convex Hausdorff space. For this topology, which we call the weak topology, the convergence of a sequence $\{T_n\}$, and therefore also that of a series, is equivalent to pointwise convergence on $\mathcal{D}(\Omega)$.

Proposition 1.72. *The sequence $\{T_n\}$ in $\mathcal{D}'(\Omega)$ converges to T in $\mathcal{D}'$ for the weak topology on the dual if*

$$\forall \varphi \in \mathcal{D}(\Omega), \quad \langle T_n, \varphi \rangle \longrightarrow \langle T, \varphi \rangle.$$

The proof of the following proposition can be found in [22].

Proposition 1.73. *If (T_n) is a sequence in $\mathcal{D}'(\Omega)$ such that for any $\varphi \in \mathcal{D}(\Omega)$, $\langle T_n, \varphi \rangle$ converges to a finite limit, then the T_n converge weakly, that is (see Remark 1.74 below), converge in the sense of distributions.*

Norm Topology on $\mathcal{D}'(\Omega)$. Let B be a bounded subset of $\mathcal{D}(\Omega)$. By Proposition 1.60, this means that B is included in some $\mathcal{D}_K(\Omega)$ and that the seminorms $\eta_{m,K}$ are bounded on B. By analogy with the case of normed spaces, we replace the finite subsets by bounded subsets in the previous definition. In other words, we consider the seminorms p_B and the associated closed balls. The resulting topology of locally convex Hausdorff space is called the norm topology on the dual $\mathcal{D}'(\Omega)$ (cf. Exercise 1.19).

Remark 1.74. We will admit the following property without proof: a *sequence* of distributions converges to 0 for the weak topology on the dual if and only if it converges to 0 for the norm topology on the dual.

Consequently, in statements concerning sequences or series we will not specify the topology in question. We will simply talk of convergence.

1.4.6 Operations on Distributions

In addition to the algebraic operations associated with the structure of vector space, we will consider the following operations.

Definition 1.75. Let α be a $\mathcal{C}^\infty$ function on Ω and let $T \in \mathcal{D}'(\Omega)$. We let αT denote the distribution such that

$$\forall \varphi \in \mathcal{D}(\Omega), \quad \langle \alpha T, \varphi \rangle = \langle T, \alpha \varphi \rangle.$$

We can verify that αT is indeed a distribution, and that the linear map $T \mapsto \alpha T$ from $\mathcal{D}'(\Omega)$ to itself is continuous, both for the norm topology and for the weak topology.

For example, we easily see that, for any locally summable function f on $\mathbb{R}^N$, we have $\alpha[f] = [\alpha f]$, and that $\alpha \delta_a = \alpha(a)\delta_a$. In particular if $\alpha(a) = 0$, we get $\alpha \delta_a = 0$. When $N = 1$, if $(x-a)T = 0$, there exists a constant C such that $T = C\delta_a$. We can also verify that $x \operatorname{Vp}(1/x) = 1$.

Definition 1.76. Let $h \in \mathbb{R}^N$ and let $T \in \mathcal{D}'(\mathbb{R}^N)$. We define the translation of T with index h, denoted by $\tau_h T$ or T_h, by

$$\forall \varphi \in \mathcal{D}(\mathbb{R}^N), \quad \langle T_h, \varphi \rangle = \langle T, \tau_{-h}\varphi \rangle,$$

where $(\tau_{-h}\varphi)(x) = \varphi(x + h)$.

We can easily see that T_h is a distribution.

1.4.7 Support of a Distribution

Definition 1.77. We call an open subset $\mathcal{O}$ of Ω a vanishing set for an element T of $\mathcal{D}'(\Omega)$ if for every $\varphi \in \mathcal{D}(\Omega)$ with compact support in $\mathcal{O}$, we have $\langle T, \varphi \rangle = 0$.

We can show that the union of all vanishing sets of T is also a vanishing set. Consequently, we can give the following definition.

Definition 1.78. The support of T, denoted by $\operatorname{supp} T$, is the complement of the largest vanishing set of T.

Example 1.79. The support of the distribution δ_a is $\{a\}$. If f is a locally summable function on Ω, then the support of the distribution $[f]$ equals the support of the function f, which is $\mathrm{supp}(f) = \overline{\{x \mid f(x) \neq 0\}}$.

Let us consider the following theorem.

Theorem 1.80. *Let T be a distribution with compact support K; then T can be extended to a continuous linear functional on the locally convex space $\mathcal{E}(\Omega)$ of C^∞ functions on Ω. In other words, it can be identified with an element of the dual $\mathcal{E}'(\Omega)$. In particular, if T has compact support, then the symbol $\langle T, \varphi \rangle$ is still defined if φ is only C^∞ on Ω.*

In the proof (cf. Exercise 1.20), we use a function $\alpha \in \mathcal{D}(\Omega)$ with value 1 on a neighborhood of K and extend T to $\widetilde{T}$ by setting

$$\forall \varphi \in \mathcal{E}(\Omega), \quad \langle \widetilde{T}, \varphi \rangle = \langle T, \alpha \varphi \rangle.$$

1.4.8 Derivation of Distributions

Definition 1.81. Let α be a multi-index and let T be a distribution on an open subset Ω of $\mathbb{R}^N$. The derivative $D^\alpha T$ is the linear functional on $\mathcal{D}(\Omega)$ defined by
$$\forall \varphi \in \mathcal{D}(\Omega), \quad \langle D^\alpha T, \varphi \rangle = (-1)^{|\alpha|} \langle T, D^\alpha \varphi \rangle.$$
This functional is a distribution on Ω.

When f is a $C^{|\alpha|}$ function, we have $D^\alpha[f] = [D^\alpha f]$. We can show that for the weak topology on $\mathcal{D}'$, given $h \in \mathbb{R}^N$ with $h = h_i e_i$, we have

$$\lim_{h_i \to 0} \frac{\tau_{-h} T - T}{h_i} = \frac{\partial T}{\partial x_i}.$$

Let us note the following property that follows from the definitions. If the sequence $\{T_n\}$ converges to T in $\mathcal{D}'$, then the sequence $\{D^\alpha(T_n)\}$ converges to $D^\alpha(T)$.

Example 1.82. The distribution $\mathrm{Vp}(1/x)$ is the derivative of the distribution $[f]$ associated with the locally summable function $x \mapsto f(x) = \ln|x|$.

The proof of the following proposition is given in [22].

Proposition 1.83. *If T is a distribution on $\mathbb{R}$ of order at most k, then the order of T' is at most $k + 1$. If T is of order $k \geqslant 1$, then T' is of order $k + 1$.*

Example 1.84 (of a derivation). Consider the function f on $\mathbb{R}^2$ defined by $f(x, y) = \min(x, y)$. Let us determine the mixed partial derivative of f in the sense of distributions. This example can be generalized to $\mathbb{R}^N$.

$$\left\langle \frac{\partial^2}{\partial x \partial y}[f], \varphi \right\rangle = \int_{-\infty}^{+\infty} \left[\int_{-\infty}^{+\infty} \min(x, y) \frac{\partial^2 \varphi}{\partial x \partial y}(x, y) dy \right] dx$$

$$= \int_{-\infty}^{+\infty} \left[\int_{-\infty}^{x} y \frac{\partial^2 \varphi}{\partial x \partial y}(x, y) dy + x \int_{x}^{+\infty} \frac{\partial^2 \varphi}{\partial x \partial y}(x, y) dy \right] dx.$$

The sum $J + K$ of the two integrals inside the square brackets can be computed as follows:

$$J + K = \left[y \frac{\partial \varphi}{\partial x}(x, y) \right]_{-\infty}^{x} - \int_{-\infty}^{x} \frac{\partial \varphi}{\partial x}(x, y) dy + x \left[\frac{\partial \varphi}{\partial x}(x, y) \right]_{x}^{+\infty}$$

$$= - \int_{-\infty}^{x} \frac{\partial \varphi}{\partial x}(x, y) dy.$$

Consequently, using Fubini's theorem one more time, we have

$$\left\langle \frac{\partial^2}{\partial x \partial y}[f], \varphi \right\rangle = - \int_{-\infty}^{+\infty} \int_{y}^{+\infty} \frac{\partial \varphi}{\partial x}(x, y) dy \, dx$$

$$= - \int_{-\infty}^{+\infty} \left[\varphi(x, y) \right]_{x=y}^{+\infty} dy$$

$$= \int_{-\infty}^{+\infty} \varphi(y, y) dy = \int_{-\infty}^{+\infty} \varphi(x, x) dx.$$

The result can be written as $\langle \delta_\Delta, \varphi \rangle$ and can be interpreted as the action on the test function φ of the Dirac distribution with support the line Δ in $\mathbb{R}^2$ with equation $y = x$.

Example 1.85. On $\mathbb{R}^N$, consider a continuous function h of the $N - 1$ variables $x_1, \ldots, x_{N-1}$. We define the function $\mathcal{U}_h$ by setting $\mathcal{U}_h(x) = 1$ if $x_N \geqslant h(x_1, \ldots, x_{N-1})$ and $\mathcal{U}_h(x) = 0$ otherwise. Let us take the derivative with respect to x_N.

Let $x' = (x_1, x_2, \ldots, x_{N-1})$. By applying Fubini's theorem, we obtain

$$\left\langle \frac{\partial}{\partial x_N}[\mathcal{U}_h], \varphi \right\rangle = - \left\langle [\mathcal{U}_h], \frac{\partial}{\partial x_N} \varphi \right\rangle = - \int_{\mathbb{R}^N} \left[\mathcal{U}_h \frac{\partial}{\partial x_N} \varphi \right] dx$$

$$= - \int_{\mathbb{R}^{N-1}} \left[\int_{h(x')}^{+\infty} \frac{\partial}{\partial x_N} \varphi(x', x_N) dx_N \right] dx'$$

$$= \int_{\mathbb{R}^{N-1}} \varphi(x', h(x')) dx'.$$

This result can be interpreted as the action of φ on a Dirac distribution with support the surface with Cartesian equation $x_N = h(x')$.

Indefinite Integration.

Proposition 1.86. *If $T \in \mathcal{D}'(\Omega)$, then T admits infinitely many indefinite integrals that can be deduced from each other by adding a constant.*

This concludes our summary of results on distributions. We will give additional information on tempered distributions in Chapter 4.

1.5 The Spaces L^p for $p \in [1, +\infty]$

We assume known the definitions of (Lebesgue) measurable functions and of the space $L^1(\Omega)$ of summable functions on Ω, endowed with the norm defined by $\|f\|_1 = \int_{\Omega} |f(x)| dx$.

Definition 1.87. The space of functions on Ω with summable pth powers is defined by

$$L^p(\Omega, \mathbb{C}) = \{u \text{ measurable on } \Omega, \text{ with values in } \mathbb{C} \mid |u|^p \in L^1\}.$$

This is a normed space thanks to the Minkowski inequality. The norm, which is denoted by $\|\cdot\|_p$ or $\|\cdot\|_{L^p}$, is defined by

$$\|f\|_p = \left[\int_{\Omega} |f(x)|^p dx \right]^{1/p}.$$

Definition 1.88. Let $L^\infty(\Omega)$ be the space of measurable functions f such that

$$\exists \alpha > 0, \quad \text{mes } E_\alpha = \text{mes}\{x \mid |f(x)| > \alpha\} = 0.$$

This is a normed space with norm $\|f\|_\infty = \inf_{\{\alpha \mid \text{mes}(E_\alpha)=0\}} \alpha$.

1.5.1 Hölder's Inequality and the Completeness of L^p

For $f \in L^p(\Omega)$ and $g \in L^{p'}(\Omega)$ with real numbers p and p' satisfying $1 < p < \infty$ and $1/p + 1/p' = 1$, we have the inequality

$$\int_{\Omega} |f(x)g(x)| dx \leq \left[\int_{\Omega} |f(x)|^p dx \right]^{1/p} \left[\int_{\Omega} |g(x)|^{p'} dx \right]^{1/p'}.$$

This inequality can be generalized by considering real numbers $p_j > 1$ such that the sum of their inverses equals 1:

$$\forall f_j \in L^{p_j}, \quad \int_{\Omega} \left| \prod f_j(x) \right| dx \leq \prod \left[\left(\int_{\Omega} |f_j(x)|^{p_j} dx \right)^{1/p_j} \right].$$

Theorem 1.89. *The space $L^p(\Omega)$ is complete.*

Proof of Theorem 1.89.

We begin with the case $p \in [1, \infty[$. Let (u_n) be a Cauchy sequence for the norm on L^p. We extract a subsequence such that

$$\|u_{n_{j+1}} - u_{n_j}\|_p \leqslant \frac{1}{2^j}.$$

Let

$$(1.90) \qquad v(x) = \lim_{J \to \infty} \sum_{j=1}^{j=J} (u_{n_{j+1}} - u_{n_j})(x).$$

By the Minkowski inequality, we have

$$\left(\int_\Omega |v|^p \right)^{1/p} \leqslant \lim_{J \to \infty} \sum_{1}^{J} \left(\int_\Omega |(u_{n_{j+1}} - u_{n_j})|^p \right)^{1/p}.$$

Consequently, the set of points where v is infinite has measure zero. Moreover, v is almost everywhere the limit of a sequence of measurable functions, hence is itself measurable. By the previous inequality, $v \in L^p$ and v is the limit in L^p of a subsequence of u_n because

$$\|v - u_{n_J}\|_p = \left\| \sum_{j \geqslant J+1} (u_{n_{j+1}} - u_{n_j}) \right\|_p \leqslant \frac{1}{2^J}.$$

Since any Cauchy sequence has only one limit point, the sequence $\{u_n\}$ converges to v, concluding the proof of Theorem 1.89 for $p \in [1, \infty[$. □

Next, let $p = \infty$. We consider a Cauchy sequence $\{u_n\}$. We define the sets $A_k = \{x \mid |u_k(x)| > \|u_k\|_\infty\}$ and $B_{n,m} = \{x \mid |u_n - u_m|(x) > \|u_n - u_m\|_\infty\}$. The union of the A_k and $B_{n,m}$ has measure zero. Moreover, the sequence u_n is uniformly convergent on the complement. Let u be its limit. We can easily see that $u \in L^\infty$ and $\lim \|u_n - u\|_\infty = 0$. □

Let us now consider the density of the regular functions.

1.5.2 Density of the Regular Functions

We assume know the property $\overline{\mathcal{C}_c(\Omega)}^{L^1(\Omega)} = L^1(\Omega)$.

Theorem 1.91. *Let Ω be an open subset of $\mathbb{R}^N$; then for any p with $1 < p < \infty$, the space $\mathcal{D}(\Omega)$ is dense in the normed space $L^p(\Omega)$.*

Proof of Theorem 1.91.

Let $u \in L^p(\Omega)$. We begin by approximating u by a sequence of continuous functions with values in $\mathbb{C}$ and compact support. We begin by carrying out a series of reductions of the problem.

(1) We reduce to u real by noting that if u is measurable and such that $|u|^p \in L^1(\Omega)$, then its real and imaginary parts have these same properties. Moreover, if $(u_n, v_n) \in (\mathcal{C}_c(\Omega, \mathbb{R}))^2$ converge to $(\Re e\, u, \Im m\, u)$, then $u_n + iv_n \to u$.

(2) We reduce to u positive. Let $u = u^+ - u^-$. If $u \in L^p(\Omega)$, then the same holds for u^+ and u^-. Let $\{u_n^{(1)}\}$ and $\{u_n^{(2)}\}$ be sequences in $\mathcal{C}_c(\Omega, \mathbb{R})$ that converge to u^+ and u^-, respectively, in $L^p(\Omega)$; then $\{u_n^{(1)} - u_n^{(2)}\} \to u$ in $L^p(\Omega)$.

(3) Let u be nonnegative; then $u^p \in L^1(\Omega)$. By assumption, there exists a sequence $\{v_n\}$ of continuous functions with compact support that converges to u^p in $L^1(\Omega)$. By taking v_n^+, we may, and do, assume that $v_n \geq 0$ almost everywhere and that the sequence converges almost everywhere to u^p.

We may, and do, also assume that $\{v_n\}$ is dominated by an element of $L^1(\Omega)$. To reduce to this, we proceed as in the previous theorem. We extract a subsequence $\{v_{n_j}\}$ of $\{v_n\}$ and let $v_0 = 0$ and $v_J = \sum_1^J (v_{n_{j+1}} - v_{n_j})$, so that $\{\|v_J\|_{L^1}\}$ has an upper bound.

Summarizing, the sequence $\{v_J\}$ of continuous functions converges almost everywhere to u^p and has upper bound $g = \sum_0^{+\infty} |v_{n_{j+1}} - v_{n_j}|$, which belongs to $L^1(\Omega)$; hence $v_J^{1/p}$ converges almost everywhere to u and for almost all x, we have

$$\left| v_J^{1/p} - u \right|^p (x) \leq 2^{p-1} \left(\left| v_J^{p \cdot 1/p} \right| + |u^p| \right)(x) \leq 2^{p-1} (g + |u^p|)(x).$$

Consequently, by the dominated convergence theorem, $v_J^{1/p} - u$ tends to 0 in $L^p(\Omega)$.

Let ρ_ε be a regularizing sequence (cf. Section 1.4.2), let u be a function belonging to $L^p(\Omega)$, let δ be a positive integer, and let φ be a continuous function with compact support in Ω such that $\|u - \varphi\|_{L^p(\Omega)} \leq \delta$. Let ε be sufficiently small that if $|\operatorname{supp}(\varphi)|$ denotes the N-dimensional Lebesgue measure of the support of φ, we have

$$\|\rho_\varepsilon \star \varphi - \varphi\|_\infty \leq \frac{\delta}{(|(\operatorname{supp}(\varphi)| + 1)^{1/p}}.$$

Since $\rho_\varepsilon \star \varphi \in \mathcal{D}(\Omega)$, this concludes the proof thanks to

$$(1.92) \qquad \|u - \rho_\varepsilon \star \varphi\|_p \leq \|u - \varphi\|_p + \|\varphi - \rho_\varepsilon \star \varphi\|_p \leq 2\delta. \qquad \square$$

Let us note that in the case of $\mathbb{R}^N$, we have a more precise result, namely

$$(1.93) \qquad \forall u \in L^p(\mathbb{R}^N), \quad \|\rho_\varepsilon \star u\|_{L^p} \leqslant \|u\|_{L^p}.$$

Indeed, if p' denotes the conjugate of p, then Hölder's inequality gives

$$
\begin{aligned}
|\rho_\varepsilon \star u(x)| &= \left| \int_{\mathbb{R}^N} \rho_\varepsilon(x-y)u(y)dy \right| \\
&\leqslant \left(\int_{\mathbb{R}^N} \rho_\varepsilon(x-y)dy \right)^{1/p'} \left(\int_{\mathbb{R}^N} \rho_\varepsilon(x-y)|u(y)|^p dy \right)^{1/p} \\
&= \left(\int_{\mathbb{R}^N} \rho_\varepsilon(x-y)|u(y)|^p dy \right)^{1/p}.
\end{aligned}
$$

By taking the pth power, integrating with respect to x, and applying Fubini's theorem, we obtain the result (1.93).

Let us conclude with the case $\mathbb{R}^N$. Let $\delta > 0$ and let $\varphi \in C_c(\mathbb{R}^N)$ be such that $\|u - \varphi\|_p < \delta$. Moreover, let ε_0 be sufficiently small that

$$\varepsilon < \varepsilon_0 \implies \|\rho_\varepsilon \star \varphi - \varphi\|_p < \varepsilon.$$

The triangle inequality then gives the result

$$\|\rho_\varepsilon \star u - u\|_p \leqslant \|\rho_\varepsilon \star (u - \varphi)\|_p + \|\rho_\varepsilon \star \varphi - \varphi\|_p + \|\varphi - u\|_p \leqslant 3\delta. \qquad \square$$

Remark 1.94. The space $\mathcal{D}(\Omega)$ is clearly not dense in $L^\infty(\Omega)$ for the norm $\|\cdot\|_\infty$; indeed, density would imply the continuity of all functions in L^∞.

The following theorem will be useful for results concerning compact embeddings in Sobolev spaces. It gives necessary and sufficient conditions for a subset of $L^p(\Omega)$ to be precompact, that is, to have compact closure.

1.5.3 Compactness in the Spaces L^p

Theorem 1.95. *Let Ω be an open subset of $\mathbb{R}^N$ and let p be a real number with $1 \leqslant p < \infty$. A bounded subset K of $L^p(\Omega)$ is precompact in $L^p(\Omega)$ if and only if for every $\varepsilon > 0$ there exist a real number $\delta > 0$ and an open subset G with compact closure in Ω such that for every $u \in K$ and $h \in \mathbb{R}^N$ satisfying $|h| < \delta$ and $|h| < d(G, \partial\Omega)$, we have*

$$\int_G |u(x+h) - u(x)|^p dx < \varepsilon^p \quad \text{and} \quad \int_{\Omega \setminus \overline{G}} |u(x)|^p dx < \varepsilon^p.$$

Let us note that by extending u by 0 outside of Ω, we can replace G by Ω in the first condition.

Proof of Theorem 1.95.

We may assume that $\Omega = \mathbb{R}^N$. Indeed, it suffices to extend the functions by zero outside of Ω and replace K by

$$K' = \{u \in L^p(\mathbb{R}^N) \mid u \cdot 1_\Omega \in K\}.$$

The following arguments show that the precompactness of K in $L^p(\Omega)$ is equivalent to that of K' in $L^p(\mathbb{R}^N)$. Indeed, let $\varepsilon > 0$, and let $N(\varepsilon)$ be an integer such that if B_p^N is the open ball in $L^p(\mathbb{R}^N)$, we have the covering property $K' \subset \bigcup_{i \leqslant N(\varepsilon)} B_p^N(\varphi_i, \varepsilon)$ with $\varphi_i \in K'$. Then, if B_p denotes the open ball in $L^p(\Omega)$, we have

$$K \subset \bigcup_{i \leqslant N(\varepsilon)} B_p(\varphi_i|_\Omega, \varepsilon),$$

where the φ_i belong to K'. Conversely, if $K \subset \bigcup_{i \leqslant N(\varepsilon)} B_p(\varphi_i, \varepsilon)$, then $K' \subset \bigcup_{i \leqslant N(\varepsilon)} B_p^N(\widetilde{\varphi}_i, \varepsilon)$, where $\widetilde{\varphi}_i$ is the extension of φ by 0.

Let us now assume that K is a precompact bounded subset of $L^p(\mathbb{R}^N)$. We begin by showing that the condition in the theorem is necessary.

Given $\varepsilon > 0$, we can cover the precompact subset K by a finite number of balls $K_j = B_j(\psi_j, \varepsilon/6)$. By the density of the continuous functions with compact support in $L^p(\mathbb{R}^N)$, there exists a finite set S of such functions φ_j such that $\|\varphi_j - \psi_j\|_p \leqslant \varepsilon/6$. Consequently, if $u \in K$, there exists a j such that $u \in K_j$, whence

$$(1.96) \qquad \forall u \in K, \ \exists \varphi_u \in S, \quad \|u - \varphi_u\|_p < \frac{\varepsilon}{3}.$$

Since the set S is finite, there exists a ball B_r of radius r such that

$$\forall \varphi \in S, \quad \mathrm{supp}(\varphi) \subset B_r;$$

hence, outside of B_r, we have $u = u - \varphi_u$. We can therefore conclude that

$$(1.97) \qquad \forall u \in K, \ \int_{\mathbb{R}^N \setminus B_r} |u(x)|^p dx \leqslant \int_{\mathbb{R}^N} |u - \varphi_u|^p < \varepsilon^p.$$

The second condition of the theorem is therefore satisfied by taking $G = B_r$.

For the first condition, let h_0 be such that $|h| \leqslant h_0$ implies

$$(1.98) \qquad \forall \varphi \in S, \ \forall x \in B_r, \quad |\varphi(x+h) - \varphi(x)| < \frac{\varepsilon}{3|B_{r+h_0}|^{1/p}}.$$

This implies that $\int_\Omega |\varphi(x+h) - \varphi(x)|^p dx \leqslant \varepsilon^p/3^p$. It follows that for all $u \in K$,

$$\left(\int_\Omega |u(x+h) - u(x)|^p dx \right)^{1/p} \leqslant \left(\int_\Omega |u(x+h) - \varphi_u(x+h)|^p dx \right)^{1/p}$$
$$+ \left(\int_{B_r} |\varphi_u(x) - \varphi_u(x+h)|^p dx \right)^{1/p}$$
$$+ \left(\int_\Omega |u(x) - \varphi_u(x)|^p dx \right)^{1/p} \leqslant 3\frac{\varepsilon}{3}.$$

Conversely, let us show that if the conditions of Theorem 1.95 are verified, then K is precompact in $L^p(\mathbb{R}^N)$. In order to do this, let $\rho \in \mathcal{D}(\mathbb{R}^N)$ with $\rho \geqslant 0$, $\int_{\mathbb{R}^N} \rho(x) dx = 1$ and, for $\eta > 0$, let $\rho_\eta(x) = \eta^{-N} \rho(x/\eta)$ be the so-called *regularizing* function. Let us begin by verifying that given $\varepsilon > 0$ and the compact subset G of $\mathbb{R}^N$ of the theorem, there exists an $h_0 > 0$ such that if $\eta < h_0$, then

$$(1.99) \qquad \forall u \in K, \quad \int_G \left| (\rho_\eta \star u - u)(x) \right|^p dx \leqslant \varepsilon.$$

Indeed, thanks to Hölder's inequality and $\int_{\mathbb{R}^N} \rho(x) dx = 1$, we have almost everywhere

$$\left| \rho_\eta \star u - u \right|^p(x) \leqslant \int \rho_\eta(y) |u(x-y) - u(x)|^p dy$$
$$\leqslant \int \rho_\eta(y) |\tau_y u - u|^p(x) dy.$$

Integrating with respect to x in G, we have for h_0 sufficiently small:

$$\int_G \left| \rho_\eta \star u - u \right|^p \leqslant \sup_{h \in B_\eta} \int_G |\tau_h u - u|^p(x) dx \leqslant \varepsilon.$$

In particular, $\int_G |\rho_\eta \star u - u|^p$ uniformly tends to 0 for $u \in K$ when $\eta \to 0$. Let therefore η be fixed such that for every $u \in K$,

$$\int_G \left| \rho_\eta \star u - u \right|^p dx \leqslant \frac{\varepsilon}{3 \cdot 2^{p-1}}.$$

Let us show, keeping η fixed, that the subset of $\mathcal{C}(\mathbb{R}^N)$ defined by $K_\eta = \{ \rho_\eta \star u \mid u \in K \}$ verifies the hypotheses of the Ascoli–Arzelà theorem on the compact set G. In order to do this, we first use the inequality

$$(1.100) \qquad \left| \rho_\eta \star u(x) \right| \leqslant \sup_{x \in \mathbb{R}^N} \left[\rho_\eta(x) \right]^{1/p} \| u \|_p,$$

to prove that the function $\rho_\eta \star u$ is uniformly bounded for $x \in G$ and u in K. Indeed, this inequality results from the upper bound

$$\int \rho_\eta^{1/p}(t)\rho_\eta^{(1-1/p)}(t)|u(x-t)|dt \leqslant \sup_{x \in \mathbb{R}^N} \left[\rho_\eta(x)\right]^{1/p} \left(\int \rho_\eta^{(1-1/p)(p')}\right)^{1-1/p} \|u\|_p.$$

Next, for $x \in G$, we have

$$(1.101) \quad \left|\rho_\eta \star u(x+h) - \rho_\eta \star u(x)\right| \leqslant \sup_{x \in \mathbb{R}^N} \left[\rho_\eta(x)\right]^{1/p} \left(\int_G |\tau_{-h}u - u|^p\right)^{1/p},$$

whence $\rho_\eta \star u$ is equicontinuous.

Finally, $\{\rho_\eta \star u \mid u \in K\}$ is precompact in $\mathcal{C}(G)$, so that there exist finite subsets (ψ_j) of $\mathcal{C}(G)$, $j = 1, 2, \ldots, k$, such that

$$(1.102) \qquad \forall u \in K, \ \exists j, \quad \left|\rho_\eta \star u - \psi_j\right|^p_{\mathcal{C}(G)} \leqslant \frac{\varepsilon}{3 \cdot 2^{p-1}|G|}.$$

Let $\widetilde{\psi}_j$ be the extension of ψ_j by 0 outside of G. This belongs to $L^p(\mathbb{R}^N)$. We have

$$\int_{\mathbb{R}^N} |u - \widetilde{\psi}_j|^p \leqslant \int_{\mathbb{R}^N - G} |u|^p + \int_G |u - \psi_j|^p$$

$$\leqslant \frac{\varepsilon}{3} + 2^{p-1} \left(\int_G |u - \rho_\eta \star u|^p + \int_G |\rho_\eta \star u - \psi_j|^p\right) \leqslant \varepsilon.$$

By the above, K can be covered by a finite number of balls of radius ε in L^p. Moreover, let us show that the centers of these balls can be chosen in K. We will need the following result.

If K is a subset of a normed space X such that for every $\varepsilon > 0$ there exists a finite number of balls of radius ε with center v_i covering K, then K can be covered by a finite number of balls of radius 2ε with centers in K.

Indeed, let $\varepsilon > 0$ and let $v_1, v_2, \ldots, v_p$ be elements of X such that $K \subset \bigcup_{1 \leqslant i \leqslant p} B(v_i, \varepsilon)$. Deleting some of the balls is necessary; we may, and do, assume that for every $i \in [1, p]$, $B(v_i, \varepsilon) \cap K \neq \varnothing$. Let $u_i \in B(v_i, \varepsilon) \cap K$ for $i \in [1, p]$. The finite set of the $B(u_i, 2\varepsilon)$ then covers K. Indeed, if $u \in K$, then for every i, there exists a v_i such that $|u - v_i| \leqslant \varepsilon$. Consequently, we have the following result, which concludes the proof:

$$|u - u_i| \leqslant 2\varepsilon. \qquad \qquad \square$$

1.5.4 Duality of the Spaces L^p

Theorem 1.103. *Let Ω be an open subset of $\mathbb{R}^N$ and let p be a real number with $1 < p < +\infty$. The topological dual of $L^p(\Omega)$ is $L^{p'}(\Omega)$, where p' is the conjugate of p, that is,*

$$\frac{1}{p} + \frac{1}{p'} = 1.$$

Remark 1.104. The following proof uses the uniform convexity of L^p for $1 < p < +\infty$.

Proof of Theorem 1.103.

We first show that if $g \in L^{p'}(\Omega)$, then we can define an element of the dual $L^p(\Omega)$ as follows: to any g in $L^{p'}(\Omega)$ we associate a linear functional L_g on $L^p(\Omega)$ defined by $\int_\Omega fg = L_g(f)$. We verify that L_g is linear and that

$$(1.105) \qquad \|L_g\|_{L^p(\Omega)'} \leqslant |g|_{p'},$$

which implies that L_g is indeed an element of the dual of $L^p(\Omega)$.

Next, let $f = g|g|^{p'-2}$ if $g \neq 0$ and $f = 0$ otherwise; then $f \in L^p(\Omega)$ and $\int_\Omega |f|^p = \int_\Omega |g|^{p'}$. Moreover,

$$(1.106) \qquad |L_g(f)| \leqslant \|L_g\|_{(L^p(\Omega))'} \|f\|_p.$$

However,

$$(1.107) \qquad L_g(f) = \int_\Omega |g|^{p'} = \|g\|_{p'}^{p'} = \|f\|_p^p.$$

We therefore have

$$(1.108) \qquad \|g\|_{p'}^{p'} \leqslant \|L_g\|_{L^p(\Omega)'} \left(\int_\Omega \|f\|^p \right)^{1/p},$$

whence

$$(1.109) \qquad \|g\|_{p'}^{p'(1-1/p)} = \|L_g\|_{L^p(\Omega)'} = \|g\|_{p'}.$$

This implies that the map associating L_g to g is an isometry.

Conversely, we want to show that every linear functional on $L^p(\Omega)$ can be identified with an element of $L^{p'}(\Omega)$. Let L be a linear functional on $L^p(\Omega)$ of norm 1. We begin by showing the existence of a w of norm 1 in $L^p(\Omega)$ such that $L(w) = \|L\|_{(L^p(\Omega))'} = 1$. In order to do this, note that by the definition of $\|L\|_{(L^p(\Omega))'}$, there exists a sequence $\{w_n\}$ in $L^p(\Omega)$ such that $\|w_n\|_p = 1$ and $L(w_n) \to \|L\|_{(L^p(\Omega))'}$. Let us show that $\{w_n\}$ is a Cauchy sequence in $L^p(\Omega)$. If not, there would exist an $\varepsilon > 0$ such that

$$\forall N \in \mathbb{N} \quad \exists n, m \geqslant N, \quad \|w_n - w_m\|_p > \varepsilon.$$

By the uniform convexity of $L^p(\Omega)$, there exists a $\delta > 0$ such that for n, m as above, we have $\|\frac{w_n + w_m}{2}\|_p < 1 - \delta$. Moreover, we can choose N sufficiently large that $\|w_n + w_m\|_p \neq 0$, as $\|w_n + w_m\|_p \|L\| \geqslant L(w_n) + L(w_m) \to 2$. We then have

$$(1.110) \qquad 1 \geqslant L\left(\frac{w_n + w_m}{\|w_n + w_m\|_p} \right) \geqslant (1-\delta)^{-1} L\left(\frac{w_n + w_m}{2} \right).$$

Since n and m tend to infinity, $L(w_n) + L(w_m) \to 2$. This gives a contradiction, whence $\{w_n\}$ is a Cauchy sequence.

Let w be its limit in $L^p(\Omega)$. We have $L(w) = \|L\|$. Let $g = w|w|^{p-2}$. It is clear that $g \in L^{p'}(\Omega)$ and $\|g\|_{p'}^{p'} = \|w\|_p^p = 1$. We want to show that $L = L_g$. We already have $L(w) = L_g(w)$. For u in L^p, we have

$$(1.111) \qquad u = \left(\int_\Omega ug \right) w + u - \left(\int_\Omega ug \right) w.$$

Let us show that if v satisfies $\int_\Omega vg = 0$, then $L(v) = 0$. For $t > 0$ sufficiently small that $\|w + tv\|_p > 1/2$, we have

$$(1.112) \qquad L\left(\frac{w + tv}{\|w + tv\|_p} \right) \leqslant L(w) = 1.$$

Consequently,

$$(1.113) \qquad tL(v) + 1 \leqslant \|w\|_p + o(t).$$

Indeed, by the mean value theorem applied to the function $t \to |w + tv|^p$, we have

$$\int_\Omega |w + tv|^p - \int_\Omega |w|^p = pt \int_\Omega v(w + \theta(t)v)|w + \theta(t)v|^{p-2},$$

where $\theta(t)$ is a function such that $|\theta(t)| < t$. For every t, the sequence of functions g_t defined by $g_t(x) = pv(w + \theta(t)v)|w + \theta(t)v|^{p-2}$ belongs to L^1. For almost all x it converges to $g_0(x) = pwv|w|^{p-2}(x)$ when t tends to 0. Moreover, g_t is dominated by an L^1 function that is independent of t, as

$$|g_t(x)| \leqslant p|v|(|v| + |w|)(|v| + |w|)^{p-2}(x) \leqslant p(|v| + |w|)^p(x).$$

By the dominated convergence theorem, we have

$$\int_\Omega g_t(x)dx \longrightarrow \int_\Omega g_0(x) = 0.$$

In particular, $|w + tv|_p = 1 + to(1)$. Dividing by $t > 0$ gives $L(v) \leqslant o(1)$, whence $L(v) \leqslant 0$. Replacing v by $-v$, which verifies the same properties, we have $L(v) \geqslant 0$; whence, finally, $L(v) = 0$. We conclude the proof by using (1.111):

$$(1.114) \qquad L(u) = \int_\Omega (ug)L(w) = \int_\Omega (ug) = L_g(u). \qquad \square$$

Proposition 1.115. Let Ω be an open subset of $\mathbb{R}^N$. The dual of $L^1(\Omega, \mathbb{R})$ is $L^\infty(\Omega, \mathbb{R})$.

Proof of Proposition 1.115.

Let us first treat the case where Ω is bounded. Let $T \in L^1(\Omega)'$; then, as $L^p(\Omega)$ has a continuous embedding into $L^1(\Omega)$ $\forall p \in]1, +\infty[$, we have $T \in (L^p(\Omega))'$. Let $g_p \in L^{p'}(\Omega)$ be the element constructed in the proof of Theorem 1.103, so that $\forall f \in L^p(\Omega)$, $\langle T, f \rangle = \int_\Omega g_p f$. In particular, when we suppose that $f \in \mathcal{C}_c(\Omega)$, we have

$$(1.116) \qquad \int_\Omega g_{p_1}(x) f(x) dx = \int_\Omega g_{p_2}(x) f(x) dx$$

for all $p_1, p_2 > 1$. Consequently $g = g_p$ is independent of p and $g \in L^{p'}(\Omega)$, $\forall p' < \infty$. Moreover,

$$(1.117) \qquad |\langle T, f \rangle| \leqslant \|T\|_{(L^1(\Omega))'} \|f\|_1.$$

Let $\varphi_{p'} = |g|^{p'-2} g$; then $\varphi_{p'} \in L^p(\Omega)$, whence by Hölder's inequality, we have

$$\langle T, \varphi_{p'} \rangle = \int_\Omega g \varphi_{p'} = \int_\Omega |g|^{p'} \leqslant \|\varphi_{p'}\|_1 \|T\|_{L^1(\Omega)'}$$

$$= \left(\int_\Omega |g|^{p'-1} \right) \|T\|_{L^1(\Omega)'} \leqslant \left(\int_\Omega |g|^{p'} \right)^{(p'-1)/p'} (\text{mes } \Omega)^{1/p'} \|T\|_{L^1(\Omega)'}.$$

Finally, by dividing by $\|g\|_{p'}^{p'-1}$, we have $\|g\|_{p'} \leqslant (\text{mes } \Omega)^{1/p'} \|T\|_{L^1(\Omega)'}$. Letting p' tend to infinity, we obtain

$$(1.118) \qquad g \in L^\infty \quad \text{and} \quad \|g\|_\infty \leqslant \|T\|_{L^1(\Omega)'}.$$

Let us verify that this is actually an equality. Indeed,

$$\|T\| = \sup_{\substack{f \in L^1 \\ |f|_1 \leqslant 1}} |\langle T, f \rangle| = \sup_{\substack{f \in L^1 \\ |f|_1 \leqslant 1}} \left| \int fg \right| \leqslant \|g\|_\infty \|f\|_1 = \|g\|_\infty.$$

Next, let Ω be unbounded. Let $\Omega_n = \Omega \cap \{x \mid |x| \leqslant n\}$ and let T_n be defined on Ω_n by

$$(1.119) \qquad \langle T_n, f \rangle = \langle T, \widetilde{f_n} \rangle,$$

where $\widetilde{f_n}$ is the extension of $f \in L^1(\Omega_n)$ by 0 outside of Ω_n. Note that $\widetilde{f_n}$ belongs to $L^1(\Omega)$ whenever $f \in L^1(\Omega_n)$. The formula easily implies that $\|T_n\|_{(L^1(\Omega_n))'} \leqslant \|T\|_{(L^1(\Omega))'}$.

By the first part of the proof, there exist $g_n \in L^\infty(\Omega_n)$ such that $\langle T_n, f \rangle = \int_{\Omega_n} g_n f$. Taking functions f in $\mathcal{D}(\Omega_n)$, we see that if $n \leqslant m$, we have the equality $g_n = g_m$ on Ω_n. In particular, $g = \lim g_n$ is well defined. Let χ_n be the characteristic function of Ω_n and let $f \in L^1(\Omega)$; then $f\chi_n \to f$ in $L^1(\Omega)$. As $f\chi_n \in L^1(\Omega_n)$ and $T \in (L^1(\Omega))'$, it follows that

$$(1.120) \qquad \langle T_n, f\chi_n \rangle = \langle T, f\chi_n \rangle \longrightarrow \langle T, f \rangle.$$

Finally, using $\||T_n|\|_{(L^1(\Omega_n))'} = \|g_n\|_{L^\infty(\Omega)}$, we conclude that

$$(1.121) \qquad g \in L^\infty(\Omega) \quad \text{and} \quad \|g\|_\infty = \||T|\|_{(L^1(\Omega))'}. \qquad \square$$

Comments

The results of this chapter cover different notions from functional analysis. The reader can consult the work of Yosida [76] for functional analysis and that of Schwartz [59] for distributions. The Clarkson inequalities are shown in Adams [1], Clarkson [16]. The notions of weak topology and locally convex spaces are, for example, developed in Bourbaki [9].

1.6 Exercises for Chapter 1

Exercise [∗] 1.1 (Completeness of the Space $\mathcal{L}(X,Y)$).
Let X be a normed space and let Y be a Banach space. Show that the space $\mathcal{L}(X,Y)$ of continuous linear maps from X to Y, normed using $L \mapsto \||L|\| = \sup_{\|x\|_X=1} \|L(x)\|_Y$, is a Banach space.

Hints. Let $\{L_n\}$ be a Cauchy sequence in $\mathcal{L}(X,Y)$. Show that for every $x \in X$, the sequence $\{L_n(x)\}$ converges in Y. Next, show that the limit $L(x)$ is such that $L : x \mapsto L(x)$ is linear. By passing to the limit with respect to the norms, show that L is continuous. Finally, prove that $\||L_n - L|\| \to 0$.

Exercise [∗] 1.2 (Examples of Baire Spaces).
Prove that a complete metric space X is a Baire space (cf. Definition 1.8).

Hints. You must, for example, show that if O_n is a sequence of open subsets such that for every n, $\overline{O_n} = X$, then $\overline{\bigcap O_n} = X$. Let W be an open subset of X. You must show that $W \cap (\bigcap O_n) \neq \varnothing$. Let x_1 be such that $B(x_1, r_1) \subset W \cap O_1$. By recursion, let x_i and $r_i < 1/i$ be such that $B(x_i, r_i) \subset B(x_{i-1}, r_{i-1}) \cap O_i$. Show that $\{x_n\}$ is a Cauchy sequence and that its limit belongs to $W \cap (\bigcap_n O_n)$.

Exercise [∗] 1.3 (Completeness of the Space of Summable Sequences).
Let $\ell^1(\mathbb{C})$ be the space of summable complex sequences. Show that the map $x = \{x_n\} \mapsto \sum_0^{+\infty} |x_n|$ is a norm for this space and that the space is Banach for this norm.

Hints. Let $\{x^{(m)}\}$ be a Cauchy sequence. Show that for every n, the sequence $\{x_n^{(m)}\}_{m \in \mathbb{N}}$ is convergent. Show that if x_n denotes the limit, then the sequence x with terms x_n is summable and $\|x^{(m)} - x\| \to 0$.

Exercise 1.4 (Topology on the Space $\mathcal{D}^k(\Omega)$).

Let $E = \mathcal{D}^k(\Omega)$. Using the notations of Subsection 1.4.1 (cf. *Countable family of fundamental systems of neighborhoods*), we know that E is the union of an increasing sequence of topological vector spaces, namely the $E_j = \mathcal{D}^k_{K_j}$. We consider the family $\mathcal{B}$ of convex, balanced and absorbing subsets B of E such that

$$\forall j, \quad B \cap E_j \text{ is a neighborhood of } 0 \text{ in } E_j.$$

Prove that $\mathcal{B}$ is a fundamental system of neighborhoods of 0_E for the TVS topology on E.

Hints. Use Proposition 1.5. To be able to do this, first show that if $B \in \mathcal{B}$ and $\lambda > 0$, then $\lambda B \in \mathcal{B}$ and, moreover, that the intersection of two elements of $\mathcal{B}$ is also an element of $\mathcal{B}$.

Exercise [∗] 1.5 (Weak Topology on the Dual of a Normed Space X).

We consider a family $\mathcal{B}$ of subsets of X defined as follows using elements $x_0 \in X$, finite subsets F' of X', and real numbers $\varepsilon > 0$:

$$B_{x_0, F', \varepsilon} = \{x \in X \mid \forall\, x' \in F', |\langle x - x_0, x' \rangle| < \varepsilon\}.$$

(1) Prove that $\mathcal{B}$ is a fundamental system of neighborhoods for the topology on X. In order to do this, show the following two properties:
   a) $\bigcup \{B \mid B \in \mathcal{B}\} = X$.
   b) If B_1 and B_2 are elements of $\mathcal{B}$ and if $x \in B_1 \cap B_2$, then

$$\exists\, B_3 \in \mathcal{B}, \quad x \in B_3 \subset B_1 \cap B_2.$$

(2) Prove that the resulting topology on X, denoted by $\sigma(X, X')$, is Hausdorff and that scalar multiplication and addition on X are continuous for this topology. Show that this is a topology of locally convex space.

(3) Prove that every open subset of X for the weak topology is an open subset of the normed space X. That is, show that the norm topology is finer than the weak topology.

Hints. Use Propositions 1.5 and 1.6. For question (3), note that the set $B_{x_0, F', \varepsilon}$ is a finite intersection of inverse images of open subsets of $\mathbb{R}$ under the continuous maps x' from the normed space X to $\mathbb{R}$.

Exercise 1.6 (Example of a Sequence of Continuous Linear Functionals).

Let $X = \ell^1$ be the space of summable sequences. Let $\{u_n\}$ be the sequence of linear maps from X to $\mathbb{C}$ defined by $u_n(x) = x_n$.

(1) Show that u_n is continuous and determine its norm.

(2) Show that the sequence of linear maps (u_n) converges pointwise to 0, that is, that for any $x \in \ell^1$, $u_n(x) \to 0$.

Note that the norm of u_n in $\mathcal{L}(X, \mathbb{C})$ equals 1. Deduce from this that u_n does not tend to 0 for the operator norm on $\mathcal{L}(X, \mathbb{C})$.

Exercise 1.7 (Minkowski Functional).

We use the definitions of balanced and absorbing convex subsets given in this book (Definition 1.1).

(1) Let M be a balanced absorbing convex subset of a topological vector space X containing 0. We define the Minkowski functional p of the convex set M as follows:

$$\forall x \in X, \quad p(x) = \inf_{t > 0}\{t \mid x/t \in M\}.$$

Show that p is subadditive, positively homogeneous of degree 1 (that is, p is a seminorm on X). Also show that $\forall x \in M$, $p(x) \leqslant 1$.

(2) Conversely, show that if p is a seminorm, then the subset M defined by $M = \{x \mid p(x) \leqslant 1\}$ is convex, balanced, and absorbing and contains 0.

(3) Show that M is open in X if and only if p is continuous.

Hints. Note that for $\varepsilon > 0$, $x/(p(x) + \varepsilon) \in M$. Use the convexity to deduce from this that

$$\frac{p(x) + \varepsilon}{p(x) + p(y) + 2\varepsilon} \cdot \frac{x}{p(x) + \varepsilon} + \frac{p(y) + \varepsilon}{p(x) + p(y) + 2\varepsilon} \cdot \frac{y}{p(y) + \varepsilon} \in M.$$

Conclude that

$$p(x + y) \leqslant p(x) + p(y) + 2\varepsilon.$$

Exercise 1.8 (Mazur's Theorem).

Let M be a convex set containing 0 in its interior. Prove that if $x_0 \notin M$, then there exists a continuous linear functional f such that $f_0(x_0) \geqslant \sup_{x \in M} |f_0(x)|$.

Hints. By the previous exercise, the Minkowski functional M is a continuous seminorm. Next, apply the geometric form of the Hahn–Banach theorem (Theorem 1.19).

Exercise [∗] 1.9 (Closed Graph Theorem).

Let T be a linear map from a Banach space X to a Banach space Y with closed graph. Prove that T is continuous.

Hints. By assumption, the graph is closed in $X \times Y$, which is a Banach space. Consequently, the graph is a complete subset. The projection p_1 of the graph on the first space (that is, $p_1(x, Tx) = x$) is linear, continuous and bijective. It therefore admits a continuous inverse U. If p_2 is the projection on the second space, we have $T = p_2 \circ U$, which is the composition of two continuous linear maps. Complete the proof.

Exercise 1.10 (Embeddings in Lebesgue Spaces).

(1) Let Ω be an open set with finite Lebesgue measure. Show that if $p \geqslant q$, then we have
$$L^p(\Omega) \hookrightarrow L^q(\Omega).$$

(2) Use a counterexample to show that this is false if Ω has infinite measure.

(3) Let Ω be an arbitrary open set. Show that
$$p \leqslant r \leqslant q \implies L^p(\Omega) \cap L^q(\Omega) \hookrightarrow L^r(\Omega).$$

Also show that
$$\forall f \in L^p(\Omega) \cap L^q(\Omega), \quad \|f\|_r \leqslant \sup(\|f\|_p, \|f\|_q).$$

Exercise 1.11 (The Limit of L^p Norms when $p \to +\infty$).
Recall the definition of $L^\infty(\Omega)$ and of the norm $\|\cdot\|_\infty$ on this space. Prove that if $f \in L^\infty(\Omega) \cap L^r(\Omega)$ for at least one index $r \geqslant 1$, then
$$\lim_{r \to +\infty} \|f\|_r = \|f\|_\infty.$$

Exercise 1.12 (Means of f for $f \in L^p(\mathbb{R}^+)$).
Let $p \in \,]1, \infty[$ and let $f \in L^p(\mathbb{R}^+)$. Define F as follows on $\mathbb{R}^+$:
$$F(x) = \frac{1}{x} \int_0^x f(t)dt.$$

(1) Show that $F \in L^p(\mathbb{R}^+)$ and $\|F\|_p \leqslant \dfrac{p}{p-1}\|f\|_p$.

(2) Using, for example, functions with compact support, show that there exists an $f \in L^1(\mathbb{R}^+)$ such that F does not belong to $L^1(\mathbb{R}^+)$.

Hints. Apply Lemma 3.14 of Chapter 3 with $\nu = 0$.

Exercise 1.13 (Compact Operators Theory).
Let K be a continuous function on $[a,b] \times [a,b]$ where $a < b$, $(a,b) \in \mathbb{R}^2$. Define an operator as follows:
$$\forall f \in \mathcal{C}([a,b]), \quad Tf(x) = \int_a^b K(x,y)f(y)dy.$$

Use the Ascoli–Arzelà theorem to prove that T is an operator that transforms the unit ball in $\mathcal{C}([a,b])$ into a relatively compact subset of $\mathcal{C}([a,b])$.

Exercise 1.14 (Compact Operators Theory, Continued).
Let Ω be an open subset of $\mathbb{R}^N$. Let $K \in L^2(\Omega \times \Omega)$ and define T as follows:

$$\forall f \in L^2(\Omega), \quad Tf(x) = \int_\Omega K(x,y)f(y)dy.$$

Prove that T sends $L^2(\Omega)$ to itself and that the image of the unit ball in $L^2(\Omega)$ is a relatively compact subset of $L^2(\Omega)$.

Hints. Let $\{f_n\}$ be a sequence such that $\|f_n\|_{L^2} \leqslant 1$; then Tf_n is bounded in L^2. You can therefore extract a subsequence that converges weakly in L^2. Show that $(Tf_n)^2$ is dominated by a fixed function belonging to L^1. Use the dominated convergence theorem to conclude the proof. Another proof uses the criterion 1.95 given in this book.

Exercise 1.15 (Space of Sequences, Completeness and Duals).
We define the spaces c_0, ℓ^1, ℓ^p, and ℓ^∞ as follows as subsets of $\mathbb{C}^N$:

$$(x_n) \in c_0 \text{ if } \lim_{n \to +\infty} x_n = 0 \quad (x_n) \in \ell^1 \text{ if } \sum_0^{+\infty} |x_n| < \infty$$

$$(x_n) \in \ell^p \text{ if } \sum_0^{+\infty} |x_n|^p < \infty \quad (x_n) \in \ell^\infty \text{ if } \exists M, \, \forall n \, |x_n| \leqslant M$$

(1) Show that these are Banach spaces.
(2) Show that $c_0' = \ell^1$, $(\ell^p)' = \ell^{p'}$ with $1/p + 1/p' = 1$ for $p \in]1, +\infty[$. Show that $(\ell^1)' = \ell^\infty$, while $(\ell^\infty)' \neq \ell^1$.

Exercise 1.16 (Jensen's Inequality).
Let j be a convex function on $\mathbb{R}$ and let μ be a probability measure on $[a,b]$, where $a < b$ (that is, the measure μ satisfies $\int d\mu = 1$). Let $f \in \mathcal{C}(]a,b[)$. Show that

$$j\left(\int_a^b f d\mu\right) \leqslant \int_a^b j \circ f d\mu.$$

Deduce from this that if $p \in [1, +\infty[$ and $f \in L^p(]a,b[)$, then

$$\int_a^b |f(x)|dx \leqslant |a-b|^{(p-1)/p}\left(\int_a^b |f(x)|^p dx\right)^{1/p}.$$

Exercise 1.17 (Separable Hilbert Spaces).
Let f be an element of $L^2(]0, 2\pi[)$, extended periodically to $\mathbb{R}$. Recall the Bessel–Parseval theorem, which states that if the Fourier coefficients of f are $c_n(f)$, then

$$\frac{1}{2\pi}\int_0^{2\pi} |f(t)|^2 dt = \sum_{-\infty}^{+\infty} |c_n(f)|^2.$$

Prove that $L^2(]0, 2\pi[)$ is a separable space.

Exercise 1.18 (Sum of Two Lebesgue Spaces).

Show that if $p \in [p_1, p_2]$, $p_1 < p_2$, then

$$L^p(\Omega) \longrightarrow L^{p_1}(\Omega) + L^{p_2}(\Omega).$$

Hints. Given $\alpha > 0$, let

$$f_1(x) = \begin{cases} f(x) & \text{if } |f(x)| \geqslant \alpha, \\ 0 & \text{otherwise}; \end{cases}$$

then $f_1 \in L^{p_1}$ and $f_2 \in L^{p_2}$, where $f_2 = f - f_1$.

Exercise [∗] 1.19 (Weak or Norm Convergence of Sequences of Distributions).

Let $\{a_j\}_{j \in \mathbb{N}}$ be a sequence of elements of $\mathbb{R}^N$ such that $|a_j| \to +\infty$. Let $\{\lambda_j\}_{j \in \mathbb{N}}$ be a sequence of complex numbers. Prove that the sequence of distributions $\{\lambda_j \delta_{a_j}\}$ converges to 0 in $\mathcal{D}'(\mathbb{R}^N)$.

Exercise [∗] 1.20 (Extension of a Distribution with Compact Support).

We will only consider the case $N = 1$. Let T be a distribution with compact support K. Let $V_\varepsilon(K) = K + [-\varepsilon, +\varepsilon]$ be the closed neighborhood of K of order $\varepsilon > 0$.

(a) Show that there exist functions $\alpha \in \mathcal{D}(\mathbb{R})$ such that

$$\forall x \in V_\varepsilon(K), \quad \alpha(x) = 1.$$

(b) For every function φ in $\mathcal{E}(\mathbb{R})$, let

$$\langle U, \varphi \rangle = \langle T, \alpha\varphi \rangle.$$

Show that U is a continuous linear functional on the locally convex space $\mathcal{E}(\mathbb{R})$. Show that U does not depend on the choice of α and that U is an extension of T to the space $\mathcal{E}(\mathbb{R})$.

(c) Conversely, show that every element of $\mathcal{E}'(\mathbb{R})$ can be identified with a distribution with compact support.

Hints. Consider a continuous function with compact support that equals 1 on a neighborhood of K. Taking a convolution with a regularizing function ρ_ε (cf. Subsection 1.4.2) gives a suitable function. For the independence of α, consider $\langle T, (\alpha_2 - \alpha_1)\varphi \rangle$ and use the definition of the support of T.

For (c), the linearity and continuity are immediate. Show the result on the support by contradiction, using the continuity of U on $\mathcal{E}(\mathbb{R})$.

Exercise [*] 1.21 (Relatively Weak-Star Sequentially Compact Subset of $L^1(\Omega)$).

Let Ω be a bounded open subset of $\mathbb{R}^N$. Let A be a subset of $L^1(\Omega)$ with the following properties:

(1) $\exists M > 0, \forall f \in A, \int_\Omega |f(x)|dx \leqslant M$.
(2) $\forall \varepsilon > 0, \exists \delta > 0$ such that

$$\forall B \subset \Omega, \quad \mathrm{mes}(B) < \delta \implies \forall f \in A, \int_B |f(x)|dx \leqslant \varepsilon.$$

Show that A is relatively weak-star sequentially compact in $L^1(\Omega)$.

Hints. Begin by extracting from $\{f_n\}$, a sequence of functions on A, a subsequence that converges for the weak-star topology to a bounded measure μ on Ω. The next step consists in using the lower semicontinuity of the integral on an open space for the weak-star topology (cf. Chapter 6). Use this to show that μ is absolutely continuous with respect to the Lebesgue measure.

Exercise 1.22 (Equi-integrable Functions in L^1).

We call a sequence $\{f_n\}$ functions in L^1 equi-integrable if for every $\varepsilon > 0$, there exists a $\delta > 0$ such that $\mathrm{mes}(E) < \delta$ implies that for every n, $\int_E |f_n(x)|dx \leqslant \varepsilon$.

(1) Show the following property:
    Let X be a subset of $\mathbb{R}^N$ with finite Lebesgue measure. Let $\{f_n\}$ be an equi-integrable sequence of functions in $L^1(X)$ that converges almost everywhere to f; then $f \in L^1(X)$ and $\{f_n\}$ converges to f in $L^1(X)$ for the norm topology.
(2) Show that this result is false if X is not of finite measure.
(3) Show the analogous result for L^p, that is, if $\{f_n\}$ converges almost everywhere to f and if $|f_n|^p$ is equi-integrable, then $\{f_n\}$ converges to f in L^p for the norm topology.

Hints. Show that the hypothesis that X has finite measure implies the existence of a finite number N of sets E_i of measure $< \delta$ such that $X \subset \bigcup_{1 \leqslant i \leqslant N} E_i$. Consequently, by Fatou's lemma,

$$\int_X |f(x)|dx \leqslant \varliminf \int_X |f_n(x)|dx \leqslant N\varepsilon.$$

Conclude that $f \in L^1(X)$. For the norm convergence, let δ be associated with $\varepsilon/3$ in the definition of equi-integrability and such that $\mathrm{mes}\, E < \delta \Rightarrow \int_E |f(x)|dx \leqslant \varepsilon/3$. Extract from $\{f_n\}$ a subsequence that converges in measure, that is, for which there exists an N_0 such that

$$n \geqslant N_0 \implies \mathrm{mes}[\{x \in X \mid |f_n - f|(x) \geqslant \varepsilon/3\,\mathrm{mes}(X)\}] < \delta.$$

Conclude with the following inequalities, where $A_n = \{x \mid |f_n - f|(x) \leqslant \varepsilon/3\,\mathrm{mes}(X)\}$:

$$\int_X |f_n - f| \leqslant \int_{A_n} |f_n - f| + \int_{X \setminus A_n} [|f_n| + |f|] \leqslant \frac{\varepsilon}{3} + \frac{\varepsilon}{3} + \frac{\varepsilon}{3}.$$

(2) Consider the sequence $\{f_n\}$ on $\mathbb{R}$ defined by $f_n = \frac{1}{n}\chi_{[n,2n]}$.

Exercise 1.23 (Rearrangement Function, cf. Chapter 7).

Let f be a measurable function on the measured space X with values in $\mathbb{C}$ and almost everywhere finite. Let $\lambda(s) = \big|\{x \in X \mid |f(x)| > s\}\big|$.

(1) Show that λ is decreasing and right-continuous on $\mathbb{R}^+$.

(2) If $f \in L^p$ with $p < +\infty$, show that $s\lambda(s)^{1/p} \leqslant \left(\int |f(x)|^p dx\right)^{1/p}$. We then define the decreasing rearrangement function of f on $\mathbb{R}^+$ to be $f^*(t) = \inf\{s \mid \lambda(s) \leqslant t\}$. Show that f^* is decreasing and right-continuous.

(3) Let f be a simple function, that is $f(x) = c_j$ for $x \in E_j$, where the E_j are disjoint measurable sets. Assume that $|c_j| > |c_{j-1}|$ for every j. Let $d_j = \sum_{k \leqslant j} |E_k|$. Show that

$$\forall t, \quad d_{j-1} \leqslant t < d_j \implies f^*(t) = c_j.$$

(4) Suppose that $p \in [1, \infty[$. Show that if $f \in L^p(\mathbb{R})$, then there exists a sequence of simple functions f_n such that $\{|f_n|\}$ is an increasing sequence that converges almost everywhere to $|f|$. Also show that $\lambda_n(s)$ converges to $\lambda(s)$ as n increases and that for every $t > 0$, $f_n^*(t)$ tends to $f^*(t)$ as n increases. Conclude that

$$\forall f \in L^p, \quad f^* \in L^p \quad \text{and} \quad \|f\|_p = \|f^*\|_p.$$

Exercise [*] 1.24 (Continuous Linear Functionals on a Locally Convex Space).

On a locally convex space X, consider a linear functional f generated by a family of seminorms $\{\eta_\lambda\}$. Show that f is continuous if and only if there exist an $M > 0$ and a seminorm η_λ such that $\forall x \in X$, $|f(x)| \leqslant M\eta_\lambda(x)$.

Hints. For every open disc D in $\mathbb{C}$, $f^{-1}(D)$ is a neighborhood of 0 in X, and hence contains a closed ball associated with one of the seminorms η_λ. Conclude the proof as in a normed space.

Exercise [*] 1.25 (Bounded Subsets of a Locally Convex Space).

By definition, a bounded subset B of a locally convex space X is a subset of X such that for every neighborhood U of 0, there exists an $\alpha > 0$ such that $|\beta| \geqslant \alpha \Rightarrow B \subset \beta U$. Let $\{\eta_\lambda\}$ be a family of seminorms defining the topology on X. Show that B is bounded if all of these seminorms are bounded on B.

Hints. The unit ball associated with η_λ is a neighborhood of 0, and hence absorbs B. The inequality follows from this. Conversely, suppose that $\sup_{x \in B} \eta_\lambda(x) \leqslant M_\lambda$ for every λ. Denoting the unit balls by B_λ, we then have

$$\forall r > 0, \quad B \subset B_\lambda(0, M_\lambda) = M_\lambda B_\lambda = \frac{M_\lambda}{r} B_\lambda(0, r);$$

hence B is absorbed by every neighborhood of 0 in X.

Exercise 1.26 (Dense Subsets of $L^p(I)$, where I Is an Interval).
Let I be an open interval of $\mathbb{R}$. Consider the space $L^p(I)$, where $p \in [1, +\infty[$. Let $S(I)$ denote the space of simple functions on I, that is, of functions that can be written as $s = \sum_1^N c_i \chi_{A_i}$, where the A_i are measurable spaces. Let $E(I)$ denote the space of step functions on I, and let $\mathcal{C}_c(I)$ be the space of continuous functions with compact support in I.

(1) Show that $S(I)$ is dense in $L^p(I)$. In order to do this, given a nonnegative $f \in L^p$, use the sets $f^{-1}([\frac{i-1}{2^n}, \frac{i}{2^n}[)$ and $f^{-1}([n, +\infty[)$.
(2) Use the following property of the Lebesgue measure μ on I:
    if $J \subset I$ is measurable, then there exists a sequence $\{J_n\}$ of subsets of I that are finite unions of disjoint open intervals such that $\mu(J) = \lim_{n \to +\infty} \mu(J_n)$,
    to show that if I is bounded, then every simple function is the limit in $L^p(I)$ of a sequence of step functions.

Conclude that $E(I)$ is dense in $L^p(I)$, and then that $\mathcal{C}_c(I)$ is dense in $L^p(I)$. Show the same results when I is unbounded.

Hints. For (1), use the following simple functions, where $F_{i,n}$ and F_n are the inverse images introduced in (1):

$$s_n = \sum_1^{n2^n} (i-1)2^{-n}\chi_{F_{i,n}} + n\chi_{F_n}.$$

Show that $0 \leqslant s_n \leqslant f$ and apply the dominated convergence theorem. Conclude for f with arbitrary sign.
    For the density of $\mathcal{C}_c(I)$, approximate $\chi_{[a,b]}$ by a continuous function with compact support in I that is piecewise affine.
    For an unbounded I, write I as an increasing union of bounded intervals $I_n = [a_n, b_n]$ with $\|f - f\chi_{I_n}\|_p \to 0$.

Exercise [**] 1.27 (Finite Subsets Distributions (cf. [22])).
In this exercise, we restrict ourselves to functions $\mathcal{U}(t)t^\alpha$, where $\mathcal{U}$ is the Heaviside step function. These functions are not locally summable when $\alpha \leqslant -1$.

(1) The case of $\mathcal{U}(t)t^\alpha$, where $\alpha = -n$ and $n \geqslant 1$ is an integer.
    The integral $J_\varepsilon = \int_\varepsilon^{+\infty} \varphi(t)t^{-n}\, dt$, where φ is an element of $\mathcal{D}(\mathbb{R})$, in general does not have a limit when $\varepsilon \to 0$. If $\varphi_{n-1}^*(t)$ denotes the Taylor polynomial of degree $n-1$ about the origin for the function φ and A is an upper bound for the support of φ, then we can write J_ε as

$$J_\varepsilon = \int_\varepsilon^A \left[\varphi(t) - \varphi_{n-1}^*(t)\right]t^{-n}\, dt + \int_\varepsilon^A \varphi_{n-1}^*(t)t^{-n}\, dt.$$

Show that the first integral has a finite limit when $\varepsilon \to 0$, so that the nonexistence of $\lim J_\varepsilon$ in a sense comes from the second term. This second term can be written as

$$\int_{\varepsilon}^{A} \varphi_{n-1}^{*}(t)t^{-n}\, dt = K_A - \mathcal{I}_{\varepsilon}(\varphi_{n-1}^{*}(t)t^{-n}),$$

where $\mathcal{I}_{\varepsilon}(\varphi_{n-1}^{*}(t)t^{-n})$ denotes the value in ε of the primitive without constant term of the function $\varphi_{n-1}^{*}(t)t^{-n}$, and K_A is the value of this primitive at the point A. The function $-\mathcal{I}_{\varepsilon}(\varphi_{n-1}^{*}(t)t^{-n})$ can be qualified as the *infinite part*.

Next, we cut off this infinite part from the integral J_{ε}, making it possible to take the limit for $\varepsilon \to 0$. Show that this gives a distribution T, denoted by $\mathrm{Pf}(\mathcal{U}(t)t^{-n})$, and defined by

$$(*) \quad \forall \varphi \in \mathcal{D}, \quad \langle T, \varphi \rangle = \lim_{\varepsilon \to 0}\left[\int_{\varepsilon}^{+\infty} \varphi(t)t^{-n}dt + \mathcal{I}_{\varepsilon}(\varphi_{n-1}^{*}(t)t^{-n}) \right]$$

$$= \lim_{\varepsilon \to 0}\left[\int_{\varepsilon}^{+\infty} \varphi(t)t^{-n}dt + \sum_{k=0}^{k=n-2} \frac{\varphi^{(k)}(0)}{k!}\left[\frac{\varepsilon^{k-n+1}}{k-n+1}\right] + \left[\frac{\varphi^{(n-1)}(0)}{(n-1)!}\ln(\varepsilon)\right] \right].$$

Show that $\operatorname{supp} T \subset \mathbb{R}^{+}$. Prove that if p is an integer > 0, then

$$t^{p}\,\mathrm{Pf}(\mathcal{U}(t)t^{-n}) = \mathrm{Pf}(\mathcal{U}(t)t^{-(n-p)}),$$

where the symbol Pf vanishes when $p > n - 1$. Determine the derivative of $\mathrm{Pf}(\mathcal{U}(t)t^{-n})$.

(2) The case where $\mathcal{U}(t)t^{\alpha}$, α is complex, non integer, with $\Re(\alpha) < -1$. Assume that $-n-1 < \Re(\alpha) < -n$, where n is still an integer with $n \geqslant 1$. Applying the previous method, give the definition of the finite part T_{α} of $\mathcal{U}(t)t^{\alpha}$ through an equality analogous to $(*)$. Show the formula

$$\langle T_{\alpha}, \varphi \rangle = \lim_{\varepsilon \to 0}\left[\int_{\varepsilon}^{+\infty} \varphi(t)t^{\alpha}dt + \sum_{k=0}^{k=n-1} \frac{\varphi^{(k)}(0)}{k!}\left[\frac{\varepsilon^{k+\alpha+1}}{k+\alpha+1}\right] \right].$$

Determine the products $t^{n}\,\mathrm{Pf}(\mathcal{U}(t)t^{\alpha})$. Find the derivative of $\mathrm{Pf}(\mathcal{U}(t)t^{\alpha})$.

(3) Likewise, we define the left-finite subsets $\mathrm{Pf}(\mathcal{U}(-t)|t|^{-n})$, $\mathrm{Pf}(\mathcal{U}(-t)t^{-n})$, and $\mathrm{Pf}(\mathcal{U}(-t)|t|^{\alpha})$, and the two-sided finite subsets:

$$\mathrm{Pf}(|t|^{\alpha}) = \mathrm{Pf}(\mathcal{U}(t)t^{\alpha}) + \mathrm{Pf}(\mathcal{U}(-t)|t|^{\alpha}),$$
$$\mathrm{Pf}(t^{-n}) = \mathrm{Pf}(\mathcal{U}(t)t^{-n}) + \mathrm{Pf}(\mathcal{U}(-t)t^{-n}).$$

Determine the derivative of $\mathrm{Pf}(t^{-n})$.

(4) Examples of logarithmic finite subsets.

  a) Use the same method as above to justify the following definition:

$$\left\langle \mathrm{Pf}\left(\mathcal{U}(t)\frac{\ln^2 t}{t}\right), \varphi \right\rangle = \lim_{\varepsilon \to 0}\left[\int_{\varepsilon}^{+\infty} \frac{\ln^2 t}{t}\varphi(t)dt + \frac{1}{3}\varphi(0)(\ln^3 \varepsilon) \right].$$

b) Let $f(t) = \mathcal{U}(t)t^{-5/2}\ln t$. Justify the following definition:

$$\langle \mathrm{Pf}(f), \varphi \rangle = \lim_{\varepsilon \to 0}\left[\int_{\varepsilon}^{+\infty} f(t)\varphi(t)dt - \frac{2\varphi(0)}{9\varepsilon^{3/2}}\Big[3\ln(\varepsilon) + 2\Big] - \frac{2\varphi'(0)}{\varepsilon^{1/2}}\Big[\ln(\varepsilon) + 2\Big]\right].$$

After defining the distribution $\mathrm{Pf}(|t|^{-3/2}\ln|t|)$, determine its derivative.

c) Show that for the function f defined by $t \mapsto f(t) = \ln t/t$, we have

$$[\mathrm{Pf}(\mathcal{U}(t)f(t))]' = [\mathrm{Pf}(\mathcal{U}(t)f'(t))].$$

Also determine the second derivative $[\mathrm{Pf}(\mathcal{U}(t)f(t))]''$.

Exercise 1.28 (Norm in a Quotient Space).
Let X be a normed space and let Y be a vector subspace of X. We define the classes modulo Y by

$$\forall x \in X, \quad \widetilde{x} = \{x + y \mid y \in Y\}.$$

Classically, the set of these classes is a vector space, denoted by X/Y and called the *quotient space* of X modulo Y.

(1) Show that the map $\widetilde{x} \mapsto \inf_{y \in Y}\{\|x + y\|\}$ is a seminorm and that it is a norm on X/Y if and only if Y is closed in X.

(2) Suppose that X is a Banach space and Y is a close subspace of X. Show that if $\{z_n\}$ is a sequence in X/Y, then there exists a sequence $\{x_n\}$ in X such that for every n, $\widetilde{x_n} = z_n$ and $\|x_n\|_X \leqslant \|z_n\|_{X/Y} + 1/2^n$. Deduce from this that all sequences converging normally in X/Y, that is, such that $\sum_0^{+\infty}\|z_n\| < +\infty$, converge in X/Y. Conclude that X/Y is a Banach space.

Hints. For the last conclusion, consider a Cauchy sequence $\{z_n\}$ in X/Y. There exists a strictly increasing map σ from $\mathbb{N}$ to itself such that

$$\|z_{\sigma(p+1)} - z_{\sigma(p)}\|_{X/Y} \leqslant 2^{-p}.$$

Setting $u_0 = z_{\sigma(0)}$ and $u_p = z_{\sigma(p)} - z_{\sigma(p-1)}$, show that the resulting sequence converges normally. Deduce from this the convergence of a subsequence extracted from the sequence $\{z_n\}$. Conclude that $\{z_n\}$ converges.

Exercise [**] 1.29 (Absolutely Continuous Functions and Distributions on an Interval I).
A function f on an interval I in $\mathbb{R}$ is called absolutely continuous if there exists a function $g: I \mapsto \mathbb{R}$ belonging to $L^1_{\mathrm{loc}}(I)$ such that for every pair of points (x, y) of I, we have $f(x) - f(y) = \int_y^x g(t)dt$.

An absolutely continuous function on I is almost everywhere derivable on I, and its derivative is almost everywhere equal to g.

(1) Let U and V be absolutely continuous functions on I with almost everywhere derivatives u and v. Using the density of $C_c(]a, b[)$ in $L^1(]a, b[)$ (cf. Exercise 1.26), show the formula for integration by parts, that is, for every pair (a, b) of points of I,

$$(1.122) \qquad \int_a^b U(t)v(t)dt = U(b)V(b) - U(a)V(a) - \int_a^b V(t)u(t)dt.$$

(2) Let $u \in L^1_{\text{loc}}(I)$ be such that its derivative in the sense of distributions satisfies $[u]' \in L^1_{\text{loc}}(I)$. Let $a \in I$ be a point at which u is well defined. Let $v(x) = u(a) - \int_a^x [u]'(t)dt$, and let $\varphi \in \mathcal{D}(I)$ have support in $[\alpha, \beta]$. Using formula (1.122), show that $[v]' = [u]'$ and deduce from this that $v - u$ is almost everywhere a constant C on I. Show that if u is moreover continuous on I, then u is absolutely continuous on I and $u' = [u]'$ almost everywhere on I. Finally, show that if u and $[u]'$ are continuous on I, then $u \in \mathcal{C}^1(I)$.

Hints. For (1), as the sequences $\{u_n\}$ and $\{v_n\}$ in $C_c(I)$ converge to u and v, respectively, in $L^1(]a, b[)$, let $U_n(x) = U(a) + \int_a^x u_n(t)dt$. Write down the integration by parts for the functions u_n and v_n and show that U_n converges uniformly to U in $]a, b[$, and the analogous result for V_n.

2

Sobolev Spaces and Embedding Theorems

2.1 Definitions and First Properties

Definition 2.1. Let Ω be an open subset of $\mathbb{R}^N$. For $m \in \mathbb{N}$ and $1 \leqslant p \leqslant +\infty$, the Sobolev space denoted by $W^{m,p}(\Omega)$ consists of the functions in $L^p(\Omega)$ whose partial derivatives up to order m, in the sense of distributions, can be identified with functions in $L^p(\Omega)$.

For these derivatives, we set $\alpha = (\alpha_1, \ldots, \alpha_N)$ and $|\alpha| = \sum_1^N \alpha_i$. Moreover, we use the notation

$$(2.2) \qquad D^\alpha u = \frac{\partial^{|\alpha|} u}{\partial^{\alpha_1} x_1 \cdots \partial^{\alpha_N} x_N}.$$

The definition above can now be written as

$$(2.3) \qquad W^{m,p}(\Omega) = \{u \in L^p(\Omega) \mid \forall \alpha \in \mathbb{N}^N, \ |\alpha| \leqslant m \Rightarrow D^\alpha u \in L^p(\Omega)\}.$$

Remark 2.4 (on the structure of the derivatives in $W^{1,p}(\Omega)$). We will use the notion of the derivative of an absolutely continuous function in the usual sense (cf. Exercise 2.3) to better understand what it means for u to belong to $W^{1,p}(\Omega)$.

Let $u \in W^{1,p}(\Omega)$; then for every i, the function u is absolutely continuous along almost all lines parallel to the vector $\vec{e_i}$ of the canonical basis of $\mathbb{R}^N$. Moreover, the derivative $\partial_i u$ of u in the usual sense, which exists almost everywhere on Ω, belongs to $L^p(\Omega)$ and is almost everywhere equal to the derivative in the sense of distributions. Conversely, if for every i, $u \in L^p(\Omega)$ is absolutely continuous along almost all lines parallel to e_i, with derivatives $\partial_i u$ in $L^p(\Omega)$, then $u \in W^{1,p}(\Omega)$.

It follows that if u is of class $\mathcal{C}^1$ on Ω, then we can verify that $u \in W^{1,p}(\Omega)$ by showing that the functions u and $\partial_i u$ belong to $L^p(\Omega)$. The following examples use this property.

F. Demengel, G. Demengel, *Functional Spaces for the Theory of Elliptic Partial Differential Equations*, Universitext, DOI 10.1007/978-1-4471-2807-6_2, © Springer-Verlag London Limited 2012

Remark 2.5. For $p = 2$, the notation $W^{m,2}(\Omega)$ is generally replaced by $H^m(\Omega)$.

Remark 2.6. When $\Omega = \mathbb{R}^N$, we can use the Fourier transform $\xi \mapsto \widehat{u}(\xi)$ of a function u in $L^2(\mathbb{R}^N)$ to give the following equivalent definition:

$$W^{m,2}(\mathbb{R}^N) = H^m(\mathbb{R}^N) = \{u \in L^2(\mathbb{R}^N) \mid \xi \mapsto (1 + |\xi|^2)^{m/2}\,\widehat{u}(\xi) \in L^2(\mathbb{R}^N)\}.$$

Example 2.7. Consider the open unit ball $\Omega = B(0,1)$ in $\mathbb{R}^2$. Let us determine under which condition the function u on Ω defined by $u(x,y) = xy(x^2 + y^2)^{-\beta}$ outside of the origin, with $\beta > 0$, is an element of $H^1(\Omega)$.

More precisely, let us show that $u \in H^1(\Omega)$ if and only if $\beta < 1$. The integral of $|u|^2$ on Ω exists if $5 - 4\beta > -1$ or, equivalently, if $\beta < 3/2$. Indeed, in polar coordinates, the integrand can be written as

$$|u|^2 r\,dr\,d\theta = r^{5-4\beta}(\sin\theta\cos\theta)^2 dr\,d\theta.$$

For the derivative in x in the usual sense, this gives

$$\partial_x u = y(x^2 + y^2)^{-\beta} - 2\beta x^2 y(x^2 + y^2)^{-\beta-1}.$$

This derivative is continuous outside of $(0,0)$. The integral of its square consists of three terms in which the exponent of r is equal to $3 - 4\beta$. These exponents are all greater than -1 if and only if the condition $\beta < 1$ is satisfied. Since the function is symmetric in x and y, it follows that if $\beta < 1$, then u and its derivatives belong to $L^2(B)$. By Remark 2.4 above, this implies that the latter are derivatives in the sense of distributions.

This concludes the proof of the necessity and sufficiency of the condition stated above.

Example 2.8. Consider the open unit ball $\Omega = B(0,1)$ in $\mathbb{R}^N$. Let $r^2 = \sum_1^N x_j^2$ and let u be defined on Ω by $u(x) = (1-r)^\beta(-\ln(1-r))^\alpha$, where α is an arbitrary real number and $\beta > 0$. We want to know under which conditions on α and β that u is an element of $W^{1,p}(\Omega)$.

The function u admits two singularities, at $r = 0$ and at $r = 1$. As the logarithm is equivalent to r^α at 0, the function $|u|^p$ is summable on Ω if $N - 1 + \alpha p > -1$, that is, if $\alpha > -N/p$. At $r = 1$, the function can be extended by continuity. The derivative in the usual sense, for example at x_1, is then

$$\partial_1 u(x) = \frac{x_1}{r}(1-r)^{\beta-1}|\ln(1-r)|^{\alpha-1}\big(\beta|\ln(1-r)| + \alpha\big).$$

At $r = 0$, as the first logarithm on the right-hand side is equivalent to $r^{\alpha-1}$, we find that u and its derivative both belong to L^p in a neighborhood of 0 if $1 - \alpha < N/p$.

At $r = 1$, the integral of $|\partial_1 u|^p$ converges if

- either $\beta > 1 - 1/p$, or
- $\beta = 1 - 1/p$ and $\alpha p < -1$.

Summarizing, $u \in W^{1,p}(B(0,1))$ if and only if either $\beta > 1 - 1/p$ and $\alpha > -N/p$, or $\beta = 1 - 1/p$ and $-N/p < \alpha < -1/p$.

Example 2.9. Given $k > 0$, consider the open subset

$$\Omega = \{(x,y) \mid 0 < x < 1, \, x^k < y < 2x^k\}$$

of $\mathbb{R}^2$. We will study for which $\alpha \in \mathbb{R}$, $(x,y) \mapsto u(x,y) = y^\alpha$ belongs to H^m, where $m \in \{1, 2, 3, \dots\}$.

For $\alpha > 0$, the function u admits a continuous extension to $\partial\Omega$, so that $u \in L^2(\Omega)$. The first derivative $\partial_y u(x,y) = \alpha y^{\alpha-1}$ cannot be extended by continuity to the point $x = 0$ if $\alpha < 1$. Nevertheless, it does belong to $L^2(\Omega)$ if the integral

$$\int_0^1 \left[\int_{x^k}^{2x^k} y^{2\alpha-2} dy \right] dx$$

exists, or, equivalently, if $(2\alpha - 1)k > -1$. We can deduce from this that for $k > 0$, we have $u \in H^1(\Omega)$ if $\alpha > 1/2 - 1/2k$.

The second derivative belongs to $L^2(\Omega)$ if $(2\alpha - 3)k > -1$, that is, if $\alpha > 3/2 - 1/2k$. Under this condition, $u \in H^2(\Omega)$. This holds, for example, when $k = 1/6$ (cf. Figure 2.1) and $\alpha > -3/2$, in which case u need not be bounded on Ω.

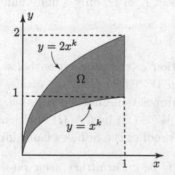

Fig. 2.1. An open subset Ω and elements of H^m.

Let us continue. We find that the condition under which u belongs to $H^m(\Omega)$ can be written as $(2\alpha - 2m + 1)k > -1$. Given m, we can choose α and k such that this necessary condition is satisfied.

Proposition 2.10. *The space $W^{m,p}(\Omega)$ endowed with the norm defined by*

$$\|u\|_{W^{m,p}(\Omega)} = \begin{cases} \left[\sum_{0\leqslant|\alpha|\leqslant m}\|D^\alpha u\|_{L^p(\Omega)}^p\right]^{1/p} & if\ 1\leqslant p < +\infty; \\ \max_{0\leqslant|\alpha|\leqslant m}\|D^\alpha u\|_{L^\infty(\Omega)} & if\ p = +\infty, \end{cases}$$

is a Banach space. For $p \in\ ]1, +\infty[$, this space is uniformly convex and therefore a reflexive space. The space $H^m(\Omega)$ endowed with the inner product

$$\langle u, v\rangle = \sum_{0\leqslant|\alpha|\leqslant m}\left(D^\alpha u, D^\alpha v\right)_{L^2(\Omega)}$$

is a Hilbert space.

Exercise 2.1 offers a proof of these statements. Many propositions in this chapter are concerned with the approximation of functions in $W^{1,p}(\Omega)$ or the density of certain subspaces. For such problems, we often use a cover of the open set Ω by a family of open subsets $\{A_j\}$. We admit (cf. Exercise 2.2) that to such a cover, we can associate a family of functions $\{\psi_j\}$ called a *partition of unity subordinate to the cover $\{A_j\}$ of Ω.*

Definition 2.11. A $\mathcal{C}^\infty$ partition of unity subordinate to an open cover $\{A_j\}_{j\in\mathbb{N}}$ of the open set Ω is a set of functions ψ_j with the following properties:

(1) For every j, the function ψ_j is a nonnegative element of $\mathcal{C}^\infty(\Omega)$ with support in A_j.
(2) For any compact subset K of Ω, only a finite number of the functions ψ_j are not zero on K.
(3) For all $x \in \Omega$, $\sum_{j\in\mathbb{N}}\psi_j(x) = 1$.

We use such a partition in the proposition below, where it allows us to approximate functions in $W^{m,p}(\Omega)$ *from the inside*, without any regularity assumption on Ω. The proposition makes it possible, for example, to replace functions that belong to $W^{m,p}(\Omega)$ by $\mathcal{C}^\infty(\Omega)$ functions during computations, in particular during the proof of the Sobolev embedding theorem.

Proposition 2.12. *Let Ω be an arbitrary open subset of $\mathbb{R}^N$. The subspace $\mathcal{C}^\infty(\Omega) \cap W^{m,p}(\Omega)$ is dense in $W^{m,p}(\Omega)$.*

Proof of Proposition 2.12.

We begin with the case $\Omega = \mathbb{R}^N$. Let $u \in W^{m,p}(\mathbb{R}^N)$. Consider a regularizing sequence (cf. Section 1.4.2) $x \mapsto \rho_\varepsilon(x) = 1/\varepsilon^N\rho(x/\varepsilon)$ and a real number $\delta > 0$. In Section 1.4.2, and in particular in the proof of Theorem 1.91, we saw that the function $\rho_\varepsilon \star u \in \mathcal{C}^\infty(\mathbb{R}^N)$ and its derivatives, which satisfy

$D^\alpha(\rho_\varepsilon \star u) = \rho_\varepsilon \star D^\alpha u$, are elements of $L^p(\mathbb{R}^N)$. Moreover, we saw that there exists an ε_0 such that for all $\varepsilon < \varepsilon_0$, we have

$$(2.13) \quad \|u - \rho_\varepsilon \star u\|_{L^p} \leqslant \delta \quad \text{and} \quad \forall \alpha, \ |\alpha| \leqslant m, \quad \|D^\alpha u - \rho_\varepsilon \star D^\alpha u\|_{L^p} \leqslant \delta$$

(cf. (1.92)). It follows that $\rho_\varepsilon \star u \in W^{m,p}(\mathbb{R}^N)$ and that there exists a constant C_m such that

$$(2.14) \qquad \|u - \rho_\varepsilon \star u\|_{W^{m,p}} \leqslant C_m \delta,$$

which concludes the proof in the case of $\mathbb{R}^N$.

Next, consider an open subset $\Omega \neq \mathbb{R}^N$. We will use an open cover $\{\Omega_j\}_{j\in\mathbb{N}^*}$ of Ω defined by

$$\Omega_j = \{x \in \Omega \mid |x| \leqslant jC_1 \text{ and } d(x, \partial\Omega) > C_2/j + 1\}.$$

The constants C_1 and C_2 are chosen such that $\Omega_2 \neq \varnothing$. The resulting sequence of bounded open subsets is increasing and covers Ω. After setting $\Omega_0 = \Omega_{-1} = \varnothing$, we define the sequence of open subsets $\{A_j\}$ by setting $A_j = \Omega_{j+2} \setminus \overline{\Omega_{j-1}}$ for $j > 1$ and $A_0 = \Omega_2$, $A_1 = \Omega_3$.

The family $\{A_j\}$ is again an open cover of Ω, and we can easily verify that if $|j - j'| \geqslant 3$, then $A_j \cap A_{j'} = \varnothing$. Let $\{\psi_j\}$ be a partition of unity associated with the cover $\{A_j\}$. Let ε_j be sufficiently small that for a given ε, we have

$$\forall j \geqslant 2, \quad A_j + B(0, \varepsilon_j) \subset A_{j-1} \cup A_j \cup A_{j+1},$$

$$\forall j \geqslant 0, \quad \|\rho_{\varepsilon_j} \star (\psi_j u) - (\psi_j u)\|_{W^{m,p}} < \frac{\varepsilon}{2^{j+1}}.$$

Next, consider the function $v^{(\varepsilon)}$ defined by

$$(2.15) \qquad v^{(\varepsilon)} = \sum_0^{+\infty} (\rho_{\varepsilon_j} \star (\psi_j u)).$$

This function is well defined, as the sum on the right-hand side is locally finite. We can deduce from the inequalities above that $v^{(\varepsilon)} \in W^{m,p}(\Omega)$.

Setting $u = \sum_0^{+\infty} (\psi_j u)$, we can conclude the proof using the following inequality:

$$(2.16) \qquad \|v^{(\varepsilon)} - u\|_{W^{m,p}(\Omega)} \leqslant \sum_0^{+\infty} \|\rho_{\varepsilon_j} \star (\psi_j u) - (\psi_j u)\|_{W^{m,p}}$$

$$\leqslant \sum_0^{+\infty} \frac{\varepsilon}{2^{j+1}} = \varepsilon. \qquad \square$$

Corollary 2.17. (1) *Let $u \in W^{1,p}(\Omega)$ and let $v \in W^{1,p'}(\Omega)$, where p and p' satisfy $1/p + 1/p' = 1$. The product uv is then an element of $W^{1,1}(\Omega)$, and*

$$\forall i \in [1, N], \quad \partial_i(uv) = u\partial_i v + v\partial_i u,$$

where the expressions in the equality are all well defined under the assumptions.

(2) *Let u be an element of $W^{1,N}(\Omega)$; then $|u|^{N-1}u$ and $|u|^N$ both belong to $W^{1,1}(\Omega)$, while*

$$\nabla(|u|^{N-1}u) = N|u|^{N-1}\nabla u. \quad \text{and} \quad \nabla(|u|^N) = N|u|^{N-2}u\nabla u.$$

Remark 2.18. In (2), $W^{1,N}(\Omega)$ may be replaced by $W^{1,q}(\Omega)$ for $q \in]1, \infty[$. The result is then

Let $u \in W^{1,q}(\Omega)$; then $|u|^{q-1}u$ and $|u|^q$ both belong to $W^{1,1}(\Omega)$, while

$$\nabla(|u|^{q-1}u) \doteqdot q|u|^{q-1}\nabla u \quad \text{and} \quad \nabla(|u|^q) = q|u|^{q-2}u\nabla u.$$

$$\nabla(|u|^{q-1}u) = q|u|^{q-1}\nabla u \quad \text{and} \quad \nabla(|u|^q) = q|u|^{q-2}u\nabla u.$$

Proof of the Corollary. (1) By the proposition above, there exists a sequence $\{u_n\} \subset \mathcal{C}^\infty(\Omega) \cap W^{1,p}(\Omega)$ that converges to u in $W^{1,p}(\Omega)$. For this sequence, we have

$$\partial_i(u_n v) = \partial_i(u_n)v + u_n\partial_i v,$$

where each term is seen as a product of a $\mathcal{C}^\infty$ function and a distribution. Let us take the limit of the left-hand side in the sense of distributions. We have $u_n v \in L^1(\Omega)$ and $\|u_n v - uv\|_{L^1} \leqslant \|u_n - u\|_{L^p}\|v\|_{L^{p'}} \to 0$. It follows that $\{u_n v\} \to uv$ in L^1, and consequently also in the sense of distributions. By a property of distributions stated in Section (1.4.8), $\partial_i(u_n v) \to \partial_i(uv)$ in the sense of distributions. Likewise, as $u_n \to u$ and $\partial_i u_n \to \partial_i u$ in L^p, the right-hand side converges in $\mathcal{D}'(\Omega)$. Taking the limit therefore gives the desired equality and, moreover, shows that $\partial_i(uv) \in L^1$, whence $uv \in W^{1,1}(\Omega)$.

(2) Consider a sequence $u_n \in \mathcal{C}^\infty(\Omega) \cap W^{1,p}(\Omega)$ that converges to u in $W^{1,N}(\Omega)$. We can easily show that the gradient of $|u_n|^N$ is given by

$$N|u_n|^{N-2}u_n[\nabla u_n].$$

Since $|u_n|^{N-2}u_n$ converges to $|u|^{N-2}u$ in $L^{N/(N-1)}$ and ∇u_n converges to ∇u in L^N, it follows that $N|u_n|^{N-2}u_n\nabla u_n$ converges to $N|u|^{N-2}u\nabla u$ in L^1. Moreover, as $|u_n|^N \to |u|^N$ in L^1, the convergence also holds in $\mathcal{D}'(\Omega)$. Consequently, $\nabla(|u_n|^N)$ converges to $\nabla(|u|^N)$ in $\mathcal{D}'(\Omega)$. Taking the limit therefore provides us with the identity

$$\nabla(|u|^N) = N|u|^{N-2}u\nabla u.$$

Finally, using Hölder's inequality with the conjugate exponents $N/(N-1)$ and N, we have

$$\int_\Omega |\nabla(|u|^N)|dx \leqslant N\left(\int_\Omega |u|^N dx\right)^{N-1/N}\left(\int_\Omega |\nabla u|^N dx\right)^{1/N}.$$

We have therefore proved that $|u|^{N-1}u \in W^{1,1}(\Omega)$.

The reasoning for the second statement concerning the gradient of $|u|^{N-1}u$ is similar. □

Corollary 2.19. *Let* $u \in W^{1,p}_{loc}(\Omega)$. *This means that for every function* $\varphi \in \mathcal{D}(\Omega)$, *we have* $\varphi u \in W^{1,p}(\Omega)$. *Let* x_0 *be the point* $(x'_0, t) \in \Omega$, *where* $x'_0 \in \mathbb{R}^{N-1}$ *and* $t \in \mathbb{R}$. *Let* $B'(x'_0, r)$ *denote an open ball in* $\mathbb{R}^{N-1}$, *and let* $B^*(x_0, r)$ *denote the open cylinder* $B'(x'_0, r) \times]-r, r[$ *whose closure, for* r *sufficiently small, is included in* Ω. *Then, for almost all pairs* (x', t) *and* (x', t') *of elements of* $B^*(x_0, r)$, *we have*

$$(2.20) \qquad u(x', t) - u(x', t') = \int_{t'}^t \partial_N u(x', s)ds.$$

Proof of Corollary 2.19.

For $(t, t') \in (]-r, r[)^2$ and $x' \in B'(x'_0, r)$, let

$$v(x') = \int_{t'}^t \partial_N u(x', s)ds.$$

Let us show that $v \in L^p(B'(x'_0, r))$. The function $(x', s) \mapsto \partial_N u(x', s)$ is an element of $L^p(\Omega)$, as $\overline{B^*(x_0, r)} \subset \Omega$, and hence is summable in s on the interval $[t', t]$ in $]-r, r[$. It follows that v is defined almost everywhere on $B'(x'_0, r)$. Next, by Hölder's inequality and Fubini's theorem, the following holds for almost every pair (t, t'):

$$\|v\|^p_{L^p(B')} = \int_{B'}\left|\int_t^{t'} \partial_N u(x', s)ds\right|^p dx'$$

$$\leqslant \int_{B'} |t - t'|^{p-1}\int_t^{t'} |\partial_N u(x', s)|^p ds dx'$$

$$\leqslant |t - t'|^{p-1}\int_{B^*} |\partial_N u(x)|^p dx < +\infty.$$

Let $\{u_n\}$ be a sequence of elements of $\mathcal{C}^\infty(B^*) \cap W^{1,p}(B^*)$ that converges to u (cf. Proposition 2.12). We define the sequence $\{v_n\}$ on B' by setting

$$v_n(x') = \int_{t'}^t \partial_N u_n(x', s)ds.$$

Replacing u by $u_n - u$ in the preceding computation, we see that $v_n \to v$ in $L^p(B')$. We can therefore extract a subsequence $\{v_{n_j}\}$ that converges almost everywhere to v on B'. Likewise, we can extract from $\{u_{n_j}\}$ a subsequence $\{u_{\sigma(n)}\}$ that converges almost everywhere to u on B^*. Since the functions $u_{\sigma(n)}$ are regular, we have

$$u_{\sigma(n)}(x', t) - u_{\sigma(n)}(x', t') = \int_{t'}^{t} \partial_N u_{\sigma(n)}(x', s) ds = v_{\sigma(n)}(x').$$

The corollary's formula follows from the almost everywhere convergence on both sides. □

Below we give another consequence of Theorem 2.12, which is very useful, in particular when extending a function in $W^{m,p}(\Omega)$ to a function in $W^{m,p}(\mathbb{R}^N)$ when Ω is a Lipschitz open set. For a function in $W^{m,p}(\Omega)$, such an extension requires a technical lemma about changes of variables.

Corollary 2.21. *Consider two bounded open subsets Ω and Ω' of $\mathbb{R}^N$. Let a be a function giving a bijection from Ω' to Ω, where a and a^{-1} are moreover both Lipschitz. Let $p \geqslant 1$ be given. If $u \in W^{1,p}(\Omega)$, then the composed function $v = u \circ a$ is an element of $W^{1,p}(\Omega')$ and the derivatives of v in the sense of distributions are given by the usual derivation formulas for composed functions. Moreover, there exists a constant $C(|\nabla a|_\infty)$ depending on $|\nabla a|_\infty$, such that*

$$\|u \circ a\|_{W^{1,p}(\Omega')} \leqslant C(|\nabla a|_\infty) \|u\|_{W^{1,p}(\Omega)}.$$

Proof of Corollary 2.21.

Let $\{u_n\}$ be a sequence in $W^{1,p}(\Omega) \cap \mathcal{C}^\infty(\Omega)$ that converges to u in $W^{1,p}(\Omega)$. The function $y \mapsto v_n(y) = u_n(a(y))$ is Lipschitz on Ω', and therefore on all lines parallel to any of the coordinate axes y_i. Since Lipschitz implies absolute continuity, it follows (cf. Remark 2.4) that v_n is almost everywhere derivable on Ω' and

$$(*) \qquad \text{for almost all } y \in \Omega', \quad \partial_i(v_n)(y) = \sum_1^N \partial_j(u_n)(a(y)) \partial_i(a_j)(y).$$

We now need the following lemma.

Lemma 2.22. *Given bounded open sets Ω and Ω', let a be a continuous bijection from Ω' to Ω such that a^{-1} is Lipschitz. Then, if $u \in L^p(\Omega)$, we have $u \circ a \in L^p(\Omega')$ and there exists a constant c such that $\|u \circ a\|_{L^p(\Omega')} \leqslant c \|u\|_{L^p(\Omega)}$.*

Let us continue the proof of Corollary 2.21 using this result. Applying it to $\partial_i(u_n - u)$, the inequality of the lemma gives us

$$\|\partial_i(u_n) \circ a - \partial_i(u) \circ a\|_{L^p(\Omega')} \leqslant c \|\partial_i u_n - \partial_i u\|_{L^p(\Omega)}.$$

Since we know that $\partial_i(u_n) \to \partial_i u$ in $L^p(\Omega)$, we deduce that $\{\partial_i(u_n) \circ a\}$ converges to $\partial_i u \circ a$ in $L^p(\Omega')$. Consequently, we can use (*) and the assumptions of the corollary to show that the open sets and derivatives $\partial_i(a_j)$ are bounded, and that the sequence $\{\partial_i(v_n)\}$ converges in $L^p(\Omega')$ to the function $\sum_1^N (\partial_j u \circ a)\,\partial_i(a_j)$, which itself belongs to $L^p(\Omega')$. Taking the limit of a subsequence, the inequality (*) then gives

$$\text{for almost all } y \in \Omega', \quad \partial_i(u \circ a)(y) = \textstyle\sum_1^N \partial_j(u)(a(y))\partial_i(a_j)(y).$$

Since these almost everywhere derivatives are in $L^p(\Omega')$, it follows from Remark 2.4 that they are derivatives in the sense of distributions. By the lemma, we have $u \circ a \in L^p(\Omega')$. Consequently, $u \circ a \in W^{1,p}(\Omega')$. Moreover, $\|u \circ a\|_{L^p(\Omega')} \leqslant c\|u\|_{L^p(\Omega)}$ and $\|\partial_i(u \circ a)\|_{L^p(\Omega')} \leqslant c'\|u\|_{W^{1,p}(\Omega)}\|\nabla(a)\|_{L^\infty(\Omega')}$. From this, we deduce the existence of a constant C that depends only on the Lipschitz constants of a and a^{-1}, such that $\|u \circ a\|_{W^{1,p}(\Omega')} \leqslant C\|u\|_{W^{1,p}(\Omega)}$.   □

Proof of Lemma 2.22. Let L denote the Lipschitz constant of a^{-1}. Let us take a sequence $\{u_n\}$ as in the proof of the corollary above. If we cover $\overline{\Omega'}$ by a finite number n_η of N-*hypercubes* C_k with edge of length 2η and extend $u_n \circ a$ by 0 outside of Ω', then the definition of the Riemann-integrability of $|u_n \circ a|^p$ gives

$$\int_{\Omega'} |u_n(a(y))|^p dy = \lim_{\eta \to 0} \sum_1^{n_\eta} (2\eta)^N \inf_{y \in C_k} |u_n(a(y))|^p.$$

We may, and do, assume that the hypercubes all satisfy $\overline{C_k} \subset \Omega'$. Let y_k be the center of C_k, so that $x_k = a(y_k) \in \Omega$. If $x \in \partial(a(C_k))$, then the properties of a imply that $y = a^{-1}(x) \in \partial C_k$. Hence, as $|y_k - y| \geqslant \eta$, we have the following inequalities for the distances in $\mathbb{R}^N$: $\eta \leqslant |y - y_k| = |a^{-1}(x) - a^{-1}(x_k)| \leqslant L|x - x_k|$. It follows that $a(C_k)$ contains the ball of radius η/L with center x_k, whence $\operatorname{mes}(a(C_k)) \geqslant \omega_N \eta^N / L^N \geqslant K \operatorname{mes}(C_k)$, where K depends only on N and L. We can now deduce the following upper bound:

$$\sum_1^{n_\eta} \operatorname{mes}(C_k) \inf_{y \in C_k} |u_n(a(y))|^p \leqslant \frac{1}{K} \sum_1^{n_\eta} \operatorname{mes}(a(C_k)) \inf_{x \in a(C_k)} |u_n(x)|^p$$

$$\leqslant \frac{1}{K} \int_\Omega |u_n(x)|^p dx.$$

Taking the limit for $\eta \to 0$ gives

$$(**) \qquad \int_{\Omega'} |u_n(a(y))|^p dy \leqslant \frac{1}{K} \int_\Omega |u_n(x)|^p dx.$$

We can find a subsequence $u_{\sigma(n)}$ that converges almost everywhere to u. The result of the lemma then follows from (**) using Fatou's lemma.   □

Let us now give a definition of $W^{1,p}$, using approximations of the derivatives by translation operators.

Proposition 2.23. *For $1 < p < \infty$, the following properties are equivalent:*

(1) $u \in W^{1,p}(\Omega)$.

(2) $u \in L^p(\Omega)$ *and there exists a constant $C > 0$ such that for any open set ω with closure contained in Ω, we have*

$$\forall h \in \mathbb{R}^N, \quad |h| \leqslant d(\omega, \partial\Omega) \Longrightarrow \|\tau_h u - u\|_{L^p(\omega)} \leqslant C|h|.$$

In the case $p = 1$, property (2) must be replaced by

(2′) *For every open set ω with closure contained in Ω, there exists a constant $c(\omega)$ such that $c(\omega) \leqslant C$, $c(\omega) \to 0$ when $|\omega| \to 0$, and $\|\tau_h u - u\|_{L^1(\omega)} \leqslant c(\omega)|h|$.*

Proof of Proposition 2.23.

Let us assume that $1 < p < +\infty$. We will first show that $(1) \Rightarrow (2)$ when the translation is parallel to a base vector.

Consider $u \in W^{1,p}(\Omega)$ and $\overline{\omega} \subset \Omega$. Let e_i be the ith vector of the canonical basis of $\mathbb{R}^N$, and let $h_0 = d(\omega, \partial\Omega)$. Then $\overline{\omega} \subset \Omega$ implies that $h_0 > 0$ and if $|h| < h_0$, we have $x \in \omega \Rightarrow x + he_i \in \Omega$. Corollary 2.19 subsequently tells us that for every h such that $|h| < h_0$ and that for almost all x in ω, we have

$$(2.24) \qquad u(x + he_i) - u(x) = \int_0^h \partial_i u(x + se_i)ds.$$

Consequently, by Hölder's inequality,

$$(2.25) \qquad |u(x + he_i) - u(x)|^p \leqslant |h|^{p-1} \int_0^h |\partial_i u(x + se_i)|^p ds.$$

Since $|u|^p \in L^1(\Omega)$, we can integrate this inequality over ω, whence, using Fubini and noting that $\omega + B(0, h) \subset \Omega$,

$$(2.26) \qquad \begin{aligned} \int_\omega |\tau_{he_i} u - u|^p(x)dx &\leqslant |h|^{p-1} \int_0^h \int_\omega |\partial_i u(x + se_i)|^p dx\, ds \\ &\leqslant |h|^p \|\partial_i u\|_{L^p(\Omega)}^p. \end{aligned}$$

Taking the $1/p$th power of this inequality gives property (2) for the translation τ_{he_i}.

For $h \in \mathbb{R}^N$ such that $\omega + B(0, h) \subset \Omega$, it suffices to replace ∂_i by the derivative along h, namely $\partial_h u = \nabla u \cdot (h/|h|)$. This leads to property (2) with, for example, constant $C = (\sum_1^N \|\partial_i u\|_{L^p(\Omega)}^2)^{1/2}$.

Let us now show the implication $(2) \Rightarrow (1)$.

Let u satisfy (2). We must prove that $\partial_i u \in L^p(\omega)$. Setting, for example, $h = 1/n$, consider the sequence $\{(\tau_{he_i} u - u)/h\}$ of distributions on ω. We know (Subsection 1.4.8) that this sequence converges in $\mathcal{D}'(\omega)$ to the distribution $\partial_i u$. Consequently,

$$(*) \qquad \forall \varphi \in \mathcal{D}(\omega), \quad \left\langle \frac{\tau_{he_i} u - u}{h}, \varphi \right\rangle \longrightarrow \langle \partial_i u, \varphi \rangle.$$

Now, by Hölder's inequality and property (2), we have

$$\left| \left\langle \frac{\tau_{he_i} u - u}{h}, \varphi \right\rangle \right| \leqslant C \|\varphi\|_{L^{p'}}.$$

Using $(*)$, taking the limit of this inequality for $h \to 0$ gives us the inequality $|\langle \partial_i u, \varphi \rangle| \leqslant C \|\varphi\|_{L^{p'}}$. Now, as $p' < \infty$, $\mathcal{D}(\omega)$ is dense in $L^{p'}(\omega)$ (cf. Theorem 1.91). The distribution $\partial_i u$ therefore defines a linear functional on $L^{p'}(\omega)$ and the previous inequality becomes

$$\forall g \in L^{p'}(\omega), \quad |\langle \partial_i u, g \rangle| \leqslant C \|g\|_{L^{p'}(\omega)},$$

proving that $\partial_i u$ can therefore be identified with a function in $L^p(\omega)$ whose norm moreover satisfies $\|\partial_i u\|_{L^p(\omega)} \leqslant C$. Since this is true for every relatively compact open subset ω of Ω, we can use an increasing sequence of such open subsets on which the L^p norms of $\partial_i u$ are uniformly bounded to show that $\partial_i u \in L^p(\Omega)$. Since this result holds for every i, it follows that $u \in W^{1,p}(\Omega)$, which concludes the proof.

Let us now consider the case $p = 1$. For the implication $(1) \Rightarrow (2')$, the reasoning remains the same as above and we see in inequality (2.25) that we can use a constant $c(\omega)$ such that $c(\omega) \leqslant \int_{\omega + B(0,h)} |\nabla u(x)| dx$, which therefore tends to $\int_\omega |\nabla u(x)| dx$ when h tends to 0. In particular, as $\nabla u \in L^1$, this inequality tends to 0 when $\mathrm{mes}(\omega) \to 0$ (in the sense of Lebesgue).

Conversely, by an argument similar to that in the case $p > 1$, the inequality in $(2')$ implies that ∇u is in the dual of $\mathcal{C}_c(\Omega)$, which means that ∇u is a measure (cf. Chapter 6). Since this estimate does not depend on the support of φ, we deduce from it that ∇u is a bounded measure.

Moreover, the inequality $\int_\omega |\nabla u| \leqslant c(\omega)$ shows that the measure ∇u is absolutely continuous with respect to the Lebesgue measure (cf. Chapter 6), which proves that $\nabla u \in L^1(\omega)$. Since ω is arbitrary and $c(\omega)$ is bounded independently of ω, we conclude that $\nabla u \in L^1(\Omega)$. $\qquad \square$

Remark 2.27. In the case $p = 1$, the above proof shows that property (2) for $p > 1$ only implies that $u \in BV(\Omega)$, the space of functions with bounded variation (cf. Chapter 6).

Definition 2.28. Let Ω be an open subset of $\mathbb{R}^N$, either bounded or not. We let $W_0^{m,p}(\Omega)$ denote the closure of the space $\mathcal{D}(\Omega)$ in $W^{m,p}(\Omega)$ for the norm $\|\cdot\|_{m,p}$.

In general, finding an intrinsic characterization of the functions in $W_0^{m,p}(\Omega)$ is not obvious and depends strongly on the structure of Ω. When $\Omega = \mathbb{R}^N$, a method involving truncation and regularization allows us to show the following result.

Proposition 2.29. *The space $\mathcal{D}(\mathbb{R}^N)$ is dense in $W^{m,p}(\mathbb{R}^N)$, so that*

$$W^{m,p}(\mathbb{R}^N) = W_0^{m,p}(\mathbb{R}^N).$$

Proof of Proposition 2.29.

Let $u \in W^{m,p}(\mathbb{R}^N)$ and let $n \in \mathbb{N}^*$. Let φ be a function in $\mathcal{D}(B(0,2))$ with value 1 on $B(0,1)$ and such that $0 \leqslant \varphi \leqslant 1$. Let $\varphi_n(x) = \varphi(x/n)$; then the sequence u_n defined by $u_n(x) = \varphi(x/n)u(x)$ converges to u in $W^{m,p}(\mathbb{R}^N)$. Indeed, as $|u|^p \in L^1$, we have

$$\|u - u_n\|_p^p = \|(1 - \varphi_n)u\|_p^p \leqslant \int_{|x| \geqslant n} |u(x)|^p dx \longrightarrow 0.$$

On the other hand, the Leibniz formula for the derivative of the product of a $\mathcal{C}^\infty$ function and a distribution implies that if $|\alpha| = m$, then $D^\alpha(\varphi_n u)$ is the sum of $\varphi_n D^\alpha u$ and expressions of the form $(1/n)^j D^{\alpha_1}\varphi(x/n)D^{\alpha_2}u$, where $|\alpha_1| + |\alpha_2| = m$ and $|\alpha_1| = j \geqslant 1$. We can bound the L^p norm of these expressions from above by

$$\frac{1}{n^j}|D^{\alpha_1}\varphi|_\infty \left(\int_{|x| \geqslant n} |D^{\alpha_2}u(x)|^p dx \right)^{1/p},$$

which tends to 0 because $j \geqslant 1$. It follows that

$$|D^\alpha(\varphi_n u) - D^\alpha u|_p \leqslant |D^\alpha(\varphi_n u) - \varphi_n D^\alpha u|_p + |\varphi_n D^\alpha u - D^\alpha u|_p,$$

where the right-hand side is the sum of two quantities that both tend to 0.

We will now use regularization. Given a regularizing function ρ, we let $\rho_n(x) = n^N \rho(nx)$ and $u_n = \rho_n \star (\varphi_n u)$. The functions u_n then belong to $\mathcal{D}(\mathbb{R}^N)$, and the sequence $\{u_n\}$ converges to u in $W^{1,p}$. □

In general, we will see that under regularity conditions on Ω, a sufficient condition for the inclusion $u \in W_0^{m,p}(\Omega)$ is that the extension $\tilde{u}$ of u by 0 outside of Ω belongs to $W^{m,p}(\mathbb{R}^N)$.

Remark 2.30. Later on, we will give a result concerning the density of $\mathcal{C}^1(\overline{\Omega})$ in $W^{m,p}(\Omega)$ when Ω is Lipschitz.

2.2 Sobolev Embeddings for $W^{m,p}(\mathbb{R}^N)$

2.2.1 Definitions of Functional Spaces

Given an integer $j \geqslant 0$, we define the family of spaces $\mathcal{C}_b^j(\mathbb{R}^N)$ by setting

$$\mathcal{C}_b^j(\mathbb{R}^N) = \{u \in C^j(\mathbb{R}^N) \mid \forall \alpha \in \mathbb{N}^N,\ |\alpha| \leqslant j,\ \exists K_\alpha,\ \left\|D^{(\alpha)}u\right\|_\infty \leqslant K_\alpha\}.$$

For a positive real number λ, the subspace $\mathcal{C}_b^{j,\lambda}(\mathbb{R}^N)$ consist of the functions in $\mathcal{C}_b^j(\mathbb{R}^N)$ such that if $|\alpha| \leqslant j$, then

$$\exists C_{\alpha,\lambda},\ \forall x, y \in \mathbb{R}^N,\quad \left|D^{(\alpha)}u(x) - D^{(\alpha)}u(y)\right| \leqslant C_{\alpha,\lambda}\,|x - y|^\lambda.$$

2.2.2 Statement of the Theorem and Preliminary Remarks

Theorem 2.31 (Sobolev embedding theorem). *For $p \geqslant 1$ and $m \in \mathbb{N}$, we have:*

(1) *If $N > mp$, then for every q satisfying $p \leqslant q \leqslant Np/(N - mp)$, we have $W^{m,p}(\mathbb{R}^N) \hookrightarrow L^q(\mathbb{R}^N)$. More precisely, under the given conditions, there exists a constant C such that*

$$\forall \varphi \in W^{m,p}(\mathbb{R}^N),\quad \|\varphi\|_q \leqslant C\|\varphi\|_{W^{m,p}(\mathbb{R}^N)}.$$

(2) *For $p = 1$, we have $W^{N,1}(\mathbb{R}^N) \hookrightarrow C_b(\mathbb{R}^N)$.*

(3) *If $N = mp$ and $p > 1$, then for every q satisfying $p \leqslant q < \infty$, we have $W^{m,p}(\mathbb{R}^N) \hookrightarrow L^q(\mathbb{R}^N)$.*

(4) *If $p > N$, then we have*

$$0 < \lambda \leqslant 1 - N/p \implies W^{1,p}(\mathbb{R}^N) \hookrightarrow C_b^{0,\lambda}(\mathbb{R}^N).$$

(5) *If $mp > N$, $N/p \notin \mathbb{N}$, and j satisfies $(j-1)p < N < jp$, then*

$$0 < \lambda \leqslant j - N/p \implies W^{m,p}(\mathbb{R}^N) \hookrightarrow C_b^{m-j,\lambda}(\mathbb{R}^N).$$

If $N/p \in \mathbb{N}$ and $m \geqslant j = N/p + 1$, then $W^{m,p}(\mathbb{R}^N) \hookrightarrow C_b^{m-N/p-1,\lambda}(\mathbb{R}^N)$ for every $\lambda < 1$.

The following preliminary remarks allow us to better understand the proof of Theorem 2.31.

Remark 2.32 (reduction to functions in $\mathcal{D}(\mathbb{R}^N)$). By Proposition 2.29, it suffices to prove the statements of the theorem for functions in $\mathcal{D}(\mathbb{R}^N)$.

Let us, for example, assume that under the conditions of statement (1), we have proved the existence of a C depending on N, p, q, such that

$$(*) \qquad \forall \varphi \in \mathcal{D}(\mathbb{R}^N),\quad \|\varphi\|_q \leqslant C\|\varphi\|_{W^{m,p}(\mathbb{R}^N)}.$$

Consider $u \in W^{m,p}(\mathbb{R}^N)$ and a sequence $\{\varphi_n\}$ in $\mathcal{D}(\mathbb{R}^N)$ that converges to u in $W^{m,p}(\mathbb{R}^N)$. Since the inequality $(*)$ shows that this is a Cauchy sequence in $L^q(\mathbb{R}^N)$, we deduce that it converges to $v \in L^q(\mathbb{R}^N)$ in this space. As, moreover, it also converges to u in $L^p(\mathbb{R}^N)$, we conclude that $u = v$ and $u \in L^q(\mathbb{R}^N)$. Furthermore, by taking the limit in $(*)$, we obtain the existence of a constant C depending on N, p, q, such that

$$\forall u \in W^{m,p}(\mathbb{R}^N), \quad \|u\|_q \leqslant C \|u\|_{W^{m,p}(\mathbb{R}^N)},$$

which shows that the injection is continuous.

The reasoning for the other types of injections is similar.

Remark 2.33 (reduction to the case of critical injections). To prove statements (1), (4) and (5) of Theorem 2.31, it suffices to prove them in the critical cases, namely, for $q = Np/(N - mp)$ for statement (1), for $\lambda = 1 - N/p$ for statement (4), and for $\lambda = j - N/p$ for statement (5).

Indeed, let us suppose that statement (1) has been proved for $q = p^* = Np/(N - mp)$. Let $q \in \,]p, p^*[$ and $\theta \in \,]0, 1[$ satisfy $q = \theta p + (1 - \theta)p^*$. Hölder's inequality with conjugate exponents $1/\theta$ and $1/(1 - \theta)$ gives

$$\int_{\mathbb{R}^N} |u(x)|^q dx = \int_{\mathbb{R}^N} |u(x)|^{\theta p} |u(x)|^{(1-\theta) p^*} dx$$

$$\leqslant \left[\int_{\mathbb{R}^N} |u(x)|^{p \theta/\theta} dx \right]^{\theta} \left[\int_{\mathbb{R}^N} |u(x)|^{p^* (1-\theta)/(1-\theta)} dx \right]^{1-\theta}$$

$$\leqslant \|u\|_{L^p}^{p \theta} \|u\|_{L^{p^*}}^{p^*(1-\theta)}.$$

We know that $u \in L^p$, $u \in L^{p^*}$, and that there exists a C such that $\|u\|_{L^{p^*}} \leqslant C \|u\|_{W^{m,p}}$. Consequently, the previous inequality shows that $u \in L^q$ and $\|u\|_{L^q}^q \leqslant C \|u\|_{W^{m,p}}^{p\theta + (1-\theta)p^*} = C\|u\|_{W^{m,p}}^q$, which implies the continuity of the injection into L^q.

A similar reasoning makes it possible to reduce the proof of statements (4) and (5) to the critical cases mentioned above.

Remark 2.34 (on the impossibility of improving (1)). A simple scaling argument shows that when $N > p$, there cannot exist an embedding from $W^{1,p}(\mathbb{R}^N)$ to $L^q(\mathbb{R}^N)$ for $q < p$ or $q > p^*$, where $p^* = Np/(N - mp)$.

Indeed, let us assume, in either case, the existence of a C such that for every $u \in W^{1,p}(\mathbb{R}^N)$, $\|u\|_{L^q} \leqslant C\|u\|_{W^{1,p}}$. Applying this inequality to the family defined by $u_\lambda(x) = u(x/\lambda)$ gives

$$\left(\int_{\mathbb{R}^N} \left| u\left(\frac{x}{\lambda}\right) \right|^q dx \right)^{1/q} \leqslant C \left[\int_{\mathbb{R}^N} \left| u\left(\frac{x}{\lambda}\right) \right|^p dx + \sum_1^N \int_{\mathbb{R}^N} \frac{1}{\lambda^p} \left| \partial_i u\left(\frac{x}{\lambda}\right) \right|^p dx \right]^{1/p}.$$

Substituting the variable $y = x/\lambda$ and using Minkowski's inequality, this becomes

$$\|u\|_q \lambda^{N/q} \leqslant C\Big[\|u\|_p \lambda^{N/p} + \|\nabla u\|_p \lambda^{-1+N/p}\Big],$$

or an inequality of the form

$$C_1 \leqslant C_2 \lambda^{N(1/p-1/q)} + C_3 \lambda^{-1+N(1/p-1/q)},$$

where C_1, C_2, C_3 are three fixed nonnegative numbers.

The hypothesis implies, when $q < p$, that the exponents on the right-hand side are negative, giving a contradiction when $\lambda \to +\infty$. Likewise, we see that the hypothesis $q > p^*$ implies that the exponents are positive, giving a contradiction when $\lambda \to 0$.

Remark 2.35 (reasoning in Sobolev's proof). The idea Sobolev originally used to show the embedding consists in writing u formally as $u = u \star \delta = u \star \Delta E$, where E, a fundamental solution of the Laplacian, is defined as follows (cf. Exercise 2.19).

For $N > 2$, it is the function $E = k_N r^{2-N}$ with $k_N = 1/((2 - N)\omega_{N-1})$, where ω_{N-1} denotes the $(N - 1)$-dimensional surface area of the unit sphere in $\mathbb{R}^N$.

For $N = 2$, it is the function $E = k_2 \ln(r)$ with $k_2 = 1/(2\pi)$. More precisely, if ζ is a function in $\mathcal{D}(\mathbb{R}^N)$ equal to 1 in a neighborhood of 0, we can write u as

$$(*) \qquad u = u \star \Delta(\zeta E) - u \star \nabla\zeta \cdot \nabla E - u \star (\Delta\zeta)E.$$

Note that when $p \geqslant 1$, the last two terms of $(*)$, namely $u \star \nabla\zeta \cdot \nabla E$ and $u \star (\Delta\zeta)E$, can each be expressed as the convolution of $u \in L^p$ with a function in $\mathcal{D}(\mathbb{R}^N)$. It follows that this convolution is in L^k for every $k \geqslant p$. We are therefore reduced to considering the first term of $(*)$, which can be written as $u \star \Delta(\zeta E) = \nabla u \star \nabla(\zeta E)$.

Let, for example, $p = 1$. Noting that $\nabla(\zeta E) \in L^q$ with $q < N/(N-1)$, and then using the properties of a convolution with an L^1 function, we obtain, thanks to $(*)$, that $u \in L^q$ whenever $q < N/(N-1)$.

The same computation shows that if $1 < p < N$, we still have $u \in L^q$ for every $q < pN/(N-p)$.

To proceed up to the critical exponent in the case $1 < p < N$ with $N \geqslant 2$, we use the *Sobolev lemma* (cf. [60]), where one of the factors of the convolution is the radial function $x \mapsto r^{-s}$. The lemma can be applied to the present situation when $p > 1$ by choosing the exponent $s = N - 1$, in accordance with the definition of $\nabla(\zeta E)$, regardless whether $N = 2$ or not. The statement of the lemma is as follows.

Lemma 2.36 (Sobolev). *Let f be an element of $L^p(\mathbb{R}^N)$ with compact support, where $p \geqslant 1$. Consider the convolution $g = r^{-s} \star f$. The following holds:*

(1) *If $p > 1$, then the function g belongs to L^q on every compact subset of $\mathbb{R}^N$, provided that q satisfies*

$$\frac{1}{q} \geqslant \sup\left\{\frac{1}{q_1}, 0\right\}, \quad where \quad \frac{1}{q_1} = \frac{1}{p} + \frac{s}{N} - 1.$$

(2) *If $p = 1$, then the function g belongs to L^q on every compact subset, provided that $1/q > 1/q_1 = s/N$.*

(3) *If $1/p + s/N = 1$, the function g belongs to L^q on every compact subset for every $q < \infty$.*

In all cases, we have upper bounds of the following type on every compact subset:

$$\|g\|_q \leqslant C\|f\|_p,$$

where the constant C depends on q, on the compact on which we bound g, and on the compact support of f.

The proof of this lemma is difficult for the cases not covered by the Riesz–Thorin theorem and will not be given in this book.

Remark 2.37. The critical exponent $N/(N-1)$ for $p = 1$ is not covered by Sobolev's lemma. In what follows, we use more elementary arguments than those in Sobolev's proof.

2.2.3 The Structure of the Proof of Sobolev's Theorem

Step A. We establish the following inequality for the functions φ in $\mathcal{D}(\mathbb{R}^N)$:

$$\|\varphi\|_{L^{N/(N-1)}(\mathbb{R}^N)} \leqslant C\|\varphi\|_{W^{1,1}(\mathbb{R}^N)}.$$

Statement (1) of the theorem for the case $p = m = 1$ follows, using Remark 2.32.

Step B. We establish the following inequality for the functions φ in $\mathcal{D}(\mathbb{R}^N)$ in the case $p < N$:

$$\|\varphi\|_{L^{Np/(N-p)}(\mathbb{R}^N)} \leqslant C\|\varphi\|_{W^{1,p}(\mathbb{R}^N)}.$$

Step C. We use induction to establish the following inequality for the functions φ in $\mathcal{D}(\mathbb{R}^N)$ in the case $m \geqslant 2$ and $mp < N$:

$$\|\varphi\|_{L^{Np/(N-mp)}(\mathbb{R}^N)} \leqslant C\|\varphi\|_{W^{m,p}(\mathbb{R}^N)}.$$

Combining these three steps and Remarks 2.32 and 2.33 gives us statement (1).

Step D. We establish the following inequality for the functions φ in $\mathcal{D}(\mathbb{R}^N)$:

$$\|\varphi\|_\infty \leqslant C\|\varphi\|_{W^{N,1}(\mathbb{R}^N)}.$$

Using the density of the regular functions, we deduce from this statement (2) of the theorem.

Step E. We prove statement (3) of the theorem, beginning with the case $m = 1$ and $p = N$, followed by the case $m \geqslant 2$ and $Np = m$.

Step F. We show that last two statements, (4) and (5), of the theorem.

2.2.4 Proof of Sobolev's Theorem

Proof of Step A. We must prove that

$$(2.38) \qquad \exists C, \quad \forall \varphi \in \mathcal{D}(\mathbb{R}^N), \quad \|\varphi\|_{L^{N/(N-1)}} \leqslant C\|\varphi\|_{W^{1,1}}.$$

Let $\varphi \in \mathcal{D}(\mathbb{R}^N)$; then for every index $i \in [1, N]$, we have

$$\forall x \in \mathbb{R}^N, \quad \varphi(x) = \int_{-\infty}^{x_i} \partial_i \varphi(x + (s - x_i)e_i)ds.$$

Consequently,

$$(2.39) \qquad |\varphi(x)| \leqslant \int_{\mathbb{R}} |\partial_i \varphi(x + (s - x_i)e_i)|ds.$$

Note that the integral on the right-hand side of (2.39) does not depend on the component x_i of x. We denote the $(N-1)$-tuple $(x_1, \ldots, x_{i-1}, x_{i+1}, \ldots, x_N)$ by $\breve{x}_i^{(N)}$. On $\mathbb{R}^{N-1}$, we define the function φ_i with compact support by setting

$$\varphi_i(\breve{x}_i^{(N)}) = \int_{\mathbb{R}} |\partial_i \varphi(x + (s - x_i)e_i)|ds.$$

The inequalities (2.39) can now be written as

$$\forall i \in [1, N], \ \forall x \in \mathbb{R}^N, \quad |\varphi(x)| \leqslant \varphi_i(\breve{x}_i^{(N)}).$$

Since our goal is to study $\|\varphi\|_{L^{N/(N-1)}}$, we note that

$$\forall x \in \mathbb{R}^N, \quad |\varphi(x)|^{N/(N-1)} \leqslant \prod_1^N \left[\varphi_i(\breve{x}_i^{(N)})\right]^{1/(N-1)}.$$

Next, we use the following lemma.

Lemma 2.40. *Let $N \geqslant 2$. Consider N functions F_i, each belonging to $L^{N-1}(\mathbb{R}^{N-1})$. We have*

$$\prod_{1 \leqslant i \leqslant N} F_i(\breve{x}_i^{(N)}) \in L^1(\mathbb{R}^N)$$

and the inequality

$$(2.41) \quad \int_{\mathbb{R}^N} \prod_i |F_i(\breve{x}_i^{(N)})| dx \leqslant \prod_i \left(\int_{\mathbb{R}^{N-1}} |F_i(\breve{x}_i^{(N)})|^{N-1} d\breve{x}_i^{(N)} \right)^{1/(N-1)}.$$

Proof of Lemma 2.40. The proof uses induction on N. For $N = 2$, it is the following known property:

$$(2.42) \quad \int_{\mathbb{R}^2} F_1(x_2) F_2(x_1) dx_1 dx_2 = \int_{\mathbb{R}} F_1(x_2) dx_2 \int_{\mathbb{R}} F_2(x_1) dx_1.$$

Let us assume that the property has been proved up to order N. For $1 \leqslant j \leqslant N + 1$, consider elements F_j of $L^N(\mathbb{R}^N)$, each a function of the variable $\breve{x}_j^{(N+1)}$.

Fixing x_{N+1}, consider the following integration over $x = (x_1, x_2, \ldots, x_N)$:

$$I_N = \int_{\mathbb{R}^N} \Big[\prod_{1 \leqslant i \leqslant N} |F_i(\breve{x}_i^{(N)}, x_{N+1})| \Big] |F_{N+1}(x)| dx \leqslant +\infty.$$

In this integral, where x_{N+1} is fixed, we apply Hölder's inequality with exponents N and $N/(N-1)$. This consists in the inequality

$$(*) \quad I_N \leqslant \left(\int_{\mathbb{R}^N} \Big(\prod_{1 \leqslant i \leqslant N} |F_i(\breve{x}_i^{(N)}, x_{N+1})| \Big)^{N/(N-1)} dx \right)^{(N-1)/N}$$
$$\cdot \left(\int_{\mathbb{R}^N} |F_{N+1}|^N (x) dx \right)^{1/N}.$$

Next, consider the N functions h_i, which for x_{N+1} fixed and $i \leqslant N$, are defined by

$$(2.43) \quad h_i(\breve{x}_i^{(N)}, x_{N+1}) = |F_i(\breve{x}_i^{(N)}, x_{N+1})|^{N/(N-1)}.$$

By the induction hypothesis at order N, as the function $(h_i)^{N-1}$ is summable on $\mathbb{R}^{N-1}$, the product of these functions is in $L^1(\mathbb{R}^N)$. The inequality $(*)$ above then gives $I_N < +\infty$. Let

$$[g_i(x_{N+1})]^N = \int_{\mathbb{R}^{N-1}} |F_i(\breve{x}_i^{(N)}, x_{N+1})|^N d\breve{x}_i^{(N)}.$$

By the induction hypothesis, the functions h_i satisfy (2.41), namely

$$(**) \quad \left(\int_{\mathbb{R}^N} \prod_{1 \leqslant i \leqslant N} h_i(\breve{x}_i^{(N)}, x_{N+1}) dx \right)^{(N-1)/N}$$

$$\leqslant \prod_{1 \leqslant i \leqslant N} \left(\int_{\mathbb{R}^{N-1}} \left| F_i(\breve{x}_i^{(N)}, x_{N+1}) \right|^N d\breve{x}_i^{(N)} \right)^{1/N}.$$

The right-hand side of this inequality is $\prod_{1 \leqslant i \leqslant N} [g_i(x_{N+1})]$.

The integral

$$I_{N+1} = \int_{\mathbb{R}^{N+1}} \prod_{1 \leqslant j \leqslant N+1} \left| F_j(\breve{x}_j^{(N+1)}) \right| dx\, dx_{N+1}$$

is the integral of

$$I_N = \int_{\mathbb{R}^N} \prod_{1 \leqslant i \leqslant N} \left| F_i(\breve{x}_i^{(N)}, x_{N+1}) \right| \left| F_{N+1}(x) \right| dx$$

over $\mathbb{R}$. We apply Hölder's inequality to I_N and note that

$$K_N = \left[\int_{\mathbb{R}^N} \left| F_{N+1}(x) \right|^N dx \right]^{1/N}$$

is independent of x_{N+1}. By the definitions of h_i and g_i and the inequalities (*) and (**), this leads to

$$I_N \leqslant K_N \left(\int_{\mathbb{R}^N} \prod_{1 \leqslant i \leqslant N} h_i(\breve{x}_i^{(N)}, x_{N+1}) dx \right)^{(N-1)/N}$$

$$\leqslant K_N \prod_{1 \leqslant i \leqslant N} g_i(x_{N+1}).$$

Finally, integrating over $\mathbb{R}$, applying the generalized Hölder inequality (cf. Subsection 1.5.1) with N exponents that are all equal to $1/N$, and using Fubini's formula for the integrals of g_i, we obtain

$$I_{N+1} \leqslant K_N \prod_{1 \leqslant i \leqslant N} \left[\int_{\mathbb{R}} (g_i(x_{N+1}))^N dx_{N+1} \right]^{1/N}$$

$$= \left[\prod_{1 \leqslant j \leqslant N+1} \int_{\mathbb{R}^N} \left| F_j(\breve{x}_j^{(N+1)}) \right|^N d\breve{x}_j^{(N+1)} \right]^{1/N}.$$

We thus obtain relation 2.41 for the rank $N+1$ case, concluding the proof of Lemma 2.40.   □

Let us conclude Step A. We apply Lemma 2.40 to the functions $F_i = |\varphi_i|^{1/(N-1)}$. The inequality $|\varphi(x)| \leqslant \prod_{1 \leqslant i \leqslant N} |\varphi_i(\breve{x}_i)|^{1/(N-1)}$ then gives the following results for the norm $\Phi = \|\varphi\|_{L^{N/(N-1)}}$:

$$\Phi \leqslant \left[\int_{\mathbb{R}^N} \prod_{1 \leqslant i \leqslant N} F_i(\breve{x}_i) dx \right]^{(N-1)/N}$$

$$\leqslant \prod_{1 \leqslant i \leqslant N} \left[\int_{\mathbb{R}^{N-1}} |\varphi_i(\breve{x}_i)| d\breve{x}_i \right]^{1/N}$$

$$= \left[\prod_{1 \leqslant i \leqslant N} \int_{\mathbb{R}^{N-1}} \int_{\mathbb{R}} |\partial_i \varphi(x + s e_i)| ds \, d\breve{x}_i \right]^{1/N}$$

$$= \left[\prod_{1 \leqslant i \leqslant N} \|\partial_i \varphi\|_{L^1(\mathbb{R}^N)} \right]^{1/N}$$

$$\leqslant \frac{1}{N} \sum_{1 \leqslant i \leqslant N} \|\partial_i \varphi\|_{L^1(\mathbb{R}^N)} \leqslant \frac{1}{N} \|\varphi\|_{W^{1,1}(\mathbb{R}^N)}.$$

We therefore have an embedding $W^{1,1}(\mathbb{R}^N) \hookrightarrow L^{N/(N-1)}(\mathbb{R}^N)$. Moreover, by Remark 2.32, statement (1) of the theorem has now been proved in the case $p = m = 1$.

Remark 2.44. The last inequality, which states the continuity of the injection, can be written more precisely as follows:

(2.45) $$\|\varphi\|_{N/(N-1)} \leqslant C \|\nabla \varphi\|_1.$$

Proof of Step B.

Let us now assume that $m = 1$ and $p < N$. Consider, for $u \in \mathcal{D}(\mathbb{R}^N)$, the function $v = |u|^{p(N-1)/(N-p)-1} u$, where the exponent is positive since $p \geqslant 1$. By the definition $|u|^\alpha = \exp(\alpha \ln(|u|))$, the partial derivative $\partial_i v$ can be written as

$$\partial_i v = \frac{p(N-1)}{N-p} |u|^{p(N-1)/(N-p)-1} \partial_i u.$$

Moreover, the previous remark and Hölder's inequality give

$$\left(\int_{\mathbb{R}^N} |v(x)|^{N/(N-1)} dx \right)^{(N-1)/N}$$

$$\leqslant C \int_{\mathbb{R}^N} \frac{p(N-1)}{N-p} |u(x)|^{p(N-1)/(N-p)-1} |\nabla u(x)|$$

$$\leqslant C \left(\int_{\mathbb{R}^N} |\nabla u(x)|^p dx \right)^{1/p} \left(\int_{\mathbb{R}^N} |u(x)|^{Np/(N-p)} dx \right)^{1-1/p}.$$

The left-hand side is none other than $\|u\|_{Np/(N-p)}^{(N-1)p/(N-p)}$. Hence, dividing by $\|u\|_{Np/(N-p)}^{N(p-1)/(N-p)}$, we obtain the inequality

$$(2.46) \qquad \|u\|_{Np/(N-p)} \leqslant C\|\nabla u\|_p.$$

We have thus proved statement (1) of the theorem for $m = 1$ and $1 < p < N$.

Proof of Step C. Let us give a proof by induction on m.

Assume that $m \geqslant 2$ and $mp < N$. We therefore have $(m-1)p < N$ and $p < N$. Let D denote the differential operator of order 1. By the existence of an embedding $W^{m-1,p} \hookrightarrow L^{Np/(N-(m-1)p)}$ which we assume proved, we have $Du \in W^{m-1,p}$, and therefore $Du \in L^{Np/(N-(m-1)p)}$. Since $u \in W^{m,p}$, we have $u \in W^{m-1,p}$, hence also $u \in L^{Np/(N-(m-1)p)}$.

Finally, setting $q = Np/(N-(m-1)p)$, we have $u \in W^{1,q}$. By the embedding theorem for $m = 1$ and because $q < N$, we have

$$u \in L^{Nq/(N-q)} = L^{Np/(N-mp)},$$

where the equality of the spaces follows from $q/(N-q) = p/(N-mp)$. This completes the proof of step C.

We have now proved statement (1) of the theorem.

Proof of Step D.

We move on to the proof of statement (2) by showing that $W^{N,1} \hookrightarrow L^\infty$. The density of the regular functions will then imply the existence of an embedding $W^{N,1} \hookrightarrow \mathcal{C}_b(\mathbb{R}^N)$.

In the proof of result (1) (cf. (2.39)), we have already shown that if $u \in W^{1,1}(\mathbb{R}^N)$, then

$$\forall x' \in \mathbb{R}^{N-1}, \quad \|u\|_\infty(x', \cdot) \leqslant \int_{\mathbb{R}} |\partial_N u(x', t)| dt.$$

Let us make the following induction hypothesis. If $v \in W^{N-1,1}(\mathbb{R}^{N-1})$, then $v \in L^\infty(\mathbb{R}^{N-1})$ and

$$\|v\|_\infty \leqslant \sum_{\substack{\alpha \in \mathbb{N}^{N-1} \\ |\alpha| \leqslant N-1}} \int_{\mathbb{R}^{N-1}} |D^\alpha v(x')| dx'.$$

Applying this inequality to the function $\partial_N u(x', x_N)$ for fixed x_N gives

$$\sup_{x' \in \mathbb{R}^{N-1}} |\partial_N u(x', x_N)| \leqslant \sum_{\substack{\alpha \in \mathbb{N}^{N-1} \\ |\alpha| \leqslant N-1}} \int_{\mathbb{R}^{N-1}} |D^\alpha(\partial_N u)|(x', x_N) dx'.$$

We then integrate with respect to x_N:

$$\sup_{\substack{x' \in \mathbb{R}^{N-1} \\ x_N \in \mathbb{R}}} |u(x', x_N)| \leqslant \int_{\mathbb{R}} \sup_{x'} |\partial_N u(x', x_N)| dx_N$$

$$\leqslant \sum_{\substack{\alpha \in \mathbb{N}^{N-1} \\ |\alpha| \leqslant N-1}} \int_{\mathbb{R}} \int_{\mathbb{R}^{N-1}} |D^\alpha (\partial_N u)(x', x_N)| dx' dx_N$$

$$\leqslant \sum_{\substack{\alpha \in \mathbb{N}^N \\ |\alpha| \leqslant N}} \int_{\mathbb{R}^N} |D^\alpha u|(x) dx.$$

We have thus obtained the embedding $W^{N,1} \hookrightarrow L^\infty$.

Let us return to statement (2). Let $u \in W^{N,1}(\mathbb{R}^N)$ and let $\{u_n\}$ be a sequence in $\mathcal{D}(\mathbb{R}^N)$ such that $\|u_n - u\|_{W^{N,1}(\mathbb{R}^N)} \to 0$. By the above, we can deduce that $\|u_n - u\|_{L^\infty(\mathbb{R}^N)} \to 0$, which means that $\{u_n\} \to u$ uniformly on $\mathbb{R}^N$. Consequently, u is continuous on $\mathbb{R}^N$. Since $u \in L^\infty$, it follows that $u \in \mathcal{C}_b(\mathbb{R}^N)$. Moreover, the inequality $\|u\|_{L^\infty} \leqslant C\|u\|_{W^{N,1}}$ gives

$$\forall u \in W^{N,1}(\mathbb{R}^N), \quad \|u\|_{\mathcal{C}_b(\mathbb{R}^N)} \leqslant C\|u\|_{W^{N,1}}.$$

This concludes step D and the proof of statement (2).

Proof of Step E. Let us now assume that $mp = N$.

We begin with the case $m = 1$, $p = N > 1$.

Let $u \in W^{1,N}(\mathbb{R}^N)$. We will show that u belongs to L^q for every $q \geqslant N$. We begin by showing that $W^{1,N}(\mathbb{R}^N)$ has an embedding into L^q for every $q \in [N, N^2/(N-1)]$. For this, we note that if $u \in W^{1,N}$, then $u^N \in W^{1,1}$. This follows from $\nabla(u^N) = N u^{N-1} \nabla u$ and Hölder's inequality:

$$\int_{\mathbb{R}^N} |\nabla u^N| \leqslant N \int_{\mathbb{R}^N} |\nabla u||u^{N-1}| dx$$

$$\leqslant N \left(\int_{\mathbb{R}^N} |\nabla u|^N dx \right)^{1/N} \left(\int_{\mathbb{R}^N} |u|^N dx \right)^{(N-1)/N}.$$

Using the Sobolev embedding of $W^{1,1}$ into $L^{N/(N-1)}$, we deduce that u belongs to $L^{N^2/(N-1)}$.

Let us now show that u belongs to all L^q with $q > N^2/(N-1)$. For this, we note that q can be written as $q = q'N/(N-1)$ with $q' > N$. Suppose that φ is a regular function tending to u in $W^{1,N}(\mathbb{R}^N)$. We consider

$$A = \left(\int_{\mathbb{R}^N} |\varphi^{q'N/(N-1)}| dx \right)^{(N-1)/N} = \|\varphi^{q'}\|_{L^{N/(N-1)}}.$$

Using $\nabla(|\varphi|^{q'}) = q'|\varphi|^{q'-2}\varphi\nabla\varphi$, Remark 2.44, that is, the upper bound (2.45), and then Hölder's inequality, we obtain the following upper bounds for A:

$$(2.47) \quad \begin{aligned} A &\leqslant q'C \int_{\mathbb{R}^N} |\varphi|^{q'-1}|\nabla\varphi|dx \\ &\leqslant q'C\Big(\int_{\mathbb{R}^N} |\varphi|^{(q'-1)N/(N-1)}dx\Big)^{(N-1)/N}\Big(\int_{\mathbb{R}^N} |\nabla\varphi|^N dx\Big)^{1/N}. \end{aligned}$$

We see that $(q'-1)N/(N-1) \in [N, q'N/(N-1))$. Therefore, there exists a $\theta \in [0,1]$, namely $\theta = 1/(q'+1-N)$, such that

$$\frac{(q'-1)N}{(N-1)} = \theta N + (1-\theta)\frac{q'N}{(N-1)}.$$

Consequently, once more using Hölder's inequality, we obtain

$$\int_{\mathbb{R}^N} |\varphi(x)|^{(q'-1)N/(N-1)}dx$$
$$\leqslant \Big(\int_{\mathbb{R}^N} |\varphi(x)|^{q'N/(N-1)}dx\Big)^{1-\theta}\Big(\int_{\mathbb{R}^N} |\varphi(x)|^N dx\Big)^{\theta}.$$

Substituting this in inequality (2.47) above, we find

$$\Big(\int_{\mathbb{R}^N} |\varphi(x)|^{q'N/(N-1)}\Big)^{(N-1)/(Nq')}$$
$$\leqslant Cq'^{(q'-N+1)/q'}\Big(\int_{\mathbb{R}^N} |\varphi(x)|^N\Big)^{(N-1)/(Nq')}\Big(\int_{\mathbb{R}^N} |\nabla\varphi(x)|^N\Big)^{(q'-N+1)/(q'N)}.$$

We have thus established (cf. Remark 2.32) that $u \in L^{q'N/(N-1)}$.

Note that we cannot conclude that $u \in L^\infty$, as the scalar sequence $q'^{(q'-N+1)/q'}$ is not bounded. Moreover, there exist examples of unbounded $W^{1,N}$ functions with $N \geqslant 2$.

Let us assume that $m \geqslant 2$ and $mp = N$.

We then have $(m-1)p < N$. From $u \in W^{m,p}$, we deduce that $u \in W^{m-1,p}$ and that for every j, $\partial_j u \in W^{m-1,p}$. Hence, by statement (1) of the theorem, we know that u and $\partial_j u$ are elements of L^r with $r = Np/(N-(m-1)p)$.

From $mp = N$, we deduce that $r = N$. Hence $u \in W^{1,r}$, which by the above implies that $u \in L^q$ for every q, concluding the proof of step E.

Proof of Step F. Let us now assume that $mp > N$.

We begin with the case $p > N$, $m = 1$.

Let $u \in W^{1,p}(\mathbb{R}^N)$ and let $p > N$. We will give two proofs that we then have $u \in L^\infty(\mathbb{R}^N)$.

First proof that $u \in L^\infty(\mathbb{R}^N)$ in step F. This proof is based on the integration of the function over a cone $C_{h,\theta}$ with vertex 0, opening angle θ, and bounded by a sphere of radius h in $\mathbb{R}^N$. This proof can therefore also be used for an open subset Ω with the uniform cone property, that is, an open subset for which there exist h, θ such that for every $x \in \Omega$, there exists a rotation R of $\mathbb{R}^N$ with $x + R(C_{h,\theta}) \subset \Omega$. This is of course the case for Lipschitz open sets, whose definition we will give further on. It does not hold for the open set in Example 2.9, in which $\partial\Omega$ has a cusp.

We will show that

$$(2.48) \qquad \forall \varphi \in \mathcal{D}(\mathbb{R}^N), \quad \|\varphi\|_\infty \leqslant C_1 h^{-N/p}\|\varphi\|_p + C_2 h^{1-N/p}\|\nabla\varphi\|_p.$$

After applying a translation, if necessary, we reduce to finding an upper bound for $|\varphi(0)|$. We will use the polar coordinates (ρ, σ), where $\rho \in [0, h]$ and $\sigma \in A(\rho)$, with $A(\rho)$ the surface of intersection of $C_{h,\theta}$ and the sphere of radius ρ (cf. Figure 2.2 below). Let $\varphi \in \mathcal{D}(\mathbb{R}^N)$ and let $\widetilde{\varphi}(\rho, \sigma)$ be its expression in polar coordinates.

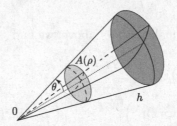

Fig. 2.2. The cone $C_{h,\theta}$.

We have

$$\varphi(0) = \widetilde{\varphi}(\rho, \sigma) + \int_\rho^0 \partial_\rho(\widetilde{\varphi})(\lambda, \sigma)d\lambda.$$

For the remainder of the proof, we set

$$I(\rho, \sigma) = \int_0^\rho |\partial_\rho(\widetilde{\varphi})(\lambda, \sigma)|d\lambda.$$

The volume element is defined by $dx = \rho^{N-1}s(\sigma)d\sigma d\rho$, where $s(\sigma)d\sigma$ is the $(N-1)$-dimensional surface element on the unit sphere S_N. Since the volume of the cone is proportional to h^N, by Fubini, integrating the inequality above over $C_{h,\theta}$ gives the following inequality, where $c_1 > 0$ is a constant bounded from below independently of h:

$$(*) \quad |\varphi(0)|h^N c_1$$

$$\leqslant \int_0^h \int_{A(\rho)} s(\sigma)|\widetilde{\varphi}(\rho,\sigma)|\rho^{N-1}d\sigma d\rho + \int_0^h \int_{A(\rho)} \rho^{N-1}s(\sigma)I(\rho,\sigma)d\sigma d\rho.$$

The first integral of $(*)$ is the same as $A = \int_{C_{h,\theta}} |\varphi(x)|dx$. Using Hölder's inequality with conjugate exponents p and p', we find

$$A \leqslant \left(\int_{C_{h,\theta}} dx\right)^{1/p'} \left(\int_{C_{h,\theta}} |\varphi(x)|^p dx\right)^{1/p}$$

$$\leqslant c_1' h^{N/p'} \|\varphi\|_{L^p(C_{h,\theta})}.$$

We will now study the second integral B of $(*)$. First consider the integral $I(\rho,\sigma)$, which we write as

$$I(\rho,\sigma) = \int_0^\rho |\partial_\rho \widetilde{\varphi}|(\lambda,\sigma)\lambda^{(N-1)/p}\lambda^{(N-1)/p'}\lambda^{-(N-1)}d\lambda,$$

giving

$$I(\rho,\sigma) \leqslant \left(\int_0^\rho |\partial_\rho(\widetilde{\varphi})(\lambda,\sigma)|^p \lambda^{N-1}d\lambda\right)^{1/p} \left(\int_0^\rho \lambda^{(N-1)(1-p')}d\lambda\right)^{1/p'}$$

when we apply Hölder's inequality to it. We note that the exponent of the last integrand satisfies the relation $(N-1)(1-p') > -1$ as $p > N$, which implies the finiteness of this integral. The second integral B in $(*)$ therefore leads to the inequality

$$B \leqslant K \int_0^h \rho^{N-1} \int_{A(\rho)} s(\sigma)$$

$$\cdot \left(\int_0^\rho |\partial_\rho(\widetilde{\varphi})(\lambda,\sigma)|^p \lambda^{N-1}d\lambda\right)^{1/p} \rho^{[(N-1)(1-p')+1]/p'} d\sigma d\rho.$$

Bounding the inner integral by the corresponding integral over $[0,h]$, we have

$$B \leqslant K \int_0^h \rho^{N/p'} \int_{A(\rho)} s(\sigma)\left(\int_0^h |\partial_\rho(\widetilde{\varphi})(\lambda,\sigma)|^p \lambda^{N-1}d\lambda\right)^{1/p} d\sigma d\rho.$$

Again applying Hölder's inequality, this time to the integral over $A(\rho)$, we have

$$B \leqslant K \int_0^h \rho^{N/p'} (\text{mes } A(\rho))^{1/p'}$$

$$\cdot \left(\int_{A(\rho)} s(\sigma)\int_0^h |\partial_\rho(\widetilde{\varphi})(\lambda,\sigma)|^p \lambda^{N-1}d\lambda d\sigma\right)^{1/p} d\rho.$$

Since the measure of $A(\rho)$ is bounded by the area of S_N, hence independently of h, the right-hand side of the inequality above can be interpreted as an integral over $C_{h,\theta}$. Since $|\partial_\rho(\widetilde{\varphi}(\lambda,\sigma)|$ is bounded from above by $|\nabla\varphi(x)|$, we can therefore write

$$B \leqslant K'h^{1+N/p'}\|\nabla\varphi\|_{L^p(C_{h,\theta})}.$$

Dividing by h^N and applying $(*)$, we obtain the desired inequality (2.48). We then extend to $W^{1,p}$ functions by density. Moreover, we will see later on that in the case of $\mathbb{R}^N$, as h can be any element of $\mathbb{R}$, the right-hand side of (2.48) is bounded from above, giving an optimal upper bound for the norm $\|\cdot\|_\infty$. $\square$

Second proof that $u \in L^\infty(\mathbb{R}^N)$ in step F. Consider the fundamental solution E of the Laplacian. We can easily verify (cf. Exercise 2.19) that $E = k_N r^{2-N}$ for $N \geqslant 3$ and $E = k_2 \ln r$ for $N = 2$, with $k_2 = 1/(2\pi)$ and $k_N = 1/((2-N)\omega_{N-1})$, where ω_{N-1} is the $(N-1)$-dimensional surface area of the unit sphere in $\mathbb{R}^N$. Let θ be a function in $\mathcal{D}(\mathbb{R}^N)$ with value 1 on a ball with center 0. Let $F = \theta E$. We then have

$$\Delta F = \theta\delta_0 + 2\nabla\theta \cdot \nabla E + (\Delta\theta)E = \delta_0 + \psi,$$

where $\psi \in \mathcal{D}(\mathbb{R}^N)$. We can write

$$u = \delta_0 \star u = \Delta F \star u - \psi \star u$$

and

$$\Delta F \star u = \sum_{1 \leqslant i \leqslant N} \partial_i F \star \partial_i u.$$

Moreover, the derivatives of F are of the form r^{1-N} in the neighborhood of 0 and have compact support on $\mathbb{R}^N$. Therefore they all belong to L^q for $q < N/(N-1)$. In particular, they belong to $L^{p'}$ because $p > N$. The convolution $\sum_i \partial_i F \star \partial_i u$ therefore belongs to L^∞. Since $\psi \in \mathcal{D}(\mathbb{R}^N)$ and, for example, $u \in L^1$, the convolution $u \star \psi$ is a bounded $\mathcal{C}^\infty$ function.

We have thus obtained the existence of a constant C such that

$$\|u\|_\infty \leqslant C\Big(\|\nabla F\|_{p'}\|\nabla u\|_p + \|\psi\|_{p'}\|u\|_p\Big),$$

completing the proof that $u \in L^\infty(\mathbb{R}^N)$. $\square$

Note that we obtain an optimal estimate by using functions of the form $u_\lambda(x) = u(x/\lambda)$, where $\lambda > 0$. Indeed, the continuity inequality $\|u\|_\infty \leqslant C_1\|u\|_p + C_2\|\nabla u\|_p$ applied to u_λ gives

$$\|u\|_\infty \leqslant C_1\lambda^{N/p}\|u\|_p + C_2\lambda^{-1+N/p}\|\nabla u\|_p.$$

In particular, the minimum of the function of λ on the right-hand side is reached for $\lambda = M\|\nabla u\|_p(\|u\|_p)^{-1}$, where $M = C_2(p - N)/(NC_1)$. We thus obtain the following inequality, where C is a constant that depends only on N, p, and universal data:

$$\|u\|_\infty \leqslant C\Big(\|u\|_p^{1-N/p}\|\nabla u\|_p^{N/p}\Big).$$

We conclude the proof of step F by studying the Hölder continuity of u. Let $h \in \mathbb{R}^N$. In Proposition 2.23, we have already noted that

$$\|\tau_h u - u\|_p \leqslant Ch\|\nabla u\|_p$$

and

$$\|\nabla(\tau_h u - u)\|_p \leqslant 2\|\nabla u\|_p,$$

so that applying the previous inequality gives

$$\|\tau_h u - u\|_\infty \leqslant Ch^{1-N/p}\|\nabla u\|_{L^p}.$$

This implies that u is a Hölder continuous function with exponent $1 - N/p$. We have thus proved that u is a Hölder continuous function for $m = 1$.

Let us now consider the case $m \geqslant 2$. If $mp > N$, $N/p \notin \mathbb{N}$, and $j = [N/p] + 1$, then

$$W^{m,p}(\mathbb{R}^N) \hookrightarrow \mathcal{C}_b^{m-j,j-N/p}(\mathbb{R}^N).$$

Indeed, let j be such that $jp > N > (j - 1)p$; then

$$u \in W^{j,p}(\mathbb{R}^N) \Longrightarrow (u, Du) \in (W^{j-1,p}(\mathbb{R}^N))^2.$$

Hence $(u, Du) \in (L^{Np/(N-(j-1)p)}(\mathbb{R}^N))^2$ by the first Sobolev embedding, since $(j - 1)p < N$. Consequently,

$$u \in W^{1,Np/(N-(j-1)p)}(\mathbb{R}^N).$$

By the above and the inequality $Np/(N - (j - 1)p) > N$, we find that $u \in \mathcal{C}_b(\mathbb{R}^N)$ or, more precisely,

$$u \in \mathcal{C}_b^{0,1-N(N-(j-1)p)/(Np)} = \mathcal{C}_b^{0,j-N/p}(\mathbb{R}^N).$$

Next, let $u \in W^{m,p}(\mathbb{R}^N)$ with $pm > N$. Let j satisfy $(j-1)p \leqslant N < jp$. By the above, $D^{(m-j)}u \in W^{j,p}(\mathbb{R}^N)$, so that $u \in \mathcal{C}_b^{(m-j)}(\mathbb{R}^N)$ with $j = [N/p]+1$. Since $D^{m-j}u \in \mathcal{C}_b^{0,j-N/p}(\mathbb{R}^N)$, we have $u \in \mathcal{C}_b^{m-j,j-N/p}(\mathbb{R}^N)$.

If $u \in W^{j,p}(\mathbb{R}^N)$ with $j = (N/p) + 1 \in \mathbb{N}$, then $Du \in W^{j-1,p}(\mathbb{R}^N)$. Moreover, as $(j - 1)p = N$, step E implies that $Du \in L^q$ for every $q < \infty$. By the above, $u \in \mathcal{C}_b^{0,\lambda}(\mathbb{R}^N)$ for every $\lambda < 1 - N/q$, that is, $u \in \mathcal{C}_b^{0,\lambda}(\mathbb{R}^N)$ for every $\lambda < 1$.

If $j = (N/p) + 1 \in \mathbb{N}$, then the above shows that $D^{m-j}u \in \mathcal{C}_b^{0,\lambda}(\mathbb{R}^N)$ for every $\lambda < 1$, whence $u \in \mathcal{C}_b^{m-N/p-1,\lambda}(\mathbb{R}^N)$ for every $\lambda < 1$.

This concludes step F and the proof of Theorem (2.31).

2.3 Generalization to Other Open Sets

In this section, we study certain classes of open subsets for which the statements of the Sobolev embedding theorem of Section 1.2 still hold.

2.3.1 Methods, Examples and Counterexamples

One method for obtaining the embeddings is as follows. If possible, we extend every function $u \in W^{m,p}(\Omega)$ outside of Ω to a function $\widetilde{u} \in W^{m,p}(\mathbb{R}^N)$. We then use the properties of Theorem 2.31 for $\widetilde{u}$. Returning to u, which is the restriction of $\widetilde{u}$ to Ω, we obtain the corresponding property for the space $W^{m,p}(\Omega)$.

We will see that the existence of such extensions are closely linked to the geometric structure of the open set Ω. Let us first give a counterexample.

Example 2.49. Consider the open set Ω defined by

$$\Omega = \{(x,y) \mid 0 < x < 1, 0 < y < x^2\}.$$

The Sobolev embeddings do not all hold for this open set (cf. [68]).

Indeed, the function $(x,y) \mapsto x^\alpha$ belongs to $H^1(\Omega)$ provided that $\alpha > -1/2$. On the other hand, it belongs to L^p if and only if $\alpha p + 2 > -1$. This implies that $u \in L^p$ for $p < 6$ but not for $p = 6$, while the classical Sobolev embedding would give the inclusion for arbitrary p.

Let us present a relatively large class of open sets for which the embedding theorems hold. The reader can consult [1] for counterexamples and more general open sets.

2.3.2 (m,p)-Extension Operators

Definition 2.50. We say that an open subset Ω of $\mathbb{R}^N$ has an (m,p)-extension if there exists a continuous linear operator E from $W^{m,p}(\Omega)$ to $W^{m,p}(\mathbb{R}^N)$ such that for every $x \in \Omega$, the operator satisfies $Eu(x) = u(x)$.

We have the following theorem.

Theorem 2.51. Let Ω be an open subset of $\mathbb{R}^N$ that has an (m,p)-extension; then the results concerning $W^{m,p}$ in Theorem 2.31 extend to the case of Ω.

Proof of Theorem 2.51.

Let us assume that $mp < N$. Let E be a continuous extension operator from $W^{m,p}(\Omega)$ to $W^{m,p}(\mathbb{R}^N)$. Let $q \leqslant Np/(N - mp)$. Since $Eu(x) = u(x)$ for x in Ω, we have

$$\|u\|_{L^q(\Omega)} \leqslant \|E(u)\|_{L^q(\mathbb{R}^N)} \leqslant C\|E(u)\|_{W^{m,p}(\mathbb{R}^N)} \leqslant C\|E\| \, \|u\|_{W^{m,p}(\Omega)}.$$

We use a similar method for the other cases (2) and (3) of the Sobolev embedding theorem. □

We will now give sufficient *geometric* conditions on the open set Ω for the existence of an (m,p)-extension.

2.3.3 The Case of the Half-Space $(\mathbb{R}^N)^+$

Let $(\mathbb{R}^N)^+ = \mathbb{R}^{N-1} \times \,]0,+\infty[$. We will show the existence of an (m,p)-extension in $W^{m,p}((\mathbb{R}^N)^+)$. We begin with a lemma stating the existence of a "trace" on the boundary. This result is a first encounter with the trace theorem that we will see in the next chapter.

Proposition 2.52. *There exists a continuous linear map*

$$\gamma_0 : W^{1,p}((\mathbb{R}^N)^+) \longrightarrow L^p(\mathbb{R}^{N-1})$$

such that if $u \in \mathcal{C}((\mathbb{R}^{N-1}) \times [0,+\infty[) \cap W^{1,p}((\mathbb{R}^N)^+)$, then $\gamma_0 u(x') = u(x',0)$. Moreover, if u has compact support in $\mathbb{R}^{N-1} \times [0,\infty[$, then $\gamma_0 u$ has compact support in $\mathbb{R}^{N-1}$ and we have

$$(2.53) \qquad \int_{\mathbb{R}^{N-1}\times]0,\infty[} \partial_N u(x)dx = -\int_{\mathbb{R}^{N-1}} \gamma_0\, u(x')dx'.$$

Proof of Proposition 2.52.

Let us show that the sequence $x' \mapsto u(x',1/n)$ of functions in $L^p(\mathbb{R}^{N-1})$ is a Cauchy sequence. By Corollary 2.19 of Proposition 2.12, we have for almost all $x' \in \mathbb{R}^{N-1}$ that

$$(*) \qquad \left|u(x',1/n) - u(x',1/m)\right| = \left|\int_{1/m}^{1/n} \partial_N u(x',t)dt\right|.$$

Applying Hölder's inequality with fixed x', taking the pth power, and integrating gives

$$\int_{\mathbb{R}^{N-1}} |u(x',1/n) - u(x',1/m)|^p dx' \leqslant \left|\frac{1}{n} - \frac{1}{m}\right|^{p-1} \int_{\mathbb{R}^{N-1}} \int_{1/m}^{1/n} |\partial_N u(x',t)|^p dt\,dx'.$$

Since the last integral is bounded by $\|\partial_N u\|_p^p$, we conclude that the sequence we are studying is a Cauchy sequence. Let $\gamma_0\, u$ be the function defined by $\gamma_0\, u(x') = \lim_{n\to+\infty} u(x',1/n)$. The above shows that $\gamma_0 u \in L^p(\mathbb{R}^{N-1})$. Moreover, the linearity of γ_0 is clear, and when $u \in \mathcal{C}^1((\mathbb{R}^N)^+)$, the limit is none other than $u(x',0)$, whence $\gamma_0(u)(x',0) = u(x',0)$.

Let us show the continuity of γ_0 on $W^{1,p}(\mathbb{R}^{N-1} \times \,]0,\infty[)$.

By applying Corollary 2.19 of Proposition 2.12 with $1/m$ and y and taking the limit in $(*)$ for m tending to $+\infty$, we find

$$(**) \qquad \text{for almost all } y \in \mathbb{R}^+, \quad \gamma_0 u(x') = u(x',y) - \int_0^y \partial_N u(x',t)dt.$$

Integrating the pth power of $(**)$ with respect to $y \in [0,1]$ and $x' \in \mathbb{R}^{N-1}$ and applying Minkowski's inequality, we obtain

$$\|\gamma_0 u\|_{L^p(\mathbb{R}^{N-1})} \leqslant \left(\int_0^1 \int_{\mathbb{R}^{N-1}} |u(x',y)|^p dx' dy\right)^{1/p} + \left(\int_0^1 \int_{\mathbb{R}^{N-1}} |\partial_N u|^p dx' dy\right)^{1/p}.$$

The continuity of the map γ_0 follows from this.

Consider u in $W^{1,p}(\mathbb{R}^{N-1} \times [0,\infty[)$ with compact support. The formula $(**)$ tells us that

$$\forall x' \in \mathbb{R}^{N-1}, \quad \gamma_0 u(x') = -\int_0^\infty \partial_N u(x',t) dt.$$

We can now obtain (2.53) by integrating with respect to x' □

This proposition is used in the proof of the following theorem.

Theorem 2.54. *For every $m \in \mathbb{N}^*$ and $1 \leqslant p < \infty$, the half-space $\mathbb{R}^{N-1} \times \mathbb{R}^+$ has an (m,p)-extension operator.*

Proof of Theorem 2.54.

For $u \in W^{m,p}(\mathbb{R}^{N+})$, we define the extension Eu of u for $x_N < 0$ by

$$(2.55) \qquad Eu(x) = \sum_{1 \leqslant j \leqslant m} \lambda_j u(x', -jx_N),$$

where the m-tuple (λ_j) consists of the unique solution of the following system:

$$(2.56) \qquad \forall k \in \{0, 1, \ldots, m-1\}, \quad \sum_{1 \leqslant j \leqslant m} (-j)^k \lambda_j = 1.$$

We can first remark that under these conditions, if $u \in \mathcal{C}^m((\mathbb{R}^N)^+)$, then for every $k \leqslant m-1$, the function u and the partial derivatives $\partial^k Eu/\partial x_N^k$ are continuous at the intersection with $\{x_N = 0\}$. Consequently, $Eu \in \mathcal{C}^{m-1}(\mathbb{R}^N)$, which we can show using the definition of the derivatives ∂_N^k along $\{x_N = 0\}$.

In Theorem 2.54, we can in fact use the given formula for Eu with m' numbers λ_j for any $m' > m$, provided that the m conditions in (2.56) are satisfied, this time with $1 \leqslant j \leqslant m'$. We apply this in the case $m = 1$ in Proposition 2.57 below, which provides a good beginning for the proof of Theorem 2.54.

Proposition 2.57. *Consider v in $W^{1,p}(\mathbb{R}^{N+})$ and $k \geqslant 1$ real numbers μ_j such that*

$$\sum_{1 \leqslant j \leqslant k} \mu_j = 1.$$

Let $\widetilde{v}$ be defined on $\mathbb{R}^N$ by

$$\widetilde{v}(x', x_N) = \begin{cases} v(x', x_N) & \text{if } x_N > 0, \\ \sum_{1 \leqslant j \leqslant k} \mu_j v(x', -jx_N) & \text{if } x_N < 0; \end{cases}$$

then $\widetilde{v} \in W^{1,p}(\mathbb{R}^N)$.

We will give the proof of Proposition 2.57 later. For the moment, we will admit the results of the proposition, in order to continue the proof of Theorem 2.54.

We must first show that $u \in W^{m,p}((\mathbb{R}^N)^+)$ implies $Eu \in W^{m,p}(\mathbb{R}^N)$. Let $u \in W^{m,p}((\mathbb{R}^N)^+)$ and let Eu be defined by (2.56). Assuming that we have proved that $Eu \in W^{m-1,p}((\mathbb{R}^N)^+)$, it suffices to verify that for every α with $|\alpha| = m - 1$, the derivative $D^\alpha(E(u))$ satisfies the conditions of the proposition. In order to do this, let $D^\alpha = D^{\alpha'} \partial_N^k$ with $\alpha = (\alpha', k)$ and $k \leqslant m - 1$; then

$$D^\alpha(Eu)(x', x_N) = \sum_1^m \lambda_j (-j)^k D^{\alpha'} \partial_N^k u(x', -jx_N).$$

Since the $m \geqslant 1$ numbers $\mu_j = \lambda_j(-j)^k$ satisfy the relation $\sum_1^m \mu_j = 1$, the conditions of Proposition 2.57 are fulfilled. Consequently, $D^\alpha(Eu) \in W^{1,p}(\mathbb{R}^N)$.

We still need to prove the continuity of E. We will give its proof after that of Proposition 2.57.

Proof of Proposition 2.57. Let us show that $\widetilde{v}$ indeed belongs to $W^{1,p}(\mathbb{R}^N)$. For this we need the following lemma.

Lemma 2.58. *Let $v \in W^{1,p}((\mathbb{R}^N)^+)$ and let $\varphi \in \mathcal{D}(\mathbb{R}^N)$; then for every $i \in [1, N-1]$,*

$$(2.59) \qquad \int_{(\mathbb{R}^N)^+} \partial_i v(x) \varphi(x) dx + \int_{(\mathbb{R}^N)^+} v(x) \partial_i \varphi(x) dx = 0.$$

If φ satisfies $\varphi(x', 0) = 0$, then

$$(2.60) \qquad \int_{(\mathbb{R}^N)^+} \partial_N v(x) \varphi(x) dx + \int_{(\mathbb{R}^N)^+} v(x) \partial_N \varphi(x) dx = 0.$$

Proof of Lemma 2.58.

Let us show equality (2.59).

Let $\varphi \in \mathcal{D}(\mathbb{R}^N)$ and let $\{v_n\}$ be a sequence in $\mathcal{C}^\infty((\mathbb{R}^N)^+) \cap W^{1,p}((\mathbb{R}^N)^+)$ that converges to v in $W^{1,p}((\mathbb{R}^N)^+)$. By the definition of the derivative $\partial_i v_n$ in the sense of distributions on $\mathbb{R}^{N-1}$, we have for almost all x_N,

$$\int_{\mathbb{R}^{N-1}} \partial_i v_n(x)(x', x_N) \varphi(x', x_N) dx' + \int_{\mathbb{R}^{N-1}} \partial_i \varphi(x', x_N) v_n(x', x_N) dx' = 0.$$

Integrating this equality with respect to x_N and taking the limit gives the desired result.

Let us now show equality (2.60).

If φ satisfies $\varphi(x',0) = 0$, then the function $u\varphi$ is an element of $W^{1,p}((\mathbb{R}^N)^+)$ and has value 0 on the boundary $\{x_N = 0\}$. By Proposition 2.52, we have

$$\int_{(\mathbb{R}^N)^+} \partial_N(u\varphi)(x)dx = 0,$$

that is,

$$\int_{(\mathbb{R}^N)^+} \partial_N u(x)\varphi(x)dx = -\int_{(\mathbb{R}^N)^+} u(x)\partial_N\varphi(x)dx. \qquad \square$$

We conclude the proof of Proposition 2.57 by using derivation in the sense of distributions and Lemma 2.58.

Let $\varphi \in \mathcal{D}(\mathbb{R})$. The function $v(x', jx_N)$ is still an element of $W^{1,p}((\mathbb{R}^N)^+)$, and $\varphi(x', -x_N)$ is still an element of $\mathcal{D}(\mathbb{R}^N)$, so that by substituting $x_N \mapsto -x_N$ twice and using the first equality of Lemma 2.58, we have

$$\int_{(\mathbb{R}^N)^-} v(x', -jx_N)\partial_i\varphi(x)dx = \int_{(\mathbb{R}^N)^+} v(x', jx_N)\partial_i\varphi(x', -x_N)dx$$

$$= -\int_{(\mathbb{R}^N)^+} \partial_i v(x', jx_N)\varphi(x', -x_N)dx$$

$$= -\int_{(\mathbb{R}^N)^-} \partial_i v(x', -jx_N)\varphi(x', x_N)dx$$

for $i \leqslant N - 1$.

Again by the first part of the lemma,

$$\langle \partial_i \widetilde{v}, \varphi \rangle = -\langle \widetilde{v}, \partial_i\varphi \rangle$$

$$= -\int_{(\mathbb{R}^N)^+} v(x)\partial_i\varphi(x)dx - \int_{(\mathbb{R}^N)^-} \sum_1^k \mu_j v(x', -jx_N)\partial_i\varphi(x)dx$$

$$= \int_{(\mathbb{R}^N)^+} \partial_i v(x)\varphi(x)dx + \int_{(\mathbb{R}^N)^-} \sum_1^k \mu_j\partial_i v(x', -jx_N)\varphi(x)dx,$$

where the right-hand side can also be written as

$$(*) \qquad \int_{\mathbb{R}^N} \left[\partial_i\widetilde{v}\,\chi_{((\mathbb{R}^N)^+)} + \left(\sum_1^k \mu_j\partial_i v(x', -jx_N)\right)\chi_{((\mathbb{R}^N)^-)}\right]\varphi(x)dx.$$

We have thus obtained

$$(2.61) \qquad \partial_i\widetilde{v} = \partial_i\widetilde{v}\,\chi_{((\mathbb{R}^N)^+)} + \left(\sum_1^k \mu_j\partial_i v(x', -jx_N)\right)\chi_{((\mathbb{R}^N)^-)}.$$

For the derivation in x_N, we substitute the variable $-jx_N$ for x_N:

$$\langle \partial_N \widetilde{v}, \varphi \rangle = -\langle \widetilde{v}, \partial_N \varphi \rangle$$

$$= -\int_{(\mathbb{R}^N)+} v(x) \partial_N \varphi(x) dx - \int_{(\mathbb{R}^N)-} \sum_1^k \mu_j v(x', -jx_N) \partial_N \varphi(x) dx$$

$$= -\int_{(\mathbb{R}^N)+} v(x) \partial_N \varphi(x) dx - \int_{(\mathbb{R}^N)+} \sum_1^k \frac{\mu_j}{j} v(x) (\partial_N \varphi)(x', -\frac{x_N}{j}) dx$$

$$= -\int_{(\mathbb{R}^N)+} v(x', x_N) \partial_N \Big(\varphi(x', x_N) - \sum_1^k \mu_j \varphi(x', -\frac{x_N}{j}))\Big) dx$$

$$= \int_{(\mathbb{R}^N)+} \partial_N v \Big(\varphi(x', x_N) - \sum_1^k \mu_j \varphi(x', -\frac{x_N}{j})\Big) dx.$$

The last equality follows from the second part of Lemma 2.58 applied to the function $\varphi(x', x_N) - \sum_1^k \mu_j \varphi(x', -x_N/j)$, which is zero on $\{x_N = 0\}$ by the hypothesis $\sum_1^k \mu_j = 1$. After another change of variables, we have

$$\langle \partial_N \widetilde{v}, \varphi \rangle = \int_{((\mathbb{R}^N)+)} \partial_N v(x) \varphi(x) dx - \int_{((\mathbb{R}^N)-)} \sum_1^k \mu_j j \partial_N v(x', -jx_N) \varphi(x) dx.$$

It follows that

$$(2.62) \qquad \partial_N \widetilde{v} = \partial_N v(x', x_N) \chi_{((\mathbb{R}^N)+)} - \sum_1^m j \mu_j \partial_N v(x', -jx_N) \chi_{((\mathbb{R}^N)-)}.$$

The two relations (2.61) and (2.62) show that all $\partial_i \widetilde{v}$ for $i \leqslant N$ belong to $L^p(\mathbb{R}^N)$.

We have thus completed the proof of Proposition 2.57.   □

Let us finish the proof of Theorem 2.54 by proving the continuity of E. The previous equalities show that for all $i \leqslant N$,

$$|\partial_i \widetilde{v}|_{L^p(\mathbb{R}^N)} \leqslant 2 \|\partial_i v\|_{L^p((\mathbb{R}^N)+)}.$$

It follows that there exists a constant C such that

$$\|Eu\|_{m,p} \leqslant C \|u\|_{W^{m,p}((\mathbb{R}^N)+)}.$$

The continuity of the operator E follows from this.   □

Corollary 2.63. *The space $W_0^{1,p}((\mathbb{R}^N)+)$ is the subspace of $W^{1,p}((\mathbb{R}^N)+)$ consisting of the functions u such that $\gamma_0 u = 0$, that is, the functions u whose extension by 0 outside of $(\mathbb{R}^N)^+$ is an element of $W^{1,p}(\mathbb{R}^N)$.*

Proof of Corollary 2.63.

It is clear, using the continuity of the trace map γ_0, that for every sequence of functions with compact support that converges in $W^{1,p}((\mathbb{R}^N)^+)$, the trace of the limit is zero. It follows that if $u \in W_0^{1,p}((\mathbb{R}^N)^+)$, then $\gamma_0 u = 0$.

Conversely, let u satisfy $\gamma_0 u = 0$. Let $\widetilde{u}$ denote the extension by 0 for $x_N < 0$. Then for $i \leqslant N - 1$, by the first equality (2.59) of Lemma 2.58, computing the derivative of this extension in the direction e_i gives

$$\forall \varphi \in \mathcal{D}(\mathbb{R}^N), \quad \langle \partial_i \widetilde{u}, \varphi \rangle = -\langle \widetilde{u}, \partial_i \varphi \rangle = -\int_{x_N > 0} u \partial_i \varphi = \int_{x_N > 0} \partial_i u \varphi.$$

For $i = N$, by the second equality (2.60) of Lemma 2.58 and since the trace of $u\varphi$ is zero, we have

$$\langle \partial_N \widetilde{u}, \varphi \rangle = -\langle \widetilde{u}, \partial_N \varphi \rangle = -\int_{x_N > 0} u \partial_N \varphi = \int_{x_N > 0} \partial_N u \varphi.$$

Let $v_n(x') = \widetilde{u}(x', x_N - 1/n)$; then the sequence $\{v_n\}$ with compact support in $(\mathbb{R}^N)^+$ converges to $\widetilde{u}$ in $W^{1,p}(\mathbb{R}^N)$. To see this, note that

(2.64) $$\forall w \in L^p(\mathbb{R}^N), \quad \lim_{h \to 0} \|\tau_h w - w\|_p = 0.$$

Indeed, let $\varepsilon > 0$ and let ψ be an element of $\mathcal{C}_c(\mathbb{R}^N)$ such that $\|w - \psi\|_p \leqslant \varepsilon/3$. By the continuity of ψ, there exists an h_0 such that

$$\forall h, \quad |h| \leqslant h_0 \Longrightarrow \|\tau_h \psi - \psi\|_\infty \leqslant \frac{\varepsilon}{3|\operatorname{supp}(\psi)|^{1/p'}}.$$

Hence, for $|h| \leqslant h_0$, we have

$$\|w - \tau_h w\|_p \leqslant \|w - \psi\|_p + \|\psi - \tau_h \psi\|_p + \|\tau_h \psi - \tau_h w\|_p \leqslant \varepsilon.$$

It follows that

$$\lim_{n \to +\infty} \|v_n - \widetilde{u}\|_p = 0 \quad \text{and} \quad \forall j \in [1, N], \quad \lim_{n \to +\infty} \|\partial_j v_n - \partial_j \widetilde{u}\|_p = 0.$$

Next, let ρ be a function in $\mathcal{D}(\mathbb{R}^N)$. We set $\rho_{2n} = (2n)^N \rho(2nx)$ and $u_n = \rho_{2n} \star v_n$; then $\{u_n\}$ is a sequence of regular functions with compact support in $(\mathbb{R}^N)^+$ that converges to u in $W^{1,p}(\mathbb{R}^N)$, completing the proof. $\qquad\square$

2.3.4 Lipschitz Open Sets, $\mathcal{C}^m$ Open Sets

Let us begin with the definition of a uniformly Lipschitz open set, followed by that of a uniformly $\mathcal{C}^1$ open set.

Definition 2.65. We call Ω a uniformly Lipschitz open set if:

(1) There exists an open cover $(\Omega_i)_{i \geqslant 0}$ of Ω such that $d(\Omega_0, \partial\Omega) > 0$, for every $i \geqslant 1$, Ω_i is bounded and $\Omega_i \cap \partial\Omega \neq \varnothing$, and either the family $\{\Omega_i\}$ is finite or

$$\exists k \geqslant 2, \quad |i - j| \geqslant k \implies \Omega_i \cap \Omega_j = \varnothing.$$

(2) There exists an open subset $\mathcal{O}'_i$ of $\mathbb{R}^{N-1}$, a function a_i that is Lipschitz on $\mathcal{O}'_i$, and a system of coordinates such that, after permuting the coordinates if necessary,

$$\Omega_i \cap \Omega \subset \{(x', x_N) \mid x' \in \mathcal{O}'_i, \, x_N > a_i(x')\},$$
$$\Omega_i \cap \partial\Omega = \{(x', a_i(x')) \mid x' \in \mathcal{O}'_i\}.$$

(3) There exist a partition of unity $(\varphi_i)_i$ subordinate to the cover of Ω by the Ω_i (cf. Definition 2.11) and constants C_1 and C_2 such that

$$\forall i, \quad \|\varphi_i\|_{W^{1,\infty}(\mathbb{R}^N)} \leqslant C_1 \quad \text{and} \quad \|a_i\|_{W^{1,\infty}(\mathcal{O}'_i)} \leqslant C_2.$$

Definition 2.66. We say that an open set is uniformly of class $\mathcal{C}^1$ if it is uniformly Lipschitz with functions a_i of class $\mathcal{C}^1$.

Remark 2.67. To simplify the terminology, we will from now on often omit the adjective *regular* or *uniformly* and simply use the terms $\mathcal{C}^1$, $\mathcal{C}^k$, or *Lipschitz*.

Lipschitz open sets have the $(1, p)$-extension property. Proposition 2.70 below states this result. Further on, we will define a class of open sets that have the (m, p)-extension property. Note that the latter is not necessary for the embedding theorems, as we will see that being "Lipschitz" is sufficient. However, when an open set is of class $\mathcal{C}^m$ with $m > 1$, it is possible to define higher order traces (cf. next chapter) and, consequently, to obtain results concerning the regularity up to the boundary. We will use these results when studying the solutions of elliptic equations (cf. Chapter 5).

When using the definition above, it helps to know the relation between the inclusion of restrictions of $u \in W^{1,p}(\Omega)$ in each of the spaces $W^{1,p}(\Omega \cap \Omega_i)$, as well as the relation between the corresponding norms. These are as follows.

Proposition 2.68. *Let Ω be a Lipschitz open set. If for every i, $u \in L^p(\Omega)$ satisfies $u \in W^{1,p}(\Omega \cap \Omega_i)$, then $u \in W^{1,p}(\Omega)$. Moreover, there exist constants C and C' that do not depend on u such that*

(2.69)
$$\begin{cases} \sum_i \|\varphi_i u\|_{W^{1,p}(\Omega_i \cap \Omega)} \leqslant C\|u\|_{W^{1,p}(\Omega)}, \\ \|u\|_{W^{1,p}(\Omega)} \leqslant C' \sum_i \|u\|_{W^{1,p}(\Omega \cap \Omega_i)}. \end{cases}$$

Proof of Proposition 2.68. The first part of the proposition is obvious. Let us show the inequalities concerning the norms.

Let $u \in L^p(\Omega)$. By condition (1) of Definition 2.65, we can divide up the sequence $\{\Omega_i\}$ into the union of k sequences of open sets $\{\Omega_{i_n}\}$ such that the intersections $\Omega \cap \Omega_{i_n}$ are two-by-two disjoint. For such a sequence, the sum $\sum_n \|u\|_{L^p(\Omega_{i_n})}^p$ is bounded from above by $\|u\|_{L^p(\Omega)}^p$.

From this, we can deduce the inequality $\sum_i \|u\|_{L^p(\Omega \cap \Omega_i)}^p \leqslant k\|u\|_{L^p(\Omega)}^p$. Next, let $u \in W^{1,p}(\Omega)$. Using the chain rule for $\varphi_i u$ and the uniform upper bounds, we find that in condition (3) of Definition 2.65, the norm $\|\varphi_i u\|_{W^{1,p}(\Omega \cap \Omega_i)}$ is uniformly bounded from above by $K\|u\|_{W^{1,p}(\Omega \cap \Omega_i)}$. The previous upper bound therefore leads to

$$\sum_i \|\varphi_i u\|_{W^{1,p}(\Omega \cap \Omega_i)}^p \leqslant kK\|u\|_{W^{1,p}(\Omega)}^p.$$

The second inequality follows from $u = \sum_i \varphi_i u$.   □

We will now give a first important extension result for Lipschitz open sets.

Proposition 2.70. *If Ω is Lipschitz, then for every $p \geqslant 1$, there exists a $(1, p)$-extension operator from Ω to $\mathbb{R}^N$.*

Proof of Proposition 2.70.

Let $u \in W^{1,p}(\Omega)$ and let $i \in \mathbb{N}$; then by the definition of the partition of unity $\{\varphi_i\}$, the function $\varphi_i u$ has compact support contained in $\Omega_i \cap \overline{\Omega}$. Moreover, $\varphi_i u \in W^{1,p}(\Omega_i \cap \Omega)$. We use the composition of $\varphi_i u$ and a *symmetry* on $\mathcal{O}'_i \times \mathbb{R}$ with respect to the hypersurface $\{x_N = a_i(x')\}$ (see Figure 2.3).

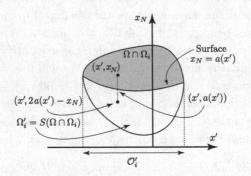

Fig. 2.3. Construction of the $(1, p)$-extension.

This *symmetry* S is defined on $\mathcal{O}'_i \times \mathbb{R}$ by $S(x', x_N) = (x', 2a_i(x') - x_N)$. The image of the bounded open set $\Omega_i \cap \Omega$ under S is a bounded open set Ω'_i. We let $U_i = (\Omega_i \cap \Omega) \cup (\partial\Omega \cap \Omega_i) \cup \Omega'_i$.

Let us begin by extending $\varphi_i u$. We will use local coordinates to define the extension $P_i(\varphi_i u)$ from $\Omega_i \cap \Omega$ to U_i. For every $(x', x_N) \in U_i$, we set

$$P_i(\varphi_i u)(x', x_N) = \begin{cases} (\varphi_i u)(x', x_N) & \text{if } x_N > a_i(x'), \\ (\varphi_i u)(x', 2a_i(x') - x_N) & \text{if } x_N < a_i(x'). \end{cases}$$

For $(x', x_N) \notin U_i$, we set $P_i(\varphi_i u) = 0$.

Let us verify that this extended function is an element of $W^{1,p}(\mathbb{R}^N)$ with norm in $W^{1,p}(\mathbb{R}^N)$ bounded from above by the norm $\|u\|_{W^{1,p}(\Omega)}$ multiplied by a constant depending only on the constants C_1 and C_2 of Definition 2.65.

We note that the symmetry S, which is its own inverse, is continuous because a_i is. Moreover, it satisfies

$$|S(x_1) - S(x_2)| \leqslant \left(1 + 4\|\nabla a_i\|_\infty\right)^{1/2}|x_1 - x_2|.$$

It follows that we can apply Lemma 2.22 to the function $P_i(\varphi_i u)$ on the open set $\Omega_i \cap \Omega$ and on its image under S. Let v be defined on $\mathbb{R}^{N-1} \times]0, +\infty[$ by

$$v(x', t) = \varphi_i u(x', a_i(x') + t).$$

The extension of v by reflection, that is, $\widetilde{v}(x', t) = \varphi_i u(x', a_i(x') - t)$ for $t < 0$, is the same as the previous reflection after the change of variable $t = x_N - a_i(x')$. It follows from Lemma 2.22 that $v \in W^{1,p}(\mathbb{R}^{N-1} \times]0, +\infty[)$. Since $\widetilde{v}$ results from a $(1, p)$-extension on $\mathbb{R}^N$, we find that $\widetilde{\varphi_i u} \in W^{1,p}(\mathbb{R}^N)$. Moreover, the constant c in Lemma 2.22 depends only on the Lipschitz constants of S and S^{-1}, and hence depends only on $\|\nabla a_i\|_\infty$, by the upper bound given earlier. We therefore have

$$\|\widetilde{v}\|_{W^{1,p}(\mathbb{R}^N)} \leqslant C(1 + \|\nabla a_i\|_\infty)\|\varphi_i u\|_{W^{1,p}(\Omega \cap \Omega_i)}.$$

Moreover, as the norms $\|\nabla a_i\|_\infty$ are bounded from above by C_2 (cf. Definition 2.65), setting $C_3 = C(1 + C_2)$, we have

$$\|\widetilde{\varphi_i u}\|_{W^{1,p}(\mathbb{R}^N)} \leqslant (1 + C_2)\|\widetilde{v}\|_{W^{1,p}(\mathbb{R}^N)}$$
$$\leqslant C_3\|\varphi_i u\|_{W^{1,p}(\Omega)}.$$

Let us return to the open set Ω. Let

$$E(u) = \sum_i P_i(\varphi_i u).$$

By Proposition 2.68, we have $E(u) \in W^{1,p}(\mathbb{R}^N)$. The same proposition also gives

$$\|E(u)\|_{W^{1,p}(\mathbb{R}^N)} \leqslant \sum_i \|P_i(\varphi_i u)\|_{W^{1,p}(\mathbb{R}^N)} \leqslant C_3\|u\|_{W^{1,p}(\Omega)}$$

This inequality implies the continuity of the extension operator E, completing the proof of Proposition 2.70. □

Corollary 2.71. *If Ω is Lipschitz, then $C^\infty(\overline{\Omega})$ is dense in $W^{m,p}(\Omega)$.*

Proof of the Corollary.

Let $u \in W^{m,p}(\Omega)$ and let $v_n \in \mathcal{D}(\mathbb{R}^N)$ converge to $E(u)$ in $W^{m,p}(\mathbb{R}^N)$. The restrictions of the v_n to Ω then converge to the restriction of u to Ω, which is u itself.   □

In compliance with the principles announced earlier, Proposition 2.70 allows us to prove the Sobolev embedding theorem.

Theorem 2.72. *Given a Lipschitz open set Ω, we have:*

(1) *If $N > mp$, then $W^{m,p}(\Omega) \hookrightarrow L^q(\Omega)$ for every $q \leqslant Np/(N - mp)$.*

(2) *If $N = mp$, then $W^{m,p}(\Omega) \hookrightarrow L^q(\Omega)$ for every $q < \infty$. If $p = 1$, then $W^{N,1} \hookrightarrow C_b(\Omega)$.*

(3) *If $mp > N$ with $N/p \notin \mathbb{N}$ and if j satisfies $(j-1)p < N < jp$, then we have*

$$W^{m,p}(\Omega) \longhookrightarrow C_b^{m-j,\lambda}(\Omega), \quad \forall \lambda \leqslant j - N/p.$$

If $N/p \in \mathbb{N}$ and $m \geqslant j = N/p + 1$, then $W^{m,p}(\Omega) \hookrightarrow C_b^{m-(N/p)-1,\lambda}(\Omega)$ for every $\lambda < 1$.

For the proof, which is left to the reader, it suffices to first understand that we can use the techniques of the proof of Theorem 2.31 to reduce to the case $m = 1$. After that, use the extension operator given in Proposition 2.70.

Let us continue with the (m,p)-extension operators, where $m > 1$.

Definition 2.73. An open set is called uniformly C^m if it is Lipschitz with functions a_i of class C^m and with the following uniform upper bounds in condition (3) of Definition 2.65:

(2.74) $\|a_i\|_{C^m(\mathcal{O}_i)} + \|\varphi_i\|_{C^m} \leqslant C_3.$

Theorem 2.75. *A C^m open set has the (m,p)-extension property for every $p \in [1, \infty[$.*

Proof of Theorem 2.75.

Using local coordinate systems, we reduce the problem to the extension of a function of type $\varphi_i u$. Leaving out the indexes i in the function a_i and in the local coordinates for the sake of simplicity, we define

$$v(x', t) = u(x', a(x') + t),$$

which gives an element of $W^{m,p}((\mathbb{R}^N)^+)$ thanks to the properties of a. We then use the extension provided by Theorem 2.54. The continuity of the extension is an immediate consequence of the properties of C^m-regularity, and the property of an extension on $\mathbb{R}^N$.   □

Note that we can also define $\widetilde{u}$ directly using the formula

$$\widetilde{u}(x', x_N) = \sum_{j=1}^{m} \lambda_j u(x', -jx_N + (1+j)a(x')),$$

where the λ_j satisfy

$$\forall k \in [0, m-1], \quad \sum_j (-j)^k \lambda_j = 1.$$

However, in this case the computations are longer as we need to use the conservation of the tangential derivatives along $\partial\Omega$, for example, at order 1, $\partial_i u + \partial_i(a)\partial_N u$ for every $i \in [1, N-1]$.

2.4 Compact Embeddings in the Case of a Bounded Open Set

Let us now give compactness results for the Sobolev embeddings in bounded Lipschitz open sets. We begin by giving counterexamples in the case of the critical exponent for a bounded set, and for all embeddings in the unbounded case.

2.4.1 Two Preliminary Counterexamples

Example 2.76. Let us show that if $\Omega = B(0,1)$, $N > p$, and $m = 1$, then the embedding $W^{m,p}(\Omega) \hookrightarrow L^q(\Omega)$, where q is the critical exponent $Np/(N-p)$, is not compact.

Let F be a $\mathcal{C}^1$ function on $\mathbb{R}^N$ with compact support in $B(0,1)$ that is not identically equal to zero. Let $\{F_n\}$ be the sequence of functions on $B(0,1)$ defined by $F_n(x) = n^{(N/p)-1}F(nx)$. We can easily see that $\{F_n\}$ tends to 0 almost everywhere and in $L^p(B(0,1))$. Moreover, its gradient is bounded in $L^p(B(0,1))$. Indeed,

$$(2.77) \qquad \int_{B(0,1)} n^{(N/p-1+1)p} |\nabla F|^p (nx) dx = \|\nabla F\|_{L^p}^p.$$

In particular, $\{F_n\}$ is bounded in $W^{1,p}(\Omega)$. Moreover, we have

$$(2.78) \qquad \|F_n\|_{L^{Np/(N-p)}(\Omega)} = \|F\|_{L^{Np/(N-p)}(\Omega)}.$$

It easily follows (cf. Section 6.1) that $|F_n|^{Np/(N-p)}$ converges vaguely to $|F|_{L^{Np/(N-p)}(\Omega)}^{Np/(N-p)} \delta_0$, where δ_0 denotes the Dirac measure at zero. Nevertheless, $\{F_n\}$ does not tend to 0 in $L^{Np/(N-p)}$.

Let us now give a counterexample to the existence of the compact embeddings when Ω is unbounded.

Example 2.79. Let us show that the embedding of $W^{1,1}(\mathbb{R}^N)$ in $L^1(\mathbb{R}^N)$ is not compact.

Consider $F \in \mathcal{D}(\mathbb{R}^N)$, non-identically zero, and a sequence $\{x_n\}$ that tends to infinity; then the sequence $\{F_n\}$ defined by $F_n(x) = F(x - x_n)$ is bounded in $W^{1,p}(\mathbb{R}^N)$ and converges almost everywhere to 0. Therefore, if it were to converge strongly in L^1, we would have $\|F_n\|_1 = \|F\|_1 = 0$, giving a contradiction.

2.4.2 Compactness Results

Theorem 2.80. *Let Ω be a bounded Lipschitz open subset of $\mathbb{R}^N$, where $N > 1$. If $N > mp$, then the embedding*

$$W^{m,p}(\Omega) \hookrightarrow L^q(\Omega)$$

is compact for $q < Np/(N - mp)$.

Proof of Theorem 2.80. Let us first prove two lemmas.

Lemma 2.81. *For any bounded Lipschitz open subset Ω of $\mathbb{R}^N$, we have*

$$W^{1,1}(\Omega) \hookrightarrow_c L^1(\Omega).$$

Proof of Lemma 2.81. Let B be a bounded subset of $W^{1,1}(\Omega)$. We use the criteria for the compactness of bounded subsets of $L^p(\Omega)$ given in Theorem 1.95 of Chapter 1. Let us verify the two conditions of that theorem.

Let $\varepsilon > 0$ be given. We first show that there exists a compact subset K of Ω such that

$$\forall u \in B, \quad \int_{\Omega \smallsetminus K} |u(x)| dx \leqslant \varepsilon.$$

Indeed, using Hölder's inequality with exponents N and $N/(N-1)$, we have

$$\int_{\Omega \smallsetminus K} |u(x)| dx \leqslant \left[\int_{\Omega \smallsetminus K} dx \right]^{1/N} \left[\int_{\Omega \smallsetminus K} |u(x)|^{N/(N-1)} dx \right]^{(N-1)/N}.$$

Since the open set Ω is bounded, we can choose mes K sufficiently large that the measure of $(\Omega \smallsetminus K)$ is arbitrarily small, giving the desired result.

Next, we prove that there exists a δ such that if $\tilde{u}$ denotes the extension of $u \in B$ by 0 outside of Ω, we have

$$\forall h, \quad |h| \leqslant \delta \implies \int_{\Omega} \left| \tilde{u}(x+h) - u(x) \right| dx \leqslant \varepsilon.$$

Let $h_0 > 0$ be given. Let B_0 denote the closure of the union of the family $\mathcal{B}_{h_0}$ of all open balls with center in $\partial\Omega$ and radius h_0. Let $\omega = \Omega \smallsetminus B_0$. This is an open set contained in Ω for which we can easily see that if $|h| < h_0$, then $x \in \omega \Rightarrow x + h \in \Omega$. Consequently, for every $x \in \omega$, $\tilde{u}(x+h) = u(x+h)$. Consider the composed function $t \mapsto u(x+th)$. For $u \in B$, we have

$$\int_\omega |u(x+h) - u(x)| = \int_\omega \left| \int_0^1 \frac{d}{dt}(u(x+th)dt \right| dx.$$

Differentiating the absolutely continuous function $t \mapsto u(x+th)$ (cf. Exercise 2.3), we obtain

$$\frac{d}{dt}u(x+th) = \sum_1^N h_j \partial_j(u)(x+th) = h \cdot \nabla u(x+th),$$

whence

$$\int_\omega |u(x+h) - u(x)| \leqslant \int_\omega |h|\, |\nabla u(x+th)| dx.$$

Consequently, the last integral is bounded from above by $|h|\, \|\nabla u\|_{L^1(\Omega)}$, as $x + th \in \Omega$, hence by $C|h|$, as $u \in B$. Therefore, there exists an $h_1 < h_0$ such that

$$|h| \leqslant h_1 \Longrightarrow \int_\omega |u(x+h) - u(x)| \leqslant C|h| \leqslant \frac{\varepsilon}{2}.$$

We still need to bound the integral over $\Omega \smallsetminus \omega$. For this, we use the inequality

$$\int_{\Omega \smallsetminus \omega} |\tilde{u}(x+h) - u(x)| \leqslant \int_{\Omega \smallsetminus \omega} \big(|u(x+h)| + |u(x)| \big).$$

The argument given in the first part of the proof then implies the existence of a $\delta < h_1$ such that $|h| \leqslant \delta \Rightarrow 2 \int_{d(x,\partial\Omega) \leqslant 2\delta} |u(x)| dx < \varepsilon$. Finally,

$$\forall u \in B, \quad |h| \leqslant \delta \Longrightarrow \int_\Omega |\tilde{u}(x+h) - u(x)| dx \leqslant \varepsilon.$$

Theorem 1.95 now implies that B is relatively compact in $L^1(\Omega)$. $\qquad\square$

Lemma 2.82. *Let Ω be an open subset of $\mathbb{R}^N$. Let $\{u_n\}$ be a sequence that is convergent in $L^k(\Omega)$ and bounded in $L^q(\Omega)$ for some $q > k$; then it converges in every $L^p(\Omega)$ with $k \leqslant p < q$.*

Proof of Lemma 2.82. We use Hölder's inequality to write $p = \theta k + (1-\theta)q$, where $\theta \in\,]0, 1[$. We have

$$(2.83) \qquad \|u_n - u_m\|_{L^p(\Omega)} \leqslant \|u_n - u_m\|_{L^k(\Omega)}^\theta \|u_n - u_m\|_{L^q(\Omega)}^{1-\theta}.$$

The right-hand side tends to zero when n and m tend to infinity, as it is the product of a bounded sequence and a sequence that tends to zero. We conclude that $\{u_n\}$ is a Cauchy sequence in $L^p(\Omega)$, and therefore converges in $L^p(\Omega)$. $\qquad\square$

Let us return to the proof of Theorem 2.80.

Let $\{u_n\}$ be a bounded sequence in $W^{m,p}(\Omega)$. As Ω is bounded, $L^p(\Omega) \hookrightarrow L^1(\Omega)$ and $\{u_n\}$ is also bounded in $W^{1,1}(\Omega)$. By Lemma 2.81, the latter is relatively compact in $L^1(\Omega)$. Moreover, by Theorem 2.72, the sequence $\{u_n\}$ is bounded in $L^q(\Omega)$ with $q \leqslant Np/(N - mp)$. By Lemma 2.82, $\{u_n\}$ is relatively compact in all $L^q(\Omega)$ with $p \leqslant q < Np/(N - mp)$.   □

Let us now consider, when $mp > N$, the compact embeddings into the spaces of Hölder continuous functions.

Theorem 2.84. *Let Ω be a Lipschitz open set. Let $mp > N$ and let $j = [N/p] + 1$; then for all $\lambda < j - N/p$, the embeddings*

$$W^{m,p}(\Omega) \hookrightarrow C^{m-j,\lambda}(\overline{\Omega})$$

are compact.

Proof of Theorem 2.84.

Let us begin with the case $m = 1$ and $p > N$. We will use the following result, whose proof we will give later.

Lemma 2.85. *Let Ω be a bounded open subset of $\mathbb{R}^N$ and let $\{u_n\}$ be a sequence in $C^{0,\lambda}(\Omega)$ that is relatively compact in $C(\overline{\Omega})$; then for every μ satisfying $0 < \mu < \lambda$, the sequence $\{u_n\}$ is relatively compact in $C_b^{0,\mu}(\Omega)$.*

Let us now show that the embedding of $W^{1,p}(\Omega)$ in $C(\overline{\Omega})$ is compact. We will use the Ascoli–Arzelà theorem. Let K be a bounded set in $W^{1,p}(\Omega)$. The set $\{u(x) \mid u \in K\}$ is then uniformly bounded for every $x \in \Omega$. Indeed, as we already know that the injection is continuous (cf. Theorem 2.72), we have

$$\|u(x)\|_\infty \leqslant \|u\|_{W^{1,p}(\Omega)} \leqslant C$$

for all $u \in K$. Let us show that K is equicontinuous. Indeed, by the continuity of the embedding of $W^{1,p}(\Omega)$ in $C^{0,1-N/p}(\Omega)$ (Theorem 2.72, again), we have

$$\forall\, (x, x + h) \in \overline{\Omega}^2, \quad |u(x + h) - u(x)| \leqslant Ch^{1-N/p}\left(\int_\Omega |\nabla u|^p dx\right)^{1/p}.$$

This implies that K is uniformly Hölder, hence in particular equicontinuous. Lemma 2.85 allows us to conclude the proof in the case $m = 1$ and $p > N$.

Next, let K be a bounded subset of $W^{j,p}(\Omega)$ with $(j - 1)p \leqslant N < jp$. We can easily see as above that K is relatively compact in $C(\overline{\Omega})$. We again use Lemma 2.85 to conclude that K is compact in $C^{0,\lambda}(\Omega)$ for every $\lambda < j-(N/p)$.

For the general case, let K be a bounded subset of $W^{m,p}(\Omega)$ and let $j = [N/p] + 1$. Let $\{u_n\}$ be a sequence of points of K. Since $\{u_n\}$ is bounded in $W^{m,p}(\Omega)$, both this sequence and the sequences consisting of its derivatives $\{D^{m-j}u_n\}$ are bounded in $W^{j,p}(\Omega)$. By the above, we can extract subsequences that converge in $\mathcal{C}_b^{0,\lambda}(\Omega)$ to u and $v_{m,j}$, respectively. For the sake of simplicity, we keep the same notation for the subsequences. They satisfy

$$\|u_n - u\|_\infty \longrightarrow 0 \quad \text{and} \quad \|D^{m-j}u_n - v_{m,j}\|_\infty \longrightarrow 0.$$

Since the convergence in L^∞ implies the convergence in the sense of distributions, we have $v_{m,j} = D^{m-j}u$. Moreover, by the above, $\{D^{m-j}u_n\}$ converges to $D^{m-j}u$ in $\mathcal{C}^{0,\lambda}(\Omega)$ for every $\lambda < j - N/p$.

It follows that for every $\lambda < j - N/p$, $\{u_n\}$ tends to u in $\mathcal{C}_b^{m-j,\lambda}(\Omega)$. This implies the compactness of the embedding of $W^{m,p}(\Omega)$ in $\mathcal{C}_b^{0,\mu}(\Omega)$, for every $\mu < j - N/p$. $\qquad \square$

Proof of Lemma 2.85. Let $\theta \in \,]0,1[$ satisfy $\mu = \theta\lambda$. Let $\{u_{\sigma(n)}\}$ be a subsequence of $\{u_n\}$ that converges in $\mathcal{C}(\overline{\Omega})$. For any pair of indexes (n,m), set

$$d_{n,m} = \left| (u_{\sigma(n)} - u_{\sigma(m)})(x + h) - (u_{\sigma(n)} - u_{\sigma(m)})(x) \right|.$$

We have $d_{n,m} = d_{n,m}^\theta d_{n,m}^{1-\theta}$. Thanks to the convergence of $\{u_{\sigma(n)}\}$ in $\mathcal{C}(\overline{\Omega}))$, we can choose n_0 sufficiently large that if $n, m \geqslant n_0$ and x and $x+h$ are elements of Ω with $|h| < h_0$, we have the following inequality:

$$d_{n,m}^{1-\theta} = \left| (u_{\sigma(n)} - u_{\sigma(m)})(x + h) - (u_{\sigma(n)} - u_{\sigma(m)})(x) \right|^{(1-\theta)} \leqslant \varepsilon.$$

Hence, under these conditions,

$$d_{n,m} \leqslant 2h^{\theta\lambda}\varepsilon.$$

Consequently,

$$\|u_{\sigma(n)} - u_{\sigma(m)}\|_{\mathcal{C}^{0,\mu}(\Omega)} \leqslant 2\varepsilon. \qquad \square$$

2.5 The Trace on the Boundary of a $\mathcal{C}^1$ Open Set

Recall that we defined a uniformly $\mathcal{C}^1$ open set to be an open subset of $\mathbb{R}^N$ that is Lipschitz with functions a_i of class $\mathcal{C}^1$. In this situation, we can define the integration on the subsets $U_i = \partial\Omega \cap \Omega_i$ of the boundary, each of which is a dimension $N - 1$ submanifold of class $\mathcal{C}^1$ in $\mathbb{R}^N$. Such a submanifold is defined by a Cartesian equation $x' \mapsto x_N = a_i(x')$, where a_i is $\mathcal{C}^1$ on the open subset $\mathcal{O}_i'$ of $\mathbb{R}^{N-1}$, so that the $(N - 1)$-dimensional surface element on U_i is given by $d\sigma(m) = \sqrt{1 + |\nabla(a_i)|^2}(m)\, dm$. Recall that in this case, the integral of a function f that is summable in U_i is defined by

$$\int_{U_i} f(m)dm = \int_{\mathcal{O}_i'} f(x', a_i(x'))\sqrt{1 + |\nabla(a_i)(x')|^2}dx'.$$

In this section, we define the trace of a function u in $W^{1,p}(\Omega)$ on the boundary of Ω in the same manner as in the case of $(\mathbb{R}^N)^+$, or more generally, in the case of a straight boundary. More precisely, we have the following theorem.

Theorem 2.86. *Let Ω be a uniformly $\mathcal{C}^1$ open subset of $\mathbb{R}^N$; then there exists a continuous linear map γ_0, called the* trace *map, from $W^{1,p}(\Omega)$ into $L^p(\partial\Omega)$ such that if $u \in \mathcal{C}(\overline{\Omega}) \cap W^{1,p}(\Omega)$, then its image $\gamma_0(u)$ is the function $x \mapsto u(x)$, which is well defined on $\partial\Omega$.*

To see the importance of the *class $\mathcal{C}^1$* hypothesis on Ω, let us give an example of a non $\mathcal{C}^1$ open set on which the functions of $W^{1,p}(\Omega)$ do not have a restriction to $\partial\Omega$ in L^p.

Example 2.87. Consider the open sets defined in Example 2.9. We take the function $u(x,y) = 1/y^2$ that belongs to $H^1(\Omega)$, where the open set Ω is defined using $k = 1/6$. This function is the restriction of a function v defined everywhere on $\overline{\Omega}$ except at the point $x = 0$. Let us study whether $v|_{\partial\Omega}$ is an element of $L^2(\partial\Omega)$.

We have already proved in Example 2.9 that this is the case. Let us restrict ourselves to the part of $\partial\Omega$ that can be identified with either the arc Γ defined by $\{x \in [0,1] \mid y = x^{1/6}\}$ or the arc $\{x = y^6 \mid y \in [0,1]\}$. The infinitesimal element of arc is $ds(y) = \sqrt{1 + 36t^{25}}\, dt$, hence $\int_0^1 v(y)^2 ds(y)$ diverges at 0. It follows that this restriction, or trace, does not belong to $L^2(\partial\Omega)$.

Proof of Theorem 2.86. Even though the existence of the trace in the case of a Lipschitz open set can be shown in a manner similar to the one used in the case of $W^{1,p}((\mathbb{R}^N)^+)$, we will give a proof in which the importance of the notions of Definitions 2.65 and 2.66 is more evident.

Let us assume that $u \in \mathcal{C}^\infty(\Omega) \cap W^{1,p}(\Omega)$. We begin by defining the trace of $v_i = \varphi_i u$ using the partition of unity and local coordinates. This function, which is an element of $W^{1,p}(\Omega_i)$, can be extended by 0 outside of its support in the open set $\mathcal{O}_i' \times \{x_N > a_i(x')\}$. By Corollary 2.19, we have the following equality for every integer $n > 0$ and every $y > 0$:

$$(*) \quad v_i(x', a_i(x') + 1/n) - v_i(x', a(x') + y) = -\int_{1/n}^{y} \partial_N(v_i)(x', a_i(x') + t)dt.$$

Let $u_n(x') = v_i(x', a_i(x') + 1/n)$. From $(*)$, we deduce that for every pair (n, m) of nonzero integers, we have

$$\left|u_n(x') - u_m(x')\right| \leqslant \left|\int_{1/m}^{1/n} \left|\partial_N(v_i)(x', a_i(x') + t)\right|dt\right|.$$

We then apply Hölder's inequality and take the pth power. Next, we multiply on the left by the element of surface $d\sigma_i$ and integrate with respect to $x' \in \mathcal{O}'_i$. This allows us to prove that $A_{n,m} = \|u_n - u_m\|_{L^p(\mathcal{O}'_i, d\sigma_i)} \to 0$:

$$A_{n,m} \leqslant \left| \frac{1}{n} - \frac{1}{m} \right|^{1-1/p}$$
$$\cdot \left[\int_{\mathcal{O}'_i} \sqrt{1 + |\nabla a_i(x')|^2} \left(\int_{\{a_i(x')-1/m \leqslant x_N \leqslant a_i(x')-1/n\}} |\partial_N v_i(x)|^p \right) \right]^{1/p},$$

whence

$$(2.88) \qquad A_{n,m} \leqslant \left| \frac{1}{n} - \frac{1}{m} \right|^{1-1/p} \left(\sqrt{1 + \|\nabla a_i\|_\infty^2} \right)^{1/p} \|\partial_N(v_i)\|_{L^p(\Omega_i)}.$$

By Definition 2.66, this expresses the fact that $|\nabla a_i(x')|$ is bounded from above. When $p > 1$ and n and m tend to infinity, the right-hand side tends to zero, and therefore so does the left-hand side. When $p = 1$, the right-hand side still tends to zero, by the definition of L^1 functions. In all cases, $\{u_n\}$ is a Cauchy sequence in $L^p(\mathcal{O}'_i, d\sigma_i)$, the Lebesgue space for the bounded measure $d\sigma_i$, which is therefore complete. This sequence therefore converges in $L^p(\mathcal{O}'_i, d\sigma_i)$ to a function $w_i \in L^p(\mathcal{O}'_i, d\sigma_i)$. Moreover, there exists a subsequence $\{u_{\eta(n)}\}$ of $\{u_n\}$ that converges almost everywhere in $\mathcal{O}'_i$ to $w_i(x')$. Now, saying that $\lim(\varphi_i u)(x', a(x') + 1/(\eta(n)))$ exists almost everywhere is equivalent to saying that the function $x' \mapsto \varphi_i u(x', a(x')) = w_i(x')$ is well defined.

This extension w_i of $\varphi_i u$ on $\partial\Omega \cap \Omega_i$ is the desired trace. We therefore set $\gamma_0(\varphi_i u) = w_i$. By the above, this function belongs to $L^p(\mathcal{O}'_i, d\sigma_i)$, and therefore to $L^p(\partial\Omega \cap \Omega_i)$. Moreover, by taking the limit in $(*)$ and taking y sufficiently large that $v_i(x', a_i(x') + y) = 0$, we find that

$$(2.89)$$
$$\text{for almost all } x' \in \mathcal{O}'_i, \quad \gamma_0(\varphi_i u)(x') = -\lim \left[\int_{1/\eta(n)}^{+\infty} \partial_N(v_i)(x', a_i(x') + t) dt \right]$$
$$= - \int_0^{+\infty} \partial_N(\varphi_i u)(x', a_i(x') + t) dt.$$

We must now define the trace of u by *gluing*.

Let $\gamma_0 u = \sum_i \gamma_0(\varphi_i u)$. This sum is locally finite, and by condition (1) of Definition (2.65), we conclude that $\gamma_0(u) \in L^p(\partial\Omega)$. We can show that the resulting trace does not depend on the choice of the elements in Definition (2.65).

If we assume that $u \in \mathcal{C}^1(\overline{\Omega})$, we can use the previous arguments. In particular, equality (2.89) gives us $\gamma_0(\varphi_i u)(x', a_i(x')) = \varphi_i \widetilde{u}(x', a_i(x'))$. It follows that $\gamma_0 u$ is the extension by continuity of u to the boundary $\partial\Omega$ (cf. the definition of $\mathcal{C}(\overline{\Omega})$).

To conclude we need only prove that the map γ_0 is continuous. For this, we start out with equality (2.89) and carry out the same computations we used to obtain (2.88). This gives

$$\|\gamma_0(\varphi_i u)\|_{L^p(\mathcal{O}'_i, d\sigma_i)} \leqslant C\left(\sqrt{1 + \|\nabla a_i\|_\infty^2}\right)^{1/p} \|\partial_N(\varphi_i u)\|_{L^p(\Omega_i)}.$$

By condition (3) of Definition 2.65, this leads to the inequalities

$$\|\gamma_0 u\|_{L^p(\partial\Omega)} \leqslant C \sup_i \left(\sqrt{1 + \|\nabla a_i\|_\infty^2}\right)^{1/p} \sum_i \|\nabla(\varphi_i u)\|_{L^p(\Omega_i)}$$

$$\leqslant C' \sum_i \|u\nabla\varphi_i + \varphi_i \nabla u\|_{L^p(\Omega_i)}$$

$$\leqslant C' \sup_i\{\|\varphi_i\|_\infty, \|\partial_N \varphi_i\|_\infty\} \sum_i \|u\|_{W^{1,p}(\Omega_i)}.$$

Using condition (2.66), we deduce that there exists a constant C^* that does not depend on the elements of Definition (2.65), such that

$$\forall u \in \mathcal{C}^\infty(\Omega) \cap W^{1,p}(\Omega), \quad \|\gamma_0 u\|_{L^p(\partial\Omega)} \leqslant C^* \|u\|_{W^{1,p}(\Omega)}.$$

We have thus defined the trace of u when $u \in \mathcal{C}^\infty(\Omega) \cap W^{1,p}(\Omega)$. For $u \in W^{1,p}(\Omega)$, we use the density stated in Proposition 2.12 to approximate u with $u_n \in \mathcal{C}^\infty(\Omega) \cap W^{1,p}(\Omega)$. By taking the limit, formula (2.89) gives $\gamma_0 u = -\int_0^{+\infty} \partial_N(\varphi_i u)(x', a_i(x') + t)dt$, whence $\gamma_0 u_n \to \gamma_0 u$ in $L^p(\partial\Omega \cap \Omega_i)$. The continuity follows, namely

$$\forall u \in W^{1,p}, \quad \|\gamma_0 u\|_{L^p(\partial\Omega)} \leqslant \|u\|_{W^{1,p}(\Omega)}. \qquad \square$$

Remark 2.90. The induced norm provides a way to define a norm on the image space of the trace map without giving it explicitly. We will give an explicit and intrinsic form of the norm in Chapter 3.

Let u be the trace of a function $U \in W^{1,p}(\Omega)$ on the boundary $\partial\Omega$. Let

$$(2.91) \qquad \|\|u\|\| = \inf_{\{U \in W^{1,p}(\Omega) | u = U|_{\partial\Omega}\}} \|U\|_{W^{1,p}(\Omega)}.$$

This defines a norm for which the image space $\gamma_0(W^{1,p}(\Omega))$ is a Banach space. Indeed, let u and v be elements of $\gamma_0(W^{1,p}(\Omega))$ and let U and V be elements of $W^{1,p}(\Omega)$ such that $U = u$ and $V = v$ on $\partial\Omega$, and

$$\|U\| \leqslant \|\|u\|\| + \varepsilon \quad \text{and} \quad \|V\| \leqslant \|\|v\|\| + \varepsilon.$$

We then have $U + V = u + v$ on $\partial\Omega$ and

$$\||u + v\|| \leqslant \|U + V\| \leqslant \|U\| + \|V\| \leqslant \||u\|| + \||v\|| + 2\varepsilon,$$

concluding the proof of the subadditivity. The proof of the other properties and of the completeness of the image space are left to the reader.

We conclude this chapter by going back to the characterization of the space $W_0^{1,p}(\Omega)$ when Ω is $\mathcal{C}^1$.

Theorem 2.92. *Let Ω be an open set of class $\mathcal{C}^1$; then the following statements are equivalent.*

(1) $u \in W_0^{1,p}(\Omega)$.

(2) *(only if $p > 1$) There exists a constant C such that for every $\varphi \in \mathcal{D}(\mathbb{R}^N)$,*

$$\left| \int_\Omega (u \nabla \varphi)(x) \right| dx \leqslant C \|\nabla u\|_{L^p(\Omega)} \|\varphi\|_{L^{p'}}.$$

(3) *The function $\widetilde{u}$ defined by*

$$\widetilde{u} = \begin{cases} u(x) & \text{if } x \in \Omega, \\ 0 & \text{otherwise,} \end{cases}$$

is an element of $W^{1,p}(\mathbb{R}^N)$.

(4) *The trace of u on $\partial\Omega$ is zero, that is, $\gamma_0 u = 0$.*

Proof of Theorem 2.92.

The implication $1 \Rightarrow 2$ is always true, without any assumptions on either the open set or on p. Let $u \in W_0^{1,p}(\Omega)$ and let $\{u_n\} \in \mathcal{D}(\Omega)$ converge to u in $W^{1,p}(\Omega)$. We have

$$\left| \int_\Omega u_n(x) \partial_i(\varphi)(x) dx \right| = \left| -\int_\Omega \partial_i u_n(x) \varphi(x) dx \right| \leqslant \|\nabla u_n\|_{L^p} \|\varphi\|_{L^{p'}}.$$

The result follows by taking the limit.

It is clear that $(2) \Rightarrow (3)$, since if $\varphi \in \mathcal{D}(\mathbb{R}^N)$, then

$$\langle \widetilde{u}, \partial_i \varphi \rangle = \int_\Omega u \partial_i \varphi \, dx.$$

Moreover, using (2), we find that if $p > 1$, then $\widetilde{u} \in W^{1,p}(\mathbb{R}^N)$.

The implication $(3) \Rightarrow (4)$ follows from the uniqueness of the trace.

Let us show that $(4) \Rightarrow (1)$. We reduce it to showing that if $u = 0$ on $\partial\Omega$, then we can approximate $u\varphi_i$ with functions in $\mathcal{D}(\Omega)$. Indeed, let

$$u_{n,i} = \widetilde{u\varphi_i}\left(x', -a_i(x') + x_N - \frac{1}{n}\right).$$

The functions $u_{n,i}$ are elements of $W^{1,p}(\Omega)$ with compact support. The sequence $\{u_{n,i}\}$ converges to $\widetilde{u\varphi_i}$ in $W^{1,p}(\mathbb{R}^N)$, hence converges to $u\varphi_i$ in $W^{1,p}(\Omega)$. Regularizing by a suitable function, we find that $u \in W_0^{1,p}(\Omega)$. $\square$

Comments

There are many books on Sobolev spaces over open subsets of $\mathbb{R}^N$. The simplest and most complete, as far as we are concerned, is Adams's book [1], which has the advantage of also studying more general open sets than Lipschitz sets, for example open sets satisfying the uniform cone condition, or having the segment property. One can also consult the original papers by Sobolev and Nikolskii [53], Sobolev [62] and Uspenskii [73]. The book by Gilbarg and Trudinger [34] presents the essentials, emphasizing the main points of the results.

There also exists a vast literature on Sobolev spaces over Riemann varieties. Let us mention, for example, the book by E. Hebey [37], which gives complete results and is agreeable to read.

The case where the codomain has other topological properties than $\mathbb{R}^p$ is discussed by Bethuel [6] and Brezis, Bethuel and Coron [5].

2.6 Exercises for Chapter 2

Exercise [*] 2.1 (On the Completeness of the Sobolev Space $H^1(\Omega)$).
Let Ω be an open subset of $\mathbb{R}^N$. Recall the definition of $H^1(\Omega)$. Show that

$$(u, v) = \int_\Omega u(x)v(x)dx + \sum_1^N \left(\int_\Omega \partial_j u(x)\partial_j v(x)dx \right),$$

defines a scalar product on the space $H^1(\Omega)$. Show that $H^1(\Omega)$ is a Hilbert space.

Hints. Let $\{u_n\}_{n \in \mathbb{N}}$ be a Cauchy sequence in $H^1(\Omega)$. Prove that the sequence of derivatives $\{\partial_j u_n\}$ converges in L^2 to u_j. Next, prove that these functions are distributional derivatives of $u = \lim u_n$. Conclude.

Exercise 2.2 (On the Construction of a Partition of Unity).
We call a cover $\{\Omega'_k\}$ of Ω finer than the cover $\{\Omega_j\}$ if for every k, there exists a j such that $\Omega'_k \subset \Omega_j$. We call the cover $\{\Omega_j\}$ locally finite if every element x of Ω admits a neighborhood that meets only a finite number of open subsets in the family $\{\Omega_j\}$.

(1) Let $\{\Omega_j\}$ be an open cover of the open subset Ω of $\mathbb{R}^N$. Show that we can find a locally finite cover $\{\Omega'_k\}$ of Ω that is finer than $\{\Omega_j\}$ and consists of relatively compact sets.
(2) Consider a cover $\{\Omega_j\}$ consisting of relatively compact open sets. Show that there exist $\gamma_j \in \mathcal{D}(\Omega_j)$ such that $\gamma_j \geqslant 0$ and $\gamma_j = 1$ on $\overline{\Omega'_j}$. Use these functions to construct a partition of unity associated with the given cover.

In the general case, we will use the open cover of Ω given by question (1), which is finer than $\{\Omega_j\}$ and consists of relatively compact sets.

Hints. For (1), use an increasing sequence $\{U_k\}$ of relatively compact open sets that covers Ω and satisfies

$$U_0 = \varnothing, \quad \overline{U_k} \subset U_{k+1}.$$

Next, use the compactness of $\overline{\Omega_j}$ to determine a cover of this compact set by a finite number of U_k. It is easy to deduce a cover of Ω with the desired properties from this.

For (2), the construction of the γ_j, set $K = \overline{\Omega_j'}$. Let V be a neighborhood of 0 and let U be a compact neighborhood such that $U + U \subset V$ (first prove the existence of U). Let ρ_ε be a regularizing function (cf. Section 1.4.2) with support contained in U and let χ be the characteristic function of $K + U + U$. Let $\gamma_j = \chi \star \rho_\varepsilon$.

Since the sum $\gamma = \sum \gamma_j$ is locally finite, we can define this sum at every point of Ω and, by division, obtain the functions of a partition. Check this.

Exercise [∗] 2.3 (On the Absolute Continuity of the Functions on a Sobolev Space (cf. Remark 2.4)).

The definition of an absolutely continuous function is given in Exercise 1.29. For any two absolutely continuous functions on an interval I, the product UV is also absolutely continuous. Moreover, for every $[a, b] \subset I$, we have the following formula for integration by parts, where u and v are almost everywhere derivatives of U and V:

$$(2.93) \qquad \int_a^b U(t)v(t)dt = U(b)V(b) - U(a)V(a) - \int_a^b V(t)u(t)dt.$$

Let u be defined almost everywhere in an open set $\Omega \subset \mathbb{R}^2$.

(1) Let $\Omega \subset \mathbb{R}^2$, and let $u \in W^{1,p}(\Omega)$, where $p \geqslant 2$. Let $[\partial_x u]$ denote the L^p function equal to the derivative of u with respect to x, seen as a distribution. We can cover Ω by squares C_j and set $v_j = \psi_j u$, where $\psi_j \in \mathcal{D}(C_j)$ and $\sum \psi_j = 1$ on Ω. We extend v_j by 0 outside of C_j. Let v be defined on Ω by $v = \sum v_j$. Below we also write v for v_j, for the sake of simplicity. Show that $v \in L^p(\Omega)$. Let v^* be defined by $v^*(x) = \int_{-\infty}^x [\partial_1 v](t, y)dt$ for every y satisfying $\int_{\mathbb{R}} |[\partial_1 v](t, y)|dt < +\infty$. Deduce from this that $v = v^*$ almost everywhere and that on almost all lines parallel to Ox, the function u is almost everywhere derivable with $[\partial_1 u] = \partial_1 u$ almost everywhere.

(2) Let $u \in L^1_{\text{loc}}(\Omega)$ be absolutely continuous on almost all lines parallel to Ox and such that its derivative almost everywhere $\partial_{x_1} u$ is an element of $L^p(\Omega)$. Show that $[\partial_{x_1} u] = \partial_{x_1} u$ almost everywhere.

(3) Let $u \in W^{1,1}(\Omega)$. Suppose that $[x, x + h] \in \Omega$. Show that the derivative of $v : t \mapsto u(x + th)$ exists almost everywhere on $]0, 1[$ and that $dv/dt\,(x + th) = h \cdot \nabla u(x + th)$.

Hints. For (2), it suffices to compute $\int_\Omega \varphi \partial_{x_1} u dx$ by integrating by parts.

For (3), use the decomposition of $v(t') - v(t)$ as a sum of differences of the type $u(x + t'h) - u(x_1 + t'h_1, x_2 + t'h_2, \ldots, x_{N-1} + t'h_{N-1}, x_N + th_N)$. Write each of these differences as the integral of a partial derivative over some interval. Taking the limit uses the continuity of a Lebesgue integral with respect to its bounds.

Exercise [*] 2.4 (On the $(1,p)$-Extension in the Case of an Interval in $\mathbb{R}$).

Let $u \in W^{1,p}(]0, +\infty[)$. We extend u to $] - \infty, 0[$ by setting $\widetilde{u}(x) = u(-x)$. Prove that this extension of u is an element of $W^{1,p}(\mathbb{R})$. Let $u \in W^{1,p}(I)$ where $I =]a, b[$. Prove that we can extend u to an element of $W^{1,p}(\mathbb{R})$.

Hints. First establish that $\widetilde{u} \in W^{1,p}(] - \infty, 0[)$ by showing that $(\widetilde{u})' = -\widetilde{u'}$.

Exercise 2.5 (Product of Functions in $W^{1,p}(\Omega)$ and $W^{1,q}(\Omega)$).

Consider a Lipschitz open subset Ω of $\mathbb{R}^N$. Let $p < N$, let $q < N$ and let $1/s = 1/p + 1/q - 1/N$. Show that if $u \in W^{1,p}(\Omega)$ and $v \in W^{1,q}(\Omega)$, then $uv \in W^{1,s}(\Omega)$.

Hints. Use the Sobolev theorem 2.31 with suitable exponents and Hölder's inequality.

Exercise 2.6 (Example of a Non-Lipschitz Open Set).

Let $\Omega = \{0 < x < 1, \ 0 < y < x^4\}$. Prove that the function $x \mapsto x^{-1}$ is an element of $H^1(\Omega)$ but not an element of $L^5(\Omega)$. Conclude.

Exercise [*] 2.7 (Injection into a Non-Compact Space of Hölder Functions).

Let $p > N$. Show that the injection of $W^{1,p}(B(0,1))$ into $\mathcal{C}_b^{0,1-N/p}(B(0,1))$ is not compact, as follows.

Let $F \in \mathcal{D}(B(0,1))$ satisfy $F \geqslant 0$ and $\sup_{|x|<1} F(x) = 1$. Show that the sequence $F_n(x) = n^{-1+N/p}F(nx)$ tends to 0 in all the spaces $\mathcal{C}_b^{0,\lambda}(B(0,1))$ and has a constant norm equal to 1 in $\mathcal{C}_b^{0,1-N/p}$. Conclude.

Exercise 2.8 (Gluing Two Functions over a Straight Edge).

Let γ^- be the trace operator defined in the same manner as over $(\mathbb{R}^N)^+$ but using the open set $\mathbb{R}^{N-1} \times \mathbb{R}^-$. Let $u^+ \in W^{1,p}((\mathbb{R}^N)^+)$ and let $u^- \in W^{1,p}((\mathbb{R}^N)^-)$. We set

$$\widetilde{u} = \begin{cases} u^+(x) & \text{if } x \in (\mathbb{R}^N)^+, \\ u^-(x) & \text{if } x \in (\mathbb{R}^N)^-. \end{cases}$$

Prove that $\widetilde{u} \in W^{1,p}(\mathbb{R}^N)$ if and only if $\gamma_0 u^+ = \gamma^- u^-$ on $\mathbb{R}^{N-1}$.

Exercise 2.9 (Generalized Poincaré Inequality).

Let Ω be a Lipschitz bounded domain in $\mathbb{R}^N$. Let $p \in [1, +\infty[$ and let $\mathcal{N}$ be a continuous seminorm on $W^{1,p}(\Omega)$; that is, a norm on the constant functions.

Show that there exists a constant $C > 0$ that depends only on Ω, N, p, such that

$$\|u\|_{W^{1,p}(\Omega)} \leqslant C\left(\left(\int_\Omega |\nabla u(x)|^p dx\right)^{1/p} + \mathcal{N}(u)\right).$$

Apply this result to $\mathcal{N}(u) = \int_{\Gamma_0} |u(x)| dx$, when Ω is a $\mathcal{C}^1$ open set and Γ_0 is a subset of $\partial\Omega$ with positive $(N-1)$-dimensional Lebesgue measure.

Hints. Prove the result by contradiction. Assume that there exists a sequence $\{u_n\}$ such that

$$\|u_n\|_{W^{1,p}(\Omega)} \geqslant n\left(\left(\int_\Omega |\nabla u_n|^p\right)^{1/p} + \mathcal{N}(u_n)\right).$$

Normalizing, that is, considering $w_n = u_n(\|u_n\|_{W^{1,p}(\Omega)})^{-1}$, gives

$$\|w_n\|_{W^{1,p}(\Omega)} = 1, \quad \mathcal{N}(w_n) \longrightarrow 0, \quad \|\nabla w_n\|_p \longrightarrow 0.$$

Use the boundedness of Ω and the relative compactness of $\{w_n\}$ in L^p to deduce a contradiction.

Exercise 2.10 (Function from Ω to $\mathbb{R}^N$ Whose Deformation Tensor is an Element of $L^p(\Omega)$).

Consider the space

$$X_p(\Omega) = \{u \in L^p(\Omega, \mathbb{R}^N) \mid$$
$$\forall (i,j) \in [1,N]^2, \ \varepsilon_{ij}(u) = \tfrac{1}{2}(\partial_j u_i + \partial_i u_j) \in L^p(\Omega)\}$$

where $p \in \,]1, +\infty[$ (cf. Chapter 6). For the moment, we admit that if Ω is a bounded Lipschitz open subset of $\mathbb{R}^N$, then $W^{1,p}(\Omega, \mathbb{R}^N)$ coincides with the space above when $p > 1$. More precisely, there exists a $C > 0$ such that for every $u \in W^{1,p}(\Omega, \mathbb{R}^N)$,

$$\|u\|_{W^{1,p}(\Omega)} \leqslant C\left(\int_\Omega |u|^p dx + \int_\Omega \sum_{ij} |\varepsilon_{ij}(u)|^p dx\right)^{1/p}.$$

We will show this in Chapter 7.

(1) Show that $X_p(\Omega)$ endowed with the norm

$$|u|_{X_p} = \left[\int_\Omega |u(x)|^p dx + \int_\Omega \sum_{ij} |\varepsilon_{ij}(u)(x)|^p dx\right]^{1/p},$$

is a Banach space.

(2) Taking the derivatives in the sense of distributions, note that $u_{i,jk} = \partial_k(\varepsilon_{ij})(u) + \partial_j(\varepsilon_{ik})(u) - \partial_i(\varepsilon_{jk})(u)$. Show that the set $\mathcal{R}$ of the $W^{1,p}$ functions satisfying $\varepsilon(u) = 0$ consists of the rigid displacements, that is, the functions of the form $u = A + B(x)$, where A is a constant vector and B is an antisymmetric matrix. Determine the dimension of $\mathcal{R}$.

(3) Consider a seminorm $\mathcal{N}$ on $W^{1,p}$ that is a norm on the rigid displacements. Show that there exists a constant $C > 0$ such that

$$\forall u \in W^{1,p}(\Omega), \quad \|u\|_{W^{1,p}(\Omega)} \leqslant C\Big[\mathcal{N}(u) + \Big(\int_{\Omega} |\varepsilon(u)(x)|^p dx\Big)^{1/p}\Big].$$

Exercise 2.11 (Best Constant for the Injection of $W^{1,p}(\mathbb{R}^N)$ in $L^k(\mathbb{R}^N)$).
Let $p < N$ and let $k \leqslant Np/(N-p)$. We know that there exist two constants C_1 and C_2 such that

$$\forall u \in W^{1,p}(\mathbb{R}^N), \quad \|u\|_k \leqslant C_1\|\nabla u\|_p + C_2\|u\|_p.$$

We say that C_1 is the best constant for the injection of $W^{1,p}$ in L^k if C_1 is the smallest constant for which there exists a C_2 satisfying the inequality above. Prove that if $k < Np/(N-p)$, then there does not exist any best constant.

Hints. Assume that C_1 exists and define, for $\lambda > 1$, the sequence $u_\lambda(x) = u(x/\lambda)$. Prove that

$$\|u_\lambda\|_k \leqslant \lambda^{-1+N/p-N/k}C_1\|\nabla u\|_p + C_2\lambda^{-N/k+N/p}\|u\|_p.$$

Use this to prove that there exists a constant that is better than C_1.

Exercise 2.12 (Function with One Derivative in L^1 and the Other in L^2).
Let $X_0^{1,2}$ be the closure of the $\mathcal{D}(\mathbb{R}^2)$ functions for the norm $|\partial_1 u|_1 + |\partial_2 u|_2$. Show that $X_0^{1,2} \hookrightarrow L^4(\mathbb{R}^2)$.

Hints. For a regular function u, write

$$u^4(x_1, x_2) = u^3(x_1, x_2)u(x_1, x_2).$$

Next, use that

$$|u^3(x_1, x_2)| \leqslant 3\int_{\mathbb{R}} u^2(x_1, t)|\partial_2 u|(x_1, t)dt$$

$$\leqslant 3\Big(\int_{\mathbb{R}} |u|^4(x_1, t)dt\Big)^{1/2}\Big(\int_{\mathbb{R}} |\partial_2 u|^2(x_1, t)dt\Big)^{1/2}$$

$$= \varphi(x_1)\psi(x_1)$$

and

$$|u(x_1, x_2)| \leqslant \int_{\mathbb{R}} |\partial_1 u(t, x_2)|dt = h(x_2).$$

Finally, use Fubini's formula and Hölder's inequality as follows:

$$\int_{\mathbb{R}}\int_{\mathbb{R}} |u|^4 dx_1 dx_2 \leqslant \int_{\mathbb{R}}\int_{\mathbb{R}} \varphi(x_1)\psi(x_1)h(x_2)dx_1 dx_2$$

$$\leqslant \|\varphi\|_2\|\psi\|_2\|h\|_1$$

$$\leqslant 3\Big(\int_{\mathbb{R}}\int_{\mathbb{R}} u^4 dx_1 dx_2\Big)^{1/2}\|\partial_2 u\|_2\|\partial_1 u\|_1.$$

Conclude.

Exercise [∗] 2.13 (Upper Bound for an Element u of $W_0^{1,1}$ on an Interval).

Let $u \in W_0^{1,1}(]0,1[)$. Prove that $\|u\|_\infty \leqslant 1/2\|u'\|_1$ and that this inequality is the best possible.

Hints. Write

$$u(x) = \int_0^x u'(t)dt \quad \text{and} \quad u(x) = -\int_x^1 u'(t)dt.$$

Exercise [∗] 2.14 (Consequences of the Existence of $\gamma_0(u)$ for u Defined over an Interval in $\mathbb{R}$).

Show the following inequality, which specifies the continuity of the trace map on $W^{1,1}(]0,1[)$:

$$(2.94) \quad \forall u \in W^{1,1}(]0,1[), \quad |u(0)| + |u(1)| \leqslant \int_0^1 |u'|(t)dt + 2\int_0^1 |u(t)|dt.$$

Show that the only functions that satisfy the equality are the constant functions.

Hints. Since the function u is absolutely continuous, we have the equalities

$$\forall x \in [0,1], \quad u(x) = u(0) + \int_0^x u'(t)dt,$$

$$\forall x \in [0,1], \quad u(x) = u(1) + \int_1^x u'(t)dt.$$

Taking the absolute values and integrating the sum of the two resulting inequalities over $]0,1[$ gives (2.94).

Assuming equality in (2.94) and taking into account the inequalities

$$|u(0)| \leqslant |u(x)| + \int_0^x |u'(t)|dt \quad \text{and} \quad |u(1)| \leqslant |u(x)| + \int_x^1 |u'(t)|dt,$$

deduce that for every x, $|u(x)| \geqslant \int_0^1 |u(t)|dt$. Applying this inequality to a point x where the continuous function u reaches its minimum gives the desired result.

Exercise [∗∗] 2.15 (The Spaces $W^{1,p}(I)$ for an Interval I in $\mathbb{R}$).
Let $1 \leqslant p < \infty$.

(1) Using Exercise 1.29, show that $u \in W^{1,p}(I)$ if and only if $u \in L^p(I)$, u is absolutely continuous, and the derivative almost everywhere satisfies $u' \in L^p(I)$.

(2) Show that every function in $W^{1,p}(I)$ can be extended to a continuous function on $\overline{I}$.

(3) In this question, we will use that $W^{1,p}(\mathbb{R}) = W_0^{1,p}(\mathbb{R})$. Let u be a C^1 function on $\mathbb{R}$ with compact support. Let $v = |u|^{p-1}u$. Show that v is C^1

with compact support and that $v' = p|u|^{p-1}u'$. Use the equality $v(x) = \int_{-\infty}^{x} v'(t)dt$ to show that there exists a constant C such that

$$\forall x \in \mathbb{R}, \quad |u(x)| \leqslant C\|u\|_{W^{1,p}(\mathbb{R})}.$$

Deduce that $W^{1,p}(\mathbb{R})$ is embedded in $L^{\infty}(\mathbb{R})$. Show that the constant C can be chosen independently of p. Show that the result still holds true when the interval I is bounded.

Hints.

(1) If $u \in W^{1,p}(I)$, then Exercise 1.29 gives the desired properties. Conversely, use integration by parts to prove that

$$\forall \varphi, \quad \langle [u]', \varphi \rangle = \langle [u'], \varphi \rangle.$$

(2) Since u' is summable over I, u is absolutely continuous over $\overline{I}$, giving the continuity on $\overline{I}$.

(3) Starting with the given hint, use Hölder's inequality to determine the upper bound $p^{1/p}\|u\|_p^{1/p'}\|u'\|_p^{1/p}$ for $|u(x)|$, giving the result by using $p^{1/p} \leqslant e$ and Jensen's inequality

$$|u|_p^{1/p'}|u'|_p^{1/p} \leqslant \frac{1}{p}|u|_p + \frac{1}{p'}|u'|_p.$$

This leads to the density of the continuous functions with compact support. When I is bounded, use

$$u(x) = u(x_0) + \int_{x_0}^{t} u'(t)dt.$$

Exercise [∗∗] 2.16 (Solving Limit Problems on an Interval).

Let $I =]0, 1[$. Given $f \in L^2(I)$, we wish to find a u that, in some sense, is a solution of

$$(*) \qquad \begin{cases} -u'' + u = f, \\ u(0) = u(1). \end{cases}$$

(1) Assume that $u \in \mathcal{C}^2(\overline{I}) \cap H_0^1(I)$ satisfies $(*)$. We multiply $(*)$ by a function $v \in H_0^1(I)$ and integrate by parts over I. Prove that if $(\cdot|\cdot)$ denotes the inner product on $H_0^1(I)$, then

$$\forall v \in H_0^1(\Omega), \quad (u|v)_{H^1(I)} = \langle f, v \rangle_{L^2(I)}.$$

Conversely, prove that if $u \in H_0^1(I)$ satisfies this relation, then u is a solution to the problem, where u'' is taken in the sense of distributions. Next, prove that $v \mapsto \int_I f(t)v(t)dt$ defines an element of the dual of $H_0^1(I)$ and deduce the existence and uniqueness of a solution of the given problem in $H_0^1(I)$ (use the Riesz representation theorem for a Hilbert space). Prove that this solution is in $H^2(I)$ and that if $f \in \mathcal{C}(I)$, then the solution is in $\mathcal{C}^2(I)$.

(2) Use, for example, the fundamental solution of $u'' - u = 0$ on $\mathbb{R}^+$ or variation of the constants to determine this solution explicitly using integrals pertaining to the function f.

Exercise 2.17 (Relation Between $\|\nabla u\|_{L^2}$ and $\|u/r\|_{L^2}$).

(1) Let $u \in C_c(\mathbb{R}^N)$ with $N \geqslant 3$. By computing

$$\left| \nabla u + \frac{(N-2)}{2} \frac{u(x)\overrightarrow{x}}{r^2} \right|^2,$$

integrating over $\mathbb{R}^N$, and integrating

$$\int_{\mathbb{R}^N} 2u\, \partial_i u \frac{x_i}{r^2}\, dx = \int_{\mathbb{R}^N} \partial_i(u^2) \frac{x_i}{r^2}\, dx,$$

by parts, show that

$$\int_{\mathbb{R}^N} |\nabla u(x)|^2 dx \geqslant \frac{(N-2)^2}{4} \int_{\mathbb{R}^N} \frac{u^2}{r^2} dx.$$

(2) Deduce that if $N \geqslant 3$, we have $u \in H^1 \Rightarrow u/|x| \in L^2$. Show that this result does not hold for $N = 2$.

Exercise 2.18 (Generalization of the Previous Exercise).

(1) Show that if $u \in W^{1,p}(\mathbb{R}^N)$, $N > p$, and $1 < p < \infty$, then $u/|x| \in L^p$. In order to do this, show Jensen's inequality (where $1/p + 1/p' = 1$):

$$\forall X, Y \in \mathbb{R}^N, \quad X \cdot Y \leqslant \frac{1}{p}|Y|^p + \frac{1}{p'}|X|^{p'}.$$

(2) Apply this inequality to the vectors $Y = \nabla u$ and

$$X = \left| \frac{(N-p)u\overrightarrow{x}}{pr^2} \right|^{p-2} \frac{(p-N)u\overrightarrow{x}}{pr^2} = -\left(\frac{N-p}{p} \right)^{p-1} \frac{|u|^{p-2}u\overrightarrow{x}}{r^p}.$$

Integrating the term $\int_{\mathbb{R}^N} |u|^{p-2}u\overrightarrow{x}/r^p \cdot \nabla u\, dx$ by parts, deduce that

$$\int_{\mathbb{R}^N} |\nabla u|^p dx \geqslant \left(\frac{N-p}{p} \right)^p \int_{\mathbb{R}^N} \left(\frac{u}{r} \right)^p dx.$$

Hints. For Jensen's inequality, use $f(x) = |x|^p$, which has derivative $p|x|^{p-2}x$, giving the inequality $f(x + y) \geqslant f(x) + Df(x) \cdot y$.

Exercise [**] 2.19 (Fundamental Solutions of the Laplacian).

Show that there exists a constant k_2 such that $\Delta(\ln \sqrt{x^2 + y^2}) = k_2 \delta_0$ in $\mathbb{R}^2$ in the sense of distributions. Show that in $\mathbb{R}^N$ with $N > 2$, $\Delta(r^{2-N}) = k_N \delta_0$, where k_N can be expressed using the area ω_{N-1} of the unit sphere in $\mathbb{R}^N$. Use elementary computations of integrals in the cases $N = 2$ and $N = 3$. For the general case, use Green's second theorem.

Hints.

(1) First show that as functions and outside of the origin, we have $\partial_x[\ln r] = x/r^2$ and $\partial_y[\ln r] = y/r^2$. Next, show that these functions are locally summable. Finally, use the function $\widetilde\varphi(r, \theta) = \varphi(r\cos\theta, r\sin\theta)$, the formula

$$\partial_x\varphi = \cos\theta\,\partial_r\widetilde\varphi - \frac{\sin\theta}{r}\,\partial_\theta\widetilde\varphi,$$

and the analogous formula for φ_y to deduce that

$$\left\langle \partial_x\frac{x}{r^2} + \partial_y\frac{y}{r^2}, \varphi \right\rangle = 2\pi\varphi(0).$$

(2) Assume that $N = 3$. Show that the three derivatives of $u = r^{-1}$ are locally summable and deduce from this that

$$\langle \Delta u, \varphi \rangle = -\int_{\mathbb{R}^3} r^{-3}\big[x\partial_x\varphi + y\partial_y\varphi + z\partial_z\varphi\big]\,dx\,dy\,dz.$$

The polar coordinates are defined by

$$x = r\cos\xi\cos\eta, \quad y = r\cos\xi\sin\eta, \quad z = r\sin\eta.$$

Compute the partial derivatives using those of $\widetilde\varphi$ with respect to r, ξ and η, and show that the previous integral is equal to $-4\pi\varphi(0)$.

(3) We admit Green's second theorem: given a bounded open set Ω of class $\mathcal{C}^1$, a $\mathcal{C}^2$ function f, and $\varphi \in \mathcal{D}(\mathbb{R}^N)$, we have

$$(2.95) \quad \int_\Omega \big[f(x)\Delta\varphi(x) - \varphi(x)\Delta f(x)\big]\,dx = \int_{\partial\Omega} \big[f(x)\partial_{\vec{n}}\varphi(x) - \varphi(x)\partial_{\vec{n}}f(x)\big]\,d\sigma,$$

where the normal derivative $\partial_{\vec{n}}$ on $\partial\Omega$ is oriented outward from Ω. Deduce from this that when $\varepsilon \to 0$, $\langle \Delta(r^{2-N}), \varphi \rangle$ is the limit of

$$\int_{r\geqslant\varepsilon} \varphi\Delta(r^{2-N})\,dx + \int_{r=\varepsilon} \big[\varphi(x)\partial_{\vec{n}}(r^{2-N}) - r^{2-N}\partial_{\vec{n}}(\varphi)\big]\varepsilon^{N-1}\,d\sigma.$$

Use this to prove that $\Delta(r^{2-N}) = (2-N)\omega_{N-1}\delta_{(0)}$.

3

Traces of Functions on Sobolev Spaces

At the end of the previous chapter, we showed the existence of a trace (that is, the extension of an element u of $W^{1,p}(\Omega)$ to the boundary $\partial\Omega$) when Ω is a $\mathcal{C}^1$ open set. This function $\gamma_0(u)$ belongs to $L^p(\partial\Omega)$. However, since we do not have extensions of the derivatives $\partial_i u$ to $\partial\Omega$ when the open set is of class $\mathcal{C}^1$, it is clear that, in general, saying that $\gamma_0 u$ lies in a Sobolev space of type $W^{1,p}(\partial\Omega)$ has no sense.

However, using the notion of a *fractional derivative*, we can imagine that the inclusion $u \in W^{1,p}(\Omega)$ implies that certain *derivatives of order s* of $\gamma_0(u)$, where $0 < s < 1$, belong to $L^p(\partial\Omega)$. This chapter begins with an example where this *inclusion* holds at the order $s \leqslant 1 - 1/p$.

In order to better picture this notion, the reader can take $p = 2$. In this case, we can use the Fourier transformation, as we will do in Chapter 4. We transform a partial derivative $\partial_i u$ into the product $2i\pi\xi_i\widehat{u}$ whose inclusion in L^2 is equivalent to that of $(1 + \xi_i^2)^{1/2}\widehat{u}$. Conversely, by using the inverse Fourier transformation, it is natural to call u $1/2$ times derivable if the function $(1 + |\xi|^2)^{1/4}\widehat{u}$ belongs to L^2.

In general, in cases other than $p = 1$, the trace of a function with derivatives in L^p has better regularity than functions in $L^p(\partial\Omega)$. We propose, in this chapter, to give an intrinsic characterization of the trace $x \mapsto v(x)$, that is, one that is independent of the choice of the function u in $W^{1,p}(\Omega)$ such that $\gamma_0 u = v$. This characterization will lead us to identify, for $p > 1$, the image space of the trace γ_0 with a new space $W^{1-1/p,p}(\partial\Omega)$, our first example of a fractional Sobolev space. In Chapter 4, we will generalize this particular case to all fractional Sobolev spaces.

F. Demengel, G. Demengel, *Functional Spaces for the Theory of Elliptic Partial Differential Equations*, Universitext, DOI 10.1007/978-1-4471-2807-6_3, © Springer-Verlag London Limited 2012

3.1 The Spaces $W^{1-1/p,p}(\mathbb{R}^{N-1})$ for $p > 1$

3.1.1 Preliminary Example

Example 3.1. We propose to begin by studying the regularity properties of the traces of certain functions in $W^{1,p}$ on a simple example. This will allow us to introduce new Sobolev spaces using the notion of fractional derivative. Consider the open set $\Omega = \mathbb{R} \times]0,+\infty[$ and a function φ in $\mathcal{D}(\mathbb{R})$ such that $0 \leqslant \varphi \leqslant 1$ and φ is 1 on $[0,1]$. We define the function u by setting

$$u(x,y) = \varphi\big(\sqrt{x^2 + y^2}\big)(x^2 + y^2)^{\alpha/2} = \varphi(r)r^\alpha,$$

where, given $p > 1$, we assume that

(∗) $1 - 2/p < \alpha < 1 - 1/p.$

We then have $u \in W^{1,p}(\Omega)$. The trace, or in this case, restriction, of the function u to the boundary $\mathbb{R} \times \{0\}$ is $x \mapsto f(x) = \varphi(|x|)|x|^\alpha$.

We can verify that under the condition (∗), $\gamma_0 u = f \in L^p(\mathbb{R})$ and $f \notin W^{1,p}(\mathbb{R})$.

Remark 3.2. To justify the statement in the introduction of this chapter, we can apply the notion of fractional derivative of order s with $0 < s < 1$ to the traces of the functions u studied above. This will lead to the inequality $0 < s < 1 - 1/p$ as a condition for the inclusion of such a trace in $L^p(\partial\Omega)$. This result is a first approximation of the definition of a fractional Sobolev space, in this case $W^{1-1/p,p}(\mathbb{R})$.

This remark, which relies on the notion of fractional derivative presented in the book [60], is expanded in Exercise 3.1. Let us consider the restriction of the function u from the example above to $[0,1]$, that is, the function $x \mapsto x^\alpha$ on this interval. Its derivative of order s is $\alpha x^{\alpha-s}$. The condition under which this derivative belongs to $L^p(]0,1[)$ is $p(\alpha - s) > -1$, or $s < \alpha + 1/p$. Thanks to (∗), we have $1 - 1/p < \alpha + 1/p < 1$. It follows that the values of s for which α satisfies the relation (∗) are indeed those that satisfy the inequality $0 < s \leqslant 1 - 1/p$.

Moreover, we will see further on that the inclusion $v \in W^{1-1/p,p}(]-1,1[)$ is equivalent to the following two conditions:

$$v \in L^p(]-1,1[) \quad \text{and} \quad \int_{]-1,1[\times]-1,1[} \left|\frac{v(x) - v(y)}{x - y}\right|^p dx\,dy < +\infty.$$

To verify this, let us show that under the condition (∗) of Example 3.1, the integral above, denoted by $J(v)$, is indeed convergent for the function v on

$]-1,1[$ defined by $v(x) = |x|^{\alpha}$. We can actually reduce this to considering the function $v(x) = x^{\alpha}$ on $]0,1[$.

Setting $\beta = (\alpha - 1)p + 1$, after applying a homothety to the variable and applying Fubini's formula twice, we obtain

$$J(v) = \int_0^1 \int_0^1 \left|\frac{x^{\alpha} - y^{\alpha}}{x - y}\right|^p dx\, dy = \int_0^1 x^{\beta} \int_0^{1/x} \left|\frac{1 - \lambda^{\alpha}}{1 - \lambda}\right|^p d\lambda\, dx$$

$$= \int_0^1 x^{\beta} dx \int_0^1 \left|\frac{1 - \lambda^{\alpha}}{1 - \lambda}\right|^p d\lambda + \int_1^{+\infty} \left|\frac{1 - \lambda^{\alpha}}{1 - \lambda}\right|^p \int_0^{1/\lambda} x^{\beta} dx\, d\lambda.$$

The function $\lambda \mapsto \left|(1 - \lambda^{\alpha})/(1 - \lambda)\right|^p$ is continuous on $[0,1]$. The first integral is therefore convergent under the condition $\beta = (\alpha - 1)p + 1 > -1$. This same condition allows us to write the second integral as

$$K \int_1^{+\infty} (\lambda)^{-(\alpha-1)p-2} \left|\frac{1 - \lambda^{\alpha}}{1 - \lambda}\right|^p d\lambda.$$

It is therefore also convergent, since $(\alpha-1)p-(\alpha-1)p-2 = -2$. To summarize, $J(v)$ is well defined if $\alpha > 1 - 2/p$.

3.1.2 Definition of a Fractional Sobolev Space; Examples

Definition 3.3. Consider a real number $p > 1$ and an integer $N \geqslant 2$. The Sobolev space $W^{1-1/p,p}(\mathbb{R}^{N-1})$ is the subspace of $L^p(\mathbb{R}^{N-1})$ defined as

$$(3.4) \quad W^{1-1/p,p}(\mathbb{R}^{N-1}) = \left\{ u \in L^p(\mathbb{R}^{N-1}) \;\middle|\; \right.$$

$$\left. \int_{\mathbb{R}^{N-1}} \int_{\mathbb{R}^{N-1}} \frac{|u(x) - u(y)|^p}{|x - y|^{p+N-2}} dx\, dy < \infty \right\}.$$

Theorem 3.5. *The space $W^{1-1/p,p}(\mathbb{R}^{N-1})$ endowed with the norm*

$$\|u\|_{W^{1-1/p,p}(\mathbb{R}^{N-1})} = \left(|u|_{L^p(\mathbb{R}^{N-1})}^p + \int_{\mathbb{R}^{N-1}} \int_{\mathbb{R}^{N-1}} \frac{|u(x) - u(y)|^p}{|x - y|^{p+N-2}} dx\, dy \right)^{1/p}$$

is a Banach space.

We will give the proof of this theorem in the next chapter, for more general fractional spaces and for an arbitrary open set Ω instead of $\mathbb{R}^{N-1}$.

Likewise, for an open subset Ω of $\mathbb{R}^{N-1}$, we define

$$(3.6) \quad W^{1-1/p,p}(\Omega) = \left\{ u \in L^p(\Omega) \;\middle|\; \int_{\Omega} \int_{\Omega} \frac{|u(x) - u(y)|^p}{|x - y|^{p+N-2}} dx\, dy < \infty \right\}.$$

We begin by studying two simple examples in dimension 1.

Example 3.7. Given a real number p satisfying $1 \leqslant p \leqslant 2$, let us determine when $x \mapsto u(x) = \ln x$ belongs to $W^{1-1/p,p}(]0,1[)$.

For $1 \leqslant p$, we have $u \in L^p((]0,1[))$. Let us study the finiteness of

$$J = \int_0^1 \int_0^1 \frac{|\ln x - \ln y|^p}{|x-y|^p} dx\, dy.$$

Introducing the variable $t = y/x$ and applying Fubini's formula gives

$$J = \int_0^1 \int_0^1 \frac{|\ln x - \ln y|^p}{x^p|1 - \frac{y}{x}|^p} dx\, dy = \int_0^1 \frac{1}{x^{p-1}} \int_0^{1/x} \frac{|\ln t|^p}{|1-t|^p} dt\, dx$$

$$= \int_0^1 \frac{|\ln t|^p}{|1-t|^p} \int_0^1 \frac{1}{x^{p-1}} dx\, dt + \int_1^{+\infty} \frac{|\ln t|^p}{|1-t|^p} \int_0^{1/t} \frac{1}{x^{p-1}} dx\, dt.$$

For $p < 2$, both the function $t \mapsto |\ln t|^p/|1-t|^p$ and x^{1-p} are continuous on $]0,1]$ and integrable at $t = 0$. The first integral on the right-hand side therefore converges. The second integral, which can be written as

$$\frac{1}{2-p} \int_1^{+\infty} \frac{|\ln t|^p}{t^{2-p}|1-t|^p} dt,$$

also converges because, on the one hand, if $t \to +\infty$, then the function is bounded from above by $K|\ln t|^p/t^2$ and, on the other hand, we have $|\ln t| \sim |1-t|$ when $t \to 1$.

For p=2, J is greater than the first integral, which is equal to $+\infty$. It follows that

$$u \in W^{1-1/p,p}(]0,1[) \iff 1 < p < 2.$$

Example 3.8. Let $p > 1$. We want to show that if $(\alpha - 1)p > -2$, then $x \mapsto x^\alpha \ln x$ belongs to $W^{1-1/p,p}(]0,1[)$.

The condition under which $u(x) = x^\alpha \ln x$ belongs to $L^p((]0,1[))$ can be written as

$$(*) \qquad\qquad\qquad \alpha p > -1.$$

The inequality $|a + b|^p \leqslant 2^{p-1}(|a|^p + |b|^p)$ applied to the decomposition

$$|x^\alpha \ln x - y^\alpha \ln y| = |x^\alpha(\ln x - \ln y) + \ln y(x^\alpha - y^\alpha)|$$

shows that the inclusion of u in $W^{1-1/p,p}(]0,1[)$ is implied by the finiteness of the two integrals

$$I = \int_0^1 \int_0^1 \frac{x^{p\alpha}|\ln x - \ln y|^p}{|x-y|^p} dx\, dy \quad \text{and} \quad J = \int_0^1 \int_0^1 \frac{|\ln y|^p|x^\alpha - y^\alpha|^p}{|x-y|^p} dx\, dy.$$

Using computations similar to those of the previous example, we see that the first integral I is finite if the integrals

$$I_1 = \int_0^1 x^{p\alpha-p+1} dx \int_0^1 \frac{|\ln t|^p}{(1-t)^p} dt, \quad I_2 = \int_1^{+\infty} \frac{|\ln t|^p}{(1-t)^p} \int_0^{1/t} x^{p\alpha-p+1} dx\, dt$$

are. The integral I_1 is finite if $(\alpha-1)p+1 > -1$, that is, if $\alpha p > p-2$, a condition that implies $(*)$. Under this same condition, after applying Fubini's transformation, the integrand of the second integral I_2 is equivalent to $|\ln t|^p / t^{\alpha p+2}$ at $+\infty$. Its convergence follows because $\alpha p + 2 > 1$. We therefore have

$$I < \infty \iff \alpha p > p - 2.$$

Likewise, the second integral J is finite if the following integrals are, where $\beta = p\alpha - p + 1$:

$$J_1 = \int_0^1 y^\beta |\ln y|^p dy \int_0^1 \frac{|1-t^\alpha|^p}{|1-t|^p} dt,$$

$$J_2 = \int_1^{+\infty} \frac{|1-t^\alpha|^p}{|1-t|^p} \int_0^{1/t} y^\beta |\ln y|^p dy\, dt.$$

The integral J_1 behaves like $J(v)$ in Example 3.1. It converges if $\alpha p > p - 2$, regardless of the sign of α. Moreover, as $\beta > 1$, when $x < 1$, the function $x \mapsto x^\beta |\ln x|^p$ is dominated by $x \mapsto x^\gamma$ for every γ satisfying $1 < \gamma < \beta$. Consequently, its primitive at $1/t$ is dominated by $Kt^{-1-\gamma}$ and the integrand of J_2 is dominated by $t^{-((1-\alpha)p+\gamma+1)}$ at $+\infty$, proving the finiteness of J_2. The stated result follows.

3.1.3 Characterization of the Trace of $u \in W^{1,p}(\mathbb{R}^{N-1} \times \mathbb{R}^+)$

We will now show the following result.

Theorem 3.9. *Let $N \geqslant 2$; then the image of the trace map γ_0 satisfies*

$$\gamma_0\left(W^{1,p}(\mathbb{R}^{N-1} \times\,]0, +\infty[)\right) = W^{1-1/p,p}(\mathbb{R}^{N-1}).$$

We will first prove the theorem for $N = 2$, after which we will proceed to the general case.

Proof of Theorem 3.9 for $N = 2$.
    We begin by showing that

$$W^{1-1/p,p}(\mathbb{R}) \hookrightarrow \gamma_0(W^{1,p}(\mathbb{R} \times\,]0, +\infty[)).$$

Let $u \in W^{1-1/p,p}(\mathbb{R})$ and let φ be a function in $\mathcal{D}(\mathbb{R})$ such that $\varphi(0) = 1$. Since u belongs to $L^p(\mathbb{R})$, we can define a function v as follows:

$$(3.10) \qquad v(x,t) = \frac{\varphi(t)}{t} \int_0^t u(x+z)dz.$$

The function v vanishes for $|t|$ sufficiently large. Let us show that $v \in L^p(\mathbb{R} \times]0, +\infty[)$. By Hölder's inequality applied to the integral defining the right-hand side of (3.10), we have

$$\iint_{\mathbb{R} \times \mathbb{R}^+} |v(x,t)|^p dx\, dt \leqslant \int_{\mathbb{R}} \int_0^{+\infty} \frac{|\varphi|^p(t)}{t} \int_0^t |u|^p(x+s)ds\, dx\, dt.$$

Using Fubini's formula, we see that the last integral is bounded from above by

$$\int_0^{+\infty} |\varphi^p(t)| \frac{1}{t} \int_0^t \int_{\mathbb{R}} |u(X)|^p dX\, ds\,, dt = \int_0^{+\infty} |\varphi|^p(t)dt \int_{\mathbb{R}} |u(x)|^p dx.$$

This integral is finite, giving the desired result.

Let us now show that v belongs to $W^{1,p}(\mathbb{R} \times \mathbb{R}^+)$. For this, we need to compute its derivatives with respect to x and t. We have

$$(3.11) \qquad \partial_x v(x,t) = \frac{u(x+t) - u(x)}{t}\varphi(t).$$

Introducing $u(x+t)$ in the integral with respect to z, we also have

$$\partial_t v(x,t) = \frac{\varphi(t)}{t^2} \int_0^t (u(x+t) - u(x+z))dz + \frac{\varphi'(t)}{t} \int_0^t u(x+s)ds$$

$$= \varphi(t) \int_0^1 \frac{u(x+t) - u(x+tz)}{t}dz + \frac{\varphi'(t)}{t} \int_0^t u(x+s)ds$$

$$(3.12) \qquad = f(x,t) + \frac{\varphi'(t)}{t} \int_0^t u(x+s)ds.$$

By the definition of $W^{1-1/p,p}(\mathbb{R})$, we have

$$\int_{\mathbb{R} \times \mathbb{R}^+} |\partial_x v(x,t)|^p \leqslant \sup |\varphi|^p \int_{\mathbb{R}^2} \left| \frac{u(y) - u(x)}{y - x} \right|^p dx\, dy < +\infty,$$

where $t = y - x$. This proves that $\partial_x v \in L^p(\mathbb{R} \times]0, +\infty[)$. Replacing φ by φ' in the definition of v, we deduce from the computations above that

$$\left\{ (x,t) \longmapsto \frac{\varphi'(t)}{t} \int_0^t u(x+s)ds \right\} \in L^p(\mathbb{R} \times]0, +\infty[).$$

It remains to show that $f \in L^p(\mathbb{R} \times]0, +\infty[)$. We will, in fact, show that $f \in L^p(\mathbb{R}^2)$. Using Hölder's inequality, we first obtain the inequality

$$(3.13) \qquad \|f\|_{L^p(\mathbb{R}^2)}^p \leqslant \|\varphi\|_\infty^p \int_{\mathbb{R}^2} \left(\int_0^1 \frac{|u(x+t) - u(x+tz)|^p}{t^p} dz \right) dx\, dt.$$

We then apply the change of variables $X = x + tz, T = x + t$ with Jacobian $|dX \wedge dT| = |z - 1| |dx \wedge dt|$. From $|z - 1| < 1$ and $p > 1$, we deduce that $|1 - z|t^p \geqslant |(1 - z)t|^p = |X - T|^p$, whence

$$\int_{\mathbb{R}^2} |f(x,t)|^p dx \, dt \leqslant \|\varphi\|_\infty^p \int_{\mathbb{R}^2} \left(\int_0^1 \frac{|u(x+t) - u(x+tz)|^p}{t^p} dz \right) dx \, dt$$

$$\leqslant \|\varphi\|_\infty^p \int_{\mathbb{R}^2} \int_0^1 \frac{|u(X) - u(T)|^p}{|X - T|^p} dX \, dT \, dz$$

$$\leqslant C\|u\|_{W^{1-1/p,p}(\mathbb{R})}^p.$$

Now that we have proved that $v \in W^{1,p}(\mathbb{R} \times]0, +\infty[)$, it remains to show that $\gamma_0 v = u$ or, in other words, that $\lim_{t \to 0+} \|v(\cdot, t) - u\|_{L^p(\mathbb{R})} = 0$.

Let us write

$$v(x,t) - u(x) = \varphi(t) \int_0^1 [u(x+tz) - u(x)] dz + (\varphi(t) - 1)u(x).$$

Since $\lim_{t \to 0}[\varphi(t) - 1]\|u\|_p = 0$, the property that we wish to prove reduces to

$$\lim_{t \to 0} \int_{\mathbb{R}} \left| \int_0^1 [u(x+tz) - u(x)] dz \right|^p dx = 0.$$

After applying Hölder's and Fubini's formulas, proving this reduces further to using the continuity of translations in L^p, that is, $\lim_{h \to 0} \|\tau_h u - u\|_p = 0$. We have thus proved the equality $\gamma_0(v) = u$.

This concludes the proof of the inclusion for $N = 2$.

Conversely, we wish to show that if $u \in W^{1,p}(\mathbb{R} \times]0, +\infty[)$, then its trace belongs to $W^{1-1/p,p}(\mathbb{R} \times \{0\})$. We will need the following lemma.

Lemma 3.14. *Consider a real number ν and a function f from $]0, +\infty[$ to $\mathbb{R}$. We assume that $0 < \nu + 1/p = \theta < 1$ and $1 \leqslant p < +\infty$. The following hold:*

(i) *If the map $t \mapsto t^\nu f(t)$ belongs to $L^p(]0, +\infty[)$ and if g is defined by*

$$(3.15) \qquad g(t) = \frac{1}{t} \int_0^t f(s) ds,$$

then the map $t \mapsto t^\nu g(t)$ belongs to $L^p(]0, +\infty[)$. Moreover, there exists a constant $C(p, \nu)$ depending only on p and ν, such that

$$(3.16) \qquad \int_0^\infty t^{\nu p} |g(t)|^p dt \leqslant C(p, \nu) \int_0^\infty t^{\nu p} |f(t)|^p dt.$$

(ii) *Let $\alpha, \beta \in \overline{\mathbb{R}}$ with $\alpha < \beta$, let f be defined on $]0, +\infty[\times]\alpha, \beta[$, and let g be defined as follows on $]0, +\infty[\times]\alpha, \beta[$:*

$$g(t,x) = \frac{1}{t} \int_0^t f(s,x) ds.$$

If $t^\nu f \in L^p(]0, +\infty[\times]\alpha, \beta[)$, then we have $t^\nu g \in L^p(]0, +\infty[\times]\alpha, \beta[)$ and there exists a constant $c(p, \nu)$ depending only on p and ν, such that

$$(3.17) \qquad \int_\alpha^\beta \int_0^\infty t^{\nu p} |g(t,x)|^p dt\, dx \leqslant c(p, \nu) \int_\alpha^\beta \int_0^\infty t^{\nu p} |f(t,x)|^p dt\, dx.$$

Remark 3.18. In (ii), the results extend to the case where the variable t is in an interval $]a, b[$ instead of $]0, +\infty[$.

Remark 3.19. We only use the lemma with $\nu = 0$. We include the case $\nu \neq 0$ for the next chapter.

Proof of Lemma 3.14.

Let F be defined as follows for $x > 0$:

$$(3.20) \qquad F(x) = x^{\nu-1} \int_0^x f(s) ds.$$

We begin by remarking that the assumptions on f imply that $x|F(x)|^p$ is bounded and tends to 0 when x tends to 0. Indeed, if $p > 1$, then

$$\left| x^{\nu-1} \int_0^x f(t) dt \right| = \left| x^{\nu-1} \int_0^x t^\nu f(t) t^{-\nu} dt \right|$$

$$\leqslant x^{\nu-1} \left(\int_0^x t^{\nu p} |f(t)|^p dt \right)^{1/p} \left(\int_0^x t^{-\nu p'} dt \right)^{1/p'}$$

$$\leqslant \left(\frac{1}{p'(1-\theta)} \right)^{1/p'} x^{\nu-1} x^{(-\nu p'+1)/p'} |t^\nu f|_{L^p(]0,x[)}$$

$$= \left(\frac{1}{p'(1-\theta)} \right)^{1/p'} x^{-1/p} \|t^\nu f\|_{L^p(]0,x[)},$$

whence

$$x|F(x)|^p \leqslant C \|t^\nu f(t)\|_{L^p(]0,x[)}^p.$$

In particular, $x|F(x)|^p$ tends to 0 when x tends to 0 and, moreover, $x|F(x)|^p \leqslant C\|t^\nu f\|_{L^p(]0,+\infty[)}^p$.

This remark allows us to carry out the following integration by parts:

$$\int_0^M |F(x)|^p dx = -\int_0^M p|F|^{p-2} F(x) F'(x) x\, dx + M|F(M)|^p.$$

Now,

$$(3.21) \qquad F'(x) = (\nu-1) x^{\nu-2} \int_0^x f(t) dt + x^{\nu-1} f(x),$$

whence

$$xF'(x) = (\nu-1) F(x) + x^\nu f(x).$$

We obtain

$$(3.22) \quad \int_0^M |F|^p(x)dx = -p(\nu - 1)\int_0^M |F|^p(x)dx$$
$$- p\int_0^M x^\nu f(x)|F|^{p-2}F(x)dx + M|F(M)|^p,$$

whence

$$\int_0^M |F|^p|1 + p(\nu-1)|\,dx \leqslant p\int_0^M x^\nu |f(x)||F|^{p-2}|F(x)|dx + c\|t^\nu f(t)\|_{L^p}^p$$
$$\leqslant p\Big(\int_0^M |x^\nu\,(f(x))|^p\,dx\Big)^{1/p}\Big(\int_0^M |F|^p\Big)^{1-1/p} + c\|t^\nu f(t)\|_{L^p(]0,M[)}^p.$$

Setting $X_M = \big(\int_0^M |F(x)|^p\big)^{1/p}dx$ and $\alpha = \|t^\nu f(t)\|_{L^p(]0,+\infty[)}$, this implies the inequality

$$(1-\theta)X_M^p \leqslant p\alpha X_M^{p-1} + c\alpha^p \leqslant \frac{1}{p'}(X_M(1-\theta)^{1/p})^p + \frac{1}{(1-\theta)^{p-1}}(p\alpha)^p + c\alpha^p$$

by inequality describing the convexity of the function $x \mapsto |x|^p$. It follows that

$$X_M^p \leqslant c(p,\nu)\alpha^p.$$

Finally,

$$\Big(\int_0^\infty |F|^p\Big)^{1/p} \leqslant C\Big(\int_0^\infty |x^\nu f(x)|dx\Big)^{1/p}.$$

For the proof of (ii), we repeat the proof given above, fixing x, and then integrating with respect to x. This concludes the proof of the lemma.   □

Let us return to the proof of the theorem for $N = 2$.

Let v be an element of $W^{1,p}(\mathbb{R} \times]0,+\infty[)$ and let $u(x) = v(x,0)$. We write the integral of the function $|u(x) - u(y)|^p|x - y|^{-p}$ over $\mathbb{R}^2$ as the sum of integrals over the sets $\{y > x\}$ and $\{x > y\}$. It suffices to study the integral over $\{y > x\}$:

$$\frac{u(x) - u(y)}{x - y} = \frac{1}{x-y}\Big(v(x,0) - v\Big(x + \frac{y-x}{2}, \frac{y-x}{2}\Big)\Big)$$
$$+ \frac{1}{x-y}\Big(v\Big(\frac{x+y}{2}, \frac{y-x}{2}\Big) - v(y,0)\Big)$$
$$= \frac{-1}{x-y}\int_0^{y-x} \partial_s v(x+s/2, s/2)ds$$
$$+ \frac{1}{x-y}\int_0^{y-x} \partial_s v(y-s/2, s/2)ds.$$

Taking the pth power and integrating the first term on the right-hand side with respect to x and y gives

$$\iint_{y>x} \left| \frac{1}{x-y} \int_0^{y-x} \partial_s v\,(x+s/2,s/2)\,ds \right|^p dx\,dy$$

$$\leqslant 2 \int_{\mathbb{R}} \int_{]0,+\infty[} \left(\frac{1}{t} \int_0^t |\partial_s v\,(x+s/2,s/2)|\,ds \right)^p dt\,dx.$$

Let us now define the function f by setting

$$f(s,x) = \partial_s v\,(x+s/2,s/2)\,;$$

this satisfies $f \in L^p(\mathbb{R} \times]0,+\infty[)$. Since $v \in W^{1,p}(\mathbb{R} \times]0,+\infty[)$, we may apply Lemma 4.38, (ii):

$$\int_{\mathbb{R}} \int_{]0,+\infty[} \left| \frac{1}{t} \int_0^t \partial_s v\,(x+s/2,s/2)\,ds \right|^p dx\,dy \leqslant C\|v\|_{W^{1,p}}^p.$$

Repeating this for the integral

$$\frac{1}{x-y} \int_0^{y-x} \partial_s v\,(y-s/2,s/2)\,ds,$$

we obtain the desired result.

At the same time, we have shown that there exists a constant $C > 0$ such that

(3.23) $$\|u\|_{W^{1-1/p,p}(\mathbb{R})} \leqslant C\|v\|_{W^{1,p}(\mathbb{R}\times]0,+\infty[)},$$

giving the continuity of the trace map in this space. $\square$

Remark 3.24. At the end of this chapter, we will give a different class of liftings that is better suited to problems concerning higher order traces. The advantage of the lifting we use here is that it allows more explicit computations.

Before continuing with the general case, let us consider an example.

Example 3.25. Let us illustrate the theorem we have just proved for $N = 2$ using $\mathcal{H}\varphi$, where φ is an element of $\mathcal{D}(\mathbb{R})$ that equals 1 on $[-1/2, 1/2]$ and $\mathcal{H}$ is the Heaviside step function defined by

$$\mathcal{H}(x) = \begin{cases} 1 & \text{if } x > 0, \\ 0 & \text{otherwise.} \end{cases}$$

We will study the inclusion $\mathcal{H}\varphi \in W^{1-1/p,p}(\mathbb{R})$ for $1 < p \leqslant 2$.

To compute the seminorm

$$\iint \frac{|(\varphi\mathcal{H})(x) - (\varphi\mathcal{H})(y)|^p}{|x-y|^p} \, dx \, dy,$$

we note that its finiteness is equivalent to that of the sum A_p of the integrals over the products $]-1/2, 0[\times]0, 1/2[$ and $]0, 1/2[\times]-1/2, 0[$. It therefore suffices to show the finiteness of

$$A_p = 2 \int_{-1/2}^{0} \int_0^{1/2} \frac{1}{|x-y|^p} \, dx \, dy = \frac{2}{1-p} \int_{-1/2}^{0} \left[(\tfrac{1}{2} - x)^{1-p} - |x|^{1-p} \right] dx.$$

The existence condition can then be written as $-p + 1 > -1$, or $p < 2$. We note that $p = 2$ is a critical case, as $\mathcal{H}\varphi$ belongs to all $W^{1-1/p,p}(\mathbb{R})$ for $p < 2$, in spite of the existence of a point of discontinuity at $x = 0$, but does not belong to $H^{1/2}(\mathbb{R})$.

In this example, we can also compute the fractional derivative of $\mathcal{H}\varphi$ of order $1 - 1/p$ for $\varphi \in \mathcal{D}(\mathbb{R})$ (cf. Exercise 3.1).

The proof given above shows the existence of a *lifting* of $\mathcal{H}\varphi$ to the space $W^{1,p}(\mathbb{R} \times]0, +\infty[)$. We can also give a function belonging to $W^{1,p}(\mathbb{R} \times]0, +\infty[)$ whose trace is $\mathcal{H}\varphi$ on the boundary $\mathbb{R} \times \{0\}$ without using the intrinsic definition of $H^{1/2}(\mathbb{R})$.

Let u be defined by

$$u(x, y) = \begin{cases} 0 & \text{if } x < 0 \text{ and } 0 < y < -x, \\ \dfrac{y+x}{y} & \text{if } x < 0 \text{ and } y > -x > 0, \\ \varphi(x) & \text{if } x > 0. \end{cases}$$

Let ψ be a function in $\mathcal{D}(\mathbb{R})$ that equals 1 on $\{y = 0\}$; then for $p \in]1, 2[$, $\psi(y)u(x, y)$ belongs to $W^{1,p}(\mathbb{R} \times]0, +\infty[)$ and equals $\mathcal{H}\varphi$ on $\mathbb{R} \times \{0\}$.

Remark 3.26. When a function has a discontinuity at a point, its derivative in the sense of distributions involves a Dirac distribution, which cannot be identified with a function. We can come across functions with jump discontinuities whose *fractional derivatives* are elements of L^p for $p < 2$.

Proof of the theorem in the general case.
    We will need the following lemma.

Lemma 3.27. *The following properties are equivalent for an element u of $L^p(\mathbb{R}^K)$:*

(i) $u \in W^{1-1/p,p}(\mathbb{R}^K)$.

(ii) $\forall\, i \in [1, K]$, $\|u\|_{i,1-1/p,p}^p = \displaystyle\int_{\mathbb{R}^K} \int_{\mathbb{R}} \left| \frac{u(x + te_i) - u(x)}{t} \right|^p dx\, dt < \infty.$

Moreover, $\|u\|'_{1-1/p,p} = \|u\|_{L^p(\mathbb{R}^K)} + \sum_1^K \|u\|_{i,1-1/p,p}$ *defines a norm equivalent to* $\|\cdot\|_{W^{1-1/p,p}(\mathbb{R}^K)}$.

Corollary 3.28. *If* $p > q > 1$ *and* u *has compact support, then*

$$u \in W^{1-1/p,p}(\mathbb{R}^N) \implies u \in W^{1-1/q,q}(\mathbb{R}^N).$$

Proof of the corollary.

We apply the lemma to $U = \|u\|^q_{1-1/q,q}$ when $u \in W^{1-1/p,p}(\mathbb{R}^N)$. Hölder's inequality gives

$$U = \int_{\mathbb{R}^N} \int_{\mathbb{R}} \frac{|u(x+te_i) - u(x)|^q}{|t|^q} \, dt \, dx$$

$$\leqslant \int_{|t|\leqslant 1} \int_{\text{supp } u + B(0,1)} \frac{|u(x+te_i) - u(x)|^q}{|t|^q} \, dx \, dt + \int_{|t|>1} 2^q \frac{\|u\|^q_q}{|t|^q} \, dt$$

$$\leqslant \left(\int_{|t|\leqslant 1} \int_{\mathbb{R}^N} \frac{|u(x+te_i) - u(x)|^p}{|t|^p} \, dx \right)^{q/p} |\text{supp } u + B(0,1)|^{1-q/p}$$

$$+ 2^{(q+1)/(q-1)} \|u\|^q_q. \qquad \square$$

Proof of Lemma 3.27.

Let us show that (ii) implies (i).

Let $u \in L^p(\mathbb{R}^K)$ be such that for every i,

$$\int_{\mathbb{R}^K} \int_{\mathbb{R}} \left| \frac{u(x+te_i) - u(x)}{t} \right|^p \, dx \, dt < \infty.$$

For elements x and y of $\mathbb{R}^K$, we introduce the notation $\widehat{x}_i = \sum_1^i x_j e_j + \sum_{i+1}^K y_j e_j = (x_1, x_2, \ldots, x_i, y_{i+1}, \ldots, y_K)$, where $\widehat{x}_K = x$ and $\widehat{x}_0 = y$. We can now write $u(y) - u(x)$ as follows:

$$u(y) - u(x) = \sum_{i=0}^{i=K-1} \left[u(\widehat{x}_i) - u(\widehat{x_{i+1}}) \right].$$

We can consequently bound the pth power of the seminorm in $W^{1-1/p,p}(\mathbb{R}^K)$ from above by the sum of integrals $\sum_0^{K-1} I_i$, where

$$I_i = \int_{\mathbb{R}^K} \int_{\mathbb{R}^K} \frac{|u(\widehat{x}_i) - u(\widehat{x_{i+1}})|^p}{\left[\sum_j |x_j - y_j|^2 \right]^{(p+K-1)/2}} \, dx \, dy.$$

We therefore need to bound these integrals. For this, setting $\eta_j = |x_j - y_j|^2$ and $q = (p+K-1)/2$, we begin by bounding the denominator $(\sum_j \eta_j)^q$ from both sides. Using the equivalence of the norms in finite dimension, we see that there exist constants C_1, C_2, C_3, C_4 depending only on p and K, such that

$$C_1\left(\sum_1^K |x_j - y_j|\right)^{2q} \leqslant C_2\left(\sum_1^K \eta_j\right)^q$$

$$\leqslant \sum_1^K (\eta_j)^q \leqslant C_3\left(\sum_1^K \eta_j\right)^q \leqslant C_4\left(\sum_1^K |x_j - y_j|\right)^{2q}.$$

Let us, for example, study the integral I_{K-1} by beginning with a partial integration with respect to y_1. Using the parity of $y_1 - x_1$, the previous inequalities with constants C'_m when K is replaced by $K - 1$, plus a homothety on an integration variable, we find, for fixed x_i, $i \in [1, K]$, and fixed y_K, that

$$\int_{\mathbb{R}} \frac{|u(x) - u(\widehat{x_{K-1}})|^p}{(\sum_j \eta_j)^q} dy_1 \leqslant 2C_3^{-1} \int_{x_1}^{\infty} \frac{|u(x) - u(\widehat{x_{K-1}})|^p}{|x_1 - y_1|^{2q} + \left[\sum_{j\geqslant 2} \eta_j^q\right]} dy_1$$

$$\leqslant 2C_3^{-1} \int_{x_1}^{\infty} \frac{|u(x) - u(\widehat{x_{K-1}})|^p \, dy_1}{|x_1 - y_1|^{2q} + C'_1\left[\sum_{j\geqslant 2} |x_j - y_j|\right]^{2q}}$$

$$\leqslant 2C_3^{-1} \frac{|u(x) - u(\widehat{x_{K-1}})|^p}{\left[\sum_{j\geqslant 2} |x_j - y_j|\right]^{2q-1}} \int_0^{+\infty} \frac{d\zeta}{\zeta^{2q} + C'_1}.$$

Since $p + K > 2$, we have $2q > 1$. Consequently, the last integral converges. We must therefore consider the inequality

$$\int_{\mathbb{R}} \frac{|u(x) - u(x_1, \ldots, x_{K-1}, y_K)|^p}{(\sum_j \eta_j)^q} dy_1 \leqslant M_1 \frac{\left|u(x) - u(\widehat{x_{K-1}})\right|^p}{\left[\sum_{j\geqslant 2} |x_j - y_j|\right]^{p+K-2}},$$

where the constant M_1 depends only on p and K.

By integrating this inequality with respect to y_2, the same computations give the following upper bound for the partial integral of I_{K-1} with respect to y_1, y_2:

$$M_1 M_2 \frac{|u(x) - u(\widehat{x_{K-1}})|^p}{\left[\sum_{j\geqslant 3} |x_j - y_j|\right]^{p+K-3}}.$$

We now use induction to show that partial integration with respect to $(y_1, y_2, \ldots, y_{K-1})$ gives the upper bound

$$I_{K-1} \leqslant M_1 M_2 \cdots M_{K-1} \int_{\mathbb{R}^K} \int_{\mathbb{R}} \frac{|u(x) - u(\widehat{x_{K-1}})|^p}{|x_K - y_K|^p} dy_K dx.$$

By a last change of variables, this leads to the existence of a constant c depending only on p and K, such that

$$I_{K-1} \leqslant c \int_{\mathbb{R}^K} \int_0^{+\infty} \frac{|u(x + te_K) - u(x)|^p}{t^p} dt \, dx.$$

By hypothesis (ii), this implies the finiteness of I_{K-1}.

We proceed in the same manner with the other integrals I_i. We have thus proved the implication (ii) $\Rightarrow$ (i), as well as the inequality

$$\|u\|_{W^{1-1/p,p}(\mathbb{R}^K)}^p \leqslant c \sum_{i=1}^{i=K} \int_{\mathbb{R}^K} \int_0^{+\infty} \frac{|u(x+te_i) - u(x)|^p}{t^p} \, dt \, dx.$$

Conversely, let us show that (i) implies (ii).

We will once more use induction on the exponents of the terms in the denominator. Let us first set

$$J_1 = \int_{\mathbb{R}^K} \int_{]0,+\infty[} \frac{|u(x+t_K e_K) - u(x)|^p}{t_K^p} \, dt_K \, dx.$$

Though the notation is different, this is the integral in statement (ii). We generalize it to integrals J_k where the numerator of the integrand is of the type $|u(x') - u(x)|$ with a difference $x' - x = \sum_{K-k+1}^K t_j e_j$ of *length k* and $t_j \geqslant 0$, namely

$$J_2 = \int_{\mathbb{R}^K} \int_{(]0,+\infty[)^2} \frac{|u(x+t_{K-1}e_{K-1}+t_K e_K) - u(x)|^p}{(t_{K-1}+t_K)^{p+1}} \, dt_K \, dt_{K-1} \, dx,$$

$$\vdots$$

$$J_K = \int_{\mathbb{R}^K} \int_{(]0,+\infty[)^K} \frac{|u(x+\sum_1^K t_j e_j) - u(x)|^p}{\left(\sum_1^K t_j\right)^{p+K-1}} \prod_1^K dt_j \, dx.$$

By using the variable $x - y$ in the integrand, which expresses the seminorm of u in $W^{1-1/p,p}(\mathbb{R}^K)$ and restricting ourselves to integrations over $]0,+\infty[$, we see that, by hypothesis, $J_K < \infty$. Consequently, the implication (i)$\Rightarrow$(ii) follows for $i = K$ if we show that for every $k \in [1, K-1]$, we have

$$J_{k+1} < \infty \implies J_k < \infty.$$

Let us therefore suppose that $J_{k+1} < \infty$. Let

$$J_k = \int_{\mathbb{R}^K} \int_{(]0,+\infty[)^k} \frac{\left|u(x+\sum_{K-k+1}^K t_j e_j) - u(x)\right|^p}{\left(\sum_{K-k+1}^K t_j\right)^{p+k-1}} \prod_{K-k+1}^K dt_j \, dx.$$

It follows from the equality

$$\frac{1}{\left(\sum_{K-k+1}^K t_j\right)^{p+k-1}} = (p+k-1) \int_0^{+\infty} \frac{1}{\left(t' + \sum_{K-k+1}^K t_j\right)^{p+k}} \, dt'.$$

that J_k is bounded from above by

$$(p+k-1) \int_{\mathbb{R}^K} \int_{(]0,+\infty[)^{k+1}} \frac{\left|u(x+\sum_{K-k+1}^K t_j e_j) - u(x)\right|^p}{\left(t' + \sum_{K-k+1}^K t_j\right)^{p+k}} \, dt' \left[\prod_{K-k+1}^K dt_j \right] dx.$$

We now proceed to give an upper bound for the numerator by using a point x^* that lies between $x + \sum_{K-k+1}^{K} t_j e_j$ and x, namely $x^* = x + t' e_{K-k} + \sum_{K-k+1}^{K} (t_j/2) e_j$, and by using the inequality $|a+b|^p \leqslant 2^{p-1}(|a|^p + |b|^p)$. A lower bound for the denominators follows from the inequality $t' + \sum_{K-k+1}^{K} t_j \geqslant t' + \sum_{K-k+1}^{K} t_j/2$. Consequently, writing

$$
\left| u\left(x + \textstyle\sum_{K-k+1}^{K} t_j e_j\right) - u(x)\right|^p
$$
$$
\leqslant 2^{p-1}\left[\left| u\left(x + \sum_{K-k+1}^{K} t_j e_j\right) - u(x^*)\right|^p + \left| u(x^*) - u(x)\right|^p\right],
$$

we obtain $J_k \leqslant 2^{p-1}[A + B]$, where

$$
A \leqslant \int_{\mathbb{R}^K} \int_{(]0,+\infty[)^{k+1}} \frac{|u(x^*) - u(x)|^p}{(t' + \sum_{K-k+1}^{K}(t_j/2))^{p+k}}\, dt' \left[\prod_{K-k+1}^{K} dt_j\right] dx,
$$

$$
B \leqslant \int_{\mathbb{R}^K} \int_{(]0,+\infty[)^{k+1}} \frac{\left| u(x + \sum_{K-k+1}^{K}(t_j/2)e_j) - u(x^*)\right|^p}{(t' + \sum_{K-k+1}^{K}(t_j/2)))^{p+k}}\, dt' \left[\prod_{K-k+1}^{K} dt_j\right] dx.
$$

In these upper bounds, the numerator of the integrand is associated with a difference $x' - x$ of length k. By considering the denominator, we see that this upper bound is the integral J_{k+1}. We conclude that $A < \infty$. For the integral B, we must transform the numerator so that it is of the form $|u(y) - u(y')|$, where y is the integration variable and the difference $y - y'$ also has length k. In order to do this, we apply the following transformation in the integral B:

$$
\begin{cases}
y = x + \left(\sum_{K-k+1}^{K} t_j e_j/2\right), \\
t_j = t_j \\
t' = t_{K-k}.
\end{cases}
\qquad \forall j \in [K-k+1, K],
$$

The Jacobian matrix of this transformation is triangular with diagonal terms equal to 1. The integral B is therefore bounded from above by

$$
\int_{\mathbb{R}^K} \int_{(]0,+\infty[)^{k+1}} \frac{\left| u(y) - u(y + \sum_{K-k+1}^{K}(t_j/2)e_j + t_{K-k} e_{K-k})\right|^p}{[t_{K-k} + \sum_{K-k+1}^{K}(t_j/2)]^{p+k}} \left[\prod_{K-k}^{K} dt_j\right] dy.
$$

This last integral is of the type J_{k+1} and is therefore finite. To summarize, we have

$$
J_k \leqslant K(A + B) < \infty.
$$

The reasoning is the same for the other integrals

$$
I_i = \int_{\mathbb{R}^K} \int_{]0,+\infty[} \frac{|u(x + t e_i) - u(x)|^p}{t^p}\, dt\, dx.
$$

We have thus proved the equivalence of (i) and (ii).

Moreover, we have shown the existence of a constant c' depending only on K and p, such that

$$\sum_{1}^{K}\left[\int_{\mathbb{R}^K}\int_{]0,+\infty[}\frac{|u(x+te_i)-u(x)|^p}{t^p}dt\,dx\right]\leqslant c'\|u\|'^p_{W^{1-1/p,p}(\mathbb{R}^K)}.$$

This concludes the proof of the equivalence of the norms stated in the lemma.

$\square$

Let us return to the proof of Theorem 3.9 for $N > 2$.

Let u be an element of $W^{1-1/p,p}(\mathbb{R}^{N-1})$ and let v be defined as follows for $t > 0$:

$$(3.29)\qquad v(x',t)=\frac{\varphi(t)}{t^{N-1}}\int_{]0,t[^{N-1}}u(x'+z)dz,$$

where $\varphi\in\mathcal{D}(\mathbb{R})$ with $\varphi(0)=1$; then $\lim_{t\to0}\|v(\cdot,t)-u\|_p=0$.

This follows from

$$\|v(.,t)-u\|_p^p=\int_{\mathbb{R}^{N-1}}\left|\int_{]0,1[^{N-1}}\varphi(t)(u(x+tz)-u(x))dz\right|^p dx\longrightarrow 0,$$

because the inclusion $u\in L^p$ implies that $\lim_{h\to0}\|\tau_h u-u\|_p=0$ (cf. property (2.64)).

Next, we must verify that $v\in W^{1,p}(\mathbb{R}^N)$. The derivative with respect to x_i, where $1\leqslant i\leqslant N-1$, can be seen as a derivative with respect to the endpoints by applying Fubini's formula and using the integration variable x_i+z_i. We thus obtain

$$(3.30)\qquad \partial_i v(x',t)=\varphi(t)\int_{(]0,t[)^{N-2}}\frac{u(x'+te_i+\breve{z}_i)-u(x'+\breve{z}_i)}{t^{N-1}}d\breve{z}_i.$$

Using Hölder's inequality and the change of variables $\breve{z}_i=t\breve{Z}_i$, we have

$$|\partial_i v(x',t)|^p\leqslant|\varphi(t)|^p\int_{(]0,1[)^{N-2}}\left|\frac{u(x'+te_i+t\breve{Z}_i)-u(x'+t\breve{Z}_i)}{t}\right|^p d\breve{z}_i.$$

We then integrate with respect to x' and t and apply the change of variables

$$(x',t)\longrightarrow(X'=x'+t\breve{Z}_i,t),$$

which, by Lemma 3.27 and Fubini's formula, gives

$$\int_{\mathbb{R}^{N-1}}\int_{]0,+\infty[}|\partial_i v|^p$$
$$\leqslant\int_{\mathbb{R}^{N-1}}\int_{]0,+\infty[}\int_{(]0,1[)^{N-2}}\left|\frac{u(X'+te_i)-u(X')}{t}\right|^p dX'\,dt\,d\breve{Z}_i\leqslant C.$$

Next, we compute $\partial_t v(x', t)$, which equals

$$\partial_t v(x', t) = \varphi(t)\Big(\frac{-(N-1)}{t^N}\int_0^t \cdots \int_0^t u(x' + z)dz\Big)$$

$$+ \varphi(t)\Big(\sum_{i=1}^{i=N}\frac{1}{t^{N-1}}\int_{]0,t[^{N-2}} u(x' + \check{z}_i + te_i)d\check{z}_i\Big)$$

$$+ \varphi'(t)\frac{1}{t^{N-1}}\int_{(]0,t[)^{N-1}} u(x' + z)dz$$

$$= \varphi(t)\sum_i \frac{1}{t^{N-1}}\int_{(]0,t[)^{N-1}} \frac{u(x' + te_i + \check{z}_i) - u(x' + z)}{t}\,dz$$

$$+ \varphi'(t)\frac{1}{t^{N-1}}\int_{(]0,t[)^{N-1}} u(x' + z)\,dz.$$

It is clear that the function

$$(x', t) \longmapsto \frac{\varphi'(t)}{t^{N-1}}\int_{(]0,t[)^{N-1}} u(x' + z)\,dz$$

belongs to $L^p(\mathbb{R}^{N-1} \times]0, +\infty[)$. It remains to show that the same holds for the integrals

$$F_i(x', t) = \varphi(t)\frac{1}{t^{N-1}}\int_{(]0,t[)^{N-1}} \frac{u(x' + te_i + \check{z}_i) - u(x' + z)}{t}\,dz.$$

By applying the change of variables $z = tZ$ and then using Hölder's inequality, we obtain

$$\sum_i |F_i(x', t)|^p \leqslant |\varphi|_\infty^p \sum_i \int_{]0,1[^{N-1}} \Big|\frac{u(x' + te_i + t\check{Z}_i) - u(x' + tZ)}{t}\Big|^p dz.$$

Integrating with respect to x' and t, and then applying the change of variables $(x', t) \mapsto \big(X' = x' + tZ, \lambda = t(1 - z_i)\big)$ gives $dX' \wedge d\lambda = (1 - z_i)dx' \wedge dt$, whence, using evident upper bounds,

$$\iint \sum_i |F_i(x', t)|^p dx' dt$$

$$\leqslant \|\varphi\|_\infty^p \sum_i \int_{\mathbb{R}^{N-1}} \int_{(]0,1[)^{N-2}} \int_{]0,+\infty[} \Big|\frac{v(X' + \lambda e_i) - v(X')}{\lambda}\Big|^p d\lambda\, dX'\, dz$$

$$< \infty.$$

This concludes the proof of Theorem 3.9. $\square$

3.2 The Case of an Open Boundary Other than $\mathbb{R}^{N-1} \times \,]0, \infty[$

In Chapter 2, we showed the existence of a trace map with values in $L^p(\partial\Omega)$ when Ω is a $\mathcal{C}^1$ open set. In a manner similar to the one we used before, we define the space

$$W^{1-1/p,p}(\partial\Omega) = \Big\{ u \in L^p(\partial\Omega) \mid \int_{\partial\Omega} \int_{\partial\Omega} \frac{|u(x) - u(y)|^p}{|x - y|^{p+N-2}} d\sigma(x) d\sigma(y) < \infty \Big\},$$

where $d\sigma$ denotes the superficial density on $\partial\Omega$. With this definition, Theorem 3.9 extends to open sets of class $\mathcal{C}^1$.

Proposition 3.31. *Let Ω be a class $\mathcal{C}^1$ open set; then the image of the trace map on $W^{1,p}(\Omega)$ satisfies*

$$\gamma_0(W^{1,p}(\Omega)) = W^{1-1/p,p}(\partial\Omega).$$

Proof of Proposition 3.31.

Let $u \in W^{1,p}(\Omega)$ and let Ω_i, $\mathcal{O}'_i$, F_i, a_i, and φ_i be as in the definitions 2.65 and 2.66 of an open set of class $\mathcal{C}^1$. Let v_i be defined on $\mathbb{R}^{N-1} \times \,]0, +\infty[$ by

$$v_i(x', x_N) = \varphi_i u(x', a_i(x') + x_N).$$

Since a_i is of class $\mathcal{C}^1$ on the compact set F_i obtained by projecting the support of φ_i onto $\mathbb{R}^{N-1}$, we easily see that $v_i \in W^{1,p}(\mathbb{R}^{N-1} \times \,]0, +\infty[)$. Consequently, by Theorem 3.9, the trace $\gamma_0 v_i$ of this function belongs to $W^{1-1/p,p}(\mathbb{R}^{N-1})$.

Setting $\widehat{x}' = (x', a_i(x'))$, we will deduce from this that the composition $\widetilde{u}_i$ defined by $\widetilde{u}_i(\widehat{x}') = \varphi_i u(\widehat{x}') = \gamma_0 v_i(\widehat{x}')$ belongs to $W^{1-1/p,p}(\partial\Omega \cap \Omega_i)$. Let $\|\widetilde{u}_i\|_{1,p}^{(i)}$ denote its seminorm in this last space. We use the inequality

$$|x' - y'| \leqslant |\widehat{x}' - \widehat{y}'| = \Big(|x' - y'|^2 + |a_i(x') - a_i(y')|^2 \Big)^{1/2} \leqslant \sqrt{1 + |\nabla a_i|_\infty^2}\, |y' - x'|$$

to give an upper bound. Using the extension by 0 outside of $\mathcal{O}'_i$, the seminorm $\|\widetilde{u}_i\|_{1,p}^{(i)}$, whose pth power equals the integral

$$\int_{(\mathbb{R}^{N-1})^2} \frac{|\varphi_i u(\widehat{y}') - \varphi_i u(\widehat{x}')|^p (1 + |\nabla a_i(x')|^2)^{1/2}(1 + |\nabla a_i(y')|^2))^{1/2}}{(|\widehat{y}' - \widehat{x}'|)^{p+N-2}}\, dx' dy',$$

gives the upper bound

$$(*) \quad \|\widetilde{u}_i\|_{1,p}^{(i)} \leqslant \Big[(1 + \|\nabla a_i\|_\infty^2) \int_{\mathbb{R}^{N-1}} \int_{\mathbb{R}^{N-1}} \frac{|\gamma_0 v_i(x') - \gamma_0 v_i(y')|^p}{|x' - y'|^{p+N-2}}\, dx' dy' \Big]^{1/p}.$$

We therefore have $\widetilde{u}_i \in W^{1-1/p,p}(\partial\Omega)$.

By Theorem 2.86, the trace $\gamma_0 u$ is defined by $\sum_i \widetilde{u}_i$. Letting $|\gamma_0 u|_{1-1/p,p}$ denote the seminorm

$$\left(\int_{\partial\Omega} \int_{\partial\Omega} \frac{|\gamma_0 u(x) - \gamma_0 u(y)|^p}{|x-y|^{p+N-2}} d\sigma(x) d\sigma(y) \right)^{1/p},$$

and applying Proposition 2.68 and the continuity of the trace map, we deduce that

$$|\gamma_0 u|_{1-1/p,p} \leqslant C \sum_i \|\widetilde{u}_i\|_{1,p}^{(i)} \leqslant C' \sum_i \|v_i\|_{W^{1,p}((\mathbb{R}^N)^+)}$$

$$\leqslant C'' \sum_i \|\varphi_i u\|_{W^{1,p}(\Omega_i \cap \Omega)} \leqslant C''' \|u\|_{W^{1,p}(\Omega)}.$$

We have thus proved part of the proposition.

Conversely, let us assume that $u \in L^p(\partial\Omega)$ and that the seminorm $|u|_{1-1/p,p}$ in $W^{1-1/p,p}(\partial\Omega)$ is finite; then we can easily show that for every i, $\|\varphi_i u\|_{1,p}^{(i)} < \infty$ because φ_i is Lipschitz.

For every $x' \in \mathcal{O}'_i$, let $v_i(x') = \varphi_i u(\widehat{x}')$. Using the inequalities

$$|\widehat{x}' - \widehat{y}'| \leqslant \sqrt{(1 + \|\nabla a_i\|_\infty^2)} \, |x' - y'|,$$

we can obtain an inequality inverse to $(*)$, from which we deduce that $v_i \in W^{1-1/p,p}(\mathbb{R}^{N-1})$.

By Theorem 2.86, there exist $V_i \in W^{1,p}((\mathbb{R}^N)^+)$ with compact support in $\mathcal{O}'_i \times [0, \delta[$ such that $v_i = \gamma_0 V_i$. For $x' \in \mathcal{O}'_i$ and $x_N \in]a_i(x'), a_i(x') + \delta[$, let the function U_i be defined by $U_i(x', x_N) = V_i(x', -a_i(x') + x_N)$. It is defined on $\Omega_i \cap \Omega$, equals u_i on $\{x_N = a_i(x')\}$, and, moreover, belongs to $W^{1,p}(\Omega_i \cap \Omega)$. The previous computations show that there exists a constant C depending only on $\partial\Omega, p, N$, such that

$$\|U_i\|_{W^{1,p}(\Omega_i \cap \Omega)} \leqslant C|u_i|_{1-1/p,p}.$$

Let $U = \sum_i U_i$. We have $U(x', 0) = \sum_i U_i(x', 0) = \sum_i \varphi_i u(x') = u(x')$. Moreover, $U \in W^{1,p}(\Omega)$ because, by Proposition 2.68,

$$\|U\|_{W^{1,p}(\Omega)} \leqslant \sum_i \|U_i\|_{W^{1,p}(\Omega_i \cap \Omega)}$$

(3.32)
$$\leqslant C \sum_i \|\varphi_i u\|_{W^{1-1/p,p}(\Omega_i \cap \partial\Omega)}$$

$$\leqslant C\|u\|_{W^{1-1/p,p}(\partial\Omega)}. \qquad \square$$

3.3 Traces of Functions in $W^{1,1}(\Omega)$

Let us now study the traces of functions in $W^{1,1}(\Omega)$. The following can be seen as an extension of the previous result if we let the derivative of order $1 - 1/p = 0$ be the function itself.

Theorem 3.33. *Let Ω be an open set of class $\mathcal{C}^1$. There exists a surjective continuous linear map, denoted by γ_0, that sends $W^{1,1}(\Omega)$ to $L^1(\partial\Omega)$. When $u \in W^{1,1}(\Omega) \cap \mathcal{C}(\overline{\Omega})$, this trace coincides with the restriction to the boundary.*

Moreover, there exists a constant $C > 0$ such that, for every $u \in L^1(\partial\Omega)$, there exists a $U \in W^{1,1}(\Omega)$ satisfying $\gamma_0 U = u$ and

$$\|U\|_{W^{1,1}(\Omega)} \leqslant C\|u\|_{L^1(\partial\Omega)}.$$

Proof of Theorem 3.33.

Using the same method we used for the functions in $W^{1,p}(\Omega)$, we reduce to the case where u has compact support in $\mathbb{R}^{N-1} \times [0, 1[$. We then have, for almost all pairs (s, t) of positive real numbers, assuming for the moment that $s < t$ to illustrate the idea,

$$(3.34) \qquad \int_{\mathbb{R}^{N-1}} |u(x', t) - u(x', s)|dx' \leqslant \int_s^t \int_{\mathbb{R}^{N-1}} |\partial_N u|(x', \lambda)dx'd\lambda.$$

Since s and t tend to zero, the right-hand side also tends to zero. We conclude that $u(\cdot, t)$ is Cauchy in $L^1(\mathbb{R}^{N-1})$, which is complete. Let $\gamma_0 u$ denote the limit. We can easily see that the trace map defined in this way is continuous.

Let us show that this map is surjective onto $L^1(\mathbb{R}^{N-1})$. Consider u in $L^1(\mathbb{R}^{N-1})$ and let $\{u_k\}$ be a sequence of $\mathcal{C}^1$ functions with compact support that converges to u in $L^1(\mathbb{R}^{N-1})$. After extracting a subsequence if necessary, we may, and do, assume that

$$(3.35) \qquad \sum_1^\infty \|u_{k+1} - u_k\|_1 < \infty.$$

Let $\{\alpha_k\}$ be a sequence of positive real numbers such that

$$(3.36) \qquad \forall k \geqslant 1, \quad \alpha_k \leqslant \frac{2^{-k}}{(\|\nabla u_{k+1}\|_1 + \|\nabla u_k\|_1 + 1)}.$$

Next, consider the sequence $\{t_k\}$ of real numbers defined by

$$(3.37) \qquad t_0 = \sum_0^\infty \alpha_k,$$
$$t_{k+1} = t_k - \alpha_k \quad (\forall k \geqslant 1).$$

This sequence is monotonically decreasing and tends to zero. We define the function v on $\mathbb{R}^{N-1} \times]0, t_0[$ by setting

$$(3.38) \qquad v(t, x') = u_k(x') + \frac{t_k - t}{t_k - t_{k+1}}(u_{k+1} - u_k)(x')$$

for every $t \in]t_{k+1}, t_k[$ and for every $x' \in \mathbb{R}^{N-1}$. We then have $v \in W^{1,1}(\mathbb{R}^{N-1} \times]0, t_0[)$. Indeed, if $j \in [1, N-1]$, then for every $t \in]t_{k+1}, t_k[$,

$$\partial_j v = \partial_j u_k + \frac{t_k - t}{t_k - t_{k+1}}(\partial_j u_{k+1} - \partial_j u_k).$$

Consequently, we have

$$\|\partial_j v\|_1 \leqslant \sum_k \int_{t_{k+1}}^{t_k} (\|\partial_j u_k\|_1 + \|\partial_j u_{k+1}\|_1)$$

$$\leqslant \sum_0^\infty |t_k - t_{k+1}|(\|\partial_j u_k\|_1 + \|\partial_j u_{k+1}\|_1) \leqslant \sum_k \frac{1}{2^k}.$$

Deriving with respect to t gives

$$(3.39) \qquad \forall t \in]t_{k+1}, t_k[, \quad \partial_t v = \frac{u_{k+1} - u_k}{t_{k+1} - t_k}.$$

Hence

$$\|\partial_t v\|_1 \leqslant \sum_k \int_{t_{k+1}}^{t_k} \frac{\|u_{k+1} - u_k\|_1}{|t_{k+1} - t_k|}$$

$$\leqslant \sum \|u_k - u_{k+1}\|_1 < \infty.$$

We have thus shown that $v \in W^{1,1}(\mathbb{R}^{N-1} \times]0, t_0[)$.

By the open mapping theorem, the image under γ_0 of the open ball of radius 1 with center 0 contains an open ball $B(0, r_0)$ for some $r_0 > 0$. Hence, for every $u \in L^1(\partial\Omega)$, there exists a $U \in W^{1,1}$ such that

$$\|U\|_{W^{1,1}(\Omega)} \leqslant \frac{1}{r_0}\|u\|_{L^1(\partial\Omega)}. \qquad \square$$

3.4 Density of $\mathcal{C}^1(\partial\Omega)$ in $W^{1-1/p,p}(\partial\Omega)$

3.4.1 Density in $W^{1-1/p,p}(\partial\Omega)$, Properties of the Trace Map

Proposition 3.40. *Let Ω be a class $\mathcal{C}^1$ open subset of $\mathbb{R}^N$; then $\mathcal{C}^1(\partial\Omega) \cap W^{1-1/p,p}(\partial\Omega)$ is dense in $W^{1-1/p,p}(\partial\Omega)$.*

Remark 3.41. We can establish this result using the definition of $W^{1-1/p,p}(\partial\Omega)$. In the next chapter, we give the proof for $\mathbb{R}^{N-1}$ and $W^{s,p}$, where $s \in]0, 1[$ is arbitrary. In the following proof, we have chosen to use the properties "inherited" from $W^{1,p}(\Omega)$.

Proof of Proposition 3.40.

Since Ω is of class $\mathcal{C}^1$, there exists a continuous linear extension E of $W^{1,p}(\Omega)$ in $W^{1,p}(\mathbb{R}^N)$. Let $u \in W^{1-1/p,p}(\partial\Omega)$. There exists a lifting $U \in W^{1,p}(\Omega)$ of u, that is, a $U \in W^{1,p}(\Omega)$ such that $\gamma_0 U = u$ on $\partial\Omega$.

By the density of $\mathcal{D}(\mathbb{R}^N)$ in $W^{1,p}(\mathbb{R}^N)$, there exists a sequence $\{U_n\}$ in $\mathcal{D}(\mathbb{R}^N)$ such that $\|U_n - E(U)\|_{W^{1,p}(\mathbb{R}^N)} \to 0$. Let u_n be the restriction of U_n to Ω. Since the restriction of $E(U)$ to Ω is U, we have $\|u_n - U\|_{W^{1,p}(\Omega)} \to 0$. By the continuity of the trace map,

$$\|\gamma_0(u_n) - u\|_{W^{1-1/p,p}(\partial\Omega)} = \|\gamma_0(u_n) - \gamma_0 U\|_{W^{1-1/p,p}(\partial\Omega)}$$
$$\leqslant C\|u_n - U\|_{W^{1,p}(\Omega)} \longrightarrow 0.$$

Now, as the boundary is of class $\mathcal{C}^1$, the function $\gamma_0 u_n$, which is the restriction of u_n to $\partial\Omega$, is also of class $\mathcal{C}^1$. Consequently, $\gamma_0 u_n \in \mathcal{C}^1(\partial\Omega) \cap W^{1-1/p,p}(\partial\Omega)$, completing the proof. $\qquad\square$

We also prove the existence of a function that is regular inside Ω and has the same trace as u on the boundary when Ω is a general open set of class $\mathcal{C}^1$.

Theorem 3.42. *Let Ω be a class $\mathcal{C}^1$ open set and let $u \in W^{1,p}(\Omega)$; then there exists a sequence $\{u_n\} \subset \mathcal{C}^\infty(\Omega) \cap W^{1,p}(\Omega)$ that converges to u in $W^{1,p}(\Omega)$ and satisfies $\gamma_0 u_n = \gamma_0 u$ on $\partial\Omega$.*

Proof of Theorem 3.42.

We repeat the construction given in the proof of Proposition 2.12 of Chapter 2. Recall that

$$u_\varepsilon = \sum_j \rho_{\varepsilon_j} \star (\varphi_j u)$$

converges to u in $W^{1,p}(\Omega)$ when ε tends to 0. Let

$$v_{N,\varepsilon} = \sum_0^N \left(\rho_{\varepsilon_j} \star (\varphi_j u) - \varphi_j u \right).$$

By definition, $v_{N,\varepsilon}$ has compact support and converges to $u_\varepsilon - u$ in $W^{1,p}(\Omega)$ when $N \to +\infty$. By the continuity of the trace map, it follows that

$$\gamma_0(u_\varepsilon - u) = 0. \qquad\square$$

Proposition 3.40 and the results before it allow us, in particular, to establish generalized Green's formulas that extend the classical Green's formula for class $\mathcal{C}^1$ functions. This is the aim of the next subsection.

3.4.2 Generalization of Green's Formula and Applications

Theorem 3.43 (generalized Green's formula). *Let Ω be a class $\mathcal{C}^1$ open subset of $\mathbb{R}^N$. Let U be an element of $W^{1,p}(\Omega)$ and let $\varphi \in \mathcal{D}(\mathbb{R}^N, \mathbb{R}^N)$; then*

$$\int_\Omega \nabla U(x) \cdot \varphi(x)dx + \int_\Omega U(x) \operatorname{div}\varphi(x)dx = \int_{\partial\Omega} \gamma_0 U(s)\,\varphi(s) \cdot \overrightarrow{n}(s)d\sigma(s).$$

In this formula, $d\sigma$ is the superficial density on $\partial\Omega$, $\overrightarrow{n}$ is the outward-pointing unit normal to $\partial\Omega$, the terms $\nabla u(x) \cdot \varphi(x)$ and $\varphi(s) \cdot \overrightarrow{n}(s)$ are inner products of vectors in $\mathbb{R}^N$, and the divergence of φ is defined to be $\operatorname{div}\varphi(x) = \sum_1^N \partial_i(\varphi_i)(x)$.

Proof of Theorem 3.43.

In the current situation, where Ω is of class $\mathcal{C}^1$, we already know this formula when u is of class $\mathcal{C}^1$ on $\overline{\Omega}$. Let $u \in W^{1,p}(\Omega)$. By Proposition 3.40, there exists a sequence $\{u_n\}$ in $\mathcal{C}^1(\overline{\Omega}) \cap W^{1,p}(\Omega)$ that converges to u in $W^{1,p}(\Omega)$ with, moreover, $\gamma_0 u_n \to \gamma_0 u$ in $W^{1-1/p,p}(\partial\Omega)$.

From the convergences $\partial_i u_n \varphi_i \to \partial_i u \varphi_i$ in $L^p(\Omega)$, it follows that $\int_\Omega \nabla u_n \cdot \varphi \to \int_\Omega \nabla u \cdot \varphi$. Moreover, the term $\int_\Omega u_n \operatorname{div}\varphi$ tends to $\int_\Omega u \operatorname{div}\varphi$.

Finally, by considering the integrals $\int_{\partial\Omega}(\overrightarrow{n})_i \varphi_i \gamma_0(u - u_n)d\sigma$, we obtain the convergence of the boundary term $\int_{\partial\Omega} u_n(\varphi \cdot \overrightarrow{n})d\sigma$ to $\int_{\partial\Omega} \gamma_0 u(\varphi \cdot \overrightarrow{n})d\sigma$ because $\|\gamma_0(u_n - u)\|_{L^p(\partial\Omega)} \to 0$. This concludes the proof. $\square$

Another proof of Theorem 3.43. Let us now prove this result using a different method. We will repeat the arguments of the proof of the classical version of Green's theorem in one of the open subsets of the cover occurring in the definition of the $\mathcal{C}^1$ regularity of Ω (cf. Definition 2.65).

The components $u\varphi_i$ of the function $u\varphi$ belong to $W^{1,p}(\Omega)$, as we can see by using the definition of the derivative of $u\varphi_i$ in the sense of distributions. Let $\mathcal{O}$ be an open subset of $\mathbb{R}^N$ such that there exist an open subset $\mathcal{O}'$ of $\mathbb{R}^{N-1}$ and a piecewise $\mathcal{C}^1$ function a that is continuous on $\mathcal{O}'$ satisfying

$$\mathcal{O} \cap \Omega \subset \{(x', x_N) \mid x_N > a(x'), x' \in \mathcal{O}'\},$$
$$\mathcal{O} \cap \partial\Omega = \{(x', a(x')) \mid x' \in \mathcal{O}'\}.$$

After changing the local coordinate systems, if necessary, we may, and do, assume that for every i, $u\varphi_i \in W^{1,p}(\mathcal{O} \cap \Omega)$ has compact support in $\mathcal{O}$. In the present case, the trace of $u\varphi_i$ on the boundary of $\mathcal{O} \cap \Omega$ is zero outside of $\mathcal{O} \cap \partial\Omega$ (arc $\widehat{m\,m'}$ in Figure 3.1). The boundary term in the formula therefore reduces to

$$\int_{\mathcal{O}'} u(x', a(x'))\varphi(x', a(x')) \cdot \overrightarrow{n}(x)d\sigma(x').$$

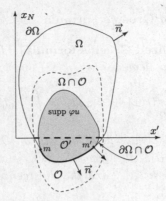

Fig. 3.1. Localization at a boundary point.

Note that the outward-pointing unit normal to $\partial\Omega$ is defined by

$$\overrightarrow{n}(x) = \frac{\nabla a - e_N}{\sqrt{1 + |\nabla a(x)|^2}}.$$

Moreover, $d\sigma(x') = \sqrt{1 + |\nabla a(x')|^2}\, dx'$, from which we deduce that

$$n_i(x')d\sigma(x') = \partial_i a(x') \quad \text{and} \quad n_N(x')d\sigma(x') = -1.$$

We must therefore show the following formulas for each of the components:

$$(*) \qquad \int_{\mathcal{O}\cap\Omega}\Big[(\partial_i u\varphi_i + u\partial_i\varphi_i)(x)\Big]dx = \int_{\mathcal{O}'} \gamma_0 u(x')\varphi_i(x', a(x'))\partial_i a(x')dx',$$

for every $i \leqslant N - 1$, and

$$(**) \qquad \int_{\mathcal{O}\cap\Omega}\Big[(\partial_N u\varphi_N + u\partial_N\varphi_N)(x)\Big]dx = -\int_{\mathcal{O}'} \gamma_0 u(x')\varphi_N(x', a(x'))dx'.$$

For the first equality, we approximate u in $W^{1,p}(\Omega\cap\mathcal{O})$ using a sequence $\{u_n\}$ of $\mathcal{C}^1$ functions. Since the function $x' \mapsto \int_{a(x')}^\infty u_n\varphi_i(x', x_N)dx_N$ has compact support in $\mathcal{O}'$, we have

$$\int_{\mathcal{O}'} \Big(\partial_i \int_{a(x')}^\infty (u_n\varphi_i)(x', x_N)dx_N\Big)dx' = 0.$$

Moreover, in this integral, we can use differentiation with respect to a parameter, giving

$$0 = \int_{\mathcal{O}'} \partial_i\Big(\int_{a(x')}^\infty (u_n\varphi_i)(x', x_N)dx_N\Big)dx'$$

$$= \int_{\mathcal{O}'} -\partial_i a(x')(u_n\varphi_i)(x', a(x'))dx' + \int_{\mathcal{O}'}\int_{a(x')}^\infty \partial_i(u_n\varphi_i)(x', x_N)dx_N dx'.$$

We now let n tend to $+\infty$. The first term of the right-hand side has the integral $-\int_{\mathcal{O}'} \partial_i a(x')(u\varphi_i)(x', a(x'))dx'$ as a limit.

By the definition of the convergence in $W^{1,p}$, the second term of the right-hand side has limit $\int_{\Omega} \partial_i(u\varphi_i)dx$. Using the derivative of the product $u\varphi_i$, we obtain the formula $(*)$.

In the case $i = N$, we obtain the formula $(**)$ by using the following definition of the trace of $x \mapsto (u\varphi)(x', a(x') + x_N)$:

$$\int_{\mathcal{O}'} \int_{a(x')}^{+\infty} \partial_N(u\varphi)(x', x_N) = -\int_{\mathcal{O}'} \gamma_0(u\varphi)(x', a(x'))dx'$$

and the derivative of $u\varphi$ with respect to x_n in the sense of distributions. $\square$

Theorem 3.44. *Let Ω be a $\mathcal{C}^1$ open set. Let u be in $W^{1,p}(\Omega)$, let v be in $W^{1,p}(\mathbb{R}^N \smallsetminus \overline{\Omega})$, and let $\tilde{u}$ be defined by*

$$\tilde{u} = \begin{cases} u & \text{in } \Omega, \\ v & \text{in } \mathbb{R}^N \smallsetminus \overline{\Omega}. \end{cases}$$

Then $\tilde{u}$ belongs to $W^{1,p}(\mathbb{R}^N)$ if and only if

$$\gamma_0 u = \gamma_0 v \text{ on } \partial\Omega.$$

Proof of Theorem 3.44.

Let us assume that $\gamma_0 u = \gamma_0 v$ on $\partial\Omega$. Let $\varphi \in \mathcal{D}(\mathbb{R}^N, \mathbb{R}^N)$. Applying the above version of Green's formula on both Ω and $\mathbb{R}^N \smallsetminus \overline{\Omega}$, with opposite normal vectors $\vec{n_1}$ and $\vec{n_2}$, we find

$$\int_{\mathbb{R}^N} \nabla\tilde{u} \cdot \varphi = -\int_{\mathbb{R}^N} \tilde{u}\,\mathrm{div}\,\varphi = -\int_{\Omega} u\,\mathrm{div}\,\varphi - \int_{\mathbb{R}^N \smallsetminus \overline{\Omega}} v\,\mathrm{div}\,\varphi$$

$$= \int_{\Omega} \nabla u \cdot \varphi + \int_{\partial\Omega} \gamma_0 u \vec{n_1} \cdot \varphi + \int_{\mathbb{R}^N \smallsetminus \overline{\Omega}} \nabla v \cdot \varphi + \int_{\partial\Omega} \gamma_0 v \vec{n_2} \cdot \varphi.$$

Since the outward-pointing unit normal to $\partial\Omega$ is the opposite of the outward-pointing unit normal to $\partial(\mathbb{R}^N \smallsetminus \Omega)$ and $\gamma_0 u = \gamma_0 v$, we obtain

(3.45) $$\nabla\tilde{u} = \nabla u\,\mathbf{1}_{\Omega} + \nabla v\,\mathbf{1}_{\mathbb{R}^N \smallsetminus \Omega};$$

hence $\tilde{u} \in W^{1,p}(\mathbb{R}^N)$.

Conversely, let us assume that $\tilde{u} \in W^{1,p}(\mathbb{R}^N)$. We denote the Dirac delta function with support $\partial\Omega$ by $\delta_{\partial\Omega}$ (cf. Example 1.85); this is a measure. The previous computation gives

$$\forall \varphi \in \mathcal{D}(\mathbb{R}^N, \mathbb{R}^N), \quad \int_{\partial\Omega} \vec{n} \cdot \varphi(x)\gamma_0(u - v)(x)d\sigma(x) = 0.$$

Let us take for φ a function whose only nonzero component is $\varphi_N \in \mathcal{D}(\mathbb{R}^N)$. The previous inequality then becomes

$$\forall \varphi \in \mathcal{D}(\mathbb{R}^N), \quad \langle \gamma_0(u-v)\delta_\Omega, n_N\varphi_N \rangle = 0.$$

We deduce from this that, seen as a function in $L^p(\partial\Omega)$, we have $\gamma_0(u-v) = 0$, concluding the proof. $\square$

Corollary 3.46. *Let Ω be a class C^1 open set; then*

$$W_0^{1,p}(\Omega) = \{u \mid \widetilde{u} \in W^{1,p}(\mathbb{R}^N)\},$$

where $\widetilde{u}$ is the extension by 0 outside of Ω. We also have

$$W_0^{1,p}(\Omega) = \{u \in W^{1,p}(\Omega) \mid \gamma_0 u = 0 \text{ on } \partial\Omega\}.$$

3.4.3 Determining the Duals of Sobolev Spaces

Dual of the Space $W^{1,p}(\Omega)$.

Proposition 3.47. *Let $1 \leqslant p < +\infty$. We consider the product space $L^p(\Omega)^{N+1}$ endowed with the norm $\|v\|_p = \left(\sum_0^{N+1} \|v_i\|_p^p\right)^{1/p}$. The map J from $W^{1,p}(\Omega)$ to $L^p(\Omega)^{N+1}$ defined by*

$$\forall u \in W^{1,p}(\Omega), \quad J(u) = (u, \partial_1 u, \partial_2 u, \dots, \partial_N u)$$

is an isometry whose image $\mathrm{Im}\, J$ is a closed subspace of $L^p(\Omega)^{N+1}$. It follows that if $T \in W^{1,p}(\Omega)'$, then

$$(3.48) \quad \exists v \in L^{p'}(\Omega)^{N+1}, \ \forall u \in W^{1,p}(\Omega), \quad T(u) = \int_\Omega uv_0 + \sum_1^N \int_\Omega \partial_i u \, v_i.$$

Conversely, when $v \in L^{p'}(\Omega)^{N+1}$, this formula defines an element T of the dual of $W^{1,p}(\Omega)$. The norm of the linear functional T is then

$$\|T\|_{(W^{1,p})'} = \inf\{\|v\|_{p'} \mid v \text{ satisfies } (3.48)\}.$$

Proof of Proposition 3.47.

The first statement concerning J is clear. Let T be an element of the dual of $W^{1,p}(\Omega)$ and let T^* be defined on $\mathrm{Im}\, J$ by $T^*(J(u)) = T(u)$. By the Hahn–Banach theorem, T^* can be extended to a continuous linear functional on the space $L^p(\Omega)^{N+1}$, that is, to an element of the dual of this space. It follows that for $0 \leqslant i \leqslant N$, there exist $v_i \in L^{p'}(\Omega)$ such that

$$\forall u \in L^p(\Omega)^{N+1}, \quad T^*(J(u)) = uv_0 + \sum_1^N \langle \partial_i u, v_i \rangle.$$

This leads to the statement about T. Since the converse is evident, we have proved that the description of an element of the dual is correct.

For the norm, we note that the $(N+1)$-tuple $(v_i)_{0 \leqslant i \leqslant N}$ is not necessarily unique. The previous extension, which conserves the norm of T^*, gives the following result using Hölder's inequality:

$$\|T(u)\| = \|T^*(J(u))\| \leqslant \|u\|_p \|v_0\|_{p'} + \sum_1^N \|v_i\|_{p'} \|\partial_i u\|_p$$
$$\leqslant \|u\|_{W^{1,p}} \left(\|v_0\|_{p'} + \sum_1^N \|v_i\|_{p'} \right).$$

It follows that for any v satisfying the condition of (3.48), we have $\|T\| \leqslant \|v\|_{p'}$. The stated equality concerning the norm of T follows.   □

The Dual $W^{-1,p'}(\Omega)$ of the Space $W_0^{1,p}(\Omega)$. The following is a consequence of the previous proposition.

Proposition 3.49. *Let $1 \leqslant p < +\infty$. Every element L of the dual of $W_0^{1,p}(\Omega)$, which we denote by $W^{-1,p'}(\Omega)$, can be identified with a distribution V satisfying*

$$\forall u \in W_0^{1,p}(\Omega), \quad L(u) = \langle V, u \rangle.$$

Indeed, V is associated with an element $(v_i) \in L^{p'}(\Omega)^{N+1}$ by setting $V = [v_0] - \sum_1^N \partial_i[v_i]$. As before, the norm of this element of $W^{-1,p'}(\Omega)$ is defined by Proposition 3.47.

Proof of Proposition 3.49.

Let L be an element of the dual. The Hahn–Banach theorem allows us to extend this element to a continuous linear functional on $W^{1,p}(\Omega)$ while preserving its norm. We deduce from this that there exist elements $v_0, v_1, \ldots, v_N$ of $L^{p'}(\Omega)^{N+1}$ such that

$$\forall u \in W_0^{1,p}(\Omega), \quad L(u) = \sum_1^N \langle \partial_i u, v_i \rangle + u v_0.$$

We know that the space $\mathcal{D}(\Omega)$ is dense in $W_0^{1,p}(\Omega)$. Consequently, the previous formula can be used for a sequence $\{\varphi_n\}$ that converges to u, giving the following equalities using differentiation in the sense of distributions and the continuity of the duality pairing of L^p with $L^{p'}$:

$$L(u) = \lim_{n \to +\infty} \left[\langle v_0, \varphi_n \rangle + \sum_1^N \langle v_i, \partial_i \varphi_n \rangle \right]$$
$$= \lim_{n \to +\infty} \langle v_0, \varphi_n \rangle - \sum_1^N \langle \partial_i v_i, \varphi_n \rangle = \langle V, u \rangle,$$

where V is the distribution $[v_0] - \sum_1^N \partial_i[v_i]$.

Conversely, we can easily see that such a distribution defines an element L of the dual of $W_0^{1,p}(\Omega)$. The norm of L is, as before, the infimum of the norms in $L^{p'}$ of the $(N+1)$-tuples (v_i) used to define V.   □

Properties of the Dual of $W^{1-1/p,p}(\partial\Omega)$. When $p = 1$, the space of traces is $L^1(\partial\Omega)$; hence its dual is $L^\infty(\partial\Omega)$. To study the dual when $p > 1$, we introduce the space $W^{p'}(\mathrm{div})$ defined by

$$W^{p'}(\mathrm{div}) = \{\sigma \in L^{p'}(\Omega) \mid \mathrm{div}(\sigma) \in L^{p'}(\Omega)\}.$$

We also define the following spaces.

Definition 3.50. Consider a class $\mathcal{C}^1$ open set $\Omega \subset \mathbb{R}^N$, a real number $p > 1$, and the conjugate exponent p' of p.

(1) If $p < N$, then we set, for $q' = Np/(Np - N + p)$,

$$(3.51) \qquad W_{q'}^{p'}(\mathrm{div}) = \{\sigma \in L^{p'}(\Omega, \mathbb{R}^N) \mid \mathrm{div}(\sigma) \in L^{q'}(\Omega)\}.$$

(2) If $p > N$, then we set

$$(3.52) \qquad W_1^{p'}(\mathrm{div}) = \{\sigma \in L^{p'}(\Omega, \mathbb{R}^N) \mid \mathrm{div}(\sigma) \in L^1(\Omega)\}.$$

(3) If $p = N$ and $\varepsilon \in \,]0, 1/(p-1)]$, then we set

$$(3.53) \qquad W_\varepsilon^{p'}(\mathrm{div}) = \{\sigma \in L^{p'}(\Omega, \mathbb{R}^N) \mid \mathrm{div}(\sigma) \in L^{1+\varepsilon}(\Omega)\}.$$

These spaces are normed using $\|\sigma\|_{p',q^*} = \|\sigma\|_{p'} + \|\operatorname{div}\sigma\|_{q^*}$, where q^* equals $Np/(Np - N + p)$ in the first case, $q^* = 1$ in the second case, and $q^* = 1 + \varepsilon$ in the third case. We have the following result.

Theorem 3.54. *Let Ω be a $\mathcal{C}^1$ open subset of $\mathbb{R}^N$. For any $\sigma \in W_{p'}^{p'}(\mathrm{div})$, consider the linear functional $S(\sigma)$ defined by*

$$\forall\, u \in W^{1-1/p,p}(\partial\Omega), \quad \langle S(\sigma), u \rangle = \int_\Omega U(x)\operatorname{div}\sigma(x)dx + \int_\Omega \sigma(x)\cdot\nabla U(x)dx,$$

where U is a lifting of u in $W^{1,p}(\Omega)$. Then $S(\sigma)$ is an element of the dual $W^{-1+1/p',p'}(\partial\Omega)$ of $W^{1-1/p,p}(\partial\Omega)$ and S is continuous and surjective onto $W_{p'}^{p'}(\mathrm{div})$. Indeed, the functional S can be extended continuously to $W_{q'}^{p'}(\mathrm{div})$ if $p < N$, to $W_1^{p'}(\mathrm{div})$ if $p > N$, and to $W_\varepsilon^{p'}(\mathrm{div})$ if $p = N$, for $\varepsilon > 0$ sufficiently small.

Remark 3.55. In principle, $p > 1$ in the above, but we can adapt the following proofs to the case $p = 1$ (cf. Exercise 3.6). In that case, we have $p' = +\infty$ and $q' = N$ and we obtain

$$S(W_N^{+\infty}(\mathrm{div})) \hookrightarrow L^1(\partial\Omega)' = L^\infty(\partial\Omega).$$

Proof of Theorem 3.54.

We begin with the case $p < N$. Let us show that the right-hand side of the equation defining $S(\sigma)$ is well defined. This follows, on the one hand, from the inclusion $\sigma \in L^{p'}(\Omega)$ and, on the other hand, from the inclusion $U \in L^q(\Omega)$, where $q = Np/(N - p)$ is the conjugate exponent of q' (cf. Theorem 2.31). This second inclusion holds because $p < N$. Moreover, the definition of $S(\sigma)$ is independent of the choice of the lifting U. To see this, it suffices to prove that the right-hand side is zero when $\gamma_0 U = 0$. Now, $\gamma_0 U = 0$ means that U belongs to $W_0^{1,p}(\Omega)$ (Corollary 3.46). Hence, there exists a sequence $\{U_n\}$ in $\mathcal{D}(\Omega)$ with limit U in $W^{1,p}(\Omega)$. By the definition of divergence in the sense of distributions, we have

$$(3.56) \qquad \int_\Omega \sigma(x) \cdot \nabla U_n(x)dx + \int_\Omega U_n(x) \operatorname{div} \sigma(x)\, dx = 0.$$

The density of the functions of $\mathcal{D}(\Omega)$ in $W_0^{1,p}(\Omega)$ implies that this equality remains true when we take the limit.

It is clear that the functional S is linear. For the continuity of S, we use the continuity of the injection of $W^{1,p}$ into L^q and the inequality of the norms (3.32) linking the function u to one of its liftings U. This gives

$$
\begin{aligned}
|\langle S(\sigma), u\rangle| &\leqslant \|U\|_{L^q}\|\operatorname{div}\sigma\|_{L^{q'}} + \|\nabla U\|_{L^p}\|\sigma\|_{L^{p'}} \\
&\leqslant C_1\|U\|_{W^{1,p}}\|\operatorname{div}\sigma\|_{L^{q'}} + \|\nabla U\|_{L^p}\|\sigma\|_{L^{p'}} \\
&\leqslant C_1\|U\|_{W^{1,p}(\Omega)}\|\sigma\|_{p',q^*} \\
&\leqslant CC_1\|u\|_{W^{1-1/p,p}(\Omega)}\|\sigma\|_{p',q^*}.
\end{aligned}
$$

The last inequality shows us the continuity of the map S, as its norm satisfies the inequality $\|\|S\|\| \leqslant CC_1\|\sigma\|_{p',q^*}$.

Let us now assume that $p > N$. We use the same definition for $S(\sigma)$. The elements U then belong to $L^\infty(\Omega)$; see step F of the proof of Theorem 2.31. It follows that $S(\sigma)$ is still well defined, since $\operatorname{div}\sigma \in L^1(\Omega)$. The independence of the choice of a lifting, the linearity and the continuity are all proved as in the previous case.

Finally, when $N = p$, Theorem 2.31 shows us that $U \in L^q$ for every $q \geqslant p$ with $q < +\infty$. As, by hypothesis, $\sigma \in W_\varepsilon^{p'}(\operatorname{div})$, we have $\sigma \in L^{p'}$ and $\operatorname{div}\sigma \in L^{1+\varepsilon}$. The integral $\int_\Omega \sigma(x) \cdot \nabla U(x)dx$ is well defined because the gradient ∇U belongs to L^p. Moreover, the conjugate exponent q of $1 + \varepsilon$ satisfies $q = 1 + 1/\varepsilon \geqslant p$ since $\varepsilon \leqslant 1/(p-1)$. It follows that the integral $\int_\Omega U(x) \operatorname{div}\sigma(x)dx$ is also finite.

We have thus proved the first part of the theorem.

We will now show that S is surjective. Let f be in the dual $W^{-1+1/p',p'}(\partial\Omega)$ of $W^{1-1/p,p}(\partial\Omega)$. We define $\tilde{f}$ on $W^{1,p}(\Omega)$ by setting

$\langle \widetilde{f}, U \rangle = \langle f, \gamma_0 U \rangle$ for every U in this space. By the continuity of the trace map, we have

$$|\langle \widetilde{f}, U \rangle| \leqslant C\|\gamma_0 U\| \leqslant C'\|U\|_{W^{1,p}(\Omega)}.$$

It follows that $\widetilde{f}$ is an element of the dual $W^{1,p}(\Omega)'$. Consequently, using Proposition 3.47, we deduce that there exist $v_0 \in L^{p'}(\Omega)$ and $\sigma \in L^{p'}(\Omega)^N$ such that

$$\forall\, u \in W^{1-1/p,p}(\Omega), \quad \langle f, u \rangle = \int_\Omega v_0(x)U(x)dx + \int_\Omega \sigma(x) \cdot \nabla U(x)dx.$$

Moreover, it is clear, using functions $U \in \mathcal{D}(\Omega)$, that when U is in $W_0^{1,p}$, the quantity $\langle f, u \rangle$ vanishes. We therefore have $v_0 = \operatorname{div} \sigma$, which is equivalent to saying that $\sigma \in W_{p'}^{p'}(\operatorname{div})$ and $S(\sigma) = f$. The surjectivity follows. $\square$

Let us now study the density of regular functions in spaces of the type $W_{q'}^{p'}(\operatorname{div})$. This will allow us to interpret the elements of the duals defined above in the setting of an extension of Green's formula.

3.4.4 Density Results and an Extension of Green's Formula

We restrict ourselves to studying $W_{q'}^{p'}(\operatorname{div})(\Omega)$ when $p < N$, in which case we can easily see that $p' > q'$. We prove the following result, which uses simplified notation.

Proposition 3.57. *Let Ω be a class $\mathcal{C}^1$ open subset of $\mathbb{R}^N$. For p and q in $[1, \infty[$ with $p > q$, let*

$$W_q^p(\operatorname{div})(\Omega) = \{\sigma \in L^p(\Omega, \mathbb{R}^N) \mid \operatorname{div} \sigma \in L^q(\Omega)\};$$

then $\mathcal{D}(\overline{\Omega}, \mathbb{R}^N)$ is dense in $W_q^p(\operatorname{div})(\Omega)$.

Proof of Proposition 3.57.

Let $\sigma \in W_q^p(\operatorname{div})(\Omega)$. Let $\Omega_i, \varphi_i, \mathcal{O}_i', a_i$ be the elements occurring in the definition of the $\mathcal{C}^1$ regularity of Ω. The vector functions $v_i = \sigma \varphi_i$, which have bounded support in $\Delta_i = \Omega_i \cap \Omega$, belong to $W_q^p(\operatorname{div})(\Delta_i)$ because $p > q$.

Indeed, first of all, we have $\|v_i\|_p \leqslant |\varphi_i|_\infty \|\sigma\|_p$. Moreover, we have $\operatorname{div}(\sigma \varphi_i) = \varphi_i \operatorname{div} \sigma + \sigma \cdot \nabla \varphi_i$. The first term belongs to L^q. By applying Hölder's inequality with exponents $t = p/q > 1$ and $t' = t/(t-1)$ to the integral $\int_{\Delta_i} |\sigma \cdot \nabla \varphi_i|^q dx$, we also obtain the inclusion of the second term in L^q. We have thus reduced the problem to approximating $\sigma \varphi_i$ by functions in $\mathcal{D}(\overline{\Omega}, \mathbb{R}^N)$.

Each function $\varphi_i \sigma$ can be extended to the open set

$$U_i = \{(x', x_N) \mid x' \in \mathcal{O}_i', \ x_N > a_i(x')\},$$

after which $\varphi_i\sigma$ belongs to $W_q^p(\operatorname{div})(U_i)$. The open set U_i is star-convex with respect to one of its points, which we denote by x_i (cf. Exercise 3.9). Let us consider the function $x \mapsto h_\lambda(x) = x_i + \lambda(x - x_i)$.

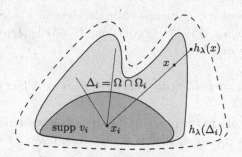

Fig. 3.2. Using star-convex open subsets of a Lipschitz cover.

If $\lambda > 1$, then the function $w_i^\lambda = \sigma\varphi_i \circ h_\lambda^{-1}$ is defined in $h_\lambda(\Delta_i)$, which is an open set containing the closure of Δ_i in its interior.

Using scaling on distributions (cf. [22, p. 103]), we have the equality $\partial_j(w_i^\lambda) = \frac{1}{\lambda}(\partial_j w_i) \circ h_\lambda^{-1}$ for every $j \in [1, N]$, and consequently $w_i^\lambda \in W_q^p(\operatorname{div})(h_\lambda(\Delta_i))$. Moreover, the restriction of w_i^λ to Δ_i converges to w_i when λ tends to 1.

Let $\varepsilon_i^\lambda = d(\partial\Omega, \partial(h_\lambda(\Delta_i))/2$, let $\Delta_i^\lambda = \{x \in h_\lambda(\Delta_i) \mid d(x, \partial\Omega) < \varepsilon_i^\lambda\}$, and let ρ be a regularizing function. The function $\rho_{\varepsilon_i^\lambda} \star w_i^\lambda$ is then well defined on Δ_i^λ and its restriction to Δ_i converges to w_i in $W_q^p(\operatorname{div})(\Delta_i)$ when λ tends to 1. If, for each Δ_i, we multiply $\rho_{\varepsilon_i^\lambda} \star w_i^\lambda$ by a function ψ_i^λ that belongs to $\mathcal{D}(\Delta_i^\lambda)$ and has value 1 on Δ_i, then the function $\sum_i \psi_i^\lambda(\rho_{\varepsilon_i^\lambda} \star w_i^\lambda)$ is a sequence in $\mathcal{D}(\mathbb{R}^N)$ that converges to σ in $W_q^p(\operatorname{div})(\Omega))$.

The same proof can be used when $p \geqslant N$. $\qquad\qquad\square$

Let us apply this density result to an extension of Green's formula.

Proposition 3.58. *Let Ω be a class $\mathcal{C}^1$ open subset of $\mathbb{R}^N$. For every $\tau \in E$, where $E = W_{q'}^p(\operatorname{div})$, $E = W_1^{p'}$, or $E = W_\varepsilon^{p'}$, depending on the value of p, we define the element $\tau \cdot \overrightarrow{n}$ of the topological dual of $W^{1-1/p,p}(\partial\Omega)$ to be the element satisfying*

$$\forall U \in W^{1,p}(\Omega), \quad \langle \tau \cdot \overrightarrow{n}, \gamma_0 U\rangle = \int_\Omega \tau(x) \cdot \nabla U(x)dx + \int_\Omega U(x)\operatorname{div}\tau(x)dx.$$

This formula is an extension of Green's formula because when $\tau \in \mathcal{D}(\overline{\Omega}, \mathbb{R}^N)$, the linear functional $\tau \cdot \overrightarrow{n}$ coincides with $U \mapsto \int_{\partial\Omega} \tau \cdot \overrightarrow{n}\gamma_0 U(\sigma)d\sigma$.

Finally, the map S on $W_{q'}^{p'}(\operatorname{div})$ defined by $S : \tau \mapsto \tau \cdot \overrightarrow{n}$ is surjective. Moreover, there exists a constant C such that if $f \in W^{-1+1/p',p'}(\partial\Omega)$, *then there exists a* $\tau \in W_{q'}^{p'}(\mathrm{div})(\Omega)$ *satisfying* $S(\tau) = f$ *and* $\|f\| \leqslant C\|\tau\|_{W_{q'}^{p'}(\mathrm{div})(\Omega)}$.

Proof of Proposition 3.58.

To a given element $\tau \in E$, we associate the element $T = S(\tau)$ of the dual of $W^{1-1/p,p}(\partial\Omega)$. When $u \in W^{1-1/p,p}(\partial\Omega)$ and $U \in W^{1,p}(\Omega)$ satisfies $\gamma_0 U = u$, we have (cf. Theorem 3.54),

$$\langle T, u \rangle = \int_\Omega U(x) \operatorname{div} \tau(x) dx + \int_\Omega \tau(x) \cdot \nabla U(x) dx.$$

In other words, thanks to the previous density result, we have a sequence $\{\varphi_k\}$ in $\mathcal{D}(\mathbb{R}^N, \mathbb{R}^N)$ that converges to τ in E. We then have

$$\langle S(\varphi_k), u \rangle = \int_\Omega U(x) \operatorname{div} \varphi_k(x) dx + \int_\Omega \varphi_k(x) \cdot \nabla U(x) dx.$$

By Green's formula (3.43), we have

$$\langle S(\varphi_k), u \rangle = \int_{\partial\Omega} \gamma_0 U(s)\, \varphi_k(s) \cdot \overrightarrow{n}(s) d\sigma(s) = \int_{\partial\Omega} u(s)\, \varphi_k(s) \cdot \overrightarrow{n}(s) d\sigma(s).$$

Now, as $U \in L^q(\Omega)$ and $\operatorname{div}(\tau - \varphi_k)$ tends to 0 in $L^{q'}(\Omega)$ when $k \to +\infty$, it follows that $\int_\Omega U(x) \operatorname{div} \varphi_k(x) dx \to \int_\Omega U(x) \operatorname{div} \tau(x) dx$. Likewise, we have $\int_\Omega \nabla U(x)\varphi_k(x) dx \to \int_\Omega \nabla U(x)\tau(x) dx$.

To φ_k, we associate the linear functional $\varphi_k \cdot \overrightarrow{n}$ on $W^{1-1/p,p}(\partial\Omega)$ defined by

$$\langle (\varphi_k \cdot \overrightarrow{n}), u \rangle = \int_{\partial\Omega} u(s)\, \varphi_k(s) \cdot \overrightarrow{n}(s) d\sigma(s).$$

By the above, this sequence converges in the dual of $W^{1-1/p,p}(\partial\Omega)$ to $S(\tau)$, which can therefore also be denoted by $\tau \cdot \overrightarrow{n}$.   □

Remark 3.59. It is clear that if, in addition to satisfying the conditions stated above, τ also belongs to $\mathcal{C}(\overline{\Omega}, \mathbb{R}^N)$, then $\tau \cdot \overrightarrow{n}$ coincides with its restriction to the boundary in the usual sense.

Corollary 3.60. *Consider a class* $\mathcal{C}^1$ *open set* Ω *and two functions* $U \in W^{1,p}(\Omega)$ *and* $V \in W^{1,q}(\Omega)$ *with exponents p and q satisfying* $1 \leqslant p < N$ *and* $1/p + 1/q = (N+1)/N$. *These two functions then satisfy Green's formula:*

$$\int_\Omega U \partial_i V dx + \int_\Omega V \partial_i U dx = \int_{\partial\Omega} \gamma_0 U \, \gamma_0 V n_i d\sigma.$$

Proof.

The proof follows from Theorem 3.54 because τ equals $V e_i$.   □

3.5 Higher Order Traces

3.5.1 Preliminary Remarks

Regularity Hypotheses on the Open Sets Ω. For $m > 1$, the term *higher order trace* of $u \in W^{m,p}(\Omega)$, for $m > 1$, refers to the trace of a derivative $D^\alpha u$ of order $|\alpha|$ with $0 \leqslant |\alpha| \leqslant m - 1$. We have seen the construction of the trace of an element u of $W^{1,p}(\Omega)$ in Chapter 2. This construction uses the existence of ∇u on the open set Ω and equality (2.89), which in local coordinates is

$$\text{for almost all } x' \in \mathcal{O}'_i, \quad \gamma_0(\varphi_i u)(x') = -\int_0^{+\infty} \partial_N(\varphi_i u)(x', a_i(x') + t)dt.$$

This relation is only well defined if the local boundary, given by $x' \mapsto a_i(x')$, is of class $\mathcal{C}^1$.

Derivatives on $\partial\Omega$. Let us first note that if $\Omega = \mathbb{R}^{N-1} \times]0, +\infty[$, then the derivatives on the boundary $\partial\Omega = \mathbb{R}^{N-1} \times \{0\}$ are the restrictions of the $N - 1$ first derivatives in $\mathbb{R}^N$. In that case, we have no trouble defining the derivatives in the sense of distributions on $\partial\Omega$ and, therefore, defining the Sobolev spaces $W^{m,p}(\partial\Omega)$.

The same cannot be said about the other cases, because the derivative with respect to the variable x_j of $x \in \mathbb{R}^N$, which is well defined in Ω, is, in general, no longer defined on the hypersurface $\partial\Omega$. The description of the derivatives in $\partial\Omega$ and the definition of the Sobolev spaces on $\partial\Omega$ are therefore no longer clear.

Let Ω_i, $\mathcal{O}'_i$, a_i be the objects that occur in the definition of the regularity of Ω. Recall that to define the induced Lebesgue measure μ_i on $\Omega_i \cap \partial\Omega$, we use the local coordinate systems from that definition. Gluing the pieces, we obtain the Lebesgue measure μ on $\partial\Omega$. We then show that this measure is unique and does not depend on the choice of local coordinate systems, allowing us to define the spaces $L^p(\partial\Omega)$. We used this same process to show that the trace $\gamma_0 U$ is indeed an element of $L^p(\partial\Omega)$, by considering limits of the integrals $\sum_i \int_{\mathcal{O}'_i} |U(x', a_i(x') + 1/n)|^p dx'$. We proceed in the same manner to define the traces of the derivatives $\partial_j U$ and the trace of ∇U. By extending the definition of a derivative with respect to a vector, we can then, using $\gamma_0 \nabla U$, define the derivatives with respect to the directions linked intrinsically to $\partial\Omega$, in particular, those along a tangent vector of $\partial\Omega$ or along the normal vector. Consequently, these derivatives are not defined, at least not directly, *in the sense of the distributions on $\partial\Omega$* (cf. [60]).

More precisely, let us assume that we are in the neighborhood of a point m_0 of $\partial\Omega$ that has a neighborhood V' where, in an orthonormal local coordinate system $\{e'_j\}$, the boundary is represented by the coordinates of the point m, that is $(x', x_N = a(x'))$ where a is a $\mathcal{C}^1$ function. The derivative of m with respect to x_j can be written as $e'_j + \partial_j a(x') e'_N$. Consequently, the vectors

$$\overrightarrow{t}_j = \frac{e'_j + \partial_j a(x') e'_N}{\sqrt{1 + |\nabla a(x')|^2}}$$

for $1 \leqslant j \leqslant N - 1$ form a basis of unit tangent vectors of $\partial\Omega$ at m. In general, it is not orthonormal.

For $1 \leqslant j \leqslant N - 1$, we can set

$$\partial_{\overrightarrow{t}_j}(\gamma_0 U)(x) = \gamma_0 \nabla U(x) \cdot \overrightarrow{t}_j(x) = \frac{\partial_j u + \partial_j a \partial_N u}{\sqrt{1 + |\nabla a(x')|^2}},$$

allowing us to define differentiation with respect to an arbitrary vector $\overrightarrow{t}$ of the tangent space $T_{N-1}(\partial\Omega)(x)$. A vector orthogonal to the tangent space can be written as

$$\frac{-\nabla a(x') + e_N}{\sqrt{1 + |\nabla a(x')|^2}}.$$

Therefore the normal derivative of u, that is, the derivative with respect to a vector orthogonal to the tangent space, can be written as

$$(3.61) \qquad \partial_{\overrightarrow{n}} u(x) = \frac{-\sum_1^{N-1} \partial_i a \partial_i u + \partial_N u}{\sqrt{1 + |\nabla a(x')|^2}}.$$

This derivative, which has already played an important role in Green's formula, is moreover essential to the formulation of the Neumann problems (cf. Chapter 5).

The generalization to derivatives of order higher than 1 demands the use of iterated operators $\nabla^{(k)}$, which are gradients of vector functions (see below).

Let us assume that we have determined the traces of U and of ∇U. In principle, we should obtain a better regularity for $\gamma_0 U$, which is an element of $W^{1-1/p,p}(\Omega)$, than for $\gamma_0 \nabla U$. Does this regularity translate to the inclusion in a subspace of $W^{1,p}(\partial\Omega)$, which would be a different fractional Sobolev space, thus generalizing the space $W^{1-1/p,p}(\partial\Omega)$?

We will devote part of this section to this question. In particular, if $k \geqslant 2$, we will see that the regularity behavior of $\gamma_0 U$ and $\gamma_0(\nabla u)$ is analogous to that of U and ∇U. Indeed, if $\gamma_0 U \in W^{k-1-1/p,p}(\partial\Omega)$, then $\gamma_0(\nabla U) \in W^{k-2-1/p,p}(\partial\Omega)$.

Notions from Differential Calculus. In what follows, the derivative $\nabla^{(k)}(u)(x)$, where k is an integer > 0, is the multilinear map whose components are the partial derivatives of order k of u at the point x. For example, for $k = 2$, consider the bilinear map $\nabla^{(2)} u(x)$, called the *Hessian* of u at x. The derivative

$\partial_{\vec{n}}^{(2)} u(x)$ is defined to be the image of the pair $(\vec{n}, \vec{n})$ under this map, that is, if the components of $\vec{n}$ are $\{n_j\}$, then

$$\nabla^{(2)} u(x) \cdot \vec{n} \cdot \vec{n} = \sum_{i+j=2} \partial_{ij} u(x) n_i n_j.$$

For α of order $|\alpha| = k$, setting $\vec{n}^{(\alpha)} = n_1^{\alpha_1} n_2^{\alpha_2} \cdots n_N^{\alpha_N}$, we generalize this to

$$\partial_{\vec{n}}^{(k)} u(x) = \sum_{|\alpha|=k} \frac{k!}{\alpha!} D^\alpha u(x) \cdot \vec{n}^\alpha.$$

When $\vec{t}$ is a tangent vector, we define the derivatives $\partial_{\vec{t}}^{(k)}$ likewise.

Exercise 3.14 concerns the computations of such derivatives when $\partial\Omega$ is a cylinder or a sphere.

3.5.2 Generalization of Liftings

To highlight the properties of traces of order greater than or equal to 1, we introduce a lifting of u that is better adapted to problems concerning higher orders than the one we used up to now.

Proposition 3.62. *Let $\rho \in \mathcal{D}(\mathbb{R}^N)$ and let $\rho_y(z) = 1/y^N \rho(z/y)$. To every $u \in W^{1-1/p,p}(\mathbb{R}^N)$, we associate the function $(x,y) \mapsto U(x,y) = \rho_y \star u$; then $U \in W^{1,p}(\mathbb{R}^N \times \,]0,1[)$ and $\gamma_0 U = \alpha u$, where $\alpha = \int_{\mathbb{R}^N} \rho(x) dx$.*

Moreover, there exists a constant C depending only on N and p, such that

$$\forall u \in W^{1-1/p,p}(\mathbb{R}^N), \quad \|\rho_y \star u\|_{W^{1,p}(\mathbb{R}^N \times]0,1[)} \leqslant C\|u\|_{W^{1-1/p,p}(\mathbb{R}^N)}.$$

Proof of Proposition 3.62.

By the properties of a convolution and the equality $\int \partial_i \rho(t) \, dt = 0$, we have

$$\partial_i U = \frac{1}{y} (\partial_i \rho)_y \star u = \int (\partial_i \rho(t)) \left(\frac{u(x-yt) - u(x)}{y} \right) dt.$$

Let us show that this derivative belongs to $L^p(\mathbb{R}^N \times \,]0,1[)$.

We use the method from the proof of Lemma 3.27. This consists in giving an upper bound for the integral

$$I = \int_0^1 \int_{\mathbb{R}^N} \left| \int_{t \in \text{supp}\,\rho} (\partial_i \rho(t)) \left(\frac{u(x-yt) - u(x)}{y} \right) dt \right|^p dx \, dy.$$

Let $\widehat{x_j} = x - y\left(\sum_1^j t_s e_s\right)$ for $1 \leqslant j \leqslant N-1$, $\widehat{x_0} = x$, and $\widehat{x_N} = x - yt$, so that

$$|u(x) - u(x-yt)| \leqslant \sum_0^{N-1} |u(\widehat{x_j}) - u(\widehat{x_{j+1}})|.$$

We first use the discrete version of Hölder's inequality, $|\sum_0^{N-1} a_i|^p \leqslant N^{p-1} \sum_0^{N-1} |a_i|^p$, and then give an upper bound for each of the integrals of the type above using Hölder's inequality, replacing the difference $u(x - yt) - u(x)$ by $u(\widehat{x_j}) - u(\widehat{x_{j+1}})$. We can then write $I \leqslant C \sum_0^{N-1} I_j$, where the integrals I_j are of the form

$$I_j = \int_0^1 \int_{\mathbb{R}^N} \left[\int_{t \in \text{supp}\, \rho} \left| \frac{u(\widehat{x_j}) - u(\widehat{x_{j+1}})}{y} \right|^p dt\, dx\, dy \right.$$

Let us determine the partial integral of the first term I_0 with respect to the variable y. Substituting the variable z_1 defined by $yt_1 = z_1$, this partial integral can be written as

$$\int_0^1 \left| \frac{u(x) - u(x - yt_1 e_1)}{y} \right|^p dy = t_1^{p-1} \int_0^{t_1} \left| \frac{u(x) - u(x - z_1 e_1)}{z_1} \right|^p dz_1.$$

Since the domain of integration of the variables t_j is bounded in $\mathbb{R}^N$ by the bounds of the support of ρ, in particular $|t_1| \leqslant K_1$, we obtain the existence of constants C_0' and C_0 such that

$$I_0 \leqslant C_0' \int_{t \in \text{supp}\, \rho} \int_{\mathbb{R}^N} \int_{-K_1}^{K_1} \left| \frac{u(x) - u(x - z_1 e_1)}{z_1} \right|^p dx\, dz_1 dt$$

$$\leqslant C_0 \int_{\mathbb{R}^N} \int_{\mathbb{R}} \left| \frac{u(x) - u(x - z_1 e_1)}{z_1} \right|^p dz_1 dx \leqslant C_0 \|u\|_{1,1-1/p}^p < +\infty.$$

The last inequality follows from Lemma 3.27, using the hypothesis $u \in W^{1-1/p,p}(\mathbb{R}^N)$. We have thus shown that I_0 is finite.

Consider the integral I_j. By setting $x' = \widehat{x_j}$, it becomes

$$I_j = \int_0^1 \int_{\mathbb{R}^N} \left[\int_{t \in \text{supp}\, \rho} \left| \frac{u(\widehat{x'}) - u(x' - yt_{j+1} e_{j+1})}{y} \right|^p dt\, dx\, dy \right.$$

Substituting the variable $z_{j+1} = yt_{j+1}$ in the partial integral with respect to y and applying Lemma 3.27, we obtain

$$I_j = \int_0^1 \int_{\mathbb{R}^N} \left[\int_{t \in \text{supp}\, \rho} \left| \frac{u(x') - u(x' - yt_{j+1} e_{j+1})}{y} \right|^p dt\, dx\, dy \right.$$

$$\leqslant C_j' \int_{\mathbb{R}^N} \int_{-K_{j+1}}^{K_{j+1}} \left| \frac{u(x') - u(x' - z_{j+1} e_{j+1})}{z_{j+1}} \right|^p dz_{j+1} dx$$

$$\leqslant C_j \|u\|_{j+1,1-1/p}^p < +\infty.$$

We can now conclude that all the derivatives $\partial_i U$ belong to $L^p(\mathbb{R}^N \times\,]0, 1[)$.

To give the derivative with respect to y explicitly, we assume that $u \in \mathcal{D}(\mathbb{R}^N)$. Setting $\tilde{u}_t(x, y) = u(x - yt)$ and $\zeta_j(t) = t_j \rho(t)$, we can write

$$\partial_y U(x, y) = \frac{1}{y} \sum_1^N \int_{\mathbb{R}^N} \zeta_j \partial_{t_j} \tilde{u}_t dt = -\frac{1}{y} \sum_1^N \int_{\mathbb{R}^N} \partial_j(\zeta_j)(t) u(x - yt) dt$$

(3.63)

$$= \sum_1^N \int_{\mathbb{R}^N} \partial_j(\zeta_j)(t) \left[\frac{u(x) - u(x - yt)}{y} \right] dt.$$

For u in $W^{1-1/p,p}(\mathbb{R}^N)$, let $\{u_n\}$ be a sequence in $\mathcal{D}(\mathbb{R}^N)$ that converges to u in $W^{1-1/p,p}(\mathbb{R}^N)$. It is clear that the sequence U_n defined by $U_n = \rho_y \star u_n$ converges, for example in L^p, to $U = \rho_y \star u$. Moreover, $\{\partial_y U_n\}$ is a Cauchy sequence in L^p, as is the sequence $\{\partial_x U_n\}$, thanks to their expressions as functions of u_n. Taking the limit, we find that because of identities between functions in L^p,

(3.64) $$\partial_y U(x, y) = \sum_1^N \int_{\mathbb{R}^N} \partial_j(\zeta_j)(t) \left[\frac{u(x) - u(x - yt)}{y} \right] dt$$

still holds for almost all (x, y).

Beginning with this formula, the computations are analogous to those concerning the derivatives $\partial_j U$. Thanks to Lemma 3.27, they give a well-defined result. We have thus obtained the inclusion $U \in W^{1,p}(\mathbb{R}^N \times]0, 1[)$. Moreover, the different upper bounds imply the existence of a constant C depending only on ρ, N, p, such that

$$\|U\|_{W^{1,p}(\mathbb{R}^N \times]0,1[)} \leqslant C\|u\|_{1-1/p,p} \leqslant C\|u\|_{W^{1-1/p,p}(\mathbb{R}^N)}. \qquad \square$$

To generalize this proposition, we need to define new spaces.

3.5.3 Fractional Sobolev Spaces with Higher Order Derivatives

The definition of $W^{2-1/p,p}(\mathbb{R}^N)$ can be obtained by generalizing that of $W^{1-1/p,p}(\mathbb{R}^N)$. More precisely, we replace the inclusion $u \in L^p(\mathbb{R}^N)$ by $u \in W^{1-1/p,p}(\mathbb{R}^N)$ and replace u by the derivatives $\partial_i u$ in the seminorm

$$\|u\|' = \left[\int_{\mathbb{R}^{2N}} \frac{|u(x) - u(y)|^p}{|x - y|^{p+N-2}} dx\, dy \right]^{1/p}.$$

We continue this extension for a class $\mathcal{C}^m$ open subset Ω of $\mathbb{R}^N$ by considering tangential derivatives, that is, derivatives with respect to vectors $\overrightarrow{t}$ of the space $T_{N-1}(x)$, which is tangent to $\partial\Omega$ at x.

Definition 3.65. For $f \in \mathcal{C}^m(\overline{\Omega})$ and a tangent vector $\overrightarrow{t}$ of $\partial\Omega$ at x, we set

$$\forall j \leqslant m, \quad \partial_{\overrightarrow{t}}^{(j)} f(x) = \nabla^{(j)} f(x) \cdot \overrightarrow{t} \cdots \overrightarrow{t}.$$

(1) Let Ω be a class $\mathcal{C}^k$ open set with $k \geqslant 1$ and let $1 < p < \infty$. We can write the seminorm, denoted by $\|\cdot\|'_{k-1,p,N}$, explicitly as follows:

$$\|u\|'_{k-1,p,N} = \left(\int_{\partial\Omega} \int_{\partial\Omega} \frac{|\partial_{\overrightarrow{t}}^{(k-1)} u(x) - \partial_{\overrightarrow{t}}^{(k-1)} u(y)|^p}{|x-y|^{p+N-2}} d\sigma(x) d\sigma(y) \right)^{1/p}.$$

(2) The space $W^{k-1/p,p}(\partial\Omega)$ is defined by

$$W^{k-1/p,p}(\partial\Omega) = \{ u \in W^{k-1,p}(\partial\Omega) \mid \forall \overrightarrow{t} \in T_{N-1}, \, \|u\|'_{k-1,p,N} < \infty \}$$
$$= \{ u \in W^{k-1,p}(\partial\Omega) \mid \forall \overrightarrow{t} \in T_{N-1},$$
$$\partial_{\overrightarrow{t}}^{k-1} u \in W^{1-1/p,p}(\partial\Omega) \}.$$

Remark 3.66. When $\Omega = \mathbb{R}^N \times \,]0,+\infty[$, this corresponds to the space $W^{k-1/p,p}(\mathbb{R}^N)$ defined before. For an element u, the partial derivatives $\partial_i u$ with respect to the N variables x_i of $\mathbb{R}^N$ belong to $W^{k-1-1/p,p}(\mathbb{R}^N)$.

Theorem 3.67. *Under the assumptions of the definition above, we have*

$$W^{k-1/p,p}(\partial\Omega) = \gamma_0(W^{k,p}(\Omega)).$$

We begin by giving the proof for $N = 2$ and $\Omega = \mathbb{R} \times \,]0,+\infty[$. For this, we propose to use the lifting used at the beginning of the chapter (cf. (3.10)). This lifting, which works well in dimension 1, is not suitable for higher dimensions. This is why, in the general case $N \geqslant 2$, we will use the *regularizing* lifting introduced in Proposition 3.62 (cf. Remark 3.24).

The difference between the two liftings is as follows. In the first case, we take the convolution with the characteristic function of a product of intervals. In the second case, the convolution is with a $\mathcal{C}^\infty$ function with compact support, which allows us to derive more easily at an arbitrary order and to use induction. In Exercise 3.12, we propose to prove the theorem for $N = 3$ and $\Omega = \mathbb{R}^2 \times \,]0,+\infty[$ using a lifting where the convolution is with a characteristic function.

Let us also note that for $\Omega = \mathbb{R}^{N-1} \times \,]0,+\infty[$, when $N = 1$, the tangential derivative is the derivative with respect to x in $\mathbb{R}$ and when $N \geqslant 2$, the tangential derivatives are the derivatives $\partial_i u$ with respect to the coordinates x_i in $\mathbb{R}^{N-1}$.

Proof of Theorem 3.67 for $\Omega = \mathbb{R} \times \mathbb{R}^+$.
   We begin by showing that

$$\gamma_0(W^{k,p}(\mathbb{R} \times \mathbb{R}^+)) \hookrightarrow W^{k-1/p,p}(\mathbb{R}).$$

Let us note that this proof does not require that the dimension is 2 and can therefore be generalized.

We use the *commutativity* of differentiation with respect to x and restriction to $\{y = 0\}$. We also use induction on k. If $k = 1$, we know the result. Assuming the result proved for $k - 1$, suppose that $u \in W^{k,p}(\mathbb{R} \times \mathbb{R}^+)$. Then $\partial_x u \in W^{k-1,p}(\mathbb{R} \times \mathbb{R}^+)$, hence by the induction hypothesis, $\partial_x u(x, 0) \in W^{k-1-1/p}(\mathbb{R})$, which means that $\partial_x u(x, 0) \in W^{k-2,p}(\mathbb{R})$ and $(\partial_x u)^{(k-2)}(\cdot, 0) \in W^{1-1/p,p}(\mathbb{R})$. This implies that $u(\cdot, 0) \in W^{k-1-1/p,p}(\mathbb{R})$.

Consider the converse.

Since the property is clear for $k = 1$, we suppose that $k \geqslant 2$. Let $u \in W^{k-1/p,p}(\mathbb{R})$ satisfy $\|u\|'_{k-1,p,2} < \infty$. We define the lifting U by setting

$$\forall x \in \mathbb{R}, \, \forall y > 0, \quad U(x, y) = \frac{1}{y} \int_0^y u(x + z) dz.$$

We will show that $U \in W^{k,p}(\mathbb{R} \times \,]0, 1[)$ and $U(x, 0) = u(x)$.

The proof once again uses induction on k. We therefore assume proved that for all j with $1 \leqslant j \leqslant k - 1$,

$$(3.68) \qquad u \in W^{j-1/p,p}(\mathbb{R}) \implies U \in W^{j,p}(\mathbb{R} \times \,]0, 1[).$$

By assumption, $u \in W^{k-1/p,p}(\mathbb{R})$; hence by Definition 3.65, $\partial_x u \in W^{k-2,p}(\mathbb{R})$ and $\|\partial_x u\|'_{k-2,p} < +\infty$. Consequently, we have $\partial_x u \in W^{k-1-1/p,p}(\mathbb{R})$. Using the formula of the lifting, and the induction hypothesis (3.68), we deduce that

$$\partial_x U \in W^{k-1,p}(\mathbb{R} \times \,]0, 1[).$$

We now only need to prove that

$$(3.69) \qquad \partial_y^k U \in L^p(\mathbb{R} \times \,]0, 1[).$$

To prove this, let us first use induction to show the following formula, where $K_k = k!(-1)^{k+1}/y^{k+1}$:

$$(3.70) \quad \partial_y^k U(x, y) = K_k \int_0^y \left(u(x+z) - u(x+y) - \sum_1^{k-1} \frac{(z-y)^j}{j!} u^{(j)}(x+y) \right) dz.$$

We assume this result, which is true for $k = 1$, established for $\partial_y^{k-1} U$. Since the function U can be written as $U(x, y) = \int_0^1 u(x + zy) dz$, differentiating it gives

$$\partial_y^{(k)} U(x, y) = \int_0^1 z^k u^{(k)}(x + zy) dz.$$

Integrating by parts then gives

$$
\partial_y^k U(x,y) = \left[\frac{z^k u^{(k-1)}(x+zy)}{y}\right]_0^1 - k\int_0^1 z^{k-1}\frac{u^{(k-1)}(x+zy)}{y}dy
$$

$$
= \frac{u^{(k-1)}(x+y)}{y} - k\frac{1}{y}\partial_y^{k-1}U(x,y)
$$

$$
= -\frac{k(-1)^{k+1}}{y^{k+1}}\int_0^y (z-y)^{k-1}u^{(k-1)}(x+y)dz - k\frac{1}{y}\partial_y^{(k-1)}U(x,y).
$$

By the induction hypothesis (3.70) for the exponent $k-1$, we see that $\partial_y^k U(x,y)$ can be written as

$$
-\frac{kK_{k-1}}{y}\int_0^y \left(u(x+z) - u(x+y) - \sum_{1\leqslant j\leqslant k-2}\frac{(z-y)^j u^{(j)}(x+y)}{j!}\right)dz
$$

$$
-\frac{k(-1)^{k+1}}{y^{k+1}}\int_0^y (z-y)^{k-1}u^{(k-1)}(x+y)dz
$$

$$
= \check{K}_k\int_0^y \left(u(x+z) - u(x+y) - \sum_{1\leqslant j\leqslant k-1}\frac{(z-y)^j u^{(j)}(x+y)}{j!}\right)dz.
$$

Formula (3.70) follows.

For the rest of the proof, let us set

$$
(3.71)\quad A_k(u)(x,y,z) = (u(x+z) - u(x+y) - \sum_1^{k-1}\frac{(z-y)^j}{j!}u^{(j)}(x+y)).
$$

We note that

$$
\partial_z^{k-1}A_k(u)(x,y,z) = u^{(k-1)}(x+z) - u^{(k-1)}(x+y),
$$

and that $A_k(u)(x,y,y) = \partial_z^j A_k(u)(x,y,y) = 0$ for every index j satisfying $j \leqslant k-1$. Integrating $k-1$ times, we deduce the relation

$$
(3.72)\quad A_k(u)(x,y,z)
$$

$$
= \int_y^z \int_y^{t_2} \cdots \int_y^{t_{k-1}} \left(u^{(k-1)}(x+t_k) - u^{(k-1)}(x+y)\right)dt_k\cdots dt_2.
$$

Using homotheties on the variables, we can write the right-hand side of the relation as

$$
y^{k-1}\int_1^{z/y} \cdots \int_1^{t_{k-1}} \left(u^{(k-1)}(x+t_k y) - u^{(k-1)}(x+y)\right)dt_k dt_{k-1}\cdots dt_2.
$$

Fixing y, we apply the change of variables $z = yt_1$ in the integral $K_k \int_0^y A_k(x, y, z)dz$, giving

$$K_k \int_0^y A_k(u)(x, y, z)dz = K_k y \int_0^1 A_k(x, y, t_1 y)dt_1$$

$$= K_k y^k \int_0^1 \int_1^{t_1} \cdots \int_1^{t_{k-1}} \left(u^{(k-1)}(x + t_k y) - u^{(k-1)}(x + y) \right) dt_k dt_{k-1} \cdots dt_1$$

$$= K_k' \int_0^1 \int_1^{t_1} \cdots \int_1^{t_{k-1}} \left(u^{(k-1)}(x + t_k y) - u^{(k-1)}(x + y) \right) dt_k dt_{k-1} \cdots dt_1,$$

where $K_k' = (-1)^{k-1}k!/(ky)$. We can bound the norm $\|\cdot\|_{L^p(\mathbb{R}\times]0,1[)}^p$ of the function $\partial_y^{(k)}U$, which satisfies $\partial_y^{(k)}U(x, y) = K_k \int_0^y A_k(u)(x, y, z)dz$, from above by

$$\int_0^1 \int_{\mathbb{R}} \left[\int_0^1 \int_{t_1}^1 \cdots \int_{t_{k-1}}^1 \left| \frac{u^{(k-1)}(x + t_k y) - u^{(k-1)}(x + y)}{y} \right|^p dt_k \cdots dt_1 \right] dx\, dy.$$

We apply the change of variables $(x, y) \mapsto (X, Y) = (x + y, x + t_k y)$ with Jacobian $1 - t_k$. The denominator can then be written as $y = (X - Y)/(1 - t_k)$ and the domain of integration becomes $\{X > Y\}$. Exchanging x and y, we obtain the previous upper bound with domain $\{Y > X\}$. Using Fubini's formula and the inequality $(1 - t_k)^{p-1} \leqslant 1$, we obtain

$$\|\partial_y^{(k)}U\|_{L^p(\mathbb{R}\times]0,1[)}^p$$

$$\leqslant \int_0^1 \cdots \int_{t_{k-1}}^1 \int_{\mathbb{R}} \int_{\mathbb{R}} (1 - t_k)^{p-1} \left| \frac{u^{(k-1)}(X) - u^{(k-1)}(Y)}{(X - Y)} \right|^p dX\, dY\, dt_1 \cdots dt_k$$

$$\leqslant \int_{\mathbb{R}} \int_{\mathbb{R}} \left| \frac{u^{(k-1)}(X) - u^{(k-1)}(Y)}{(X - Y)} \right|^p dX\, dY$$

$$\leqslant \|u^{(k-1)}\|_{k-1,p,2}^{'p} < +\infty.$$

Summarizing, we have shown that $\partial_y^{(k)}U \in L^p(\mathbb{R}\times]0,1[)$, concluding the proof of (3.69), and therefore the proof of the theorem for $N = 2$.   □

We continue for $N > 2$ with results concerning the new lifting, starting with a theorem generalizing Proposition 3.62, which in fact completes the proof of Theorem 3.67.

Theorem 3.73. *Let $\rho \in \mathcal{D}(\mathbb{R}^N)$ and, as above, let $\rho_y(z) = (1/y^N)\rho(z/y)$. To a function u in $W^{k-1/p,p}(\mathbb{R}^N)$, we associate the function U defined by $U(x, y) = \rho_y \star u$. The following hold:*

(1) *We have $U \in W^{k,p}(\mathbb{R}^N \times]0,1[)$.*

(2) *If, moreover,*

$$\forall s = \{s_i\}, \quad 0 < |s| \leqslant k-1, \quad \text{we have} \quad \int_{\mathbb{R}^N} \vec{t^s} \rho(t) dt = 0,$$

where $\vec{t^s} = \Pi_i(t_i^{s_i})$, *then the trace of U satisfies*

(3.74) $U(x,0) = \left(\int_{\mathbb{R}^N} \rho(t) dt \right) u(x) \quad \text{and} \quad \forall j \in [1, k-1], \quad \partial_y^j U(x,0) = 0.$

Remark 3.75. The existence of such a function ρ can be shown, for example, using a function $\varphi \in \mathcal{D}(\mathbb{R})$ such that for every integer ℓ satisfying $0 < \ell \leqslant k-1$, we have $\int_{\mathbb{R}} \varphi(t) t^\ell dt = \delta_0^\ell$. The existence of such a function φ is the aim of Exercise 3.8.

It is now easy to see that $\rho(t) = \Pi_1^N \varphi(t_j)$ satisfies the condition stated above.

Proof of Theorem 3.73.

We make the following induction hypothesis on k:

$$\forall \rho \in \mathcal{D}(\mathbb{R}^N), \quad u \in W^{k-1/p,p}(\mathbb{R}^N) \Longrightarrow \rho_y \star u \in W^{k,p}(\mathbb{R}^N \times \,]0,1[).$$

For $k = 1$, this is Proposition 3.62.

Let us assume the theorem proved up to rank $k-1$. Let $u \in W^{k-1/p,p}(\mathbb{R}^N)$ with $k \geqslant 2$. By the induction hypothesis, we already know that $U(x,y) = \rho_y \star u \in W^{k-1,p}(\mathbb{R}^N \times \,]0,1[)$.

By Remark 3.66, we know that $\partial_i u \in W^{k-1-1/p,p}(\mathbb{R}^N)$, where $k-1 \geqslant 1$. We can therefore compute $\partial_i U = \rho_y \star \partial_i u$ as a convolution of functions. The induction hypothesis gives $\partial_i U \in W^{k-1,p}(\mathbb{R}^N \times \,]0,1[)$. In order to obtain the conclusion that $U \in W^{k,p}(\mathbb{R}^N \times \,]0,1[)$, it now suffices to prove that $\partial_y U \in W^{k-1,p}(\mathbb{R}^N \times \,]0,1[)$.

For this derivative, we traditionally have

$$\partial_y U(x,y) = \sum_1^N \int \rho(t)(-t_i)\partial_i u(x-yt).$$

Setting $\zeta_i(t) = t_i \rho(t)$, an arbitrary term of the sum can be written as

$$-\int_{\mathbb{R}^N} \zeta_i(z/y)\partial_i u(x-z) dz = -(\zeta_i)_y \star \partial_i u.$$

By the induction hypothesis, as $\zeta_i \in \mathcal{D}(\mathbb{R}^N)$ and $\partial_i u \in W^{k-1-1/p,p}(\mathbb{R}^N)$, we deduce that each of these terms belongs to $W^{k-1,p}(\mathbb{R}^N \times \,]0,1[)$, giving the conclusion for $\partial_y U$. We have thus proved that $U \in W^{k,p}(\mathbb{R}^N \times \,]0,1[)$.

It remains to see that $\partial_y^\ell U(x,0) = 0$ for $\ell \leqslant k-1$. To illustrate the ideas behind our method, we first consider the case $\ell = 1$. We have

$\partial_y U(x,y) = \sum_i \int_{\mathbb{R}^N} \zeta_i(t)\partial_i u(x - yt)dt$. Moreover, as $\partial_i u \in W^{1-1/p,p}$, using the equalities $\int_{\mathbb{R}^N} \rho(t)t_j dt = 0$ for every $j \in [1, N]$, Proposition 3.62 tells us that $\partial_y U(x,0) = 0$.

Let us now assume that $\ell > 1$ with $\ell \leqslant k - 1$. Since the convolution can be differentiated up to order $k - 1$, we deduce the following formula by differentiating the function u:

$$\partial_y^\ell U(x,y) = \sum_{|s|=\ell} C_j^s \int_{\mathbb{R}^N} \rho(\vec{t})D^s u(x - y\,\vec{t})\cdot(\vec{t^s})dt.$$

It follows that $\partial_y^\ell U(x,0)$ is a sum of terms $\int_{\mathbb{R}^N} \rho(t)\vec{t^s}\,dt\, D^s u(x)$ that are all zero for the chosen ρ because $s \neq 0$ and $|s| \leqslant k - 1$. $\square$

The next two propositions specify the previous liftings so that they satisfy boundary conditions. These conditions are related to Neumann conditions, as they concern derivatives.

Proposition 3.76. *Let $k \geqslant 1$; then for every $u \in W^{1-1/p,p}(\mathbb{R}^N)$ and for every $\rho \in \mathcal{D}(\mathbb{R}^N)$, the function V defined by $V(x,y) = (y^{k-1}/(k-1)!)\rho_y \star u(x)$ has the following properties:*

$$V \in W^{k,p}(\mathbb{R}^N \times \,]0,1[), \quad \partial_y^{k-1}V(x,0) = u(x)\int_{\mathbb{R}^N} \rho(t)dt,$$

and $\forall \ell \leqslant k - 2, \quad \partial_y^\ell V(x,0) = 0.$

Proof of Proposition 3.76.

We use induction on k.

When $k = 1$, this is Proposition 3.62. We assume that the result is true at the exponent $k - 1$. Let

$$V(x,y) = \frac{y^{k-1}}{(k-1)!}\rho_y \star u = y\frac{y^{k-2}}{(k-1)!}\rho_y \star u = yv,$$

where $v \in W^{k-1,p}(\mathbb{R}^N \times \,]0,1[)$ by the induction hypothesis.

Let α be a differentiation index satisfying $|\alpha| = k - 1$.

- If $\alpha_N = 0$, then we have $D^\alpha(yv) = yD^\alpha v \in L^p(\mathbb{R}^N \times \,]0,1[)$.
- If $\alpha_N = j > 0$, then the Leibniz formula gives

$$D_y^j D^{\alpha'}(yv) = yD_y^j D^{\alpha'}(v) + jD_y^{j-1}D^{\alpha'}(v),$$

which also proves that this derivative is in $L^p(\mathbb{R}^N \times\,]0,1[)$ because $j+|\alpha'| = k - 1$. We conclude that $V \in W^{k-1,p}(\mathbb{R}^N \times \,]0,1[)$.

From here on, we use the notation $\widetilde{u}_{x,y}(t) = u(x - yt)$, giving

$$\partial_{x_j}\widetilde{u}_{x,y}(t) = -\frac{1}{y}\partial_{t_j}\widetilde{u}_{x,y}(t).$$

Following the method of Proposition 3.62 (cf. relations (3.63) and (3.64)), that is, integrating the term $\int_{\mathbb{R}^N} \rho(t)\partial_{t_j}u(x - yt)dt$ by parts, we find that

$$\partial_j V(x,y) = \frac{y^{k-1}}{(k-1)!}\rho_y \star \partial_j u = \frac{-y^{k-2}}{(k-1)!}\int_{\mathbb{R}^N}\rho(t)\partial_{t_j}\widetilde{u}_{x,y}$$

$$= \frac{y^{k-2}}{(k-1)!}(\partial_j\rho)_y \star u.$$

Since the function $(\partial_j\rho)_y$ belongs to $\mathcal{D}(\mathbb{R}^N)$ and u belongs to $W^{1-1/p,p}(\mathbb{R}^N)$, the induction hypothesis implies that $\partial_j V \in W^{k-1,p}(\mathbb{R}^N \times]0,1[)$. We still need to prove the same property for $\partial_y V$. We once more use the process described in the relations (3.63) and (3.64). This gives

$$\partial_y V(x,y) = \frac{y^{k-2}}{(k-2)!}\rho_y \star u + \frac{y^{k-1}}{(k-1)!}\sum_1^N \left[\rho_y \star (-t_j\partial_j u)\right]$$

$$= \frac{y^{k-2}}{(k-2)!}\rho_y \star u - \frac{y^{k-2}}{(k-1)!}\sum_1^N \int_{\mathbb{R}^N} t_j\rho(t)\partial_{t_j}u(x - yt)dt$$

$$= \frac{y^{k-2}}{(k-2)!}\rho_y \star u - \frac{y^{k-2}}{(k-1)!}\sum_1^N \int_{\mathbb{R}^N} -\partial_j(t_j\rho(t))u(x - yt)dt,$$

whence

$$(3.77) \qquad \partial_y V(x,y) = \frac{y^{k-2}}{(k-2)!}\rho_y \star u + \frac{y^{k-2}}{(k-1)!}\sum_1^N \left[(\eta_j)_y \star u\right].$$

The left-hand side belongs to $W^{k-1,p}(\mathbb{R}^N \times]0,1[)$. All the terms on the right-hand side also do, thanks to the induction hypothesis applied to the functions $\eta_j = \partial_j(t_j\rho)$, which belong to $\mathcal{D}(\mathbb{R}^N)$.

To summarize, we have shown that $V \in W^{k,p}(\mathbb{R}^N \times]0,1[)$.

The relations at the boundary are obvious. Indeed, for $y = 0$, the Leibniz formula applied to the derivative of order $k - 1$ in y implies that all terms vanish except for one, namely,

$$\partial_y^{k-1}\left(\frac{y^{k-1}}{(k-1)!}\right)[\rho_y \star u]_{y=0} = u(x)\int_{\mathbb{R}^N}\rho(t)dt. \qquad \square$$

Proposition 3.78. *Let* $u \in W^{j-1/p,p}(\mathbb{R}^N)$. *For* $k \geqslant 0$, *set*

$$U(x,y) = \frac{y^k}{k!} \rho_y \star u,$$

where ρ *satisfies*

$$\forall s, \quad |s| \in [1, j-1] \Longrightarrow \int_{\mathbb{R}^N} \rho(t) \vec{t^s} \, dt = 0.$$

We then have:

(1) *The function* U *belongs to* $W^{k+j,p}(\mathbb{R}^N \times \,]0,1[)$. *Its norm in this space is controlled by that of* u *in* $W^{j-1/p,p}(\mathbb{R}^N)$.

(2) *The traces of* U *satisfy*

$$\partial_y^k U(x,0) = u(x) \int_{\mathbb{R}^N} \rho(t) dt,$$

$$\forall \ell \in [0, k+j-1], \quad \ell \neq k \Longrightarrow \partial_y^\ell U(x,0) = 0.$$

Proof of Proposition 3.78.

Part of the proof is by induction on k. We begin by noting that if $|\alpha| = j-1$ and $\alpha_N = 0$, then we have $D^\alpha u \in W^{1-1/p,p}(\mathbb{R}^N)$. Hence, by the previous proposition,

$$D^\alpha U = \frac{y^k}{k!} \rho_y \star D^\alpha u \in W^{k+1,p}(\mathbb{R}^N),$$

which implies that all the derivatives other than $\partial_y^{k+j} U$ are in L^p. It remains to prove that $\partial_y^{k+j} U$ is in $L^p(\mathbb{R}^N \times \,]0,1[)$. Now,

$$\partial_y U = \frac{y^{k-1}}{(k-1)!} \rho_y \star u + \frac{y^{k-1}}{k!} \sum (\eta_j)_y \star u.$$

Since the recursion hypothesis tells us that $\partial_y U \in W^{k+j-1,p}(\mathbb{R}^N \times \,]0,1[)$, we can deduce that $U \in W^{k+j,p}(\mathbb{R}^N \times \,]0,1[)$. This proves the first statement.

The previous computations show that, up to a constant, the norm of U in $W^{j+k,p}(\mathbb{R}^N \times \,]0,1[)$ is bounded from above by that of u in $W^{j-1/p,p}(\mathbb{R}^N)$. For the boundary conditions, we first note that, by the Leibniz formula, we have $\partial_y^\ell U(x,0) = 0$ for every l satisfying $l < k$ and $\partial_y^k U(x,0) = \left(\int_{\mathbb{R}^N} \rho(t) dt \right) u(x)$.

For the exponents l satisfying $k < l \leqslant k + j - 1$, we once more give a proof by recursion on k, for fixed j. For $k = 0$, this is Theorem 3.73, where k is replaced by j. We assume the proposition proved for j and $k-1$, that is, if $U(x,y) = (y^{k-1}/((k-1)!)) \rho_y \star u$, then U is in $W^{k+j-1,p}(\mathbb{R}^N \times \,]0,1[)$ and satisfies

$$\forall \ell \leqslant k+j-2, \quad \partial_y^\ell U(x,0) = \delta_l^{k-1} \left(\int_{\mathbb{R}^N} \rho(t) dt \right) u(x).$$

Let $V(x, y) = (y^k/k!)\rho_y \star u$. Once more setting $\eta_j = \partial_j(t_j\rho)$ and using previous computations (cf. relation (3.77) and the ones following it), the derivative with respect to y can be written as

$$\partial_y V = \frac{y^{k-1}}{(k-1)!}\rho_y \star u + \frac{y^{k-1}}{k!}\sum_1^N [(\eta_j)_y \star u] = V_1 + V_2.$$

By the recursion hypothesis, as the function ρ is in $\mathcal{D}(\mathbb{R}^N)$ and satisfies the condition $\int_{\mathbb{R}^N} \rho(t)\vec{t^\ell}\, dt = 0$ for $\ell \in [1, j-1]$, we have

$$\forall \ell \leqslant k+j-1, \quad \partial_y^\ell V_1(x, 0) = \delta_\ell^{k-1}\Big(\int_{\mathbb{R}^N} \rho(t)dt\Big)u(x).$$

To conclude for the terms of the sum V_2, we must verify the orthogonality of the function η_j.

For $|s| \in [1, j-1]$, consider the integral $\int_{\mathbb{R}^N} \eta_j(t)\vec{t^s}\, dt$. Since $\eta_j = \partial_j(t_j\rho)$, integrating by parts with respect to t_j gives

$$\int_{\mathbb{R}^N} \eta_j(t)\vec{t^s}\, dt = \int_{\mathbb{R}^N} \partial_j(t_j\rho)\Big[\prod_k t_k^{s_k}\Big] dt$$

$$= -s_j \int_{\mathbb{R}^N} \rho(t)t_j t_j^{s_j-1}\Big[\prod_{k\neq j} t_k^{s_k}\Big] dt = -s_j \int_{\mathbb{R}^N} \rho(t)\vec{t^s}\, dt = 0.$$

We can therefore apply the recursion hypothesis to the terms of V_2. We deduce that

$$\forall |\ell| \leqslant k+j-2, \quad \partial_y^\ell V(x, 0) = u(x)\delta_\ell^k\Big(\int_{\mathbb{R}^N} \rho(t)dt\Big).$$

Consequently, $\partial_y^\ell V(x, 0) = 0$ for $k < |\ell| \leqslant k+j-1$. $\qquad \square$

In the following theorem, we extend the previous results to the case of an arbitrary open set.

Theorem 3.79. *Let Ω be a class $\mathcal{C}^m$ open subset of $\mathbb{R}^N$.*

(1) *For $0 \leqslant j \leqslant m-1$, the map $\varphi \mapsto \partial_{\vec{n}}^{(j)}\varphi$ from $\mathcal{C}^m(\overline{\Omega})$ to $\mathcal{C}^{m-j}(\partial\Omega)$ can be extended to a continuous linear map from $W^{m,p}(\Omega)$ to $W^{m-j-1/p,p}(\partial\Omega)$. We will denote this extension by γ_j.*

(2) *Moreover, the map γ that sends $u \in W^{m,p}(\Omega)$ to the m-tuple*

$$\Big(u, \partial_{\vec{n}}u, \ldots, \partial_{\vec{n}}^{(j)}u, \ldots, \partial_{\vec{n}}^{(m-1)}u\Big)$$

is linear, continuous and surjective onto the product space

$$W^{m-1/p,p}(\partial\Omega) \times \cdots \times W^{m-j-1/p,p}(\partial\Omega) \times \cdots \times W^{1-1/p,p}(\partial\Omega).$$

Proof of Theorem 3.79.

Let us prove the first statement.

We begin by showing the continuity of $U \mapsto \gamma_j U$, where $j \leqslant m - 1$. By definition, $\partial_{\vec{n}}^j = \nabla^{(j)} \cdot \vec{n} \cdot \vec{n} \cdots \vec{n}$. Expanding, we obtain

$$\partial_{\vec{n}}^k = \sum_{|\alpha|=k} \frac{k!}{\alpha!} \gamma_0(D^\alpha U) n_1^{\alpha_1} n_2^{\alpha_2} \cdots n_N^{\alpha_N}.$$

By the above, the maps $U \mapsto \gamma_0(D^\alpha U)$, where $|\alpha| = j$, are continuous because the open set is of class $\mathcal{C}^m$. Taking the normal derivatives introduces the product of a function v in $W^{j-1/p,p}(\partial\Omega)$ and a function f in $\mathcal{C}^m$. We then show (cf. Exercise 3.13) that we have

$$\|vf\|_{W^{j-1/p,p}(\partial\Omega)} \leqslant C\|v\|_{W^{j-1/p,p}(\partial\Omega)}$$

where the constant C depends on the norms of f. We deduce from this the existence of constants c_j such that

$$\|\gamma_j U\|_{W^{m-j-1/p,p}(\partial\Omega)} \leqslant c_j \|U\|_{W^{m,p}(\Omega)}.$$

Since the maps γ_j are linear and continuous, we also obtain this result for the map γ with values in the product space endowed with the corresponding norm topology.

To prove the surjectivity of γ, we first consider the case $\Omega = \mathbb{R}^{N-1} \times]0, +\infty[$.

Let $u = (u_m, u_{m-1}, \ldots, u_1)$ be a function in the product space. We let $U_{u_j,k}$ denote the function of Proposition 3.78 that satisfies

$$\partial_y^k U_{u_j,k} = u_j$$

and, for $\ell \neq k$,

$$\partial_y^\ell U_{u_j,k} = 0.$$

We then let $U = \sum_1^m U_{u_j,m-j}$. This is an element of $W^{m,p}$ that satisfies the equality $\gamma(U) = u$, proving the surjectivity.

Let us now consider an arbitrary Ω. When defining the liftings, we can use the objects of the definition of the regularity of Ω to reduce to reasoning on the open set $\Delta_i = \Omega_i \cap \Omega$.

Let $u\varphi_i \in W^{k-1/p,p}(\partial^* \Delta_i)$, where $\partial^* \Delta_i = \partial\Omega \cap \Omega_i$. For the sake of simplicity, we denote $u\varphi_i$ by u and omit the indexes i. We may, and do, assume that $\mathcal{O}' = B_{N-1}$, the open unit ball in $\mathbb{R}^{N-1}$. Let us consider the map Φ from Δ to $\mathbb{R}^{N-1} \times]0, +\infty[$ that sends the point (x', x_N) of Δ to the point $(\widetilde{x}', y)$ defined by $\widetilde{x}' = x'$, $y = x_N - a(x')$.

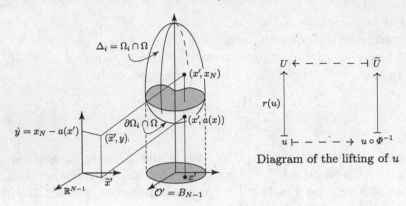

Fig. 3.3. Surjectivity of γ.

We can easily see that this map is invertible and that it is a class $\mathcal{C}^m$ diffeomorphism onto its image. The image of $\partial^*\Delta$ is an open subset of $\mathbb{R}^{N-1}$. The inclusions in Sobolev spaces are conserved by Φ. Figure 3.3 illustrates the situation.

Let us now study the surjectivity of γ onto $\partial\Omega$. To simplify the ideas, we study the case $m = 2$.

Let $u \in W^{1-1/p,p}(\Delta)$. Let us show the existence of a $V \in W^{2,p}(\Omega)$ such that

$$V(x', a(x')) = 0 \quad \text{and} \quad \partial_{\vec{n}} V(x', a(x')) = u(x', a(x')).$$

In order to do this, let $U \in W^{2,p}(\mathbb{R}^{N-1} \times \,]0, +\infty[)$ be an element satisfying

$$U(x', 0) = 0 \quad \text{and} \quad \partial_N U(x', 0) = u(x', a(x'))\sqrt{1 + |\nabla a(x')|^2}.$$

The existence of such a function is guaranteed by Proposition 3.78. We let

$$V(x', x_N) = U(x', x_N - a(x'));$$

then $V(x', a(x')) = 0$. Moreover, by taking the derivative with respect to x_i, we have

$$\partial_i V(x', x_N) = \partial_i U(x', x_N - a(x')) - \partial_i a(x')\partial_N U(x', x_N - a(x')),$$

whence

$$\partial_i V(x', a(x')) = \partial_i U(x', 0) - \partial_i a(x')\partial_N U(x', 0).$$

Using $\partial_i U(x', 0) = 0$ and the expression of the normal derivative (cf. (3.61)) along the boundary, we obtain

$$\begin{aligned}
\partial_{\vec{n}} V(x', a(x')) &= \frac{-\sum_i \partial_i a(x') \partial_i V(x', a(x')) + \partial_N V(x', a(x'))}{\sqrt{1 + |\nabla a(x')|^2}} \\
&= \frac{\sum_i (\partial_i a(x'))^2 \partial_N U(x', 0) + \partial_N U(x', 0)}{\sqrt{1 + |\nabla a(x')|^2}} \\
&= \sqrt{1 + |\nabla a(x')|^2}\, \partial_N U(x', 0) \\
&= u(x', a(x')).
\end{aligned}$$

To conclude the proof of the surjectivity, it suffices, under the hypothesis $u \in W^{2-1/p,p}(\Delta)$, to show the existence of a V in $W^{2,p}(\Omega)$ such that

$$V(x', a(x')) = u(x', a(x')).$$

Let $U \in W^{2,p}(\mathbb{R}^{N-1} \times \,]0, +\infty[)$ satisfy

$$U(x', 0) = u(x', a(x')) \quad \text{and} \quad \partial_N U(x', 0) = 0.$$

Then, if $V(x', x_N) = U(x', x_N - a(x'))$, we indeed have

$$V(x', a(x')) = U(x', 0). \qquad \square$$

Remarks (concerning specific cases).

Notations in the Case $p = 2$. When $p = 2$ and k is a nonzero integer, we let $H^{k-1/2}(\partial\Omega)$ denote the space $W^{k-1/2,2}(\partial\Omega)$.

The Case $p = 1$. Let $u \in W^{2,1}(\mathbb{R}^{N-1} \times \,]0, +\infty[)$. It is clear that $\gamma_0 u \in W^{1,1}(\mathbb{R}^{N-1})$. However, as has been shown in [19], the space of traces is smaller than $W^{1,1}(\mathbb{R}^{N-1})$. Describing the space $\gamma_0\big(W^{2,1}(\mathbb{R}^{N-1} \times \,]0, +\infty[)\big)$ is still an open problem. However, we can describe the normal derivative on the boundary. More generally, we have the following result.

Proposition 3.80. *Let $m \geqslant 1$; then the image of the trace map γ_{m-1} satisfies*

$$\gamma_{m-1}\big(W^{m,1}(\Omega)\big) = L^1(\partial\Omega).$$

Proof of Proposition 3.80. It is clear that $\gamma_{m-1}(W^{m,1}(\Omega)) \hookrightarrow L^1(\partial\Omega)$.

Let us show the result for $m = 2$ (cf. [19]).

Let $g \in L^1(\mathbb{R}^{N-1})$ and let $\{\varphi_p\}_{p \geqslant 0}$ be a sequence in $\mathcal{C}_c^2(\mathbb{R}^{N-1})$ that converges to g in $L^1(\mathbb{R}^{N-1})$. We can extract a subsequence, which we will denote in the same way, satisfying

$$\|\varphi_{p+1} - \varphi_p\|_1 \leqslant 2^{-p}\|g\|_1.$$

Let $\{\alpha_p\}$ be a sequence of positive real numbers such that

$$\forall p \in \mathbb{N}, \quad \alpha_p \leqslant \frac{2^{-p}\|g\|_1}{\sum_{\{i\in\{1,2\},k\in[p,p+1]\}} \|\varphi_k^{(i)}\|_1 + 1}.$$

Let $t_0 = \sum_0^\infty \alpha_p$ and let $t_{p+1} = t_p - \alpha_p$.

The resulting sequence $\{t_p\}$ is strictly decreasing and tends to zero when p tends to infinity. Let t satisfy $0 < t \leqslant t_0$; then there exist unique t_p and $\lambda \in [0,1[$ such that $t = \lambda t_{p+1} + (1-\lambda)t_p$. We define the function v on $\mathbb{R}^{N-1} \times [0, t_0]$ by

$$v(x', t) = \lambda(\varphi_{p+1}(x') - \varphi_p(x')) + \varphi_p(x').$$

For every $x' \in \mathbb{R}^{N-1}$, we have $\lim_{t\to 0} \|v(\cdot, t) - g\|_{L^1(\mathbb{R}^{N-1})} = 0$. Let us show that the following functions,

$$v, \quad \frac{\partial v}{\partial x_i} \ (1 \leqslant i \leqslant N-1), \quad \frac{\partial v}{\partial x_N}, \quad \frac{\partial^2 v}{\partial x_i^2}$$

belong to $L^1(\mathbb{R}^{N-1} \times]0, t_0[)$. For v, this follows from the inequality $\lambda < 1$ and the inclusion $\varphi_p \in L^1(\mathbb{R}^{N-1})$. For $i = 1, 2$ and $j \in [1, N-1]$, we have, thanks to the definition of α_p,

$$\int_0^{t_0} \int_{\mathbb{R}^{N-1}} |\partial_j^i v(x')| dx' dt = \sum_0^{+\infty} \int_{t_{p+1}}^{t_p} \int_{\mathbb{R}^{N-1}} |\partial_j^i v(x')| dx' dt$$

$$\leqslant 3 \sum_0^{+\infty} (t_p - t_{p+1}) \|\partial_j^i \varphi_p\|_1$$

$$\leqslant 3 \sum_0^{+\infty} \alpha_p \|\partial_j^i \varphi_p\|_1 \leqslant 3\|g\|_1.$$

On $[t_{p+1}, t_p]$ we have $\lambda = (t - t_p)/(t_{p+1} - t_p)$. Therefore the derivative in t on this interval can be written as $(\varphi_{p+1} - \varphi_p)/(t_{p+1} - t_p)$. We deduce from this that

$$\int_0^{t_0} \int_{\mathbb{R}^{N-1}} |\partial_t v(x', t)| \, dx' dt = \int_{\mathbb{R}^{N-1}} \sum_0^{+\infty} \int_{t_{p+1}}^{t_p} \frac{|\varphi_{p+1} - \varphi_p|}{t_p - t_{p+1}} \, dx' dt$$

$$\leqslant \sum_0^{+\infty} \|\varphi_{p+1} - \varphi_p\|_1 \leqslant 2\|g\|_1.$$

Next, let u be defined by $u(x', x_N) = \varphi(x_N) \int_0^{x_N} v(x', t) \, dt$, where the function φ is a function in $\mathcal{D}(\mathbb{R})$ with value 1 in the neighborhood of zero. We then have

$$u \in W^{2,1}(\mathbb{R}^{N-1} \times]0, t_0[), \quad \frac{\partial u}{\partial x_N}(x', 0) = g(x'), \quad \text{and} \quad u(x', 0) = 0. \quad \square$$

3.6 Embedding Theorems, Compact Injections

3.6.1 Results Concerning Embeddings

Theorem 3.81. *Let Ω be a class C^k open subset of $\mathbb{R}^N$. We have the following embeddings:*

(1) *If $N > kp$, then*

$$W^{k-1/p,p}(\partial\Omega) \longhookrightarrow L^{(N-1)p/(N-kp)}(\partial\Omega).$$

(2) *If $N = kp$, then*

$$\forall q < \infty, \quad W^{k-1/p,p}(\partial\Omega) \longhookrightarrow L^q(\partial\Omega).$$

(3) *If $N < kp$ and N/p is not an integer, then*

$$\forall \lambda \leqslant [N/p] + 1 - N/p, \quad W^{k-1/p,p}(\partial\Omega) \longhookrightarrow C_b^{k-[N/p]-1,\lambda}(\partial\Omega),$$

where $[N/p]$ denotes the integral part of N/p.
If $N/p \in \mathbb{N}$, then $W^{k-1/p,p}(\partial\Omega) \hookrightarrow C_b^{k-N/p-1,\lambda}(\partial\Omega)$ for every $\lambda < 1$.

Remark 3.82. If we extend the formula $W^{k,p}(\mathbb{R}^{N-1}) \hookrightarrow L^q(\mathbb{R}^{N-1})$ in the case $kp > N - 1$ to noninteger exponents k, in particular to the present situation, then we indeed find the condition

$$q \leqslant \frac{(N-1)p}{N-1-(1-1/p)p} = \frac{(N-1)p}{N-p}.$$

We can make similar remarks in the other cases, $kp > N$ and $kp = N$. Indeed, in the next chapter, after defining the spaces $W^{s,p}$ for s a positive noninteger, we will show the existence of analogous injections for every noninteger s.

In what follows, we let $(\mathbb{R}^N)^+$ denote the open set $\mathbb{R}^{N-1} \times]0, +\infty[$. We begin the proof of Theorem 3.81 by considering this specific case.

Proof of (1) and (2) for $\Omega = (\mathbb{R}^N)^+$.

Statement (1). We begin by assuming that $k = 1$, and therefore $p < N$.

Let C be a constant such that, for every $u \in W^{1,p}(\mathbb{R}^{N-1})$, there exists a lifting $U \in W^{1,p}(\mathbb{R}^{N-1} \times]0, +\infty[)$ of u, that is, satisfying $U(x',0) = u(x')$, such that

$$\|U\|_{W^{1,p}(\mathbb{R}^{N-1}\times]0,+\infty[)} \leqslant C\|u\|_{1,p}.$$

Let $\gamma = (N-1)p/(N-p)$, whence $\gamma - 1 = (N(p-1))/(N-p)$. We can then write

$$(3.83) \qquad |U(x',0)|^\gamma \leqslant \gamma \int_0^\infty |U(x',y)|^{\gamma-1} |\partial_N U(x',y)| dy.$$

By Hölder's inequality, we have

$$(3.84) \quad \big|U(x',0)\big|^{\gamma} \leqslant \gamma \Big(\int_0^{\infty} |\partial_N U(x',y)|^p \, dy\Big)^{1/p} \Big(\int_0^{\infty} |U(x',y)|^{Np/(N-p)} \, dy\Big)^{1/p'}.$$

Finally, integrating with respect to x' and applying Hölder's inequality gives the following norm for u in $L^{\gamma}(\mathbb{R}^{N-1})$:

$$\|u\|_{\gamma}^{\gamma} \leqslant \gamma \|\partial_N U\| \Big(\int_{\mathbb{R}^N \times]0,+\infty[} \big|U(x)\big|^{Np/(N-p)} \, dx\Big)^{1/p'}$$
$$\leqslant C \|U\|_{W^{1,p}(\mathbb{R}^{N-1} \times]0,+\infty[)}^{\gamma},$$

giving the result of statement (1) for $k = 1$.

For arbitrary k in statement (1) with $(\mathbb{R}^N)^+$, we use an induction on k.

Let us assume that assertion (1) has been proved for $k - 1$. Let $u \in W^{k-1/p,p}(\mathbb{R}^{N-1})$; then by definition, we have $u \in W^{k-1,p}(\mathbb{R}^{N-1})$ and $\partial_i^{k-1} u \in W^{1-1/p,p}(\mathbb{R}^{N-1})$ for every $i \leqslant N - 1$.

By the embedding theorem of Chapter 2, we have $u \in L^{(N-1)p/(N-1-(k-1)p)}$ because $(k-1)p < N - 1$.

By the induction hypothesis, the inclusion $\partial_i u \in W^{k-1-1/p,p}$ implies $\partial_i u \in L^{(N-1)p/(N-(k-1)p)}$. We therefore have

$$u \in L^p \quad \text{and} \quad u \in L^{(N-1)p/(N-1-(k-1)p)}$$

and, since

$$(N-1)p/(N-(k-1)p) \in [p, (N-1)p/(N-1-(k-1)p)],$$

we can deduce that $u \in L^{(N-1)p/(N-(k-1)p)}$.

Finally, we have $u \in W^{1,(N-1)p/(N-(k-1)p)}$. Once more applying the embedding theorem of Chapter 2, we deduce that $u \in L^{(N-1)p/(N-kp)}$. We have thus proved statement (1) in the case $(\mathbb{R}^N)^+$.

Let us show (2). If $k = 1$ and $p = N$, then $W^{1,N}(\mathbb{R}^{N-1} \times]0,\infty[) \hookrightarrow L^q(\mathbb{R}^{N-1} \times]0,\infty[)$ for every $q < \infty$. Applying the inequality (3.84) with arbitrary γ, we obtain $W^{1-1/N,N} \hookrightarrow L^q$ for every $q < \infty$.

Let us now assume that $k \geqslant 2$ and $kp = N$. We then have $(k-1)p < N$, which implies that

$$W^{k-1-1/p,p}(\mathbb{R}^{N-1}) \hookrightarrow L^{(N-1)p/(N-(k-1)p)}(\mathbb{R}^{N-1}) = L^{N-1}(\mathbb{R}^{N-1}).$$

However, u and ∇u belong to $W^{k-1-1/p,p}(\mathbb{R}^{N-1})$, whence $u \in W^{1,N-1}(\mathbb{R}^{N-1})$. By Sobolev's embedding theorem for the spaces $W^{1,N-1}(\mathbb{R}^{N-1})$, we deduce that $u \in L^q(\mathbb{R}^{N-1})$ for every $q < \infty$, concluding the proof of statement (2) in the case $(\mathbb{R}^N)^+$.   □

Proof of statements (1) *and* (2) *in the general case.*

Let Ω be a class $\mathcal{C}^k$ open set.

Using the regularity of Ω, let us show the continuity of the injections of $W^{k,p}(\Omega)$ in the cases (1) and (2). Let Ω_i be open sets that cover Ω, let $\{\mathcal{O}_i\}$ be open subsets of $\mathbb{R}^{N-1}$, and let $\{a_i\}$ be $\mathcal{C}^k$ functions on $\mathcal{O}_i$ such that, for every $i \geqslant 1$,

$$\Omega_i \cap \Omega \subset \{(x', x_N) \mid x_N > a_i(x'), \, x' \in \mathcal{O}_i\},$$
$$\Omega_i \cap \partial\Omega = \{(x', a_i(x')) \mid x' \in \mathcal{O}_i\}.$$

Let $\{\varphi_i\}$ be a $\mathcal{C}^k$ partition of unity subordinate to the cover of Ω consisting of the Ω_i. The uniform regularity assumptions on the open set Ω imply the existence of a constant C_1 such that

$$\forall i, \quad \|a_i\|_{\mathcal{C}^k(\mathcal{O}_i)} + \|\varphi_i\|_{\mathcal{C}^k(\Omega_i)} \leqslant C_1,$$

and $\forall q \geqslant 1, \, \exists c_q, \, \forall u \in L^q(\Omega), \quad \sum_i \int_{\Omega_i \cap \Omega} |u(x)|^q dx \leqslant c_q \int_\Omega |u(x)|^q dx.$

Note that this property also implies the existence of a constant C_2 such that

$$\forall u \in W^{k-1/p,p}(\partial\Omega), \quad \sum_i \|u_i\|_{W^{k-1/p,p}(\partial\Omega \cap \Omega_i)} \leqslant C_2 \|u\|_{W^{k-1/p,p}(\partial\Omega)}.$$

Let $u \in W^{k-1/p,p}(\partial\Omega)$; then the function $u_i = \varphi_i u$ belongs to the space $W^{k-1/p,p}(\partial\Omega \cap \Omega_i)$.

Let $v_i(x') = u_i(x', a_i(x'))$. By the properties of a_i, it is clear that $v_i \in W^{k-1/p,p}(\mathbb{R}^{N-1})$. It follows that $v_i \in L^q(\mathbb{R}^{N-1})$ for $q < (N-1)p/(N-kp)$, and therefore $u_i \in L^q(\Omega_i \cap \partial\Omega)$.

Moreover, there exist constants, which we all denote by C, such that

$$\|u\|_{L^q(\partial\Omega)} \leqslant \sum_i \|u_i\|_{L^q(\Omega_i \cap \partial\Omega)} \leqslant \sum_i \|v_i\|_{L^q(\mathbb{R}^{N-1})}$$
$$\leqslant C \sum_i \|u_i\|_{W^{k-1/p,p}(\Omega_i \cap \partial\Omega)} \leqslant \|u\|_{W^{k-1/p,p}(\partial\Omega)}. \qquad \square$$

Proof of statement (3) *in the case* $(\mathbb{R}^N)^+$.

We again begin by assuming that $k = 1$ and $p > N$.

Let C be a constant such that for $u \in W^{1-1/p,p}(\mathbb{R}^{N-1})$, there exists a $U \in W^{1,p}(\mathbb{R}^{N-1} \times \,]0, +\infty[)$ with $U(x', 0) = u(x')$ and

$$\|U\|_{W^{1,p}(\mathbb{R}^{N-1} \times]0,+\infty[)} \leqslant C \|u\|_{W^{1-(1/p),p}(\mathbb{R}^{N-1})}.$$

We use the embedding into $\mathcal{C}_b^{0,\lambda}$ given in the previous chapter (cf. Theorem 2.31), namely

$$U \in W^{1,p}(\mathbb{R}^{N-1} \times [0, \infty[) \implies u \in \mathcal{C}_b^{0,1-(N/p)}(\mathbb{R}^{N-1}).$$

Then, for every $t > 0$ and for every $(x, y) \in (\mathbb{R}^{N-1})^2$, we have

$$|U(x, t) - U(y, t)| \leqslant C\|U\|_{W^{1,p}(\mathbb{R}^{N-1} \times [0,\infty[)}|x - y|^{1-(N/p)}.$$

We obtain result (3) for $k = 1$ by letting t tend to 0.

Next let $k > 1$. Suppose first that $jp > N > (j-1)p$ and that $u \in W^{j-1/p,p}(\mathbb{R}^{N-1})$. Then $u \in W^{j-1,p}(\mathbb{R}^{N-1})$, which implies, since $(j-1)p < N$, that $u \in L^{(N-1)p/(N-1-(j-1)p)}$. Furthermore $Du \in W^{j-1-1/p,p}$, hence the part "$kp < N$" ensures that $Du \in L^{(N-1)p/(N-(j-1)p)}$. Since

$$\frac{(N-1)p}{(N-(j-1)p)} \in \left[p, \frac{(N-1)p}{(N-1-(j-1)p)}\right],$$

we have $u \in W^{1,(N-1)p/(N-(j-1)p)}$ hence, since $(N-1)p/(N-(j-1)p) > N-1$ and

$$1 - \frac{(N-1)}{\frac{(N-1)p}{N-(j-1)p}} = j - \frac{N}{p},$$

we have $u \in \mathcal{C}_b^{0,j-N/p}$.

If $kp > N$ and N/p is not an integer, then let $j \in \mathbb{N}$ be such that $jp > N > (j-1)p$, that is, $j = [N/p] + 1$. We have $D^{(k-j)}u \in W^{j-(1/p),p}(\mathbb{R}^{N-1})$ and, by the above, $D^{k-j}u \in \mathcal{C}_b^{0,j-N/p}(\mathbb{R}^{N-1})$. It follows that

$$u \in \mathcal{C}_b^{k-j,j-(N/p)}(\mathbb{R}^{N-1}) = \mathcal{C}_b^{k-1-[N/p],[(N/p)+1]-(N/p)}(\mathbb{R}^{N-1}).$$

The case where $N/p \in \mathbb{N}$ is left to the reader. $\square$

Proof of (3) in the general case.

In the general case of a class $\mathcal{C}^k$ open set, we define u_i and v_i as in the proofs of (1) and (2). We then have $v_i \in \mathcal{C}_b^{k-1-[N/p],[(N/p)+1]-(N/p)}(\mathbb{R}^{N-1})$. Setting

$$X(\Omega_i) = \mathcal{C}_b^{k-1-[N/p],[N/p+1]-(N/p)}(\Omega_i \cap \partial\Omega),$$

we write

$$\|u\|_{X(\partial\Omega)} = \sup_i \|u_i\|_{X(\Omega_i)} \leqslant \sup_i \|v_i\|_{X(\mathbb{R}^{N-1})}$$

$$\leqslant C \sup_i \|v_i\|_{W^{k-1/p,p}(\mathbb{R}^{N-1})}$$

$$\leqslant C \sup_i \|u_i\|_{W^{k-1/p,p}(\partial\Omega \cap \Omega_i)} \leqslant C\|u\|_{W^{k-1/p,p}(\partial\Omega)}.$$ $\square$

Let us now consider the compactness of some of these injections.

3.6.2 Compactness Results for Bounded $\partial\Omega$

Theorem 3.85. *We suppose that $\partial\Omega$ is bounded and of class $\mathcal{C}^k$.*

(1) *Let $p > 1$ and let $N - 1$ be the dimension of $\partial\Omega$. We suppose that $kp < N$. The injection of $W^{k-1/p,p}(\partial\Omega)$ into $L^q(\partial\Omega)$ is then compact for all $q < (N-1)p/(N-kp)$.*

(2) *If $kp = N$, then the injection of $W^{k-1/p,p}(\partial\Omega)$ into any $L^q(\partial\Omega)$ is compact.*

(3) *If $kp < N$, then the injection of $W^{k-1/p,p}(\partial\Omega)$ into $\mathcal{C}^{k-1-[N/p],\lambda}(\partial\Omega)$ is compact for every $\lambda < [(N/p) + 1] - N/p$.*

Proof of Theorem 3.85.

In the first case, it suffices to show that the injection of $W^{k-1/p,p}(\partial\Omega)$ into $L^p(\partial\Omega)$ is compact and then use Lemma 2.82 from Chapter 2. Moreover, it suffices to show the result for $k = 1$ and for functions in $W^{1-1/p,p}(\mathbb{R}^{N-1} \times \{0\})$ with support in a fixed compact set. Therefore, let $\{u_n\}$ be a bounded sequence in $W^{1-1/p,p}(\mathbb{R}^{N-1})$ with support in a fixed compact set. By the continuity of the lifting of $W^{1-1/p,p}(\mathbb{R}^{N-1})$ in $W^{1,p}((\mathbb{R}^N)^+)$, there exists a $\widetilde{u}_n$ equal to u_n on the boundary and such that $\widetilde{u}_n$ is bounded in $W^{1,p}((\mathbb{R}^N)^+)$. Consider a function $\psi \in \mathcal{D}(\mathbb{R}^{N-1})$ that is equal to 1 at 0. The sequence v_n defined by $v_n(x) = \widetilde{u}_n(x)\psi(x')\varphi(x_N)$ then has the same trace as $\widetilde{u}_n$ and has support in a fixed compact subset of $\mathbb{R}^{N-1} \times [0, \infty[$.

The sequence $\{v_n\}$ is relatively compact in $L^p(\mathbb{R}^N)$, by the compactness theorem for bounded subsets of $W^{1,p}(\Omega)$ when Ω is bounded. For two indexes n and m of a convergent subsequence in L^p, which we also denote by $\{v_n\}$, we have

$$|u_n - u_m|^p(x', 0) \leqslant p \int_0^1 |v_n - v_m|^{p-1}(|v_{n,N} - v_{m,N}|)(x', s)ds.$$

Moreover, integrating with respect to x' and using Hölder's inequality gives

$$\|u_n - u_m\|_{L^p(\mathbb{R}^{N-1} \times \{0\})}^p \leqslant p\|v_n - v_m\|_p^{p-1}\Big(\|v_{n,N}\|_p + \|v_{m,N}\|_p\Big),$$

which tends to 0 when $n, m \to \infty$. The sequence $\{u_n\}$ is therefore a Cauchy sequence in $L^p(\mathbb{R}^{N-1})$ and consequently converges in $L^p(\mathbb{R}^{N-1})$, namely to $x' \mapsto u(x', 0)$.

Let us now assume that $kp > N$. It suffices to show that the injection

$$W^{k-1/p,p}(]-1, 1[^{N-1} \times \{0\}) \longrightarrow \mathcal{C}([-1, 1]^{N-1} \times \{0\})$$

is compact and to apply Lemma 2.85.

Let $\{u_n\}$ be a bounded sequence in $W^{k-1/p,p}(]-1,1[^{N-1}\times\{0\})$ and let $\widetilde{u}_n$ be a bounded sequence in $W^{k,p}(]-1,1[^{N-1}\times]0,1[)$ that equals u_n on the boundary. By the compactness of the injection of $W^{k,p}(]-1,1[^{N-1}\times]0,1[)$ into $\mathcal{C}([-1,1]^{N-1}\times[0,1])$, we can extract a subsequence of u_n that converges in $\mathcal{C}([-1,1]^{N-1}\times[0,1])$. In particular, it converges in $\mathcal{C}([-1,1]^{N-1}\times\{0\})$, giving the desired result. $\qquad\qquad\square$

3.6.3 Comments

Few books give a simple approach to trace spaces. In general, the given definition uses interpolation spaces, which is more abstract than what we present here. For these other approaches, the reader can consult Adams [1], J.-L. Lions [47, 48] and Peetre [56].

3.7 Exercises for Chapter 3

Exercise [∗∗] 3.1 (Fractional Derivatives).
The aim of this exercise is to determine properties of the fractional differentiation of distributions. In particular, we will be able to justify Remark 3.2, which was made at the beginning of this chapter. We denote by $\mathcal{H}$ the function equal to 1 on $]0,+\infty[$ and zero elsewhere. For the definition of the finite parts used here, we refer, for example, to Exercise 1.27 of Chapter 1. The following formula, which holds for $\alpha \in]0,1[$, also suffices:

$$(*) \qquad \forall \varphi \in \mathcal{D}(\mathbb{R}), \quad \langle \mathrm{Pf}(\mathcal{H}(x)x^{-1-\alpha}),\varphi\rangle = \int_0^{+\infty} \frac{\varphi(x)-\varphi(0)}{x^{1+\alpha}}dx.$$

We recall the definition of the convolution of two distributions T and S in $\mathcal{D}'_+(\mathbb{R})$. Suppose that the function $\eta \in \mathcal{D}(\mathbb{R})$ has value 1 in a neighborhood of $\mathrm{supp}(\varphi)$, this convolution is defined by

$$\langle T \star S, \varphi\rangle = \Big\langle T, \big((\langle S, \eta(x)\eta(y)\varphi(x+y)\rangle)\big)\Big\rangle.$$

In most cases, it suffices to do formal computations where we disregard the function η.

We will admit without proof that the derivative of the resulting distribution is either the convolution $S' \star T$ or the convolution $S \star T'$.

Let us recall the definition of the Euler function $\mathcal{B}$, namely

$$\forall \alpha > 0, \forall \beta > 0 \quad \mathcal{B}(\alpha,\beta) = \int_0^1 t^{\alpha-1}(1-t)^{\beta-1}dt.$$

This function satisfies the relations

$$\mathcal{B}(\alpha, \beta) = \frac{\Gamma(\alpha)\Gamma(\beta)}{\Gamma(\alpha + \beta)} \quad \text{and} \quad \mathcal{B}(\alpha, 1 - \alpha) = \frac{\pi}{\sin(\pi\alpha)}.$$

Finally, we extend Γ to the nonpositive real numbers that are not integers using the following formulas:

$$\forall x \in \,]-1, 0[, \quad \Gamma^*(x) = \frac{\Gamma(x+1)}{x}; \quad \forall x \in \,]-2, -1[, \quad \Gamma^*(x) = \frac{\Gamma^*(x+1)}{x}$$

and so on, on all segments $]-n-1, -n[$.

For noninteger $m > 0$, the fractional derivative of order m of the distribution $T \in \mathcal{D}'_+(\mathbb{R})$ (cf. [60]) is defined to be

$$d^m(T) = \frac{1}{\Gamma^*(-m)} \, \mathrm{Pf}\left(\frac{\mathcal{H}(x)}{x^{m+1}}\right) \star T.$$

When m is an integer, it is $d^m(T) = \delta^{(m)} \star T = T^{(m)}$.

(1) As a first example, we consider the derivative of order $1/2$ of $\mathcal{H}(x)x^\alpha$ for $\alpha > 0$. Prove the following result, where K is a constant:

$$d^{1/2}\left[\mathcal{H}(x)x^\alpha\right] = \frac{1}{\Gamma^*(-\frac{1}{2})} \, \mathrm{Pf}\left(\frac{\mathcal{H}(x)}{x^{3/2}}\right) \star \mathcal{H}(x)x^\alpha = K\mathcal{H}(x)x^{\alpha-1/2}.$$

More generally, determine the derivative of order s of the function $\mathcal{H}(x)x^\alpha$ for $s \in \,]0, 1[$ (use Definition $(*)$).
Using the differentiation of a convolution and the derivatives of the finite parts, deduce the derivative of order s of $\mathcal{H}(x)x^\alpha$ for $s \in \,]1, 2[$ from the previous result. Generalize to an arbitrary noninteger nonnegative differentiation order.

(2) For α and β in $]0, 1[$, determine the convolution of the distributions $S = \mathcal{H}(x)x^{-\alpha}$ and $T = \mathcal{H}(x)x^{-\beta}$, which can also be considered as a convolution in the sense of functions. Give an explicit result for $\alpha + \beta = 1$.
Deduce from this an explicit description of the composition of the two derivatives of noninteger orders $m > 0$ and $k > 0$, using the derivative of order $m + k$.

(3) (Question related to Example 3.25). Let f be the function with value 1 on $]0, 1[$ and 0 elsewhere. We assume that $p > 1$. Determine the convolution of functions $\mathcal{H}(x)x^{1/p-1} \star f$. Deduce from this the fractional derivative of order $1 - 1/p$ of f. The result is a function, in contrast to the derivatives of integer order, which involve Dirac distributions. Show that this fractional derivative belongs to $L^p(\mathbb{R})$ only if $p < 2$ (cf. Example 3.25).

Hints. For (1), apply the definition of a convolution of distributions to obtain

$$\langle T, \varphi \rangle = \langle \mathcal{H}(x)x^{\alpha}, \langle \mathrm{Pf}(\mathcal{H}(y)/y^{3/2}), \varphi(x+y) \rangle \rangle$$

$$= \int_0^{+\infty} x^{\alpha} \int_0^{+\infty} \frac{\varphi(x+y) - \varphi(x)}{y^{3/2}} \, dy \, dx.$$

Next, integration by parts gives

$$\int_0^{+\infty} \frac{\varphi(x+y) - \varphi(x)}{y^{3/2}} dy = 2 \int_0^{+\infty} \frac{\varphi'(x+y)}{y^{1/2}} dy.$$

Using a translation applied to the variable, it follows that

$$\langle T, \varphi \rangle = 2 \int_0^{+\infty} x^{\alpha} \int_x^{+\infty} \frac{\varphi'(z)}{(z-x)^{1/2}} dz \, dx.$$

Use Fubini's formula and the Euler function $\mathcal{B}(\alpha + 1, 1/2)$ to deduce that $\langle T, \varphi \rangle = K' \int_0^{+\infty} z^{\alpha+1/2} \varphi'(z)$. Finally, integrating by parts gives the desired result, since $\alpha > 0$:

$$\langle T, \varphi \rangle = K \int_0^{+\infty} z^{\alpha-1/2} \varphi(z) dz.$$

Use an analogous computation to determine the derivative of order $s \in \,]0,1[$. This will again give the function $K_s \mathcal{H}(x) x^{\alpha-s}$.

When $\alpha - s \leqslant -1$, generalize the formula by replacing the power function by the associated finite part. For example, when $s \in \,]1,2[$ (whence $\sigma = s - 1 \in \,]0,1[$) and $\alpha - s \leqslant -1$, this gives

$$d^s(\mathcal{H}(x)x^{\alpha}) = d[d^{\sigma}(\mathcal{H}(x)x^{\alpha})] = K_{\sigma} d[(\mathcal{H}(x)x^{\alpha-\sigma})] = K_s \, \mathrm{Pf}(\mathcal{H}(x)x^{\alpha-s}).$$

Use a derivative of integer order to show that this formula holds in general.

For (2), the analogous computation holds, giving the function $\mathcal{H}(x)x^{1-(\alpha+\beta)}$ up to a constant that can be expressed using the Euler function $\mathcal{B}$. Taking the derivative of the resulting formula gives the desired property.

For (3), the convolution is $px^{1/p}$ on $]0,1[$ and $p[x^{1/p} - (x-1)^{1/p}]$ for $x > 1$. The fractional derivative is the order one derivative of this function. The inclusion in $L^p(\mathbb{R})$ poses no difficulty.

Exercise 3.2 (Weak Continuity of a Trace Map).

Let Ω be a class $\mathcal{C}^1$ open subset of $\mathbb{R}^N$ and let $p > 1$. Show that the trace map is continuous for the weak topology on $W^{1,p}(\Omega)$. More precisely, if $\{u_n\}$ converges weakly to u in $W^{1,p}(\Omega)$, that is, if both $u_n \rightharpoonup u$ in L^p and ∇u_n tends to ∇u, then $\gamma_0 u_n$ converges weakly to $\gamma_0 u$ in $W^{1-1/p,p}(\partial\Omega)$.

Hints. Let $f \in W^{-1+1/p',p'}(\partial\Omega)$. Use the surjectivity of the map S introduced in Theorem 3.58 to show that there exists a $\sigma \in W^{p'}(\mathrm{div})(\Omega)$ such that

$$f = \sigma \cdot \overrightarrow{n}.$$

We have

$$\int_{\partial\Omega} f(\gamma_0 u_n - \gamma_0 u) = \int_{\Omega} (u_n - u) \, \mathrm{div}\, \sigma + \int_{\Omega} (\nabla u_n - \nabla u) \cdot \sigma \longrightarrow 0,$$

giving the result.

Exercise 3.3 (Example of a Non-Weakly Continuous Trace Map).
Verify that the trace of the space $W^{1,1}(]0,1[^N)$ in $L^1(]0,1[^{N-1}\times\{0\})$ is not weakly star continuous. For this, use the sequence $\{u_n\}$ defined by

$$u_n(x', x_N) = (1 - nx_N)\chi_{]0,1/n]}(x_N).$$

(1) Show that $\{u_n\}$ is bounded in $W^{1,1}(]0,1[^N)$.
(2) The sequence $\{u_n\}$ is in the space BV of functions in $L^1(]0,1[^N)$ whose gradient is a bounded measure on $]0,1[^N$ (cf. Section 6.3 of Chapter 6). In Chapter 6, we define the weak convergence of the sequence $\{u_n\}$ to u in BV by the conditions

$$\|u_n - u\|_1 \longrightarrow 0 \quad \text{and} \quad \forall \varphi \in \mathcal{C}_c(]0,1[^N), \quad |\langle \nabla u_n - \nabla u, \varphi\rangle| \longrightarrow 0.$$

Show that this weak convergence is indeed verified with $u = 0$.
Consider the trace of u_n on $\{x_N = 0\}$ and compare this to the trace of the zero function to deduce that the trace map is not weakly continuous.

Exercise 3.4 (Noncompact Injection Into a Trace Space).

(1) Let $N \geq 2$ and let $0 < p - 1 < N$. Prove that the injection of $W^{1-1/p,p}(]0,1[^N)$ into $L^{Np/(N-p+1)}$ is not compact.
(2) Suppose that $N + 1 < p$. Prove that the injection of $W^{1-1/p,p}(]0,1[^N)$ into $\mathcal{C}^{0,1-(N+1)/p}(]0,1[^N)$ is not compact.

Hints. For (1), use a function φ in $\mathcal{D}(]0,1[^N)$ and define a sequence $\{\varphi_n\}$ by setting

$$\varphi_n(x) = n^{(N-p+1)/p}\varphi(nx).$$

Show that $\{\varphi_n\}$ is bounded in $W^{1-1/p,p}(]0,1[^N)$. Next, show that it tends to 0 in all L^q with $q < Np/(N-p+1)$ but does not converge for the critical exponent.
For (2), let $\varphi \in \mathcal{D}(]0,1[^N)$ satisfy the condition

$$\sup_{(x,y)\in (]0,1[^N)^2}\left|\frac{\varphi(x) - \varphi(y)}{|x - y|^\lambda}\right| = 1.$$

Let $\{\varphi_n\}$ be a sequence such that

$$\varphi_n(x) = n^{(N-p+1)/p}\varphi(nx).$$

Show that this sequence is bounded in $W^{1-1/p,p}(]0,1[^N)$ and that it tends to 0 in all $\mathcal{C}^{0,\lambda}$ with $\lambda < 1 - (N+1)/p$ but has a constant seminorm equal to 1 in $\mathcal{C}^{0,1-(N+1)/p}$.

Exercise 3.5 (Noncompact Injection into a Trace Space, Continued).
Prove that the injection of $W^{1-1/p,p}(\mathbb{R}^N)$ into $L^1(\mathbb{R}^N)$ is not compact. Let φ be a nonzero function in $\mathcal{D}(\mathbb{R}^N)$. Let $\varphi_n(x) = \varphi(x + ne_1)$, where e_1 is a canonical basis vector of $\mathbb{R}^N$.
Prove that φ_n has a constant norm in $W^{1-1/p,p}(\mathbb{R}^N)$ while it tends to 0 almost everywhere.

Exercise 3.6 (Function in $W_N^\infty(\mathrm{div})$ and Green's Formula).
Let Ω be a class $\mathcal{C}^1$ open set. Prove that if $\sigma \in L^\infty(\Omega)$ and $\mathrm{div}\,\sigma \in L^N(\Omega)$, then there exists an element $\sigma \cdot \overrightarrow{n} \in L^\infty$ such that for every $u \in W^{1,1}(\Omega)$, the following Green's formula holds:

$$\int_\Omega \sigma \cdot \nabla u + \int_\Omega \mathrm{div}(\sigma)\,u = \int_{\partial\Omega} \sigma \cdot \overrightarrow{n}\,u.$$

Prove that the map that sends σ to $\sigma \cdot \overrightarrow{n}$ is continuous for the topology associated with the norm

$$\|\sigma\| = \|\sigma\|_\infty + \|\mathrm{div}(\sigma)\|_N.$$

Exercise 3.7 (Traces in $W^{1,\infty}(\Omega)$).
Let Ω be a class $\mathcal{C}^1$ open set. Show that the functions in $W^{1,\infty}(\Omega)$ have a trace on $\partial\Omega$ that belongs to $W^{1,\infty}(\partial\Omega)$.

Conversely, show that every function in $W^{1,\infty}(\partial\Omega)$ is the trace of a function in $W^{1,\infty}(\Omega)$.

Exercise 3.8 (Functions in $\mathcal{D}(\mathbb{R})$ Orthogonal to the Space of Polynomials).

(1) Let $p \in \mathbb{N}$ and let $0 \leqslant k \leqslant p$. For any compact subset $[a, b]$ of $\mathbb{R}$, prove the existence of a function φ in $\mathcal{D}(]a, b[)$ such that for every $i \in [0, p]$, we have

$$\int_\mathbb{R} t^i \varphi(t)dt = \delta_i^k.$$

(2) Let $p \in \mathbb{N}$. Prove that there exists a function φ in $\mathcal{D}(\mathbb{R}^N)$ satisfying

$$\int_{\mathbb{R}^N} \varphi(t)dt = 1 \quad \text{and} \quad \int_{\mathbb{R}^N} P(t)\varphi(t)dt = 0,$$

for every polynomial P with valuation at least 1 on $\mathbb{R}^N$ and degree less than or equal to p.

Hints. For (1), take $[a, b] = [-1, 1]$ to illustrate the ideas. Let φ_j, where $j \in [0, p]$, be functions in $L^2(]-1, 1[)$ such that $\det(\int_\mathbb{R} \varphi_i t^j dt) \neq 0$. Show their existence by taking, for example, the Legendre polynomials on $]-1, 1[$ for φ_i. Next, use the density of $\mathcal{D}(]-1, 1[)$ in $L^2(]-1, 1[)$ to find φ_j in $\mathcal{D}(]-1, 1[)$ such that the determinant $\det((\int_\mathbb{R} \varphi_i t^j dt)_{i,j})$, with indexes i and j in $[0, p]$, is nonzero. Consider the system

$$\sum_{i=0}^p \lambda_i \int_\mathbb{R} \varphi_i(t)t^j\,dt = \alpha_j,$$

for given α_j. It admits a unique solution $(\lambda_0, \lambda_1, \ldots, \lambda_p)$. In particular, you can obtain the desired result by taking $\sum_0^p \lambda_i \varphi_i = \varphi$ and $\alpha_j = \delta_i^k$.

For (2), take a function φ such that $\int_\mathbb{R} \varphi(t)dt = 1$ and $\int \varphi(t)t^j dt = 0$ for every $j \geqslant 1$. Verify that $\rho(t_1, t_2, \ldots, t_N) = \prod_1^N \varphi(t_i)$ has the desired properties.

Exercise 3.9 (Proof That a Lipschitz Open Set Is Locally Star Convex).

Let Ω be the open set $\{(x', x_N) \mid x_N > a(x'), x' \in \mathcal{O}'\}$, where a is a Lipschitz function and $\mathcal{O}'$ is a bounded open ball in $\mathbb{R}^{N-1}$ or a convex subset. Show that Ω is star convex with respect to a point.

Hints. You can, and do, assume that the point $(0,0)$ belongs to $\partial\Omega$ (hence $a(0)=0$). Let $m > \|a\|_{L^\infty(\mathcal{O}')} + \|\nabla a\|_{L^\infty(\mathcal{O}')} \sup |x'|_{\mathcal{O}'}$; then the open set is star convex with respect to $(0, m)$.

Let $\lambda \in \,]0, 1[$ and let $(x', x_N) \in \Omega$. You must show that $\lambda(0, m) + (1 - \lambda)(x', x_N) \in \Omega$. For this, it suffices to prove that $a((1 - \lambda)x') < \lambda m + (1 - \lambda)a(x')$. Consider the function $\varphi(\lambda) = \lambda m + (1 - \lambda)a(x') - a((1 - \lambda)x')$. It has value 0 on $\{\lambda = 0\}$ and is increasing because if a is $\mathcal{C}^1$, then

$$\varphi'(\lambda) = m - a(x') + \nabla(a(1 - \lambda)x') \cdot x' > 0$$

on the ball $\mathcal{O}'$, by the hypotheses on m.

This proof also works when a is Lipschitz, because φ is an increasing function. Indeed, if $\lambda > \lambda'$, then using the Lipschitz property of a, we find that

$$\varphi(\lambda) - \varphi(\lambda') = (\lambda - \lambda')(m - a(x') + a((1 - \lambda)x') - a((1 - \lambda')x'))$$
$$\geqslant (\lambda - \lambda')(m - a(x') - K\|\nabla a\|_\infty).$$

Exercise 3.10 (Inclusion of $x \mapsto \sin\sqrt{x}$ in Sobolev Spaces).

Prove that the function $x \mapsto \sin\sqrt{x}$ belongs to $W^{1,p}(]0, 1[)$ for every $p < 2$ and that it belongs to $W^{1-1/p,p}(]0, 1[)$ for every $p < 4$.

Hints. Show that the following is an upper bound for the seminorm

$$A = \int_0^1 \int_0^1 \frac{|\sin\sqrt{x} - \sin\sqrt{y}|^p}{|x - y|^p} dx\, dy:$$

$$A \leqslant \int_0^1 \int_0^1 \frac{dx\, dy}{(\sqrt{x} + \sqrt{y})^p} \leqslant \int_0^1 \int_0^1 \frac{dx\, dy}{(x + y)^{p/2}}$$
$$\leqslant \int_0^1 x^{1-p/2} \int_0^{1/x} \frac{du}{(1 + u)^{p/2}} \leqslant C \int_0^1 x^{1-p/2} \left|1 - (1 + 1/x)^{-p/2+1}\right| dx.$$

If $p > 2$, then the integrand is equivalent to $x^{1-p/2}$ at 0 and if $p < 2$, then it is equivalent to

$$x^{1-p/2}\left((1 + 1/x)^{1-p/2} - 1\right) \sim 1.$$

This integral therefore converges when $1 - p/2 > -1$, that is, when $p < 4$. To see that it does not converge for $p = 4$, use

$$\frac{1}{(\sqrt{x} + \sqrt{y})^4} \geqslant \frac{1}{8(x^2 + y^2)}.$$

Exercise 3.11 (Function in $W^{1-1/p,p}(\Omega)$ That Does Not Belong To $W^{1,p}(\Omega)$).

Let $\Omega = \,]0, 1[$ and let $\varphi(x) = x^{-1/k}$, where $k \in \mathbb{N}^*$. Note that φ does not belong to any $W^{1,p}(]0, 1[)$. Prove that $\varphi \in W^{1-1/p,p}(]0, 1[)$ if and only if $p < 2k/(k + 1)$.

Hints. The function φ is not bounded and therefore cannot be in any $W^{1,p}(]0,1[)$. Determine an upper bound for the seminorm $\|\varphi\|'_{1-1/p,p}$ as follows:

$$\|\varphi\|'^p_{1-1/p,p} = \int_0^1 \int_0^1 \frac{|x^{-1/k} - y^{-1/k}|^p}{|x-y|^p} \, dx\, dy$$

$$\leqslant \int_0^1 \int_0^1 \frac{|x^{1/k} - y^{1/k}|^p}{x^{p/k} y^{p/k} |x-y|^p} \, dx\, dy$$

$$\leqslant C \int_0^1 \int_0^1 \frac{1}{x^{p/k} y^{p/k} |x+y|^{p(k-1)/k}} \, dx\, dy$$

$$\leqslant C \int_0^1 \frac{x\,dx}{x^{2p/k + p(1-1/k)-1}} \int_0^{1/x} \frac{du}{u^{p/k}(1+u)^{p(1-1/k)}}$$

$$\leqslant C \Big[\int_0^1 \frac{x\,dx}{x^{2p/k+p(1-1/k)-1}} \Big] \Big[\int_0^{+\infty} \frac{du}{u^{p/k}(1+u)^{p(1-1/k)}} \Big] = C J_1 J_2.$$

The second integral J_2 converges at $u = 0$ if $p/k < 1$, which implies that $\varphi \in L^p(]0,1[)$. It also converges at $+\infty$ if $p > 1$. The integral J_1 is finite if and only if $1 - p - p/k > -1$, that is, $p < 2k/(k+1)$. We have $2k/(k+1) \leqslant k$, hence $p < 2k/(k+1)$ is a sufficient condition for $\varphi \in W^{1-1/p,p}(]0,1[)$. It is easy to see that this condition is also necessary.

Exercise [∗∗] 3.12 (Lifting in $\Omega = \mathbb{R}^2 \times \mathbb{R}^+$).

For $u \in W^{k-1/p,p}(\mathbb{R}^2)$, set $\overrightarrow{x} = (x_1, x_2)$ and define the lifting

$$U(\overrightarrow{x}, y) = Tu(\overrightarrow{x}, y) = \frac{\varphi(y)}{y^2} \int_0^y \int_0^y u(\overrightarrow{x} + \overrightarrow{z}) dz_1 dz_2,$$

where $\varphi \in \mathcal{D}(\mathbb{R})$ with $\varphi(0) = 1$ (cf. Theorem 3.67). Show that this function is indeed a lifting.

Hints. As in the theorem mentioned above, use a proof by induction to show that for $|\alpha| \leqslant k - 1$, we have $D^\alpha U \in W^{1,p}(\Omega)$. Suppose that

$$(3.86) \qquad \forall j, \quad j \leqslant k-1 \text{ and } u \in W^{j-1/p,p}(\mathbb{R}^2) \Longrightarrow U \in W^{j,p}(\Omega).$$

Show that if $u \in W^{k-1/p,p}(\mathbb{R})$, then $\partial_x u \in W^{k-1-1/p,p}(\mathbb{R}^2)$. Use the formula of the lifting and the induction hypothesis (3.86) to deduce that U satisfies

$$\partial_x U \in W^{k-1,p}(\mathbb{R}^2 \times]0, +\infty[).$$

You now only need to show that

$$(3.87) \qquad \partial_y^k U \in L^p(\mathbb{R}^2 \times]0, +\infty[).$$

By treating the terms of $\varphi'(y)$ that are simple separately, reduce to

$$U(\overrightarrow{x}, y) = \frac{1}{y^2} \int_0^y \int_0^y u(\overrightarrow{x} + \overrightarrow{z}) dz_1 dz_2 = \int_{(]0,1[)^2} u(\overrightarrow{x} + y \overrightarrow{t}) dt_1 dt_2.$$

For the derivative of order one, show that the following formula holds for $\partial_y U$:

$$\partial_y U = \int_{(]0,1[)^2} \Big[t_1 \partial_1 u(\overrightarrow{x} + y \overrightarrow{t}) + t_2 \partial_2 u(\overrightarrow{x} + y \overrightarrow{t}) \Big] dt_1 dt_2.$$

Let $I_1(\overrightarrow{x}, y) = \int_{(]0,1[)^2} t_1 \partial_1 u(\overrightarrow{x} + y\overrightarrow{t}) dt_1 dt_2$. Show that

$$
\begin{aligned}
I_1(\overrightarrow{x}, y) &= \frac{1}{y^3} \int_0^y \int_0^y z_1 \partial_1 u(\overrightarrow{x} + \overrightarrow{z}) dz_1 dz_2 \\
&= \frac{1}{y^3} \int_0^y \left(\left[z_1 u(\overrightarrow{x} + \overrightarrow{z}) \right]_0^y - \int_0^y u(\overrightarrow{x} + \overrightarrow{z}) dz_1 \right) dz_2 \\
&= \frac{1}{y^3} \int_0^y \int_0^y \left[u(x_1 + y, x_2 + z_2) - u(x_1 + z_1, x_2 + z_2) \right] dz_1 dz_2 \\
&= \frac{1}{y} \int_0^1 \int_0^1 \left[u(x_1 + y, x_2 + t_2 y) - u(x_1 + t_1 y, x_2 + t_2 y) \right] dt_1 dt_2.
\end{aligned}
$$

Deduce that $\|I_1\|_p^p$, which is in $\mathbb{R}^2 \times]0, +\infty[)$, is bounded from above by the integral of

$$
\int_{\mathbb{R}^2} \left[\int_0^1 \int_0^1 \left| \frac{[u(x_1 + y, x_2 + t_2 y) - u(x_1 + t_1 y, x_2 + t_2 y)]}{y} \right| dt_1 dt_2 \right]^p dx_1 dx_2
$$

with respect to y over $]0, +\infty[$. Next, use the variables $X_1 = x_1 + t_1 y$, $X_2 = x_2 + t_2 y$ and $Y = x_1 + y$ to prove that

$$
\|I_1\|_p^p \leqslant \int_{\mathbb{R}} \int_{\mathbb{R}} \int_{X_1}^{+\infty} \left[\int_0^1 \int_0^1 \left| \frac{u(Y, X_2) - u(X_1, X_2)}{Y - X_1} \right| dt_1 dt_2 \right]^p dX_2 dX_1 dY.
$$

Finally, use an upper bound for the inner integral and a translation, and set $\overrightarrow{X} = (X_1, X_2)$ to obtain

$$
\begin{aligned}
\|I_1\|_p^p &\leqslant \int_{\mathbb{R}} \int_{\mathbb{R}} \int_{X_1}^{+\infty} \left| \frac{u(Y, X_2) - u(X_1, X_2)}{Y - X_1} \right|^p dX_2 dX_1 dY \\
&= \int_{\mathbb{R}^2} \int_0^{+\infty} \left| \frac{u(\overrightarrow{X} + t\overrightarrow{e_1}) - u(\overrightarrow{X})}{t} \right|^p dX \, dt.
\end{aligned}
$$

Conclude by applying Lemma 3.27 that the inclusion $u \in W^{1-1/p,p}(\mathbb{R}^2)$ implies that the norm $\|I_1\|_p^p$ is bounded from above by

$$
\int_{\mathbb{R}^2} \int_{\mathbb{R}} \left| \frac{u(\overrightarrow{X} + t\overrightarrow{e_1}) - u(\overrightarrow{X})}{t} \right|^p dX \, dt \leqslant c \int_{\mathbb{R}^4} \frac{|u(\overrightarrow{X}) - u(\overrightarrow{Y})|^p}{|\overrightarrow{X} - \overrightarrow{Y}|^{p+1}} dX \, dY < \infty.
$$

Apply the same reasoning to the integral

$$
I_2(\overrightarrow{x}, y) = \int_{(]0,1[)^2} t_2 \partial_2 u(\overrightarrow{x} + y\overrightarrow{t}) dt_1 dt_2.
$$

For the derivative in y of arbitrary order k, observe that $\partial_y^k U$ is the sum of integrals of the type

$$
\int_{(]0,1[)^2} \left[t_i \partial_i (D^\alpha u(\overrightarrow{x} + y\overrightarrow{t})) \right] dt_1 dt_2
$$

with $|\alpha| = k - 1$. Apply the induction hypothesis to the derivative $D^\alpha u$ and use arguments similar to the ones above to complete the proof.

Exercise 3.13 (Map Sending U to the Normal Derivative of its Trace).

(1) Consider $U \in W^{k,p}(\Omega)$ with regular Ω. Show that if f belongs to $\mathcal{C}^{k-1}(\overline{\Omega})$ and $D^{\alpha}f$ is Lipschitz for $|\alpha| = k$, then the product Uf is still in $W^{k,p}(\Omega)$ and we have $\|fu\|_{W^{k,p}(\Omega)} \leqslant C_f \|u\|_{W^{k,p}(\Omega)}$.

(2) Let Ω be of class $\mathcal{C}^k$. Show the existence of a constant C such that

$$\forall \ell \leqslant k-1, \forall U \in W^{k,p}(\Omega), \quad \left\| \partial_{\vec{n}}^{\ell} \gamma_0 u \right\|_{W^{k-\ell-1/p,p}(\partial\Omega)} \leqslant C \|U\|_{W^{k,p}(\Omega)}.$$

Exercise 3.14 (Determining Iterated Gradients and the Normal Derivative).

The aim of this exercise is to determine iterated gradients and tangential or normal derivatives on cylinders and spheres in dimension $N = 3$.

(1) Since the function U is in $\mathcal{C}^2(\mathbb{R}^3)$, use the chain rule for differentiation to determine the partial derivatives of U with the help of the cylindrical coordinates $x = r\cos\theta$, $y = r\sin\theta$ and z. Likewise, determine the partial derivatives of order 2.

(2) Consider the cylinder $\Omega = \{(\dot{x}, y, z) \mid x^2 + y^2 < 1, z \in \mathbb{R}\}$. Let the tangent vector of $\partial\Omega$ at $x \in \partial\Omega$ be defined by $\vec{t} = (-\sin\theta, \cos\theta, 0)$. Determine the tangential derivative $\partial_{\vec{t}} u$, where u is the trace of U on $\partial\Omega$. Next, determine the derivatives $\partial_{\vec{t}}^2 u$ and $\partial_{\vec{n}}^2 u$.

(3) Determine the previous results using a different method. Namely, find the relation between the operators $D = x\partial_x + y\partial_y$ and ∂_r. Derive from it an explicit description of $\nabla^2 u \cdot \vec{n} \cdot \vec{n}$ using D and D^2, and deduce the previous result.

Likewise, find the relation between the operators $D_1 = -y\partial_x + x\partial_y$ and ∂_θ. Use D and D_1^2 to determine the tangential derivative $\nabla^2 u \cdot \vec{t} \cdot \vec{t}$ explicitly.

(4) Use a similar method to compute normal derivatives of orders one and two when Ω is the ball of center O with radius 1, using the spherical coordinates:

$$x = r\cos\theta\cos\varphi, \quad y = r\sin\theta\cos\varphi, \quad z = r\sin\varphi.$$

Exercise 3.15 (The Zygmund Space).

Recall the definition of the deformation tensor (cf. Exercise 2.10):

$$\forall i, j \in [1, N]^2, \quad \varepsilon_{ij}(u) = \frac{\partial_j u_i + \partial_i u_j}{2}.$$

Let $u \in L^{\infty}(\mathbb{R}^2, \mathbb{R}^2)$ satisfy $\varepsilon(u) \in L^{\infty}(\mathbb{R}^2)$. Show that $x \mapsto u_1(x, 0) \in W^{1,\infty}(\mathbb{R})$ and that $u_2(x, 0)$ belongs to the Zygmund space

$$Z = \left\{ v \in L^{\infty}(\mathbb{R}) \sup_{(x,y)} \left| \frac{v(x+y) + v(x-y) - 2v(x)}{y} \right| < \infty \right\}.$$

Hints. Write $\Delta_2 u = u_2(x+y,0) + u_2(x-y,0) - 2u_2(x,0)$ as

$$\Delta_2 u = u_2(x+y,0) - u_1(x+y,0) + (u_2(x-y,0) + u_1(x-y,0)$$
$$+ u_1(x+y,0) - u_1(x-y,0) - 2u_2(x,0)$$
$$= [-(u_2-u_1)(x+y-t,t)|_0^y + [-(u_2+u_1)(x-y+t,t)|_0^y$$
$$+ [u_1(x+t),0)]_{-y}^y + 2[u_2(x,t)]_0^y$$
$$= -\int_0^y \partial_s(u_2-u_1)(x+y-s,s)ds - \int_0^y \partial_t(u_2+u_1)(x-y+t,t)dt$$
$$+ \int_{-y}^y u_{1,1}(x+t,0)dt + 2\int_0^y \partial_t u_2(x,t)dt$$
$$= -\int_0^y (\varepsilon_{22}(u) + \varepsilon_{11}(u) - 2\varepsilon_{12}(u))(x+y-s,s)ds$$
$$- \int_0^y (\varepsilon_{22}(u) + \varepsilon_{11}(u) + 2\varepsilon_{12}(u))(u)(x-y+t,t)dt$$
$$+ \int_{-y}^y u_{1,1}(x+t,0)dt + 2\int_0^y \varepsilon_{22}(u)(x,t)dt.$$

By the assumptions, the absolute value of $\Delta_2 u$ is bounded from above by $|y|\|\varepsilon(u)\|_{L^\infty}$.

Exercise 3.16 (Explicit Converse of the Previous Result).

Let $\varphi \in Z$. Let $H(x,y) = (1/y)\int_{-y}^y \varphi(x-t)(y-|t|)dt$ and let $u_1(x,y) = -\partial_x H$, $u_2(x,y) = \partial_y H$.

Prove that $\varepsilon(u) \in L^\infty$. We have $\varepsilon_{12}(u) = 0$; hence

$$\frac{\partial H}{\partial x} = \frac{1}{y}\int_{-y}^y \varphi'(x-t)(y-|t|)dt \longrightarrow 0$$

when y tends to 0, while

$$u_2 = -(1/y^2)\int_{-y}^y \varphi(x-t)(y-|t|)dt + (1/y)\int_{-y}^y \varphi(x-t)dt,$$

which tends to $-\varphi(x) + 2\varphi(x)$ when $y \to 0$. Using integration by parts, show that $u_{1,1} = (1/y)(\varphi(x+y) + \varphi(x-y) - 2\varphi(x))$ and

$$u_{2,2} = \frac{2}{y^3}\int_{-y}^y \varphi(x-t)(y-|t|)dt - \frac{2}{y^2}\int_{-y}^y \varphi(x-t)dt$$
$$+ \frac{1}{y}(\varphi(x-y) + \varphi(x+y))$$
$$= \frac{-2}{y^3}\int_0^y (\varphi(x-t) + \varphi(x+t))t\,dt + \frac{1}{y}(\varphi(x+y) + \varphi(x-y))$$
$$= \frac{-2}{y^3}\int_0^y (\varphi(x-t) + \varphi(x+t) - 2\varphi(x))t\,dt$$
$$+ \frac{1}{y}(\varphi(x+y) + \varphi(x-y) - 2\varphi(x)),$$

proving that $u_{2,2}$ is bounded.

4

Fractional Sobolev Spaces

This chapter continues where Chapter 3 left off. We begin by recalling results
concerning the Fourier transform. In the first two sections, we use this transform to study the spaces $W^{s,2}(\mathbb{R}^N)$, where s is an arbitrary real number. The
next sections are devoted to giving different definitions of the spaces $W^{s,p}(\Omega)$,
where $0 < s < 1$ and $1 < p < +\infty$, with $p \neq 2$. These generalize the spaces
$W^{1-1/p,p}(\Omega)$ of last chapter.

In these new spaces, we establish the analogous density and regularity
results, embedding and compact embedding theorems, and the existence theorems for traces when the open set Ω has a certain regularity. After demon-
strating these properties in the case $0 < s < 1$, we extend them to the spaces
$W^{s,p}$ for $s \in \mathbb{R}$.

4.1 Tempered Distributions and Fourier Transforms

4.1.1 Rapidly Decreasing Functions and Tempered Distributions

Definition 4.1. A function φ is called rapidly decreasing in $\mathbb{R}^N$ if $\varphi \in
\mathcal{C}^\infty(\mathbb{R}^N)$ and if, when D^j denotes the differentiation operator with respect
to the multi-index $j = (j_1, j_2, \ldots, j_N)$, we have:

$$(*) \qquad \forall\, j \in \mathbb{N}^N,\ \forall\, k \in \mathbb{N}, \quad |x|^k D^j \varphi \in L^\infty(\mathbb{R}^N).$$

The set of these functions is a vector space that we denote by $\mathcal{S}(\mathbb{R}^N)$.

Remark 4.2. The condition $(*)$ has the following two equivalent forms:

$$\forall\, (j, k), \quad |x|^k D^j \varphi \in L^1(\mathbb{R}^N),$$

or $\qquad \forall\, (j, k), \quad \lim_{|x| \to +\infty} |x|^k D^j \varphi(x) = 0.$

F. Demengel, G. Demengel, *Functional Spaces for the Theory
of Elliptic Partial Differential Equations*, Universitext,
DOI 10.1007/978-1-4471-2807-6_4,
© Springer-Verlag London Limited 2012

Topological Structure and Dual. The space $\mathcal{S}(\mathbb{R}^N)$ has a natural topology generated by the following countable family of seminorms:

$$n_{k,j}(\varphi) = \||x|^k D^j \varphi\|_\infty.$$

We let $\mathcal{S}'(\mathbb{R}^N)$ denote the topological dual of $\mathcal{S}(\mathbb{R}^N)$. By the following proposition, this is a locally convex topological space and a subspace of $\mathcal{D}'(\mathbb{R}^N)$.

Proposition 4.3. *The space $\mathcal{D}(\mathbb{R}^N)$ is dense in $\mathcal{S}(\mathbb{R}^N)$.*

Proof of Proposition 4.3.

Let $\varphi \in \mathcal{S}(\mathbb{R}^N)$ and let $\psi \in \mathcal{D}(\mathbb{R}^N)$ with $0 \leqslant \psi \leqslant 1$ and $\psi = 1$ on the ball $B(0,1)$. We define the sequence $\{\varphi_n\}$ by setting $\varphi_n(x) = \psi(x/n)\varphi(x)$; then $\{\varphi_n\}$ converges uniformly to φ because

$$\sup_{x \in \mathbb{R}^N} |\varphi_n(x) - \varphi(x)| \leqslant \sup_{|x| \geqslant n} |\varphi(x)| \longrightarrow 0$$

since φ tends to 0 at infinity. For $k \in \mathbb{N}$ and $j \in \mathbb{N}^N$, we have

$$|x|^k D^j(\varphi_n) = |x|^k \psi(x/n) D^j \varphi + \sum_{|p| \leqslant |j|} C_j^p \frac{|x|^k}{n^p} D^p \psi(x/n) D^{j-p} \varphi.$$

It follows that

$$\left| \|x|^k D^j \varphi_n - |x|^k D^j \varphi \right|$$
$$\leqslant \sup_{|x| \geqslant n} \left\{ |x|^k |D^j \varphi| \right\} + \sum_{|p| \leqslant |j|} \frac{1}{n^p} C_j^p \|D^p \psi\|_\infty \||x|^k D^{j-p} \varphi\|_\infty,$$

giving the desired conclusion because the right-hand side tends to 0. $\qquad \square$

Thus we identify the elements of $\mathcal{S}'(\mathbb{R}^N)$ with distributions, which we call *tempered distributions*. It is easy to see that the derivatives of a tempered distribution and the product of a tempered distribution and a slowly increasing function are also tempered distributions.

4.1.2 Fourier Transform

We give the following results without proof.

Theorem 4.4. *The Fourier transform $\mathcal{F}$, defined by*

$$\forall \xi \in \mathbb{R}^N, \ \forall \varphi \in \mathcal{S}(\mathbb{R}^N), \quad \mathcal{F}(\varphi)(\xi) = \int_{\mathbb{R}^N} e^{-2i\pi \, \xi \cdot x} \varphi(x) dx,$$

is an automorphism of $\mathcal{S}(\mathbb{R}^N)$. The inverse operator of $\mathcal{F}$, which we denote by $\overline{\mathcal{F}}$, is defined by

$$\forall \xi \in \mathbb{R}, \quad \overline{\mathcal{F}}(\varphi)(\xi) = \mathcal{F}(\varphi)(-\xi).$$

The transpose of this Fourier transform is an automorphism of the dual, which we also denote by $\mathcal{F}$. We again denote its inverse by $\overline{\mathcal{F}}$.

Theorem 4.5. *The Fourier transform of $T \in \mathcal{S}'$, defined by*

$$\forall \varphi \in \mathcal{S}, \quad \langle \mathcal{F}(T), \varphi \rangle = \langle T, \mathcal{F}(\varphi) \rangle,$$

is a tempered distribution.

The Fourier transform of a function φ is often denoted by $\widehat{\varphi}$. In what follows, we will denote the transform of a distribution T either by $\mathcal{F}(T)$ or by $\widehat{T}$.

We can easily see that if $f \in L^p(\mathbb{R}^N)$, then the associated distribution $[f]$ is tempered. In particular, if $f \in L^1(\mathbb{R}^N)$, then the function $\widehat{f} = \mathcal{F}(f)$, which belongs to L^∞, coincides with the transform $\mathcal{F}([f])$.

Because of the density of the subspace $L^2 \cap L^1$ in L^2 and Plancherel's theorem, we can extend the Fourier transform on L^1 to an isometric automorphism of the Hilbert space $L^2(\mathbb{R}^N)$. The transform of $f \in L^2$, which we once more denote by $\widehat{f}$, can be identified with $\mathcal{F}([f])$.

In general, we have the following result.

Proposition 4.6. *The distributions with bounded support, which we know belong to $\mathcal{E}'(\mathbb{R}^N)$ (cf. Exercise 1.20), are tempered. The Fourier transform of such a distribution T can be identified with the function defined by*

$$\xi \longmapsto \langle T_{(x)}, \exp(-2i\pi\xi \cdot x) \rangle.$$

We thus see that $\mathcal{F}(\delta_0) = 1$ and, using the inverse Fourier transform, that $\mathcal{F}(1) = \delta_0$. For more details, the reader can consult [22].

4.2 The Sobolev Spaces $H^s(\mathbb{R}^N)$

4.2.1 Definitions, Density of the Regular Functions

Definition 4.7. Let s be a real number. If $s > 0$, then we let

$$H^s(\mathbb{R}^N) = \{u \in L^2(\mathbb{R}^N) \mid \{\xi \mapsto (1 + |\xi|^2)^{s/2} \mathcal{F}(u)(\xi)\} \in L^2(\mathbb{R}^N)\}.$$

If $s < 0$, then we let

$$H^s(\mathbb{R}^N) = \{u \in \mathcal{S}'(\mathbb{R}^N) \mid \{\xi \mapsto (1 + |\xi|^2)^{s/2} \mathcal{F}(u)(\xi)\} \in L^2(\mathbb{R}^N)\}.$$

To see that these spaces are well defined, we note that if $\varphi \in \mathcal{S}$, then the function $\xi \mapsto (1 + |\xi|^2)^{s/2} \varphi(\xi)$, which is the product of a slowly increasing $\mathcal{C}^\infty$ function and a function in $\mathcal{S}$, also belongs to $\mathcal{S}$. The definition therefore allows us to write

$$\langle (1 + |\xi|^2)^{s/2} \mathcal{F}(u), \varphi \rangle = \langle u, \mathcal{F}((1 + |\xi|^2)^{s/2} \varphi) \rangle.$$

It is then easy to verify that $(1 + |\xi|^2)^{s/2} \mathcal{F}(u)$ is a tempered distribution. In particular, it is the product of a slowly increasing $\mathcal{C}^\infty$ function and a tempered distribution.

Proposition 4.8. *The space $H^s(\mathbb{R}^N)$ endowed with the norm defined by*

$$\|u\|_{H^s(\mathbb{R}^N)} = \left\| (1 + |\xi|^2)^{s/2} \mathcal{F}(u) \right\|_{L^2(\mathbb{R}^N)}$$

is a Banach space.

Proof of Proposition 4.8.

We assume that $s > 0$. For a Cauchy sequence $\{u_n\}$, the sequence with general term $(1 + |\xi|^2)^{s/2} \mathcal{F}(u_n)$ converges to U in $L^2(\mathbb{R}^N)$. Since the function f defined by $f(\xi) = (1 + |\xi|^2)^{-s/2}$ is bounded on $\mathbb{R}^N$, it follows that $fU \in L^2$. Setting $u = \mathcal{F}^{-1}(fU)$, we obtain an element of $H^s(\mathbb{R}^N)$. Hence, using the continuity of the Fourier transform in L^2, we can conclude that $\|u_n - u\|_{H^s} \to 0$.

The same proof holds if $s < 0$, with the exception that this time, the function $f : \xi \mapsto (1 + |\xi|^2)^{-s/2}$ is not bounded. However, as f is a slowly increasing $\mathcal{C}^\infty$ function, the product of U considered as a tempered distribution and f is also a tempered distribution. We conclude in a similar manner using the continuity of $\mathcal{F}$ in $\mathcal{S}'$. $\qquad \square$

The following result concerns the case where s is an integer.

Proposition 4.9. *If $s = m \in \mathbb{N}$, then the space $H^s(\mathbb{R}^N)$ coincides with the classical Sobolev space $W^{m,2}(\mathbb{R}^N)$.*

Proof of Proposition 4.9. Indeed, if $u \in H^m(\mathbb{R}^N)$, then the function u as well as all of its derivatives up to order m belong to L^2. Using the Fourier transform, we find that $\mathcal{F}u \in L^2(\mathbb{R}^N)$ and $-2i\pi\xi^\alpha \mathcal{F}u \in L^2(\mathbb{R}^N)$, where α is a multi-index with $|\alpha| \leqslant m$ and $\xi^\alpha = \xi_1^{\alpha_1} \cdots \xi_N^{\alpha_N}$. In particular, this implies that $(1 + |\xi|^2)^{m/2} \mathcal{F}(u) \in L^2(\mathbb{R}^N)$.

Conversely, if $\mathcal{F}(u)$ satisfies $(1 + |\xi|^2)^{m/2} \mathcal{F}(u) \in L^2$, then we also have $(2i\pi\xi)^j \mathcal{F}(u) \in L^2$ for every j satisfying $|j| \leqslant m$. Consequently, the derivatives of u up to order m are in L^2.

Moreover, by expanding the mth power of $1 + \sum_1^N |\xi_i|^2$, we can show the equivalence of the norms $\|\cdot\|_{W^{m,2}}$ and $\|\cdot\|_{H^m}$, where the latter is as defined above.   □

Proposition 4.10. *For $s > 0$, the space $H^{-s}(\mathbb{R}^N)$ coincides with the dual $H^s(\mathbb{R}^N)'$.*

Proof of Proposition 4.10. Let $v \in H^{-s}(\mathbb{R}^N)$. We define a linear functional L_v on H^s by setting

$$\forall u \in H^s(\mathbb{R}^N), \quad L_v(u) = \int_{\mathbb{R}^N} \widehat{v}(\xi)\widehat{u}(\xi)d\xi.$$

We show its continuity as follows:

$$\begin{aligned}
|L_v(u)| &= \left| \int_{\mathbb{R}^N} (1+|\xi|^2)^{-s/2}\widehat{v}(\xi)(1+|\xi|^2)^{s/2}\widehat{u}(\xi)d\xi \right| \\
&\leqslant \|(1+|\xi|^2)^{-s/2}\widehat{v}(\xi)\|_2 \, \|(1+|\xi|^2)^{s/2}\widehat{u}(\xi)\|_2 \\
&\leqslant C\|u\|_{H^s(\mathbb{R}^N)}.
\end{aligned}$$

It is therefore clear that the map that sends v to L_v is an embedding; consequently,

$$H^{-s}(\mathbb{R}^N) \hookrightarrow H^s(\mathbb{R}^N)'.$$

Conversely, let $T \in (H^s)'$. Proposition 4.11 below states that the embedding of $\mathcal{S}(\mathbb{R}^N)$ into $H^s(\mathbb{R}^N)$ is dense, whence $H^s(\mathbb{R}^N)' \hookrightarrow \mathcal{S}'(\mathbb{R}^N)$. It follows that $T \in \mathcal{S}'$.

Note that if $g \in L^2$, then the Fourier transform of $(1+|\xi|^2)^{-s/2}g$ belongs to $H^s(\mathbb{R}^N)$ and has norm

$$\|\mathcal{F}\big((1+|\xi|^2)^{-s/2}g\big)\|_{H^s} = \|g\|_2.$$

Let $g \in \mathcal{S}(\mathbb{R}^N)$. By the definition of the multiplication of $\mathcal{F}(T)$ by the slowly increasing function $(1+|\xi|^2)^{-s/2}$, we have

$$\begin{aligned}
\left| \big\langle (1+|\xi|^2)^{-s/2}\mathcal{F}(T), g \big\rangle \right| &= \left| \big\langle \mathcal{F}(T), (1+|\xi|^2)^{-s/2}g \big\rangle \right| \\
&= \left| \big\langle T, \mathcal{F}\big((1+|\xi|^2)^{-s/2}g\big) \big\rangle \right| \\
&\leqslant \|T\|_{(H^s)'}\|(\mathcal{F}(1+|\xi|^2)^{-s/2}g)\|_{H^s} \\
&= \|T\|_{(H^s)'}\|g\|_2.
\end{aligned}$$

Consequently, $(1+|\xi|^2)^{-s/2}\mathcal{F}(T) \in L^2$, because it defines a continuous linear functional on L^2. We conclude that $T \in H^{-s}$.   □

Proposition 4.11. *The space $\mathcal{S}(\mathbb{R}^N)$ is dense in $H^s(\mathbb{R}^N)$.*

Proof of Proposition 4.11. The density of $\mathcal{D}(\mathbb{R}^N)$ in $L^2(\mathbb{R}^N)$ implies the existence of a sequence $\{\psi_n\} \in \mathcal{D}(\mathbb{R}^N)$ with

$$\|\psi_n - (1 + |\xi|^2)^{s/2}\mathcal{F}(v)\|_2 \longrightarrow 0.$$

The function $\varphi_n = (1+|\xi|^2)^{-s/2}\psi_n$ therefore belongs to $\mathcal{D}(\mathbb{R}^N)$ and converges to $\mathcal{F}(v)$ in L^2. By the continuity of $\mathcal{F}^{-1}$, we deduce that $\mathcal{F}^{-1}(\varphi_n)$ is in $\mathcal{S}(\mathbb{R}^N)$ and converges to v in $H^s(\mathbb{R}^N)$. $\qquad\square$

4.2.2 The Space $H^s(\mathbb{R}^N)$ Seen as a Trace Space

At this point, we are interested in a characterization of the functions in H^s for $s > 0$. In the following theorem, we establish that they are the restrictions of functions in $H^{s+1/2}(\mathbb{R}^N)$ to $\{x_N = 0\}$.

Theorem 4.12. *Let $N \geqslant 2$ and let s be a real number, integer or not, with $s > 1/2$; then the functions in $H^s(\mathbb{R}^N)$ have a trace on $\{x_N = 0\}$ that belongs to $H^{s-1/2}(\mathbb{R}^{N-1})$.*

Conversely, every function in $H^{s-1/2}(\mathbb{R}^{N-1} \times \{0\})$ can be extended in a linear and continuous manner to a function in $H^s(\mathbb{R}^N)$.

Proof of Theorem 4.12.

We begin with a lemma that expresses the Fourier transform of the restriction of the function u to $\{x_N = 0\}$ in terms of the Fourier transform of u with respect to the first $N - 1$ variables.

Lemma 4.13. *Let $v \in \mathcal{S}(\mathbb{R}^N)$ and let $u \in \mathcal{S}(\mathbb{R}^{N-1})$. If $\widehat{u}$ denotes the Fourier transform of u with respect to the first $N - 1$ variables, then we have the equivalence*

$$v(x', 0) = u(x') \iff \widehat{u}(\xi') = \int_{\mathbb{R}} \mathcal{F}(v)(\xi', \xi_N)d\xi_N.$$

Proof of Lemma 4.13.

For fixed x' in $\mathbb{R}^{N-1}$, let φ be defined by $\varphi(x_N) = v(x', x_N)$. Using $\delta_0(\varphi) = \varphi(0) = \langle \mathcal{F}(1), \varphi \rangle = \langle 1, \mathcal{F}(\varphi) \rangle$, we obtain $\varphi(0) = \int_{\mathbb{R}} \widehat{\varphi}(\xi_N)d\xi_N$, which can also be written as

$$(*) \qquad v(x', 0) = \int_{\mathbb{R}} \int_{\mathbb{R}} v(x', x_N)e^{-2i\pi\xi_N x_N}dx_N d\xi_N.$$

Taking the Fourier transform in x' on both sides of the relation $(*)$, we obtain the result, that is,

$$\widehat{u}(\xi') = \int_{\mathbb{R}^{N-1}} \int_{\mathbb{R}} \int_{\mathbb{R}} v(x', x_N)e^{-2i\pi(\xi' \cdot x' + x_N \xi_N)}dx_N dx' d\xi_N$$
$$= \int_{\mathbb{R}} \mathcal{F}(v)(\xi', \xi_N)d\xi_N.$$

The converse is evident. This concludes the proof of Lemma 4.13. $\qquad\square$

Let us return to the proof of Theorem 4.12. We suppose that $v \in H^s(\mathbb{R}^N)$ and set $u(x') = v(x', 0)$. We then show that there exists a constant $C > 0$ such that

(4.14) $\quad |\widehat{u}(\xi')|$

$$\leqslant C \left(\int_{\mathbb{R}} (1 + |\xi'|^2 + |\xi_N|^2)^s (\mathcal{F}(v))^2 (\xi', \xi_N) d\xi_N \right)^{1/2} (1 + |\xi'|^2)^{1/4 - s/2}.$$

Indeed, using the change of variables $\xi_N \mapsto \xi_N / \sqrt{1 + |\xi'|^2}$, we have

$$\widehat{u}(\xi') = \int_{\mathbb{R}} (1 + |\xi|^2)^{s/2} \mathcal{F}(v)(\xi) (1 + |\xi'|^2 + |\xi_N|^2)^{-s/2} d\xi_N$$

$$\leqslant \left(\int_{\mathbb{R}} (1 + |\xi|^2)^s |\mathcal{F}(v)|^2 (\xi', \xi_N) d\xi_N \right)^{1/2} \left(\int_{\mathbb{R}} (1 + |\xi'|^2 + |\xi_N|^2)^{-s} d\xi_N \right)^{1/2}$$

$$= C \left(\int_{\mathbb{R}} (1 + |\xi|^2)^s |\mathcal{F}(v)|^2 (\xi', \xi_N) d\xi_N \right)^{1/2} (1 + |\xi'|^2)^{1/4 - s/2}.$$

It follows that $\xi' \mapsto (1 + |\xi'|^2)^{s/2 - 1/4} \widehat{u}(\xi')$ belongs to $L^2(\mathbb{R}^{N-1})$ and that its norm in this space is lesser than or equal to $\| (1 + |\xi|^2)^{s/2} \mathcal{F}(v) \|_2$.

Let us now suppose that $u \in H^{s-1/2}(\mathbb{R}^{N-1})$. We extend this function as follows. Given $\varphi \in \mathcal{D}(\mathbb{R})$ with integral equal to 1, we write

$$\mathcal{F}(v)(\xi', \xi_N) = \mathcal{F}(u)(\xi') \varphi \left(\frac{\xi_N}{\sqrt{1 + |\xi'|^2}} \right) \frac{1}{\sqrt{1 + |\xi'|^2}}.$$

The function $\mathcal{F}(v)$ then has support in the cylinder $\{ \xi \mid |\xi_N| \leqslant C\sqrt{1 + |\xi'|^2} \}$, and $v(x', 0) = u(x')$ because

$$\int_{\mathbb{R}} \mathcal{F}(v)(\xi', \xi_N) d\xi_N = \mathcal{F}(u)(\xi') \int_{\mathbb{R}} \varphi \left(\frac{\xi_N}{\sqrt{1 + |\xi'|^2}} \right) d \left(\frac{\xi_N}{\sqrt{1 + |\xi'|^2}} \right)$$

$$= \mathcal{F}(u)(\xi').$$

It remains to show that $v \in H^s$. For this, we write

(4.15) $\quad (1 + |\xi|^2)^s (\mathcal{F}(v))^2 (\xi', \xi_N)$

$$= (1 + |\xi'|^2)^{s - 1/2} (\mathcal{F}(u))^2 (\xi') \varphi^2 \left(\frac{\xi_N}{\sqrt{1 + |\xi'|^2}} \right) \left(\frac{(1 + |\xi|^2)^s}{(1 + |\xi'|^2)^s} \right) \frac{1}{\sqrt{1 + |\xi'|^2}}.$$

The relation

$$\frac{(1 + |\xi|^2)^s}{(1 + |\xi'|^2)^s} = \left(1 + \left(\frac{|\xi_N|}{\sqrt{1 + |\xi'|^2}} \right)^2 \right)^s,$$

allows us to integrate with respect to ξ_N after applying the change of variables $t = \xi_N/(1 + |\xi'|^2)^{1/2}$. Integrating both sides of the relation (4.15) with respect to ξ then gives

$$\int_{\mathbb{R}^N} |\mathcal{F}(v)|^2(\xi)(1 + |\xi|^2)^s d\xi$$

$$\leqslant \int_{\mathbb{R}^{N-1}} (1 + |\xi'|^2)^{s-1/2} |\mathcal{F}(u)|^2(\xi') \Big(\int_{\mathbb{R}} \varphi^2(t)(1 + t^2)^s dt \Big) d\xi'$$

$$\leqslant C\|u\|^2_{H^{s-1/2}(\mathbb{R}^{N-1})}.$$

This concludes the proof of the surjectivity of the trace map from $H^s(\mathbb{R}^N)$ onto $H^{s-1/2}(\mathbb{R}^{N-1})$. $\qquad\qquad\qquad\qquad\qquad\qquad\qquad\qquad\qquad\qquad\Box$

4.2.3 Generalization for Higher Order Traces

The following proposition generalizes the trace theorem of Chapter 3.

Proposition 4.16. *Let $m \in \mathbb{N}$, let $s \in \,]m+1/2, m+1+1/2]$, and let γ be the map sending $u \in H^s(\mathbb{R}^N)$ to the $(m+1)$-tuple consisting of the traces of the successive derivatives $u(x',0), \partial_N u(x',0), \ldots, \partial_N^m u(x',0)$. Then $\gamma(u)$ belongs to the product $H^{s-1/2}(\mathbb{R}^{N-1}) \times H^{s-1-1/2}(\mathbb{R}^{N-1}) \times \cdots \times H^{s-m-1/2}(\mathbb{R}^{N-1})$ and the map γ is linear, continuous, and surjective onto the product space.*

Proof of Proposition 4.16.

Let $u \in H^{s-k-1/2}(\mathbb{R}^{N-1})$, with k fixed in $[0, m]$. Let φ be a function in $\mathcal{D}(\mathbb{R})$ such that

$$\int_{\mathbb{R}} (2i\pi t)^k \varphi(t) dt = 1 \quad \text{and} \quad \forall j \in [0, m], \ j \neq k \Longrightarrow \int_{\mathbb{R}} (2i\pi t)^j \varphi(t) dt = 0$$

(cf. Exercise 3.8 of Chapter 3). Next, let v be defined in $\mathbb{R}^N$ by its Fourier transform

$$\mathcal{F}(v)(\xi) = \mathcal{F}(v)(\xi', \xi_N) = \mathcal{F}(u)(\xi') \varphi\Big(\frac{\xi_N}{\sqrt{1 + |\xi'|^2}} \Big) (1 + |\xi'|^2)^{-(k+1)/2}.$$

Let $v^{(j)}(x') = \partial_N^j v(x', 0)$. By the characterization given in Lemma 4.13, we have

$$\mathcal{F}(v^{(j)})(\xi') = \int_{\mathbb{R}} \mathcal{F}(\partial_N^j v)(\xi', \xi_N) d\xi_N.$$

Therefore, recalling that $\mathcal{F}(\partial_N^j v) = (2i\pi\xi_N)^j \mathcal{F}(v)$ and applying a homothety to the variable ξ_N, we obtain the following results:

$$\mathcal{F}(v^{(j)})(\xi') = \int_{\mathbb{R}} \Big(\frac{(2i\pi\xi_N)^j}{(1+|\xi'|^2)^{(k+1)/2}} \Big) \mathcal{F}(u)(\xi')\varphi\Big(\frac{\xi_N}{\sqrt{1+|\xi'|^2}} \Big) d\xi_N$$

$$= 0 \quad \forall j \neq k$$

$$\mathcal{F}(v^{(k)})(\xi') = \int_{\mathbb{R}} \Big(\frac{(2i\pi\xi_N)^k}{(1+|\xi'|^2)^{k+1/2}} \mathcal{F}(u)(\xi') \Big) \varphi\Big(\frac{\xi_N}{\sqrt{1+|\xi'|^2}} \Big) d\xi_N$$

$$= \mathcal{F}(u)(\xi').$$

The traces of the successive derivatives of v are therefore all zero, with the exception of that of order k, which equals the given function u in $H^{s-k-1/2}$. It remains to show that $v \in H^s(\mathbb{R}^N)$. For this, we integrate the equality

$$(1+|\xi|^2)^s |\mathcal{F}(v)|^2(\xi)$$

$$= (1+|\xi'|^2)^{s-k-1/2} |\mathcal{F}(u)|^2(\xi')|\varphi|^2\Big(\frac{\xi_N}{\sqrt{1+|\xi'|^2}} \Big) \frac{(1+|\xi|^2)^s}{(1+|\xi'|^2)^s} \frac{1}{\sqrt{1+|\xi'|^2}}$$

with respect to ξ, using the change of variables $t = \xi_N/\sqrt{1+|\xi'|^2}$ in the integral in ξ_N and noting that $\int_{\mathbb{R}} |\varphi|^2(t)(1+t^2)^s dt < \infty$. We thus obtain

$$\|(1+|\xi|^2)^{s/2}\mathcal{F}(v)\|_2 \leqslant C\|u\|_{H^{s-k-1/2}},$$

proving the desired inclusion. $\square$

4.2.4 Other Definitions of the Spaces H^s

The following proposition will allow us to show that for $\mathbb{R}^N$, the spaces H^s coincide with the spaces $W^{s,2}$ whose definition is given in the next section.

Proposition 4.17. *Let $s \in \,]0,1[$; then $u \in H^s(\mathbb{R}^N)$ if and only if*

$$u \in L^2(\mathbb{R}^N) \quad and \quad \int_{\mathbb{R}^N} \int_{\mathbb{R}^N} \frac{|u(x)-u(y)|^2}{|x-y|^{N+2s}} \, dx \, dy < \infty.$$

Proof of Proposition 4.17.

Let $u \in H^s(\mathbb{R}^N)$. We will see further on (cf. Lemma 4.33) that the following two properties are equivalent:

$$\int_{\mathbb{R}^N} \int_{\mathbb{R}^N} \frac{|u(x)-u(y)|^2}{|x-y|^{N+2s}} \, dx \, dy < \infty$$

and $\qquad \forall i, \qquad \displaystyle\int_{\mathbb{R}} \int_{\mathbb{R}^N} \frac{|u(x)-u(x+he_i)|^2}{|h|^{1+2s}} \, dx \, dh < \infty$

To illustrate the ideas, let us take $i = 1$. Using $|1 - e^{i\alpha}|^2 = 4\sin^2(\alpha/2)$, we have

$$\int_{\mathbb{R}} \frac{1}{h^{2s+1}} \|\tau_{he_1} u - u\|_2^2 dh = \int_{\mathbb{R}} \frac{1}{h^{2s+1}} \int_{\mathbb{R}^N} |e^{2i\pi h\xi_1} - 1|^2 |\widehat{u}|^2(\xi) d\xi dh$$

$$= \int_{\mathbb{R}^N} |\widehat{u}|^2(\xi) \int_{\mathbb{R}} \frac{1}{h^{2s+1}} 4\sin^2(\pi h\xi_1) dh d\xi$$

$$= \int_{\mathbb{R}^N} (\pi|\xi_1|)^{2s} |\widehat{u}|^2(\xi) d\xi \int_{\mathbb{R}} \frac{4\sin^2 u}{u^{2s+1}} du$$

$$\leqslant C \|u\|_{H^s}^2 < \infty$$

because the integral $\int_{\mathbb{R}} 4\sin^2 u / u^{2s+1} du$ converges for $s \in \,]0, 1[$.

Conversely, these computations show that

$$\frac{\tau_h u - u}{|h|^{s+1/2}} \in L^2 \implies |\xi|^s \widehat{u} \in L^2.$$

$\square$

4.2.5 Embedding Results using the Fourier Transform $\mathcal{F}$

In Section 3.6.1, we gave the extension of the Sobolev embedding theorems of Chapters 2 for the spaces $W^{m,p}$, where m is an integer, to the spaces $W^{1-1/p,p}$. In the case of H^s, using the Fourier transform allows us to show some of these results in a somewhat elementary manner. We will state those results here. For more complete results, we refer to the more general embedding theorems for the spaces $W^{s,p}$ at the end of this chapter. In particular, the following proposition concerns neither the critical embedding for $q = 2N/(N - 2s)$, nor the embeddings into Hölder function spaces.

Proposition 4.18. *Let $s > 0$. We have the following embeddings:*

(1) *If $1/2 < s < N/2$, then $H^s(\mathbb{R}^N) \hookrightarrow L^q(\mathbb{R}^N)$ for every $q < 2N/(N - 2s)$.*
(2) *If $s = N/2$, then $H^s(\mathbb{R}^N) \hookrightarrow L^q(\mathbb{R}^N)$ for every $q < \infty$.*
(3) *If $s > N/2$, then $H^s(\mathbb{R}^N) \hookrightarrow \mathcal{C}_0(\mathbb{R}^N)$.*

Proof of Proposition 4.18.

In the case $s < N/2$, u is the inverse Fourier transform of $\mathcal{F}(u)$, which can be written as $\mathcal{F}(u) = (1+|\xi|^2)^{-s/2}(1+|\xi|^2)^{s/2}\mathcal{F}(u)$. The function $(1+|\xi|^2)^{-s/2}$ belongs to L^q for every $q > N/s$ while $(1 + |\xi|^2)^{s/2}\mathcal{F}(u)$ belongs to L^2, so that their product $\mathcal{F}(u)$ belongs to L^r with $1/r = 1/2 + 1/q$.

We can therefore apply Theorem 4.19 below (whose proof can be found in the appendix), which states that the Fourier transform of a function in L^r with $r \in [1, 2]$ belongs to $L^{r'}$, where r' is the conjugate of r, and therefore belongs to L^k for $k \in [2, 2N/(N - 2s)[$ (cf. the remarks made before the proof of

Theorem 4.59). Moreover, this same theorem applied to the conjugate Fourier transform gives the existence of a constant C such that $\|u\|_{L^k} \leqslant C\|u\|_{H^s}$.

In the case $s = N/2$, we can use that if $s' < s$, then H^s admits an embedding into $H^{s'}$. To see this, it suffices to use the definition of the norms (cf. 4.8). We will generalize this further on, in Corollary 4.34. Using the previous result with $s' < N/2$, we obtain the desired result.

In the case $s > N/2$, the transform $\mathcal{F}(u)$ can still be written as a product of the function g in L^2 defined by $g(\xi) = (1 + |\xi|^2)^{-s/2}$ and the function $(1 + |\xi|^2)^{s/2}\mathcal{F}(u)$, which is also in L^2. The product is therefore in L^1, and, consequently, u is the Fourier transform of a function in L^1. It is therefore continuous and tends to 0 at infinity. Moreover, we have

$$\|u\|_{L^\infty} \leqslant \|g\,(1 + |\xi|^2)^{s/2}\mathcal{F}(u)\|_{L^1}$$
$$\leqslant \|g\|_{L^2}\,\|(1 + |\xi|^2)^{s/2}\mathcal{F}(u)\|_{L^2} = \|g\|_{L^2}\,\|u\|_{H^s},$$

concluding the proof in this last case.   □

The theorem used above, which is proved in the appendix, is the following.

Theorem 4.19. *Let T be a linear operator defined on all the $L^p(\mathbb{R}^N)$ and continuous from $L^{p_i}(\mathbb{R}^N)$ to $L^{q_i}(\mathbb{R}^N)$ for $i = 0, 1$, where p_i and q_i are given elements of $[1, \infty]$. We let k_i denote the operator norm of T, that is,*

$$k_i = \|T\|_{p_i,q_i} = \sup_{\substack{\|f\|_{p_i}=1 \\ \|g\|_{q_i'}=1}} |\langle Tf, g\rangle|,$$

where q_i' denotes the conjugate of q_i.

If $t \in \,]0,1[$ with $1/p = t/p_0 + (1-t)/p_1$, then T is continuous from L^p to L^q with $1/q = t/q_0 + (1-t)/q_1$. Moreover, we have the continuity inequality

$$\|T\|_{p,q} \leqslant k_0^t k_1^{1-t}.$$

4.3 The Spaces $W^{s,p}(\Omega)$ for $0 < s < 1$

We begin by recalling results concerning the Lebesgue spaces of functions with values in a Banach space B.

4.3.1 The Spaces $L^p(\,]0, +\infty[, B)$

For a simple function $t \mapsto \sum_1^n \chi_{A_i}(t)a_i$, where the A_i are two-by-two disjoint measurable subspaces of $I = \,]0, +\infty[$ and the a_i are elements of B, the integral over I is defined to be $\sum_1^n |A_i|a_i$.

Let f be function from I to B. We call it *strongly measurable* if there exists a sequence $\{f_n\}$ of simple functions such that for almost all t in $]0, +\infty[$, we have

$$\lim_{n \to +\infty} \|f(t) - f_n(t)\|_B = 0.$$

If, moreover, one of these sequences satisfies $\lim_{n \to +\infty} \int_0^{+\infty} \|f(t) - f_n(t)\|_B dt = 0$, then we call f *integrable*. The integral of f is then defined to be the limit of the integrals of the simple functions f_n. We will show that this limit is independent of the choice of the approximating sequence of f.

We will admit, from now on, that a strongly measurable function f is integrable if and only if the function $t \mapsto \|f(t)\|_B$ is summable on $]0, +\infty[$. Moreover, if this function has a summable pth power, then we will write $f \in L^p(]0, +\infty[, B)$.

Definition of the Trace Spaces T. We let $t^\nu f$ denote the function $t \mapsto t^\nu f(t)$ and let f' denote the derivative of f in the sense of distributions. In particular, if f has values in the Banach space B and is locally integrable in the sense defined above, then for every function φ in $\mathcal{D}(]0, +\infty[)$, we have

$$\int_0^{+\infty} f'(t)\varphi(t)dt = -\int_0^{+\infty} f(t)\varphi'(t)dt,$$

where the integrals of functions with values in the Banach space B are defined as before.

Definition 4.20. Given real numbers ν and p with $1 \leqslant p \leqslant +\infty$ and an open subset Ω of $\mathbb{R}^N$, we let $T(p, \nu, \Omega)$ denote the space of functions f from $]0, +\infty[$ to Ω such that

$$t^\nu f \in L^p(]0, +\infty[, W^{1,p}(\Omega)) \quad \text{and} \quad t^\nu f' \in L^p(]0, +\infty[, L^p(\Omega)),$$

where the derivative of f is taken in the sense of distributions.

This space is a Banach space when endowed with the norm

$$\|f\|_T = \max\left\{ \int_0^{+\infty} \|t^\nu f\|_{W^{1,p}(\Omega)} dt, \int_0^{+\infty} \|t^\nu f'\|_{L^p(\Omega)} dt \right\}.$$

The following is a first regularity property of this space.

Proposition 4.21. *Let $f \in T(p, \nu, \Omega)$, then there exists an $a \in L^p(\Omega)$ such that*

$$\text{for almost all } t \in]0, +\infty[, \quad f(t) = a + \int_1^t f'(\tau)d\tau.$$

Proof of Proposition 4.21.

Since the factor t^ν is bounded on every compact subset of $I =]0, +\infty[$, we have the inclusions $f \in L^p_{\mathrm{loc}}(I, W^{1,p}(\Omega))$ and $f' \in L^p_{\mathrm{loc}}(I, L^p(\Omega))$. Therefore, almost everywhere on I, we can define the function g in $L^p_{\mathrm{loc}}(I, L^p(\Omega))$ by setting $g(t) = f(t) - \int_1^t f'(\tau) d\tau$.

Let b be an element of the dual $L^{p'}(\Omega)$ of $L^p(\Omega)$. To prove that g is almost everywhere a constant, we consider the function $t \mapsto g_b(t) = \langle g(t), b \rangle_p$, where $\langle , \rangle_p$ is the duality pairing of L^p with $L^{p'}$. Applying Fubini's and Hölder's formulas, we see that the function g_b belongs to $L^p_{\mathrm{loc}}(I)$. Consequently, the pairing of the derivative of g_b in the sense of distributions and a scalar function $\varphi \in \mathcal{D}(I)$, which we denote by $A = \langle (g_b)', \varphi \rangle$, satisfies

$$A = -\int_0^{+\infty} g_b(t) \varphi'(t) dt$$

$$= -\int_{\mathrm{supp}\,\varphi} \int_\Omega b(x) g(t)(x) dx \varphi'(t) dt = -\Big\langle \int_0^{+\infty} g(t) \varphi'(t) dt, b \Big\rangle_p$$

$$= -\Big\langle \int_0^{+\infty} f(t) \varphi'(t) dt - \int_0^{+\infty} \varphi'(t) \int_1^t f'(\tau) d\tau dt, b \Big\rangle_p$$

$$= \Big\langle \int_0^{+\infty} f'(t) \varphi(t) dt, b \Big\rangle_p + \int_\Omega b(x) \Big[\int_0^{+\infty} \varphi'(t) \int_1^t f'(\tau)(x) d\tau dt \Big] dx.$$

Note that applying Fubini's formula can be justified by approximating $g(t)$ on the compact set $\mathrm{supp}\,\varphi$ by simple functions, for which the validity of Fubini's formula is obvious.

The same method allows us to replace the second term in the next to last equality by

$$\int_0^{+\infty} \varphi'(t) \int_1^t \langle f'(\tau), b \rangle_p d\tau dt.$$

By the above, the function $\tau \mapsto \langle f'(\tau), b \rangle_p$ is locally summable. We can therefore differentiate its integral over $[0, t]$, in particular in the sense of distributions. Consequently, we can write

$$\int_0^{+\infty} \varphi'(t) \int_1^t \langle f'(\tau), b \rangle_p d\tau = -\int_0^{+\infty} \varphi(t) \langle f'(t), b \rangle_p dt$$

$$= -\Big\langle \int_0^{+\infty} f'(t) \varphi(t) dt, b \Big\rangle_p.$$

We deduce from this that $(g_b)' = 0$. Let t be an element of the domain of g; then we deduce from the above that for almost all t' and for all $b \in L^{p'}$, we have $\langle g(t), b \rangle_p = \langle g(t'), b \rangle_p$. We conclude that the function $g(t)$ is a fixed element a of $L^p(\Omega)$, proving the relation stated above. □

Corollary 4.22. *Under the previous assumptions, the function f from $]0, +\infty[$ to $L^p(\Omega)$ is continuous.*

This results from the continuity of the integral of a locally summable function with respect to the upper integration limit.

4.3.2 The Spaces $W^{s,p}(\Omega)$ for $0 < s < 1$

Definition 4.23. Let $s \in]0, 1[$ and let $p \in]1, \infty[$. We define the fractional Sobolev space $W^{s,p}(\Omega)$ as follows:

$$W^{s,p}(\Omega) = \left\{ u \in L^p(\Omega) \;\Big|\; \int_\Omega \int_\Omega \frac{|u(x) - u(y)|^p}{|x - y|^{sp+N}} \, dx \, dy < \infty \right\}.$$

This definition of the spaces $W^{s,p}$ generalizes that of the spaces in Chapter 3.

Proposition 4.24. *Let $s \in]0, 1[$. The space $W^{s,p}(\Omega)$ endowed with the norm*

$$\|u\|_{s,p} = \left(\|u\|_p^p + [\|u\|_{s,p}']^p \right)^{1/p}, \quad \text{where } [\|u\|_{s,p}']^p = \int_\Omega \int_\Omega \frac{|u(x) - u(y)|^p}{|x - y|^{sp+N}} dx \, dy,$$

is a Banach space.

Proof of Proposition 4.24.

Let $\{u_n\}$ be a Cauchy sequence for the norm $\|u\|_{s,p}$. In particular, $\{u_n\}$ is a Cauchy sequence in L^p. It converges to a function $u \in L^p$. Moreover, the sequence $\{v_n\}$ of functions

$$v_n(x, y) = \frac{u_n(x) - u_n(y)}{|x - y|^{s+N/p}}$$

is a Cauchy sequence in L^p. It therefore also converges to an element of L^p. Let us extract a subsequence $\{u_{\sigma(n)}\}$ of $\{u_n\}$ that converges almost everywhere to u. We note that $v_{\sigma(n)}(x, y)$ converges, for almost every pair (x, y), to $v(x, y) = (u(x) - u(y))|x - y|^{-s-N/p}$. Applying Fatou's lemma, we obtain

$$\int_\Omega \int_\Omega \frac{|u(x) - u(y)|^p}{|x - y|^{sp+N}} dx \, dy \leqslant \varliminf_{n \to \infty} \int_\Omega \int_\Omega \frac{|u_{\sigma(n)}(x) - u_{\sigma(n)}(y)|^p}{|x - y|^{sp+N}} dx \, dy.$$

Hence $u \in W^{s,p}(\Omega)$. Moreover, we find that $u_n \to u$ in $W^{s,p}(\Omega)$ by taking the limit for $m \to \infty$ in $\|v_n - v_m\|_{L^p(\Omega \times \Omega)}$. $\qquad\square$

Example 4.25. Let us study the inclusion of the function $x \mapsto \ln |x|$ in the space $W^{s,p}(]0, 1[)$ when $sp < 1$, and the inclusion of $x \mapsto |x|^\alpha \ln |x|$ in this same when $s - \alpha < 1/p$. From this, we easily deduce the conditions for the inclusion in $W^{s,p}_{\text{loc}}(\mathbb{R}^N)$ of these functions considered as radial functions on $\mathbb{R}^N$.

Let us first evaluate the seminorm $I = \| \ln |x| \|'_{s,p}$ when $sp < 1$:

$$I = \int_0^1 \int_0^1 \frac{|\ln|x| - \ln|y||^p}{|x - y|^{sp+1}} dx\, dy = \int_0^1 y^{-sp} \int_0^{1/y} \frac{|\ln u|^p}{(1-u)^{sp+1}} du\, dy$$

$$\leqslant \int_0^1 y^{-sp} \left(\int_0^1 \frac{|\ln u|^p}{(1-u)^{sp+1}} du + \int_1^{1/y} \frac{|\ln u|^p}{(1-u)^{sp+1}} du \right) dy = I_1 + I_2.$$

In the first integral between the parentheses, the integrand is equivalent to $|\ln u|^p$ at $u = 0$ and to $(1-u)^{p-sp-1}$ at $u = 1$. The integral in u is therefore convergent, and the integral in y is convergent when $sp < 1$. Under this same condition, we deduce the existence of the first term I_1. By Fubini's formula, I_2 can be written as

$$\int_0^1 y^{-sp} \int_1^{1/y} \frac{|\ln u|^p}{(1-u)^{sp+1}} du\, dy = \int_1^{+\infty} \frac{|\ln u|^p}{(1-u)^{sp+1}} \left(\int_0^{1/u} y^{-sp} dy \right) du.$$

Studying it therefore reduces to studying

$$\int_1^{+\infty} \frac{|\ln u|^p}{(1-u)^{sp+1}} u^{sp-1} du.$$

From the equivalence of the integrand in the latter to $|\ln u|^p |u|^{-2}$ in the neighborhood of $+\infty$ and to $(1-u)^{p(1-s)-1}$ at $u = 1$, we deduce the convergence of I_2, giving the desired conclusion.

For $x \mapsto x^\alpha \ln|x|$, we evaluate the seminorm in the same manner as in Chapter 3 (cf. Example 3.8). It therefore suffices to prove the finiteness of the two integrals

$$J_1 = \int_0^1 \int_0^1 x^{p\alpha} \frac{|\ln x - \ln y|^p}{|x-y|^{sp+1}} dx\, dy$$

and

$$J_2 = \int_0^1 \int_0^1 |\ln y|^p \frac{|x^\alpha - y^\alpha|^p}{|x-y|^{sp+1}} dx\, dy.$$

Following the computations we made for $s = 1 - 1/p$ (Example 3.8), we obtain the finiteness of J_1 provided that $p\alpha - sp > -1$ and $p\alpha + 2 > 1$, that is, under the conditions stated at the beginning of this example. Finally, setting $\gamma = (\alpha - s)p$, the second integral J_2 becomes

$$J_2 = \int_0^1 |\ln y|^p |y|^{\alpha p - sp} \int_0^{1/y} \frac{|1 - u^\alpha|^p}{|1-u|^{sp+1}} du\, dy$$

$$= \int_0^1 |\ln y|^p y^\gamma \int_0^1 \frac{|1-u^\alpha|^p}{|1-u|^{sp+1}} du\, dy + \int_0^1 |\ln y|^p y^\gamma \int_1^{1/y} \frac{|1-u^\alpha|^p}{|1-u|^{sp+1}} du\, dy.$$

The first term is the product of an integral in y that converges because $p(\alpha - s) > -1$ and an integral in u that converges under the same condition because the function is equivalent to $K(1 - u)^{p(1-s)-1}$ at $u = 1$. Applying Fubini's formula, we can reduce the second term to the integral

$$J_2' = \int_1^{+\infty} \frac{|1 - u^\alpha|^p}{|1 - u|^{sp+1}} \left[\int_0^{1/u} |\ln y|^p y^{(\alpha-s)p} dy \right] du.$$

When $y < 1$, we can bound $|\ln y|^p y^{(\alpha-s)p}$ from above by $y^{-\varepsilon+(\alpha-s)p}$ for every $\varepsilon > 0$. It follows that we can find, for the integrand of J_2', a bounding function equivalent to u^r at the neighborhood of $+\infty$, where $r = -2 + \varepsilon$. This shows the finiteness of J_2, whence the desired conclusion.

When the integration domain is $K \times K$ with K a compact subset of $\mathbb{R}^N$, the only additional difficulty corresponds to the case where $0 \in K$. Using polar coordinates in a neighborhood of 0, we reduce to the previous integrals with αp replaced by $\alpha p + N - 1$. We easily deduce from this the conditions for the inclusion of the function we are considering in the space $W_{\text{loc}}^{s,p}(\mathbb{R}^N)$.

4.3.3 First Properties of the Space $W^{s,p}(\Omega)$

Proposition 4.26. *The space $W^{s,p}(\Omega)$ is of local type, that is, for every u in $W^{s,p}(\Omega)$ and for every $\varphi \in \mathcal{D}(\Omega)$, the product φu belongs to $W^{s,p}(\Omega)$.*

Proof of Proposition 4.26.
Let $u \in W^{s,p}(\Omega)$ and let $\varphi \in \mathcal{D}(\Omega)$. It is clear that $u\varphi \in L^p$. We will show that

$$\int_\Omega \int_\Omega \frac{\left|(\varphi u)(x) - (\varphi u)(y)\right|^p}{|x - y|^{sp+N}} \, dx \, dy < \infty.$$

In order to do this, we write the difference in the numerator as a sum of two terms. The first is $\varphi(x)(u(x) - u(y))$, which will give a convergent integral because φ is bounded. The second gives the integral

$$J_p = \int_\Omega \int_\Omega \left| \frac{(\varphi(x) - \varphi(y))u(y)}{|x - y|^{s+N/p}} \right|^p dx \, dy.$$

This can be bounded from above by using the mean value theorem and integrating with respect to x:

$$J_p \leqslant \|\varphi'\|_\infty^p \int_{\text{supp}\,\varphi} |u(y)|^p \left[\int_{\text{supp}\,\varphi} |x - y|^{p(1-s)-N} dx \right] dy$$
$$\leqslant C\rho^{p(1-s)} \|u\|_p^p,$$

where ρ is an upper bound for the diameter of the support of φ. $\square$

Let us consider the case $\Omega = \mathbb{R}^N$.

Proposition 4.27. *The space $\mathcal{D}(\mathbb{R}^N)$ is dense in $W^{s,p}(\mathbb{R}^N)$.*

Proof of Proposition 4.27. We traditionally use a truncation and a regularization. We will give the proof in the case $N = 1$. The general case easily follows from this one.

Let us show that the functions with compact support in $W^{s,p}$ are dense in $W^{s,p}$.

Let $u \in W^{s,p}(\mathbb{R})$ and let $\varphi \in \mathcal{D}(\mathbb{R})$ have value 1 on the open ball of radius 1 with center 0, value 0 for $|x| \geqslant 2$, and satisfy $0 \leqslant \varphi \leqslant 1$ elsewhere. Let u_n be defined to be $\varphi(x/n)u(x)$. It is clear that u_n has compact support and values in $W^{s,p}$. Moreover, it is a classical result that u_n converges to u in L^p.

It remains to show that the sequence $\{v_n\}$, where

$$v_n(x,y) = ((u_n - u)(x) - (u_n - u)(y))|x - y|^{-s-1/p}$$

tends to 0 in $L^p(\mathbb{R}^2)$. To do this, we will show that the integrals

$$I_n = \int_0^n dx \Big(\int_n^\infty |v_n|^p(x,y)dy \Big), \quad J_n = \int_n^\infty dx \Big(\int_n^\infty |v_n|^p(x,y)dy \Big)$$

and those that we deduce from them by exchanging the variables x and y tend to 0. Indeed, $(u_n - u)(x) - (u_n - u)(y)$ vanishes when x and y are in $[-n,n]$. For the integral I_n, we have

$$\begin{aligned}
I_n &= \int_n^\infty |u(y)|^p \Big|1 - \varphi(y/n)\Big|^p \Big[\int_0^n \frac{dx}{(y-x)^{sp+1}} \Big] dy \\
&\leqslant C \int_n^\infty |u(y)|^p \Big|1 - \varphi(y/n)\Big|^p \frac{1}{(y-n)^{sp}} \, dy \\
&\leqslant \frac{C}{n^{sp}} \int_n^\infty |u(y)|^p \sup_{u \geqslant 1} \Big| \frac{1 - \varphi(u)}{(u-1)^s} \Big|^p \, dy.
\end{aligned}$$

The function $(1 - \varphi(u))(u-1)^{-s}$ is in fact bounded for $u \geqslant 1$. When $u > 2$, this results from the upper bound $(u-1)^{-s} \leqslant 1$, and when $u \in [1,2]$, it follows from the inequality $|(1 - \varphi(u))(u-1)^{-s}| \leqslant (u-1)^{1-s}\|\varphi'\|_\infty$. This inequality can be deduced by applying the mean value theorem to φ, because $s \in \,]0,1[$. We therefore obtain $I_n \to 0$.

Let w_n denote the function defined by

$$w_n(x,y) = (u_n(x) - u_n(y))|x - y|^{-s-1/p}.$$

We will show that $K_n = \int_n^\infty \int_n^\infty |w_n(x,y)|^p dx\, dy \to 0$, which leads to $J_n \to 0$ because, by hypothesis, $\int_n^\infty \int_n^\infty |v(x,y)|^p dx\, dy \to 0$. We first note that by the choice of φ, we have

$$K_n \leqslant \int_n^{2n} \int_n^{2n} \frac{|u_n(x) - u_n(y)|^p}{|x - y|^{sp+1}} dx\, dy + \int_{2n}^{\infty} \int_n^{2n} \frac{|u_n(x) - u_n(y)|^p}{|x - y|^{sp+1}} dx\, dy$$
$$= K_n^{(1)} + K_n^{(2)}.$$

Integrating with respect to x and then using the properties of φ, we find that the term $K_n^{(2)}$ satisfies

$$K_n^{(2)} \leqslant \int_{2n}^{\infty} \int_n^{2n} \frac{|u_n(y)|^p}{|x - y|^{sp+1}} dx\, dy \leqslant C \int_n^{2n} \frac{|(\varphi(y/n) - \varphi(2))u(y)|^p}{|2n - y|^{sp}} dy$$
$$\leqslant \frac{C}{n^{sp}} \int_n^{2n} \sup_{y \in [1,2]} \left| \frac{\varphi(2) - \varphi(y)}{(2 - y)^s} \right|^p |u(y)|^p dy \leqslant \frac{C'}{n^{sp}} \int_n^{2n} |u(y)|^p dy.$$

Since $u \in L^p$, we have $K_n^{(2)} \to 0$.

Moreover, using the triangular inequality, the mean value inequality for φ, the assumption that $u \in W^{s,p}$, and the maximum of the function $x \mapsto (2n - x)^{p(1-s)} + (x - n)^{p(1-s)}$ on $[n, 2n]$, we can write

$$K_n^{(1)} \leqslant 2^{p-1} \int_n^{2n} \int_n^{2n} \frac{|\varphi(x/n) - \varphi(y/n)|^p |u(x)|^p}{|x - y|^{sp+1}} dx\, dy$$
$$+ 2^{p-1} \int_n^{2n} \int_n^{2n} \frac{|\varphi(x/n)|^p |u(x) - u(y)|^p}{|x - y|^{sp+1}} dx\, dy$$
$$\leqslant 2^{p-1} \left(\int_n^{2n} \int_n^{2n} \frac{|x - y|^{p(1-s)-1}}{n^p} \|\varphi'\|_\infty^p |u(x)|^p dx\, dy \right.$$
$$+ \left. \int_n^{2n} \int_n^{2n} \left| \frac{u(x) - u(y)}{|x - y|^{s+1/p}} \right|^p dx\, dy \right)$$
$$\leqslant C \int_n^{2n} \frac{(2n - x)^{p(1-s)} + (x - n)^{p(1-s)}}{n^p} |u(x)|^p dx + o(1)$$
$$\leqslant C \int_n^{2n} \frac{n^{p(1-s)}}{n^p} |u(x)|^p dx \leqslant \frac{C}{n^{sp}} \int_n^{2n} |u(x)|^p dx + o(1) \longrightarrow 0,$$

where the last line follows from the inclusion of u in L^p.

Using a regularization, we now approximate the functions u with compact support by functions in $\mathcal{D}$. Let ρ be a function in $\mathcal{D}(\mathbb{R})$, let $\rho_\varepsilon(t) = \frac{1}{\varepsilon} \rho(x/\varepsilon)$, and for a function u with compact support in $\mathbb{R}$, let $u_\varepsilon = \rho_\varepsilon \star u$.

The convergence of u_ε in L^p is well known. We will prove that

$$\|u_\varepsilon\|_{s,p}' = \left| \frac{\rho_\varepsilon \star u(x) - \rho_\varepsilon \star u(y)}{|x - y|^{s+1/p}} \right|_{L^p(\mathbb{R}^2)} \leqslant \left| \frac{u(x) - u(y)}{|x - y|^{s+1/p}} \right|_{L^p(\mathbb{R}^2)}.$$

Indeed, we have

$$\left[\|u_\varepsilon\|'_{s,p}\right]^p = \int_{\mathbb{R}^2}\left|\int_{\mathbb{R}} \rho(t)(u(x-\varepsilon t) - u(y-\varepsilon t))dt\right|^p \frac{dx\,dy}{|x-y|^{sp+1}}$$

$$\leqslant \int_{\mathbb{R}^2}\int_{\mathbb{R}} \rho(t)\frac{|u(x-\varepsilon t) - u(y-\varepsilon t)|^p}{|x-y|^{sp+1}}dt\,dx\,dy$$

$$\leqslant \int_{\mathbb{R}} \rho(t)\int_{\mathbb{R}^2}\frac{|u(x-\varepsilon t) - u(y-\varepsilon t)|^p}{|x-y|^{sp+1}}dx\,dy\,dt \leqslant \left[\|u\|'_{s,p}\right]^p.$$

Moreover, setting $v(x,y) = (u(x) - u(y))|x-y|^{-s-1/p}$, the convergence

$$\frac{|\rho_\varepsilon \star u(x) - \rho_\varepsilon \star u(y)|}{|x-y|^{s+1/p}} \longrightarrow v(x,y)$$

for almost every pair (x,y) is a classical result. By Fatou's lemma, it follows that

$$\|u\|'_{s,p} \leqslant \varliminf_{\varepsilon \to 0} \|\rho_\varepsilon \star u\|'_{s,p}.$$

In particular, the sequence defined by

$$v_\varepsilon = (u_\varepsilon(x) - u_\varepsilon(y))|x-y|^{-s-1/p}$$

satisfies $\|v_\varepsilon\|_p \to \|v\|_p$.

We have thus obtained the almost everywhere convergence and the convergence of the norms. Now, the space L^p is uniformly convex because $p > 1$ and in such a space, these two convergences imply that $\|v_\varepsilon - v\|_p \to 0$ (cf. Exercise 4.5). From this, we deduce the convergence of $\|u_\varepsilon - u\|_{s,p}$ to 0, completing the proof. □

At the end of this section, we will see that if Ω is an open set of class $\mathcal{C}^1$, then the space $\mathcal{C}^1(\overline{\Omega})$ is dense in $W^{s,p}(\Omega)$.

4.3.4 Comparison of the Spaces W and T for $\Omega = \mathbb{R}^N$

We will now show that $W^{s,p}(\Omega)$ equals the space of the traces of the elements of $T(p, 1-1/p-s, \Omega)$ at the point $t = 0$. We have the following partial result.

Proposition 4.28. *Let $s \in \,]0,1[\,$ and let $u \in T(p, 1 - 1/p - s, \Omega)$. Let $\{\lambda_n\}$ be an arbitrary sequence of real numbers tending to 0, and let $u_n = u(\lambda_n)$. The sequence $\{u_n\}$ then has a limit $u(0)$ in $L^p(\Omega)$ and the resulting trace map $u \mapsto u(0)$ from T to $L^p(\Omega)$ is continuous.*

Proof of Proposition 4.28.

Let $0 < s < 1$ and set $\nu = 1 - 1/p - s$. Let $u \in T(p, \nu, \Omega)$. To illustrate the ideas, we take $\lambda_n = 1/n$. Let $\{u_n\}$ be the sequence of functions on Ω defined by $u_n = u(1/n)$. By Proposition 4.21 and Hölder's inequality, when $n > m$, we have

$$\|u_n - u_m\|^p_{L^p(\Omega)} = \left\| \int_{1/n}^{1/m} |u'(t)|dt \right\|^p_{L^p(\Omega)} = \int_\Omega \left[\int_{1/n}^{1/m} |u'(t)|(x)dt \right]^p dx$$

$$= \int_\Omega \left[\int_{1/n}^{1/m} t^{-\nu} t^\nu |u'(t)|(x)dt \right]^p dx$$

(4.29)
$$\leqslant \int_\Omega \left[\int_{1/n}^{1/m} t^{-\nu p'} dt \right]^{p/p'} \left[\int_{1/n}^{1/m} [t^\nu |u'(t)|(x)]^p dt \right] dx$$

$$\leqslant \left[\int_{1/n}^{1/m} t^{-\nu p'} dt \right]^{p/p'} \left[\int_{1/n}^{1/m} \left\| t^\nu |u'(t)| \right\|^p_{L^p(\Omega)} dt \right]$$

$$\leqslant C \left[\left(\frac{1}{m} \right)^{1-\nu p'} - \left(\frac{1}{n} \right)^{1-\nu p'} \right]^{p/p'} \|t^\nu u'\|^p_{L^p(]0,+\infty[,L^p(\Omega))},$$

where the last inequality uses the assumption that $t^\nu u'$ belongs to $L^p(]0,+\infty[,L^p(\Omega))$.

Since $\nu + 1/p < 1$, we have $\nu p' = \nu p/(p-1) < 1$. It follows that the first factor tends to 0 when m and n tend to $+\infty$, and, consequently, that $\{u_n\}$ is a Cauchy sequence in the complete space $L^p(\Omega)$. From inequality (4.29), which still holds with the same proof, we can deduce that

(4.30) $\|u(t_1) - u(t_2)\|^p_{L^p(\Omega)}$

$$\leqslant C \left| (t_1)^{1-\nu p'} - (t_2)^{1-\nu p'} \right|^{p/p'} \|t^\nu u'\|^p_{L^p(]0,+\infty[,L^p(\Omega))}.$$

Using this inequality, we see that for all sequences $\{\lambda_n\}$ that tend to 0 from above, the limits of the sequences $\{u(\lambda_n)\}$ exist and coincide. This completes the proof of the existence of the limit.

Let $u(0)$ denote the limit of these sequences in $L^p(\Omega)$. By letting t_1 tend to 0 and using the triangle inequality, we deduce the following from (4.30):

$$\forall t > 0, \ \|u(0)\|^p_{L^p(\Omega)}$$

$$\leqslant 2^{p-1} \left[\|u(t)\|^p_{L^p(\Omega)} + \frac{1}{1-\nu p'} t^{(p/p')-\nu} \|t^\nu u'\|^p_{L^p(]0,+\infty[,L^p(\Omega))} \right].$$

Integrating this inequality over $[0,1]$ and transforming $\int_0^1 \|u(t)\|_{L^p(\Omega)} dt$ by Hölder's inequality, as we did with the integral of $\|u'(t)\|$ at the beginning of (4.29), we obtain the inequality

$$\|u(0)\|_{L^p(\Omega)} \leqslant C\|u\|_T.$$

The trace map $u \mapsto u(0)$ is therefore continuous. $\square$

From now on, we let $\gamma_0(T)$ denote the subspace of $L^p(\Omega)$ consisting of the $u(0)$ for u in T. Let us now show the relation between $W^{s,p}(\mathbb{R}^N)$ and $\gamma_0\left(T(p, 1 - 1/p - s, \mathbb{R}^N)\right)$.

Proposition 4.31.

$$\gamma_0\left(T(p, 1 - 1/p - s, \mathbb{R}^N)\right) = W^{s,p}(\mathbb{R}^N).$$

Outline of the Proof. We first consider the case $N = 1$, which we show using two converse propositions (4.32 and 4.37). For the general case, we will apply Lemma 4.33 in order to use an induction on the dimension N.

Proposition 4.32. *Let $u \in W^{s,p}(\mathbb{R})$ and let v be defined on $]0, +\infty[\times \mathbb{R}$ by*

$$v(t, x) = \frac{\varphi(t)}{t} \int_0^t u(x + s) ds = \frac{\varphi(t)}{t} \int_x^{x+t} u(s) ds,$$

where $\varphi \in \mathcal{D}(\mathbb{R})$ and $\varphi(0) = 1$; then the function $t \mapsto v(t, \cdot)$ belongs to $T(p, 1 - 1/p - s, \mathbb{R})$. More precisely, if v_1 and v_2 denote the functions

$$t \longmapsto t^{1-1/p-s} v(t, \cdot) \quad and \quad t \longmapsto t^{1-1/p-s} \frac{\partial v}{\partial t}(t, \cdot),$$

respectively, then we have

$$v_1 \in L^p\left(]0, +\infty[, W^{1,p}(]0, +\infty[\times \mathbb{R})\right) \ and \ v_2 \in L^p\left(]0, +\infty[, L^p(]0, +\infty[\times \mathbb{R})\right).$$

Proof of Proposition 4.32.

We begin by verifying that if $\nu = 1 - 1/p - s$, then $v_\nu = t^\nu v \in L^p(]0, +\infty[\times \mathbb{R})$. Indeed,

$$\|v_\nu\|_p^p = \int_{\mathbb{R}} \int_0^{+\infty} t^{\nu p} |\varphi(t)|^p \left| \int_0^1 u(x + st) ds \right|^p dt\, dx$$

$$\leqslant \int_0^{+\infty} t^{\nu p} |\varphi(t)|^p dt \int_0^1 \int_{\mathbb{R}} |u(X)|^p dX\, ds < \infty.$$

We then show that $t^\nu \partial_x v \in L^p(]0, +\infty[\times \mathbb{R})$. Indeed,

$$t^\nu \partial_x v = \varphi(t) t^{-1/p-s} \left(u(x + t) - u(x)\right),$$

whence, by taking the pth power and integrating,

$$\int_{\mathbb{R}} \int_{]0,+\infty[} |\varphi(t)|^p \frac{|u(x+t) - u(x)|^p}{|t|^{sp+1}} ds \leqslant \|\varphi\|_\infty^p \|u\|_{W^{s,p}}^p < \infty.$$

Finally, we verify that $t^\nu \partial_t v \in L^p(]0, +\infty[\times \mathbb{R})$:

$$t^\nu \partial_t v = \varphi(t) t^{-1/p-s} \frac{1}{t} \int_0^t (u(x+t) - u(x+s)) ds + \varphi'(t) t^\nu \int_0^1 u(x+st) ds$$

$$= t^\nu f(t, x) + \varphi'(t) t^\nu \int_0^1 u(x+st) ds.$$

It is clear that $t \mapsto \varphi'(t) t^\nu \int_0^1 u(x+st) ds$ belongs to L^p and, moreover, has a norm in L^p bounded from above by $\|u\|_p$, up to a constant.

Using Hölder's inequality and a change of variables, we have

$$\int_\mathbb{R} \int_{\mathbb{R}^+} |t^\nu f(t,x)|^p dx \, dt \leqslant \|\varphi\|_\infty^p \int_0^1 \int_\mathbb{R} \int_{\mathbb{R}^+} \frac{|u(x+t) - u(x+tz)|^p}{t^{sp+1}} dz \, dx \, dt.$$

Next, the change of variables $(x, t, z) \to (x+t, x+tz, z)$, whose Jacobian is $|1 - z|$, allows us to deduce an upper bound for the last integral:

$$\int_0^1 \int_\mathbb{R} \int_\mathbb{R} \frac{|u(X) - u(T)|^p}{|X - T|^{sp+1}} |1 - z|^{sp} dz \, dX \, dT \leqslant \|u\|_{s,p}^p,$$

giving the desired result. □

We begin by studying the case where $N \geqslant 2$ and establishing the following equivalence result, which is the analogue of Lemma 3.27.

Lemma 4.33. *The following two properties are equivalent:*

(i) $$u \in W^{s,p}(\mathbb{R}^K),$$

(ii) $$\forall i \in [1, K], \quad \int_{\mathbb{R}^K} \int_\mathbb{R} \frac{|u(x + te_i) - u(x)|^p}{t^{sp+1}} dx \, dt < \infty$$

and there exists a universal constant c such that

$$\int_{\mathbb{R}^K} \int_\mathbb{R} \frac{|u(x + te_i) - u(x)|^p}{t^{sp+1}} dx \, dt \leqslant c \int_{\mathbb{R}^{2K}} \frac{|u(x) - u(y)|^p}{|x - y|^{sp+K}} dx \, dy.$$

The following result concerning the existence of embeddings, which will be useful later on, easily follows.

Corollary 4.34. *The spaces $W^{s,p}(\mathbb{R}^N)$ satisfy the following embedding properties:*

(i) *If $0 < s' < s < 1$, then $W^{s,p}(\mathbb{R}^N) \hookrightarrow W^{s',p}(\mathbb{R}^N)$.*
(ii) *If $s \in]0, 1[$, then $W^{1,p}(\mathbb{R}^N) \hookrightarrow W^{s,p}(\mathbb{R}^N)$.*

Proof of Lemma 4.33.

Let us show that (ii) implies (i). Let $u \in L^p(\mathbb{R}^K)$ satisfy

$$\forall i \in [1, N], \quad \int_{\mathbb{R}^K} \int_{\mathbb{R}} \frac{|u(x + te_i) - u(x)|^p}{t^{sp+1}} \, dx \, dt < \infty.$$

For x and y in $]0, 1[^K$, we use the decomposition of $[u]_x^y = -u(x) + u(y)$ introduced in the proof of Lemma 3.27 and the functions δ_i derived from it:

$$[u]_x^y = \sum_{i=1}^{i=K-1} u\Big(x - \sum_{j \leqslant i} x_j e_j + \sum_{j \leqslant i} y_j e_j\Big) - u\Big(x - \sum_{j \leqslant i+1} x_j e_j + \sum_{j \leqslant i+1} y_j e_j\Big)$$

$$\delta_i(x, y) = u\Big(x - \sum_{j \leqslant i} x_j e_j + \sum_{j \leqslant i} y_j e_j\Big) - u\Big(x - \sum_{j \leqslant i+1} x_j e_j + \sum_{j \leqslant i+1} y_j e_j\Big).$$

We can thus write the seminorm $W^{s,p}(]0, 1[^K)$ as a sum of integrals I_i, where

$$I_i = \left(\int_{\mathbb{R}^K} \int_{\mathbb{R}^K} \frac{|\delta_i(x, y)|^p}{[\sum_j |x_j - y_j|]^{sp+K}} \, dx' dy' \right)^{1/p}.$$

To bound these integrals from above, we note, as in the proof of Lemma 3.27 of Chapter 3, that there exists a constant C such that

(4.35) $$\int_{\mathbb{R}^{K-1}} \frac{1}{\sum_i |x_i - y_i|^{sp+K}} \prod_{j \geqslant 2+i} dy_j \prod_{k \leqslant i} dx_k \leqslant C \frac{1}{|x_{i+1} - y_{i+1}|^{sp+1}}.$$

In each integral I_i, we can see the numerator as depending only on x_i and y_i. Indeed, taking, for example, $i = K - 1$ and integrating with respect to $\prod_{j \leqslant K-1} dy_j$, the previous inequality leads to

(4.36) $$\int_{\mathbb{R}^K} \int_{\mathbb{R}^K} \frac{|(u(x_1, \ldots, x_K) - u(x_1, \ldots, x_{K-1}, y_K)|^p}{\sum_i (|x_i - y_i|)^{sp+K}} \prod_j dx_j \prod_l dy_l$$

$$\leqslant C \int_{\mathbb{R}^K} \int_{\mathbb{R}} \frac{|(u(x_1, \ldots, x_{K-1}, x_K) - u(x_1, \ldots, x_{K-1}, y_K)|^p}{|x_K - y_K|^{sp+1}} \prod_{j \leqslant K} dx_j dy_K,$$

giving the result by using (ii).

Let us show that (i) implies (ii). To illustrate the ideas, suppose that $i = K$. Reasoning by induction, we see that the result follows from the following implication:

If

$$\int_{\mathbb{R}^K} \int_{\mathbb{R}^{K-1}} \int_{\mathbb{R}} \frac{|u(x', x_K + t) - u(y', x_K)|^p}{(|t| + |x' - y'|)^{sp+K}} \, dx' dx_K dy' \, dt < \infty,$$

then

$$\int_{\mathbb{R}^K}\int_{\mathbb{R}^{K-2}}\int_{\mathbb{R}}\frac{|u(x'',x_{K-1},x_K+t)-u(y'',x_{K-1},x_K)|^p}{(t+|x''-y''|)^{sp+K-1}}\,dx\,dy''\,dt<\infty.$$

Integrating the quantity $(t+t'+|x''-y''|)^{-sp-K}$ with respect to t' between 0 and $+\infty$, we find that there exists a constant $c_{p,s,k}$ such that

$$c_{p,s,K}\,(t+|x''-y''|)^{-sp-K+1}\geqslant\int_0^\infty(t+t'+|x''-y''|)^{-sp-K}\,dt'.$$

Moreover, we have

$$u(x',x_K+t)-u(y'',x_{K-1},x_K)$$
$$=u(x'',x_{K-1},x_K+t)-u(\tfrac{y''+x''}{2},x_{K-1}+t',x_K+t/2)$$
$$+u(\tfrac{y''+x''}{2},x_{K-1}+t',x_K+t/2)-u(y'',x_{K-1},x_K),$$

where $t'\in[0,+\infty[$. Using the triangle inequality, the inequality $t+t'+|x''-y''|\geqslant t/2+t'+\frac{1}{2}|x''-y''|$, and the classical inequality $|a+b|^p\leqslant 2^{p-1}(|a|^p+|b|^p)$ describing the convexity, we can bound the integral

$$\int_{\mathbb{R}^K}\int_{\mathbb{R}^{K-2}}\int_0^\infty\frac{|u(x'',x_{K-1},x_K+t)-u(y'',x_{K-1},x_K)|^p}{(|x''-y''|+|t|)^{sp+K-1}}\,dt\,dx\,dy''$$

from above by the sum of the following two integrals, up to a multiplicative constant:

$$\int_{\mathbb{R}^K}\int_{\mathbb{R}^K}\frac{|u(x'',x_{K-1},x_K+t)-u(\tfrac{y''+x''}{2},x_{K-1}+t',x_K+t/2)|^p}{(\frac{1}{2}|x''-y''|+|\frac{t}{2}|+|t'|)^{sp+K}}\,dt\,dt'\,dx\,dy'',$$

$$\int_{\mathbb{R}^K}\int_{\mathbb{R}^K}\frac{|u(\tfrac{y''+x''}{2},x_{K-1}+t',x_K+t/2)-u(y'',x_{K-1},x_K)|^p}{(\frac{1}{2}|x''-y''|+|t/2|+|t'|)^{sp+K}}\,dt\,dt'\,dx\,dy'',$$

thus concluding the proof of Lemma 4.33.   □

Proof of Corollary 4.34.

We use the characterization given in the lemma. Let us write the integral

$$\int_{\mathbb{R}^N}\int_{\mathbb{R}}\frac{|u(x)-u(x+te_i)|^p}{|t|^{s'p+1}}\,dx\,dt$$

as the sum

$$\int_{\mathbb{R}^N}\int_{|t|\leqslant 1}\frac{|u(x)-u(x+te_i)|^p}{|t|^{s'p+1}}\,dx\,dt+\int_{\mathbb{R}^N}\int_{|t|>1}\frac{|u(x)-u(x+te_i)|^p}{|t|^{s'p+1}}\,dx\,dt.$$

The second integral is bounded from above by

$$2^p \int_{\mathbb{R}^N} |u(x)|^p \int_{|t|>1} \frac{1}{t^{s'p+1}} dt\, dx \leqslant c\|u\|_{L^p(\mathbb{R}^N)}^p.$$

For the first integral, we use the inequality

$$\frac{1}{|t|^{s'p+1}} \leqslant \frac{1}{|t|^{sp+1}},$$

for $|t| \leqslant 1$, which by the previous lemma gives the desired embedding. Moreover, it gives the existence of a constant C depending only on N, p, s, s', such that

$$\|u\|_{s',p}^p \leqslant C\Big(\|u\|_{s,p}^p + \|u\|_p^p\Big).$$

For the second embedding, let $u \in W^{1,p}(\mathbb{R}^N)$. For $|t| \leqslant 1$, we write $|u(x + te_i) - u(x)|$ as an integral and apply Hölder's inequality, giving

$$|u(x + te_i) - u(x)|^p \leqslant t^{p-1} \int_0^t |\partial_i u|^p (x + s)ds.$$

Using Fubini's formula, we deduce from this that

$$\int_0^1 \int_{\mathbb{R}^N} \frac{|u(x) - u(x + te_i)|^p}{t^{sp+1}} dx\, dt \leqslant \int_0^1 t^{p-sp-1} \int_{\mathbb{R}^N} |\partial_i u|^p \leqslant C|\partial_i u|^p$$

because the integral in t converges since $p - sp - 1 > -1$. Moreover, the same function integrated over $[1, \infty]$ gives a result that is bounded from above by $C\|u\|_p^p$. $\qquad\square$

Proof of Proposition 4.31 for $N \geqslant 2$.

Let $u \in W^{s,p}(\mathbb{R}^N)$. Taking a function φ in $\mathcal{D}(\mathbb{R})$ satisfying $\varphi(0) = 1$, we define v by setting

$$v(t, x) = \frac{\varphi(t)}{t^N} \int_{]0,t[^N} u(x + z)dz.$$

We use the notation

$$\breve{z}_i = \sum_{j \neq i} z_i e_i, \quad d\breve{z}_i = \prod_{j \neq i} dz_j,$$

so that

$$\partial_{x_i}\big(u(x + z)\big) = \partial_{x_i}\big(u((x_i + z_i)e_i + \breve{x}_i + \breve{z}_i)\big)$$
$$= \partial_{z_i}\big(u((x_i + z_i)e_i + \breve{x}_i + \breve{z}_i)\big) = \partial_{z_i}\big(u(x + z)\big).$$

To derive v with respect to x_i, we use the above and Fubini's formula. This leads to

$$\partial_i v(t,x) = \frac{\varphi(t)}{t^N} \int_{(]0,t[)^{N-1}} \int_0^t \partial_{z_i}\big(u(x+z_ie_i+\check{z}_i)dz_id\check{z}_i$$

$$= \frac{\varphi(t)}{t^N} \int_{(]0,t[)^{N-1}} \big[u(x+te_i+\check{z}_i) - u(x+\check{z}_i)\big]d\check{z}_i.$$

Taking the pth power, applying Hölder's inequality, and multiplying by $t^{\nu p}$, we obtain

$$\int_0^{+\infty} \int_{\mathbb{R}^N} t^{\nu p} |\partial_i v(t,x)|^p dx\, dt$$

$$\leqslant \|\varphi\|_\infty^p \int_{\mathbb{R}^+} \int_{\mathbb{R}^N} \int_{]0,1[^{N-1}} \frac{|u(x+\check{s}_it+t) - u(x+\check{s}_it)|^p}{t^{sp+1}} dx\, d\check{s}_i dt.$$

The result follows by using the change of variables $X = x + \check{s}_it$.

Setting $\psi(t,x) = \varphi'(t) \int_{]0,1[^N} u(x+zt)dz$, differentiating with respect to t gives

$$\partial_t v = \varphi(t)\left(\frac{-N}{t^{N+1}} \int_{]0,t[^N} u(x+z)dz + \frac{1}{t^N}\sum_i \int_{]0,t[^{N-1}} u(x+\check{s}_i+te_i)d\check{s}_i\right)$$

$$+ \varphi'(t) \int_{]0,1[^N} u(x+zt)dz$$

$$= \frac{\varphi(t)}{t^{N+1}} \sum_i \int_{]0,t[^N} \big(u(x+\check{z}_i+te_i) - u(x+z)\big)\,dz + \psi(x,t)$$

$$= f(t,x) + \psi(t,x).$$

It is clear that $(t,x) \mapsto t^\nu \psi(t,x)$ belongs to L^p. Moreover, multiplying $|f(t,x)|^p$ by $t^{\nu p}$ and integrating gives

$$\int_{\mathbb{R}^N \times \mathbb{R}^+} |t^\nu f(t,x)|^p dt\, dx$$

$$\leqslant C\|\varphi\|_\infty^p \int_{\mathbb{R}^N} \sum_i \int_{]0,1[^N \times \mathbb{R}^+} \frac{|u(x+\check{z}_it+te_i) - u(x+zt)|^p}{t^{sp+1}} dt\, dz\, dx.$$

Using the change of variable $X = x + zt$, we then obtain

$$\int_{\mathbb{R}^N} \int_{\mathbb{R}^+} \int_{]0,1[^N} \frac{|u(x+\check{z}_it+te_i) - u(x+zt)|^p}{t^{sp+1}} dt dz\, dx$$

$$= \int_{\mathbb{R}^N} \int_{]0,1[^N} \int_{\mathbb{R}^+} \frac{|u(X) - u(X+t(1-z_i)e_i)|^p}{t^{sp+1}} dz\, dt\, dX$$

$$= \int_{\mathbb{R}^N} \int_0^1 dz_i \int_0^{1-z_i} (1-z_i)^{sp} \frac{|u(X) - u(X+Te_i)|^p}{T^{sp+1}}\, dT\, dX < \infty,$$

completing the proof. $\qquad\square$

The following is the converse of Proposition 4.32.

Proposition 4.37. *Let ν be a real number such that $0 < \nu + 1/p < 1$. Let u satisfy $t^\nu u(t, \cdot) \in L^p(]0, 1[, W^{1,p}(\mathbb{R}^N))$ and $t^\nu \partial_t u \in L^p(]0, +\infty[\times \mathbb{R}^N)$; then $u(0, \cdot) \in W^{1-1/p-\nu, p}(\mathbb{R}^N)$.*

Proof of Proposition 4.37.

To prove this proposition, we recall the following lemma from Chapter 3.

Lemma 4.38. *Let ν be a real number and let f be a function from $\mathbb{R}$ to $\mathbb{R}$. We assume that $0 < 1/p + \nu = \theta < 1$ and $1 \leqslant p < \infty$. The following holds:*

(i) *If the map $t \mapsto t^\nu f(t)$ belongs to $L^p(\mathbb{R}^+)$ and if g is defined by*

$$(4.39) \qquad g(t) = \frac{1}{t} \int_0^t f(s)ds,$$

then the map $t \mapsto t^\nu g(t)$ belongs to $L^p(\mathbb{R}^+)$ and there exists a constant $c(p, \nu)$ depending only on p and ν such that

$$(4.40) \qquad \int_0^\infty t^{\nu p} |g(t)|^p dt \leqslant c(p, \nu) \int_0^\infty t^{\nu p} |f(t)|^p dt.$$

(ii) *Let α, β be elements of $\overline{\mathbb{R}}$ with $\alpha < \beta$. Let f be defined on $\mathbb{R}^+ \times]\alpha, \beta[$ and let g be defined by $g(t, x) = 1/t \int_0^t f(s, x)ds$. If $t^\nu f \in L^p(\mathbb{R}^+ \times]\alpha, \beta[)$, then $t^\nu g$ belongs to $L^p(\mathbb{R}^+ \times]\alpha, \beta[)$ and there exists a constant $c(p, \nu)$ depending only on p and ν, such that*

$$(4.41) \qquad \int_\alpha^\beta \int_0^\infty t^{\nu p} |g(t, x)|^p dt\, dx \leqslant c(p, \nu) \int_\alpha^\beta \int_0^\infty t^{\nu p} |f(t, x)|^p dt\, dx.$$

We can now show Proposition 4.37. By Lemma 4.33, we can reduce to proving that

$$\int_{\mathbb{R}^N} \int_0^\infty \frac{|u(0, x) - u(0, x + t)|^p}{t^{sp+1}} dx\, dt < \infty.$$

To show this, we write $u(0, x) - u(0, x + t)$ as a sum of three differences:

$$u(0,x) - u(0, x+t) = u(0,x) - u(t,x) + u(t,x) - u(t,x+t) + u(t,x+t) - u(0,x+t)$$

that we replace by

$$\int_0^t \partial_\lambda u(\lambda, x)d\lambda, \qquad \int_0^t \partial_x u(t, x + \lambda)d\lambda \quad \text{and} \quad \int_0^t \partial_\lambda u(\lambda, x + t)d\lambda,$$

respectively. We then apply Lemma 4.38 to each of these integrals with the functions $f(t, x, \lambda) = \partial_t u(\lambda, x)$, $f(t, x, \lambda) = \partial_x u(t, x + \lambda)$ and $f(t, x, \lambda) = \partial_t u(\lambda, x + t)$, respectively . This gives

$$\int_{\mathbb{R}^N} \int_{\mathbb{R}^+} t^{\nu p} \left| \frac{1}{t} \int_0^t f(x, \lambda)d\lambda \right|^p d\lambda dx < \infty,$$

which implies that

$$\int_{\mathbb{R}^N} \int_{\mathbb{R}^+} t^{(\nu-1)p} |u(0,x) - u(t,x)|^p = \int_{\mathbb{R}^N} \int_{\mathbb{R}^+} \frac{1}{t^{sp+1}} |u(0,x) - u(t,x)|^p < \infty. \quad \square$$

After studying the difference between the cases $\mathbb{R}$ and $\mathbb{R}^N$, we now consider the case of a general open set Ω.

4.3.5 Comparison of the Spaces W and T when $\Omega \neq \mathbb{R}^N$

Before we begin, we need to recall certain results concerning (s,p)-extensions, which will also be useful when we establish embedding theorems.

Preliminary Results on (s,p)-Extensions.

Definition 4.42. We say that Ω admits an (s,p)-extension if there exists a continuous linear operator E that sends $u \in W^{s,p}(\Omega)$ to $E(u) = \widetilde{u} \in W^{s,p}(\mathbb{R}^N)$, such that
$$\forall x \in \Omega, \quad Eu(x) = u(x).$$

In the case of a class $\mathcal{C}^1$ or Lipschitz open set, we have the following result.

Proposition 4.43. *Any Lipschitz open set Ω admits an (s,p)-extension.*

Proof of Proposition 4.43.

By assumption, there exists a cover of Ω by bounded open sets Ω_i, open subsets $\mathcal{O}'_i$ of $\mathbb{R}^{N-1}$ and Lipschitz functions a_i on $\mathcal{O}'_i$ with uniformly bounded gradient norms, such that, for $i \geqslant 1$,

$$\Omega_i \cap \Omega \subset \{(x', x_N) \mid x' \in \mathcal{O}'_i, \, x_N > a_i(x')\},$$
$$\Omega_i \cap \partial\Omega = \{(x', a_i(x')) \mid x' \in \mathcal{O}'_i\}.$$

Let $\{\theta_i\}$ denote a partition of unity subordinate to the cover $\{\Omega_i\}$ of Ω.

Given the function $u \in W^{s,p}(\Omega)$, we are going to construct $E(u)$ locally. Consider the product $u_i = u\theta_i$ on the open set $U_i = \Omega \cap \Omega_i$. If we define a function Eu_i that extends u_i outside of $\Omega \cap \Omega_i$ and that belongs to $W^{s,p}(\mathbb{R}^N)$, then, as usual, it will suffice to glue these extensions Eu_i to obtain the desired (s,p)-extension and thus complete the proof of the proposition.

Let us first show that $u_i \in W^{s,p}(U_i)$.

We already have $u_i \in L^p(U_i)$. For the seminorm $\|u_i\|'_{s,p}$, we write

$$(\theta_i u)(x) - (\theta_i u)(y) = \theta_i(x)(u(x) - u(y)) + u(y)(\theta_i(x) - \theta_i(y)).$$

Hence, using $(|a| + |b|)^p \leqslant 2^{p-1}[|a|^p + |b|^p]$ for the numerator and the mean value theorem for θ_i, we obtain the following inequality for $2^{-p+1}\|u_i\|'^p_{s,p}$:

$$2^{-p+1} \int_{U_i} \int_{U_i} \frac{|u_i(x) - u_i(y)|^p}{|x - y|^{sp+N}}$$

$$\leqslant \int_{U_i} \int_{U_i} \frac{|\theta_i|^p(x)|u(x) - u(y)|^p}{|x - y|^{sp+N}} dx\, dy + \int_{U_i} |u(y)|^p \int_{U_i} \frac{|\theta_i(x) - \theta_i(y)|^p}{|x - y|^{sp+N}} dx\, dy$$

$$\leqslant C_1 \|u\|'^p_{s,p} + \|\nabla \theta_i\|^p_\infty \int_{U_i} |u(y)|^p \Big[\int_{U_i} |x - y|^{p-sp-N} dx \Big] dy.$$

Now, the last integral is finite. Indeed, taking the origin at y and supposing that $U_i \subset B(y, R)$, which we may by our assumptions, we have

$$\int_{U_i} |x - y|^{p-sp-N} dx \leqslant \omega_{N-1} \int_0^R \rho^{p-sp-N+N-1} d\rho < \infty$$

because of the relation $p - 1 - sp = (1 - s)p - 1 > -1$, which results from $s < 1$. It then follows from the previous inequality that $u_i \in W^{s,p}(U_i)$ and that there exist constants H and K such that

$$\|u_i\|'^p_{s,p} \leqslant K\|u\|'^p_{s,p} + H\|u\|^p_p \leqslant C_1\|u\|^p_{s,p}.$$

Construction of the (s,p)-extension. For the sake of simplicity, we omit the factor θ_i. We have reduced the problem to extending the function $u \in W^{s,p}(\Omega)$ to the open set Ω' defined by $\Omega' = \{x' \in \mathcal{O}' \mid x_N < a_i(x')\}$. We will use the reflexion P defined by

$$\text{if} \quad (x', x_N) \in \mathbb{R}^N, \quad \text{then} \quad x_N < a(x') \Longrightarrow P(x', x_N) = (x', 2a_i(x') - x_N).$$

Let $\widetilde{u}(x', x_N) = u(x', x_N)$ if $x \in \Omega$ and $\widetilde{u}(x', x_N) = u(P(x', x_N))$ if $x \in \Omega'$.

Let us verify that $\widetilde{u} \in W^{s,p}(\mathbb{R}^N)$.

We write the seminorm $\|\widetilde{u}\|'_{W^{s,p}(\mathbb{R}^N)}$ as the sum of four integrals J_1, J_2, J_3 and J_4 over the sets $\Omega \times \Omega$, $\Omega \times \Omega'$, $\Omega' \times \Omega$ and $\Omega' \times \Omega'$, respectively. By assumption, $|J_1| < +\infty$. For the three other integrals, we will give a lower bound for the denominator, which is of the form $|x - y|^{sp+N}$.

We will show the existence of a constant C_2 such that

(4.44) $\qquad \forall\, (x, y) \in (\Omega')^2, \quad |P(x) - P(y)| \leqslant C_2 |x - y|$

(4.45) $\qquad$ and $\forall\, (x, y) \in \Omega \times \Omega', \quad |x - P(y)| \leqslant C_2 |x - y|.$

Note that these properties generalize those of an oblique reflection *symmetry*. Figure 4.1 illustrates this for the case $N = 2$, where the boundary is straight and the norm is the sum of the absolute values of the coordinates.

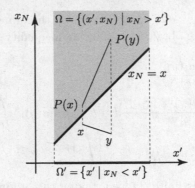

Fig. 4.1. A *symmetry* for the (s, p)-extension.
Case $N = 2$, $a(x') = x'$; norm: $|(a, b)|_1 = |a| + |b|$;
$\left|\overrightarrow{P(x)P(y)}\right|_1 \leqslant 3|\overrightarrow{xy}|_1$.

Indeed, for the first inequality, we use the distance function $\sum_1^N |\xi_i - \eta_i|$ in $\mathbb{R}^N$ to obtain

$$|P(x) - P(y)| = |x' - y'| + |2a_i(x') - x_N - 2a_i(y') + y_N|$$
$$\leqslant (1 + 2\|\nabla a_i\|_\infty)(|x' - y'| + |x_N - y_N|) \leqslant C_2 |x - y|,$$

and deduce (4.44).

For the second inequality, we have, on the one hand,

$$2a_i(y') - x_N - y_N = 2(a_i(y') - y_N) + y_N - x_N \geqslant y_N - x_N$$
$$\geqslant -|x_N - y_N|,$$

since $y_N < a_i(y')$, and, on the other hand,

$$2a_i(y') - y_N - x_N \leqslant 2(a_i(y') - a_i(x')) + 2a_i(x') - x_N - y_N$$
$$\leqslant 2(a_i(y') - a_i(x')) + x_N - y_N$$
$$\leqslant |y_N - x_N| + 2\|\nabla a_i\|_\infty |x' - y'|$$
$$\leqslant (1 + 2\|\nabla a_i\|_\infty)(|x - y|),$$

since $x_N > a_i(x')$. The inequality (4.45) follows from these two. Moreover, by the uniform regularity conditions on the open set Ω, we may replace the norm $\|\nabla a_i\|_\infty$ in C_2 by the supremum $\sup_i \|\nabla a_i\|_\infty$, giving a constant C_2 that does not depend on i. Using (4.45) and the change of variables $y'_N = 2a_i(y') - y_N$, we see that the second integral J_2 satisfies

$$C_2 J_2 \leqslant \int_\Omega \int_{\mathcal{O}'} \int_{-\infty}^{a_i(x')} \frac{|u(x) - u(y', 2a_i(y') - y_N)|^p}{|x - P(y)|^{sp+N}} dy_N dy' dx$$
$$\leqslant \int_\Omega \int_{\mathcal{O}'} \int_{a_i(x')}^{+\infty} \frac{|u(x) - u(y', y'_N)|^p}{|x - (y', y'_N)|^{sp+N}} dy_N dy' dx = J_1.$$

We can obtain the analogous result for J_3 by exchanging x and y. For J_4, the inequality (4.44) gives the analogous result using two changes of variables similar to the ones above. Returning to the function u_i, we can now conclude that $Eu_i \in W^{s,p}(\mathbb{R}^N)$. Moreover, we have

$$\|Eu_i\|^p_{W^{s,p}(\mathbb{R}^N)} \leqslant 2\|u_i\|^p_{L^p(\Omega)} + 4C_2^{-1}(\|u_i\|'_{s,p})^p.$$

It follows that

$$\|Eu_i\|^p_{W^{s,p}(\mathbb{R}^N)} \leqslant C\|u\|^p_{W^{s,p}(\Omega)},$$

where C does not depend on i. We have thus shown the existence of an $Eu \in W^{s,p}(\mathbb{R}^N)$ extending $u \in W^{s,p}(\Omega)$ and satisfying $\|Eu\|_{W^{s,p}(\mathbb{R}^N)} \leqslant C\|u\|_{W^{s,p}(\Omega)}$. The latter expresses the continuity of the (s,p)-extension map E. □

Comparison of the Spaces W and T, Continued. Using the above, we can generalize the previous result as follows.

Proposition 4.46. *Let $p > 1$, let $s \in {]}0,1{[}$, and let $\nu = 1 - 1/p - s$. If Ω is a Lipschitz open subset of $\mathbb{R}^N$, then*

$$\gamma_0(T(p,\nu,\Omega)) = W^{s,p}(\Omega).$$

Proof of Proposition 4.46.

To $u \in T(p,\nu,\Omega)$, we associate the function Eu in $T(p,\nu,\mathbb{R}^N)$ (cf. Proposition 4.43). Indeed, since by assumption, $t^\nu u(t,\cdot) \in W^{1,p}({]}0,+\infty{[},\mathbb{R}^N)$, it follows that for a fixed $t > 0$, $t^\nu Eu(t,\cdot) \in W^{1,p}(\mathbb{R}^N)$ while $\|t^\nu Eu(t,\cdot)\|_{W^{1,p}(\mathbb{R}^N)} \leqslant C\|t^\nu u(t,\cdot)\|_{W^{1,p}(\Omega)}$ for a constant C that is independent of t. From this property, we obtain the convergence

$$\int_0^{+\infty} \|t^\nu Eu(t,\cdot)\|_{W^{1,p}(\mathbb{R}^N)}dt \leqslant C\int_0^{+\infty} \|t^\nu u(t,\cdot)\|_{W^{1,p}(\Omega)}dt < +\infty.$$

We repeat this proof for $t^\nu\partial_t u$, giving the desired result. It follows that $\gamma_0(Eu)$, which we can also denote by $Eu(0,\cdot)$, is an element of $W^{s,p}(\mathbb{R}^N)$. By Proposition 4.28, we now have, for every $x \in \Omega$,

$$Eu(0,x) = \lim_{t\to 0} Eu(t,x) = \lim_{t\to 0} u(t,x) = u(0,x).$$

Conversely, let $u \in W^{s,p}(\Omega)$. We then have $Eu \in W^{s,p}(\mathbb{R}^N)$ and by Proposition 4.32, there exists a function v such that $v \in T(p,\nu,W^{1,p}(\mathbb{R}^N),L^p(\mathbb{R}^N))$ and $v(0,x) = Eu(x)$. By restricting the functions in x to the open set Ω, we can easily see that $(t,x) \mapsto v(t,x)$ defines an element v^* of $T(p,\nu,W^{1,p}(\Omega),L^p(\Omega))$. For every $x \in \Omega$, this restriction of v satisfies $v^*(0,x) = u(x)$. □

An immediate application of this comparison of spaces is the existence of embeddings of the spaces $W^{s,p}$ in the spaces L^q. We will study this in the next section.

4.4 Embeddings of the $W^{s,p}(\Omega)$

4.4.1 The Case $\Omega = \mathbb{R}^N$

Theorem 4.47. *Let $s \in]0,1[$ and let $p \in]1,\infty[$. We have:*

- *If $sp < N$, then $W^{s,p}(\mathbb{R}^N) \hookrightarrow L^q(\mathbb{R}^N)$ for every $q \leqslant Np/(N - sp)$.*
- *If $N = sp$, then $W^{s,p}(\mathbb{R}^N) \hookrightarrow L^q(\mathbb{R}^N)$ for every $q < \infty$.*
- *If $sp > N$, then $W^{s,p}(\mathbb{R}^N) \hookrightarrow L^\infty(\mathbb{R}^N)$ and, more precisely,*

$$W^{s,p}(\mathbb{R}^N) \longhookrightarrow \mathcal{C}_b^{0,s-N/p}(\mathbb{R}^N).$$

Remark 4.48. We have already shown this theorem for $s = 1 - 1/p$ using embeddings in Sobolev spaces of integer order.

Proof of Theorem 4.47.

Let $u \in W^{s,p}(\mathbb{R}^N)$ and let $v \in L^p(]0,+\infty[\times \mathbb{R}^N)$ with $v(0,x) = u(x)$ be such that $t \mapsto t^\nu v$ belongs to $L^p(]0,+\infty[, W^{1,p}(\mathbb{R}^N))$ and $t \mapsto t^\nu \partial_t v$ belongs to $L^p(]0,+\infty[, L^p(\mathbb{R}^N))$, where $\nu = 1 - 1/p - s$.

We begin by assuming that $N > p$. We fix x and define f by setting $f(t) = v(t,x)$; we then have

$$f(0) = f(t) - \int_0^t f'(s)ds.$$

By multiplying and dividing by t^ν, integrating over $]0,1[$, applying Hölder's inequality and the inequality $-\nu p' > -1$, we obtain

$$|f(0)| \leqslant C\left[\left(\int_0^1 |t^\nu f|^p \, dt\right)^{1/p} + \left(\int_0^1 |t^\nu \partial_t f|^p \, dt\right)^{1/p}\right]$$
$$\leqslant C\left[\left(\int_0^\infty |t^\nu f|^p dt\right)^{1/p} + \left(\int_0^\infty |t^\nu f'|^p dt\right)^{1/p}\right].$$

Using the function $f_\lambda(t) = f(\lambda t)$, we find that for every $\lambda > 0$, this leads to the inequality

$$|f(0)| \leqslant C\left[\lambda^{-\nu-1/p}\left(\int_0^\infty |t^\nu f|^p dt\right)^{1/p} + \lambda^{1-\nu-1/p}\left(\int_0^\infty |t^\nu \partial_t f|^p dt\right)^{1/p}\right],$$

giving the optimal upper bound

$$|f(0)| \leqslant C'\left[\left(\int_0^\infty |t^\nu f|^p dt\right)^{1/p}\right]^s \left[\left(\int_0^\infty |t^\nu \partial_t f|^p dt\right)^{1/p}\right]^{1-s}.$$

Let r satisfy

$$\frac{1}{r} = \frac{s(N-p)}{Np} + \frac{(1-s)}{p}, \quad \text{that is,} \quad r = \frac{Np}{(N-sp)}.$$

Let $|g|_p = (\int_0^1 |g(t)|^p dt)^{1/p}$. By Hölder's inequality, we have the following upper bound for $\int_{\mathbb{R}^N} |v(0,x)|^r dx$:

$$\int_{\mathbb{R}^N} \left|t^\nu v(t,x)\right|_p^{sr} \left|t^\nu \partial_t v\right|_p^{(1-s)r} dx$$

$$\leqslant \left(\int_{\mathbb{R}^N} \left|t^\nu v\right|_p^{Np/(N-p)} dx\right)^{(N-p)s/(N-sp)} \left(\int_{\mathbb{R}^N} \left|t^\nu \partial_t v\right|_p^p dx\right)^{(1-s)N/(N-sp)}.$$

Consequently, by taking the $1/r$th power, we obtain

$$\|v(0,x)\|_{L^r(\mathbb{R}^N)} \leqslant C \left\|t^\nu v\right\|_{L^p(]0,1[,L^{Np/(N-p)}(\mathbb{R}^N))}^s \left\|t^\nu \partial_t v\right\|_{L^p(]0,1[,L^p(\mathbb{R}^N))}^{1-s}.$$

This relation gives the result in the case $N > p$. Note that this method cannot be adapted to the case $p > N$.

When $p > N$ and $sp < N$, we need to use different arguments. We will use the fundamental solution E of the Laplacian. Recall that in dimension $N+1$, it is defined by $E(t,x) = k_{N+1}(|x|^2 + t^2)^{(1-N)/2}$, where k_{N+1} is chosen in such a way that we have $\Delta E = \delta_0$ (cf. Exercise 2.19 of Chapter 2).

Let θ and ψ be functions in $\mathcal{D}(\mathbb{R}^N)$ and $\mathcal{D}(\mathbb{R})$, respectively, with values between 0 and 1 and equal to 1 in neighborhoods of 0. We can replace δ_0, which has support $\{0\}$, by the product $\theta(x)\psi(t)\delta_0$. Using the formula giving the derivative of the product of a distribution and a $\mathcal{C}^\infty$ function, the formula giving the Laplacian of such a product, and the formula giving the derivative of a convolution, that is, $\partial_i(V) \star U = \partial_i(U \star V) = \partial_i U \star V$, we can write, for v satisfying $v(0,x) = u(x)$,

$$v = \delta_0 \star v = \Delta\big(\theta(x)\psi(t)E\big) \star v - 2\big(\nabla(\theta(x)\psi(t)) \cdot \nabla E\big) \star v - \Delta(\theta(x)\psi(t))E \star v$$

$$= \sum_{1 \leqslant i \leqslant N} \nabla_i(\theta(x)\psi(t)E) \star \nabla_i v + \partial_t(\theta(x)\psi(t)E) \star \partial_t v$$

$$- 2\big(\nabla(\theta(x)\psi(t)) \cdot \nabla E\big) \star v - E\Delta(\theta(x)\psi(t)) \star v.$$

Letting $\nabla_x E$ denote the gradient with respect to x and $\nabla_x A \star \nabla_x B$ the sum of the convolutions $\partial_i A \star \partial_i B$, we can also write

$$(4.49) \quad v = \big(\theta(x)\psi(t)\nabla_x E\big) \star \nabla_x v + \big(\psi(t)\theta(x)\partial_t E\big) \star \partial_t v$$

$$+ \big(\psi(t)E\nabla_x \theta(x)\big) \star \nabla_x v + \big(\theta(x)E\partial_t \psi\big) \star \partial_t v - 2\big(\nabla(\theta(x)\psi(t)) \cdot \nabla E\big) \star v$$

$$- \big(E\Delta\theta(x)\psi(t)\big) \star v.$$

The last four terms of the right-hand side of (4.49) are finite sums of convolutions of the type

$$(\zeta_1(t,x)E) \star v, \quad (\zeta_2(t,x)\partial_i E) \star v, \quad (\zeta_3(t,x)\partial_t E) \star v,$$
$$(\zeta_4(t,x)E) \star \partial_i v \quad \text{and} \quad (\zeta_5(t,x)E) \star \partial_t v,$$

where the ζ_i are functions in $\mathcal{D}(\mathbb{R}^{N+1})$.

We will evaluate these terms at $(0,x)$ after studying the first two terms of the right-hand side of (4.49), which involve the derivatives of both v and E. These first two terms of (4.49) are sums of convolutions of the form

$$(\theta(x)\psi(t)\partial_i E) \star \partial_i v \quad \text{and} \quad (\psi(t)\theta(x)\partial_t E) \star \partial_t v.$$

We therefore need to evaluate these convolutions at the point $(0,x)$. On the one hand, the function v is such that $t \mapsto t^\nu v(t,.)$ belongs to $L^p(]0,+\infty[, W^{1,p}(\mathbb{R}^N))$, which implies that $t^\nu \partial_i v$ belongs to $L^p(]0,+\infty[, L^p(\mathbb{R}^N))$. On the other hand, the function $t^\nu \partial_t v$ also belongs to this space. The two convolutions above can therefore be written as

$$I = (\psi(t)\theta(x)\partial_t E) \star g \quad \text{and} \quad J = (\psi(t)\theta(x)\nabla_x E) \star g,$$

for a function g such that $t \mapsto t^\nu g(t,\cdot)$ belongs to $L^p(]0,+\infty[, L^p(\mathbb{R}^N))$.

To study I, we let $h(t,x) = \theta(x)\psi(t)\, t\, (|x|^2 + t^2)^{-(N+1)/2}$ and we compute the convolution that expresses I at the point $(0,x)$:

$$(g \star h)(0,x) = \int_{\mathbb{R}^N} \int_0^{+\infty} \frac{\theta(x-x')\psi(-t)tg(t,x')}{(|x|^2 + t^2)^{(N+1)/2}} \, dt\, dx'.$$

Using Hölder's inequality in the integrals in t, we bound $(g \star h)(0,x)$ from above by the convolution $G \star H$ in $\mathbb{R}^N$, where the functions G and H are defined as follows:

$$G(x) = \left(\int_0^{+\infty} t^{\nu p}|g(t,x)|^p dt\right)^{1/p}, \quad H(x) = \left(\int_0^{+\infty} t^{-\nu p'}|h(t,x)|^{p'}\, dt\right)^{1/p'}.$$

The function H can be bounded from above by

$$|\theta(x)|\|\psi\|_\infty \left(\int_0^{+\infty} \frac{t^{(1-\nu)p'}}{(t^2 + x^2)^{(N+1)p'/2}}dt\right)^{1/p'}.$$

Moreover, as the integral in this bound equals, up to a constant, the function $|x|$ to the power $1 - \nu + 1/p' - (N + 1) = s - N$, we find that $H(x) \leqslant C|\theta(x)||x|^{s-N}$.

The product $G \star H$ is therefore bounded from above by the convolution at x of a function in L^p, which by definition is G, and a function of the form

$|x|^{s-N}$, which belongs to L^k for $k < N/(N-s)$. By Corollary 4.60 of the appendix, the function $G \star H$ therefore belongs to L^r for $1/p + 1/k = 1 + 1/r$, that is, for $r < Np/(N-sp)$. For an optimal result, we must use Sobolev's lemma 2.36.

To study J, we let $h_i(t,x) = \theta(x)\psi(t)x_i(|x|^2 + t^2)^{-(N+1)/2}$. We compute the convolution $g \star h_i$ at the point $(0, x)$, once again for $t^\nu g \in L^p(]0, +\infty[\times \mathbb{R}^N)$. By Hölder's inequality, the expression $(g \star h_i)(0, x)$ can be bounded from above by $G \star H_i(x)$, where

$$H_i(x) = \left(\int_0^{+\infty} (\theta(x)\psi(t))^{p'} \frac{t^{-\nu p'}|x_i|^{p'}}{(|x|^2 + t^2)^{(N+1)p'/2}} dt \right)^{1/p'}.$$

This convolution can be bounded from above by $C\theta(x)|x|^{s-N}$. This concludes our study of I and J, and we see that the two terms $(\zeta_2(t,x)\partial_i E) \star v$ and $(\zeta_3(t,x)\partial_t E) \star v$ have also been dealt with.

We will now consider the terms of the form $\zeta_1 E \star v$, $\zeta_4 E \star \partial_i v$, or $\zeta_5 E \star \partial_t v$, that is, the terms that involve E rather than its derivatives. The process is similar to the previous one.

We consider, for example, a term of the form $\theta_1(x)\psi_1(t)E(x,t) \star v$ at the point $(0, x)$, where θ and ψ are in $\mathcal{D}(\mathbb{R}^N)$ and $\mathcal{D}(\mathbb{R})$, respectively. We have

$$I_1(x) = \int_{\mathbb{R}^N} \int_0^\infty \frac{\theta_1(x-x')\psi(-t)v(t,x')}{(t^2 + |x-x'|^2)^{(N-1)/2}} \, dt \, dx'.$$

Using Hölder's inequality in the integrals in t and multiplying by $t^\nu t^{-\nu}$, we find that the absolute value of $I_1(x)$ is bounded from above by the convolution $G_1 \star H_1$ in $\mathbb{R}^N$, where

$$G_1(x) = \left(\int_0^\infty t^{\nu p}|v(t,x)|^p dt \right)^{1/p}$$

and $$H_1(x) = \left(\int_0^\infty \frac{|\theta_1(x)\psi_1(-t)|^{p'} t^{-\nu p'}}{(t^2 + |x|^2)^{(N-1)p'/2}} dt \right)^{1/p'}.$$

The function H_1 is bounded from above by

$$\|\psi_1\|_\infty |\theta_1|(x) \left(\int_0^\infty \frac{t^{-\nu p'}}{(t^2 + |x|^2)^{(N-1)p'/2}} dt \right)^{1/p'},$$

that is, by a function of the type

$$C|\theta_1(x)| \, |x|^{(1-\nu p' - (N-1)p')/p'} = C|\theta_1(x)| \, |x|^{s-N+1}.$$

The product $G_1 \star H_1$ is therefore the convolution of a function in L^p and a function with compact support multiplied by $|x|^{s-N+1}$, which belongs to L^k

for every $k < N/(N - s - 1)$. In particular, this product belongs to L^r for every $r < Np/(N - (s + 1)p)$, hence belongs to $L^{Np/(N-sp)}$.

The other terms are dealt with in a similar way, concluding our treatment of the case $sp < N$.

Let us now consider the case $sp = N$. By Corollary 4.34, we have $W^{s,p}(\mathbb{R}^N) \hookrightarrow W^{s',p}(\mathbb{R}^N)$ for every $s' \in \,]0, s[$. Using the embeddings we obtained for $sp < N$, we deduce that

$$W^{s',p}(\mathbb{R}^N) \longrightarrow L^{Np/(N-s'p)}(\mathbb{R}^N).$$

Moreover, since $Np/(N - s'p)$ can be arbitrarily large, we conclude that $W^{s,p}(\mathbb{R}^N)$ is embedded into $L^q(\mathbb{R}^N)$ for every $q \in [p, \infty[$.

We continue with the case $sp > N$. We once more use the fundamental solution of the Laplacian in $\mathbb{R}^{N+1}$. As in the case $sp < N$, we need to show that certain sums of convolutions of the type $\zeta_1 E \star v$, $\zeta_5 E \star \partial_t v$, $\zeta_4 E \star \partial_x v$, or $\zeta \nabla E \star \nabla v$ belong to L^∞.

For the last term, let $g(t, x)$ denote a function such that $t^\nu g(t, x) \in L^p(]0, +\infty[\times \mathbb{R}^N)$ and let $h(t, x) = \theta(x)\psi(t)t(|x|^2 + t^2)^{-(N+1)/2}$, where θ is a regular function with support in $B(0, 1)$. We will show that for $sp > N$, we have

$$x \longmapsto (h \star g)(0, x) \in L^\infty(\mathbb{R}^N).$$

Indeed,

$$(h \star g)(0, x) = \int_{\mathbb{R}^N} \int_{\mathbb{R}^+} \frac{\theta(x - x')\psi(-t)tg(x', t)}{(t^2 + |x - x'|^2)^{(N+1)/2}} dx'\, dt$$

$$\leqslant \|t^\nu g\|_p \left(\int_{\mathbb{R}^N} \int_{\mathbb{R}^+} \frac{t^{(1-\nu)p'}(\theta(x - x')\psi(t))^{p'}}{(t^2 + |x - x'|^2)^{(N+1)p'/2}} dx'\, dt \right)^{1/p'}$$

$$\leqslant \|t^\nu g\|_p \left(\int_{|x-x'|\leqslant 1} \frac{|x - x'|^{(1-\nu)p'+1}}{|x - x'|^{(N+1)p'}} dx' \right)^{1/p'} \leqslant C\|t^\nu g\|_p,$$

because the last integral can be written as

$$\left(\left[\rho^{(sp-N)/(p-1)} \right]_0^1 \right)^{1/p'},$$

which is bounded because $sp > N$. To bound the functions of the type $\zeta_1 E \star v$, $\zeta_5 E \star \partial_t v$, or $\zeta_4 E \star \partial_x v$, it suffices to remark that each of these products is bounded from above by the convolution of a function in L^p and a function in $L^{p'}$ that is of the form $\theta_i(x)|x|^{s-N+1}$ with θ_i in $\mathcal{D}(\mathbb{R}^N)$.

Let us now show that u is a Hölder continuous function with exponent $s - N/p$. For this, we need to show the existence of a constant C such that

$$(4.50) \qquad \|u\|_\infty \leqslant C\|t^\nu v\|_p^{1-\nu-(N+1)/p}\|t^\nu \nabla_{(t,x)}v\|_p^{\nu+N+1/p}.$$

Indeed, let v satisfy $v(0,x) = u(x)$. By the above, there exist constants C_1 and C_2 such that

$$\|u\|_\infty \leqslant C_1 \|t^\nu v\|_p + C_2 \|t^\nu \nabla_{(t,x)} v\|_p.$$

We define v_λ by setting $v_\lambda(t,x) = v(\lambda t, \lambda x)$. Computing the norms gives

$$\|v_\lambda\|_\infty(0,\cdot) = \|u\|_\infty, \quad \|t^\nu v_\lambda\|_p = \lambda^{-\nu-(N+1)/p} \|t^\nu v\|_{L^p(\mathbb{R}^N \times]0,+\infty[)}$$

and $\quad \|t^\nu \nabla_{(t,x)} v_\lambda\|_p = \lambda^{1-\nu-(N+1)/p} \|t^\nu \nabla_{(t,x)} v\|_p.$

Consequently, by choosing $\lambda = (\|t^\nu v\|_p)(\|t^\nu \nabla_{(t,x)} v\|_p)^{-1}$, we obtain the inequality

$$(4.51) \qquad \|u\|_\infty \leqslant C \|t^\nu v\|_p^{1-\nu-(N+1)/p} \|t^\nu \nabla_{(t,x)} v\|_p^{\nu+(N+1)/p}.$$

Let $h \in \mathbb{R}$ and let $i \in [1,N]$. To illustrate the ideas, we assume that $h > 0$. By a well-known inequality, we have

$$|v(t,x-he_i) - v(t,x)| \leqslant \int_0^h |\partial_i v(t,x-se_i)| ds.$$

Multiplying by t^ν, integrating the pth power, and using Hölder's inequality, we obtain

$$\int_0^1 \int_{\mathbb{R}^N} t^{\nu p} |v(t,x-he_i) - v(t,x)|^p dx\, dt$$

$$\leqslant \int_0^1 t^{\nu p} h^{p-1} \int_0^h \int_{\mathbb{R}^N} |\partial_i v|^p (t,x-se_i) ds$$

$$\leqslant h^p \int_0^1 \int_{\mathbb{R}^N} t^{\nu p} |\nabla v|^p dx\, dt.$$

Taking the $1/p$th power then gives

$$\|t^\nu(\tau_h v - v)\|_p \leqslant 2|h| \|t^\nu \nabla v\|_p.$$

Since we also have

$$\|t^\nu \nabla_{t,x}(\tau_h v - v)\|_p \leqslant 2\|t^\nu \nabla_{(t,x')} v\|_p,$$

applying inequality (4.51) to $u_h - u$ gives the upper bound

$$\|u_h - u\|_\infty \leqslant C|h|^{1-\nu-(N+1)/p} (\|t^\nu v\|_p + \|t^\nu \nabla_{(t,x)} v\|_p).$$

Since $1 - \nu - (N+1)/p = s - N/p$, it follows that u is a Hölder continuous function with exponent $s - N/p$. This concludes the proof of the theorem for $\Omega = \mathbb{R}^N$. $\qquad \square$

4.4.2 The Case of an Open Set Admitting an Extension

The analogue of Theorem 4.47 is true for open subsets satisfying certain regularity conditions. In particular, it is true if Ω is an open set that admits an (s, p)-extension, a property we studied before.

Consequences of the Existence of an (s, p)-extension. We can easily obtain the following density result.

Proposition 4.52. *Let $s \in [0, 1[$ and let $p > 1$. Let Ω be an open set that admits an (s, p)-extension; then $\mathcal{D}(\overline{\Omega})$, the space of restrictions to Ω of functions in $\mathcal{D}(\mathbb{R}^N)$, is dense in $W^{s,p}(\Omega)$.*

Proof of Proposition 4.52.

Let $u \in W^{s,p}(\Omega)$. Let E be a continuous extension of $W^{s,p}(\Omega)$ to $W^{s,p}(\mathbb{R}^N)$. As $E(u) \in W^{s,p}(\mathbb{R}^N)$, there exists a sequence $\{\varphi_n\}$ of functions in $\mathcal{D}(\mathbb{R}^N)$ that converges to $E(u)$ in $W^{s,p}(\mathbb{R}^N)$. The sequence of restrictions of the φ_n then converges to u in $W^{s,p}(\Omega)$. $\qquad\square$

The following is a corollary to Proposition 4.52 and Theorem 4.47.

Corollary 4.53. *Let $s \in]0, 1[$ and let $p \in]1, \infty[$. Let Ω be a Lipschitz open set. We then have:*

- *If $sp < N$, then $W^{s,p}(\Omega) \hookrightarrow L^q(\Omega)$ for every $q \leqslant Np/(N - sp)$.*
- *If $N = sp$, then $W^{s,p}(\Omega) \hookrightarrow L^q(\Omega)$ for every $q < \infty$.*
- *If $sp > N$, then $W^{s,p}(\Omega) \hookrightarrow L^\infty(\Omega)$ and, more precisely,*

$$W^{s,p}(\Omega) \hookrightarrow \mathcal{C}_b^{0, s - N/p}(\Omega).$$

4.5 Compact Embeddings of the $W^{s,p}(\Omega)$ with Bounded Ω

Theorem 4.54. *Let Ω be a bounded Lipschitz open subset of $\mathbb{R}^N$. Let $s \in [0, 1[$, let $p > 1$, and let $N \geqslant 1$. We then have:*

- *If $sp < N$, then the embedding of $W^{s,p}(\Omega)$ into L^k is compact for every $k < Np/(N - sp)$.*
- *If $sp = N$, then the embedding of $W^{s,p}(\Omega)$ into L^q is compact for every $q < \infty$.*
- *If $sp > N$, then the embedding of $W^{s,p}(\Omega)$ into $\mathcal{C}_b^{0,\lambda}(\Omega)$ is compact for $\lambda < s - N/p$.*

Proof of Theorem 4.54.

We begin with the case $sp < N$.

To prove the statement, it suffices to show that the embedding into L^1 is compact. Indeed, $W^{s,p} \hookrightarrow L^{Np/(N-sp)}$ and every bounded sequence in L^k with $k > 1$ that converges in L^1 also converges in $L^{k'}$ for $k' < k$, by Lemma 2.82.

We will therefore use the compactness criterion for bounded subsets of L^1 (cf. Theorem 1.95). Let $\mathcal{B}$ be a bounded subset of $W^{s,p}(\Omega)$. Let $u \in \mathcal{B}$, let $i \in [1, N]$, let $h > 0$, and let $\Omega_h = \{x \in \Omega \mid d(x, \partial\Omega) > h\}$. Setting $\overrightarrow{h} = he_i$, we consider the integral

$$I_{\overrightarrow{h}} = \int_{\Omega_h} \int_{B(x,h)} |u(x + he_i) - u(x)| dy\, dx.$$

Since the integrand does not depend on y, we have

(4.55) $$I_{\overrightarrow{h}} = \omega_{N-1} |h|^N \int_{\Omega_h} |u(x + \overrightarrow{h}) - u(x)|\, dx,$$

where ω_{N-1} denotes the volume of the unit ball. Next, using the equality

$$u(x + \overrightarrow{h}) - u(x) = u(x + \overrightarrow{h}) - u(y) + u(y) - u(x),$$

for $x \in \Omega_h$ and $y \in B(x, h)$ and setting $\sigma = (sp + N)/p$, the integral $I_{\overrightarrow{h}}$ can be bounded as follows:

$$I_{\overrightarrow{h}} \leqslant \int_{\Omega_h} \int_{B(x,h)} \frac{|u(x + \overrightarrow{h}) - u(y)|}{|x + \overrightarrow{h} - y|^\sigma} |x + \overrightarrow{h} - y|^\sigma dy\, dx$$

$$+ \int_{\Omega_h} \int_{B(x,h)} \frac{|u(x) - u(y)|}{|x - y|^\sigma} |x - y|^\sigma dy\, dx = I_{\overrightarrow{h}}^{(1)} + I_{\overrightarrow{h}}^{(2)}.$$

After transforming these integrals to integrals over $A_h = \Omega_h \times B(0, h)$ by applying a translation to y, we can bound the integrals $I_{\overrightarrow{h}}^{(1)}$ and $I_{\overrightarrow{h}}^{(2)}$ from above using Hölder's inequality. For example, we have

$$I_{\overrightarrow{h}}^{(2)} = \int_{A_h} \frac{|u(x) - u(z + x)|}{|z|^\sigma} |z|^\sigma dz\, dx$$

$$\leqslant \left(\int_{A_h} \frac{|u(x) - u(z + x)|^p}{|z|^{\sigma p}} dz\, dx \right)^{1/p} \left(\int_{A_h} |z|^{\sigma p'} dz\, dx \right)^{1/p'}.$$

Since by assumption, $B(x, h) \subset \Omega_h \subset \Omega$, the first integral on the right-hand side, which equals

$$\int_{\Omega_h} \int_{B(x,h)} \frac{|u(x) - u(y)|^p}{|x - y|^{sp+N}} dy\, dx,$$

can be bounded from above by the integral

$$\int_{\Omega \times \Omega} \frac{|u(x) - u(y)|^p}{|x - y|^{sp+N}} dy \, dx,$$

which is bounded for u in $\mathcal{B}$. Moreover, we have

$$\left(\int_{A_h} |z|^{\sigma p'}\right)^{1/p'} \leqslant (\text{mes } \Omega)^{1-1/p} \left(\int_0^h \rho^{((sp+N)/(p-1))+N-1} d\rho\right)^{1-1/p}$$

$$\leqslant (\text{mes } \Omega)^{1-1/p} C' |h|^{N+s},$$

where the constant on the right depends only on the seminorm $\|u\|'_{s,p}$. We can proceed in a similar manner for the integral $I^{(1)}_{\vec{h}}$. Finally, using inequality (4.55) and the relations following it, we obtain

$$|h|^N \int_{\Omega_h} |u(x + \vec{h}) - u(x)| dx \leqslant C |h|^{N+s},$$

that is, the first condition of the compactness criterion in $L^1(\Omega)$:

$$\int_{\Omega_h} |u(x + \vec{h}) - u(x)| \leqslant C |h|^s.$$

Moreover, as the set $\mathcal{B}$ is bounded in $L^p(\Omega)$ and the set Ω itself is bounded, we can find a compact set K that is sufficiently large that for every $u \in \mathcal{B}$, we have

$$\int_{\Omega-K} |u(x)| \leqslant \left(\int_{\Omega-K} |u(x)|^p\right)^{1/p} (\text{mes}(\Omega - K))^{1-1/p} \leqslant \varepsilon.$$

We have thus shown that $\mathcal{B}$ is relatively compact in $L^1(\Omega)$, hence in all the $L^k(\Omega)$ with $k < pN/(N - sp)$.

If $s = Np$, we use $W^{s,p} \hookrightarrow W^{s',p}$ with $s' < s$, giving the second statement.

Let us now suppose that $sp > N$. Let $\mathcal{B}$ be a bounded subset of $W^{s,p}(\Omega)$. We use the Ascoli–Arzelà theorem to show that $\mathcal{B}$ is relatively compact in $\mathcal{C}(\overline{\Omega})$. A consequence of Theorem 4.47 is then the existence of a constant $C > 0$ such that for every $u \in \mathcal{B}$, we have

$$\|u\|_{L^\infty(\Omega)} \leqslant C \|u\|_{W^{s,p}(\Omega)}.$$

Since for every pair of elements (x, y) of Ω, we also have

$$|u(x) - u(y)| \leqslant C \|u\|_{W^{s,p}(\Omega)} |x - y|^{s-N/p},$$

we can deduce that the set $\mathcal{B}$ is bounded in L^∞ and equicontinuous, concluding the proof of the third statement of the theorem in the case of $\mathcal{C}(\overline{\Omega})$.

Finally, we use Theorem 4.47 and Lemma 2.85 to deduce the compactness in Hölder spaces. $\qquad \square$

4.6 The Spaces $W^{s,p}(\Omega)$ with $s \in {]0,+\infty[}$

4.6.1 Definition and Embedding Theorem

Definition 4.56. Let $s \in \mathbb{R} \setminus \mathbb{N}$ with $s \geqslant 1$. The space $W^{s,p}(\Omega)$ is defined to be

$$W^{s,p}(\Omega) = \{u \in W^{[s],p}(\Omega) \mid D^j u \in W^{s-[s],p}(\Omega), \forall \overrightarrow{j}, |\overrightarrow{j}| = [s]\}.$$

It is clear that $W^{s,p}(\Omega)$ endowed with the norm

$$\|u\|_{s,p} = \left(\|u\|^p_{W^{[s],p}(\Omega)} + \sum_{j,|j|=[s]} \int_\Omega \int_\Omega \frac{|D^j u(x) - D^j u(y)|^p}{|x-y|^{(s-[s])p+N}} dx\, dy \right)^{1/p} < \infty$$

is a Banach space.

We can moreover easily verify that the functions in $\mathcal{D}(\mathbb{R}^N)$ are dense in $W^{s,p}(\mathbb{R}^N)$. The following embedding theorem is similar to the previous ones.

Theorem 4.57. *Let Ω be a Lipschitz open set. We then have:*

- *If $sp < N$, then $W^{s,p}(\Omega) \hookrightarrow L^q(\Omega)$ for every $q \leqslant Np/(N - sp)$.*
- *If $sp = N$, then $W^{s,p}(\Omega) \hookrightarrow L^q(\Omega)$ for every $q < \infty$.*
- *If $sp > N$, then we have:*
  - *If $s - N/p \notin \mathbb{N}$, then $W^{s,p}(\Omega) \hookrightarrow \mathcal{C}_b^{[s-N/p],s-N/p-[s-N/p]}(\Omega)$.*
  - *If $s - N/p \in \mathbb{N}$, then $W^{s,p}(\Omega) \hookrightarrow \mathcal{C}_b^{s-N/p-1,\lambda}(\Omega)$ for every $\lambda < 1$.*

Proof of Theorem 4.57.

For $sp < N$, we use an induction on $[s]$.

If $[s] = 0$, this is Theorem 4.47. Let us assume that the theorem has been proved for $[s] = m - 1$. Let $u \in W^{s,p}(\Omega)$ with $[s] = m$ and $sp < N$; then $\nabla u \in W^{s-1,p}(\Omega)$ and $u \in W^{[s],p}(\Omega)$. Hence, by the induction hypothesis, $\nabla u \in L^r(\Omega)$ with $r = Np/(N - (s-1)p)$ and $u \in L^{Np/(N-[s]p)}(\Omega)$.

Using the inequalities $p \leqslant Np/(N - (s-1)p) \leqslant Np/(N - [s]p)$, we deduce that $u \in W^{1,r}(\Omega)$. Since $rp < N$, we conclude that $u \in L^{Nr/(N-r)}(\Omega) = L^{Np/(N-sp)}(\Omega)$.

Let us assume that $sp = N$.

In this case, $[s]p < N$ and $(s-1)p < N$. If $u \in W^{s,p}(\Omega)$, then by the previous reasoning, $u \in W^{1,r}(\Omega)$ with $r = (Np)/(N - (s-1)p) = N$. Since $r = N$, we conclude that $u \in L^q(\Omega)$ for every $q < \infty$.

Let us now assume that $sp > N$. Let j be an integer satisfying $s-1-N/p < j < s - N/p$; then for $u \in W^{s,p}$, $v = \nabla^j u$ belongs to $W^{s-j,p}$. Therefore, v and ∇v belong to $W^{s-j-1,p}$ and the inequality $(s-j-1)p < N$ implies that v and ∇v belong to L^r with $r = (Np)/(N - (s-j-1)p)$. Consequently, $v \in W^{1,r}(\Omega)$ and $r > N$, whence $v \in \mathcal{C}_b^{0,1-N/r}(\Omega) = \mathcal{C}_b^{0,s-N/p-j}(\Omega)$. Finally, we conclude that $u \in \mathcal{C}^{[s-N/p],s-N/p-[s-N/p]}(\Omega)$.

If $s - N/p = j \in \mathbb{N}$, then $u \in W^{s,p}(\Omega)$ implies that $(D^{j-1}u, D^j u) \in \left(W^{s-j,p}(\Omega)\right)^2 = \left(W^{N/p,p}(\Omega)\right)^2$. We deduce from this that $D^{j-1}u \in W^{1,q}(\Omega)$ for every $q < \infty$, and therefore $D^{j-1}u \in \mathcal{C}_b^{0,\lambda}(\Omega)$ for every $\lambda < 1$. We conclude that $u \in \mathcal{C}_b^{s-N/p-1,\lambda}(\Omega)$ for every $\lambda < 1$. $\qquad\square$

4.6.2 Compact Embeddings

For a bounded open set we also have results concerning compact injections.

Theorem 4.58. *Let Ω be a bounded Lipschitz open set. We then have:*

- *If $sp < N$, then the embedding $W^{s,p}(\Omega) \hookrightarrow L^q(\Omega)$ is compact for all exponents q satisfying $q < Np/(N - sp)$.*
- *If $sp = N$, then the embedding $W^{s,p}(\Omega) \hookrightarrow L^q(\Omega)$ is compact for every $q < \infty$.*
- *If $sp > N$, then we have:*
  - *If $s - N/p \notin \mathbb{N}$, then the embedding $W^{s,p}(\Omega) \hookrightarrow \mathcal{C}_b^{[s-N/p],\lambda}(\Omega)$ is compact for every $\lambda < s - N/p - [s - N/p](\Omega)$;*
  - *If $s - N/p \in \mathbb{N}$, then the embedding $W^{s,p}(\Omega) \hookrightarrow \mathcal{C}_b^{s-N/p-1,\lambda}(\Omega)$ is compact for every $\lambda < 1$.*

4.7 Appendix: The Riesz–Thorin Convexity Theorem

Let T be the Fourier transform. We know that T sends a function in L^1 to a function in L^∞ and a function in L^2 to a function in L^2. In particular, for every $g \in L^1$ and every $f \in L^1$, we have

$$|\langle Tf, g\rangle| \leqslant \|Tf\|_\infty \|g\|_1 \leqslant \|f\|_1 \|g\|_1$$

and for every pair (f, g) of elements of L^2, we have

$$|\langle Tf, g\rangle| \leqslant \|f\|_2 \|g\|_2.$$

The following theorem, which is known as the Riesz–Thorin theorem, allows us to deduce that when $p \in [1, 2]$, T sends L^p into $L^{p'}$. We used this property in the proof of Proposition 4.18.

In the proof, we use the arguments of Stein and Weiss [64]. The interested reader can consult that book for the "stronger" theorem of Marcinkiewicz.

Theorem 4.59. *Let T be a linear operator defined on all of the $L^p(\mathbb{R}^N, \mathbb{C})$, such that for given p_i and q_i in $[1, \infty]$, it is continuous from $L^{p_i}(\mathbb{R}^N, \mathbb{C})$ to $L^{q_i}(\mathbb{R}^N, \mathbb{C})$. We denote its operator norms by*

$$k_i = \|T\|_{p_i, q_i} = \sup_{\substack{\|f\|_{p_i}=1 \\ \|g\|_{q_i'}=1}} |\langle Tf, g\rangle|,$$

where q_i' is the conjugate of q_i.

If $t \in {]0,1[}$ and $1/p = t/p_0 + (1-t)/p_1$, then T is continuous from $L^p(\mathbb{R}^N, \mathbb{C})$ to $L^q(\mathbb{R}^N, \mathbb{C})$, where $1/q = t/q_0 + (1-t)/q_1$. Moreover, we have the continuity inequality

$$\|T\|_{p,q} \leqslant k_0^t k_1^{1-t}.$$

Proof of the theorem.

We begin by showing the result for simple functions. Let $f = \sum_j a_j \chi_{E_j}$ have norm in L^p equal to 1, where the E_j are two-by-two disjoint integrable sets. We set $a_j = |a_j| e^{i\theta_j}$. Let $g = \sum_k b_k \chi_{F_k}$, where the F_k are two-by-two disjoint integrable sets, $b_k = |b_k| e^{i\varphi_k}$, and $\|g\|_p = 1$. For $p \in [1, \infty]$, let t be a real number in $[0, 1]$ that satisfies $1/p = t/p_0 + (1-t)/p_1$. Let α and β be the functions on $\mathbb{C}$ defined by

$$\alpha(z) = \frac{z}{p_0} + \frac{1-z}{p_1}, \quad \beta(z) = \frac{z}{q_0} + \frac{1-z}{q_1}.$$

We also set

$$f(z) = \sum_j |a_j|^{\alpha(z)/\alpha(t)} e^{i\theta_j} \chi_{E_j} \quad \text{and} \quad g(z) = \sum_k |b_k|^{(1-\beta(z))/(1-\beta(t))} e^{i\varphi_k} \chi_{F_k}.$$

Finally, let F be defined by

$$F(z) = \int_{\mathbb{R}^N} Tf(z)g(z)\, dx = \sum_{j,k} |a_j|^{\alpha(z)/\alpha(t)} e^{i\theta_j} |b_k|^{(1-\beta(z))/(1-\beta(t))} e^{i\varphi_k} \gamma_{j,k},$$

with $\gamma_{j,k} = \int_{\mathbb{R}^N} T(\chi_{E_j})\chi_{F_k}\, dx$. It is easy to check that $F(t) = \int_{\mathbb{R}^N} Tfg\, dx$.

To prove the result, we begin by showing that $|F(iy)| \leqslant k_1$ and that $|F(1+iy)| \leqslant k_0$. We will then use the fact that F is holomorphic and bounded on the strip $0 \leqslant x \leqslant 1, y \in \mathbb{R}$ and the Phragmén–Lindelöf principle, which implies that for every pair (x, y) with $0 \leqslant x \leqslant 1$, we have $|F(x+iy)| \leqslant k_0^x k_1^{1-x}$. From this, we will deduce the continuity inequality on the operator norm by setting $x + iy = t$.

Let us determine $|F(iy)|$. We have $\Re(\alpha(iy)) = 1/p_1$, and therefore $\Re(\alpha(iy)/\alpha(t)) = p/p_1$, so that

$$\|f(iy)\|_{p_1}^{p_1} = \sum_j |a_j|^p |E_j| = \|f\|_p^p = 1.$$

Moreover, $\Re(\beta(iy)) = 1/q_1$, so that

$$\frac{1 - \Re(\beta(iy))}{1 - \beta(t)} = \frac{1 - 1/q_1}{1 - 1/q} = \frac{q'}{q_1'}.$$

We therefore have

$$\|g(iy)\|_{q_1'}^{q_1'} = \sum_k |b_k|^{q'} |F_k| = \|g\|_{q'}^{q'} = 1.$$

We also have $\Re(\alpha(1+iy)) = 1/p_0$, so that $\Re\alpha(1+iy)/\alpha(t) = p/p_0$, and therefore

$$\|f(1+iy)\|_{p_0}^{p_0} = \sum_j |a_j|^p |E_j| = \|f\|_p^p = 1.$$

Finally, $\Re(\beta(1+iy)) = 1/q_0$, which implies that

$$\frac{1 - \Re(\beta(1+iy))}{1 - \beta(t)} = \frac{1 - 1/q_0}{1 - 1/q} = \frac{q'}{q_0'}.$$

Consequently, we have

$$\|g(1+iy)\|_{q_0'}^{q_0'} = \sum_k |b_k|^{q'} |F_k| = \|g\|_{q'}^{q'} = 1.$$

By the continuity of the operator, we then have

$$|F(iy)| = \left| \int Tf(iy)g(iy) \right| \leqslant k_1 \|f(iy)\|_{p_1} \|g(iy)\|_{q_1'} = k_1,$$

$$|F(1+iy)| \leqslant k_0 \|f(1+iy)\|_{p_0} \|g(1+iy)\|_{q_0'} = k_0,$$

giving the result for simple functions.

In the general case, let $f \in L^p(\mathbb{R}^N, \mathbb{C}^N)$. We will show that there exists a sequence f_n of simple functions such that $\|f_n - f\|_p \to 0$ and $Tf_n(x) \to Tf(x)$ for almost all x. Let us first assume that such a sequence exists and show that the result follows. The sequence $\{Tf_n\}$ is bounded in L^q. By Fatou's lemma, setting $k_t = k_0^t k_1^{1-t}$, we have

$$\|Tf\|_q \leqslant \lim_{m \to \infty} \|Tf_m\|_q \leqslant k_t \lim_{m \to \infty} \|f_m\|_p \leqslant k_t \|f\|_p,$$

and in particular $Tf \in L^q$, proving the theorem.

It remains to show the existence of the f_n. We reduce to the case where f is real and $f \geqslant 0$. Let us assume that $p_0 < p_1$. For $f \in L^p$, let f_0 equal f when $f(x) > 1$ and 0 elsewhere, and let $f^1 = f - f_0$. We then have $f_0 \in L^{p_0}$ and $f^1 \in L^{p_1}$. Let g_m be an increasing sequence of simple functions that converges almost everywhere to f. By the monotone convergence theorem, we have $\|g_m - f\|_p \to 0$. Likewise, $\|g_m^0 - f^0\|_{p_0} \to 0$ and $\|g_m^1 - f^1\|_{p_1} \to 0$. Since T is continuous from L^{p_1} to L^{q_1} and from L^{p_0} to L^{q_0}, we have

$$\|Tg_m^0 - Tf^0\|_{q_0} \longrightarrow 0 \quad \text{and} \quad \|Tg_m^1 - Tf^1\|_{q_1} \longrightarrow 0.$$

Therefore there exists a subsequence for which $Tg_m^0 \to Tf^0$ almost everywhere and $Tg_m^1 \to Tf^1$ almost everywhere. It follows that the sequence $\{f_m\}$ defined by $f_m = g_m^0 + g_m^1$ satisfies the desired conditions. $\qquad\square$

Corollary 4.60 (Hausdorff–Young inequality). *If $f \in L^p(\mathbb{R}^N)$ and $g \in L^q(\mathbb{R}^N)$ with $1/p+1/q > 1$, then the convolution of these two functions belongs to L^r for r with $1 + 1/r = 1/p + 1/q$.*

Proof of the corollary. In what follows, we fix $f \in L^p$. We associate to it the operator T_f defined by $T_f(g) = f * g$ for every g in a suitable space L^q. Let us consider two situations that correspond to the assumptions of the theorem.

If $g \in L^{p'}$, then by a known result, we have $T_f(g) \in L^\infty$ and, moreover,

$$\|f * g\|_\infty \leqslant \|f\|_p \|g\|_{p'},$$

which proves the continuity of T as an operator from $L^{p'}$ to L^∞. We can therefore take $p_0 = p'$ and $q_0 = +\infty$ in the theorem. The operator norm $\|T_f\|_{p',\infty}$ satisfies the following equalities:

$$\|T_f\|_{p',\infty} = \sup_{\substack{\|g\|_{p'}=1 \\ \|g_1\|_p=1}} |\langle T_f(g), g_1 \rangle| = \sup_{\substack{\|g\|_{p'}=1 \\ \|g_1\|_p=1}} \left| \int_{\mathbb{R}^N} (f * g)(x) g_1(x) dx \right|.$$

By the definition of the norm in a dual and the reflexivity, the last term is the supremum of $\|f * g\|_\infty$ when $\|g\|_{p'} = 1$. It follows that

$$\|T_f\|_{p',\infty} = \|f\|_p.$$

If $g \in L^1$, then since $f \in L^p$, Young's theorem guarantees that $T_f(g) \in L^p$ and that, moreover, $\|f * g\|_p \leqslant \|f\|_p \|g\|_1$. The operator T is therefore continuous from L^1 to L^p. We can then take $p_1 = 1$ and $q_1 = p$ in the theorem. The operator norm associated with this situation also satisfies

$$\|T_f\|_{1,p} = \|f\|_p.$$

Now, let q satisfy $1/p + 1/q > 1$ and let t satisfy

$$\frac{1}{q} = \frac{t}{p_0} + \frac{1-t}{p_1} = \frac{t}{p'} + 1 - t.$$

We then have $t = p(1 - 1/q)$, which indeed lies strictly between 0 and 1.

Since this condition of the theorem has thus been satisfied, we deduce that T_f sends L^q continuously into L^r, where r satisfies

$$\frac{1}{r} = \frac{t}{q_0} + \frac{1-t}{q_1} = \frac{t}{\infty} + \frac{1-t}{p} = \frac{1}{p} + \frac{1}{q} - 1.$$

The first statement of the corollary follows.

Next, consider the inequality

$$\|T_f\|_{q,r} \leqslant k_0^t (k_1)^{1-t} \leqslant \|f\|_p^t \|f\|_p^{1-t} = \|f\|_p.$$

Going back to the operator norms, it follows that

$$\|f * g\|_r \leqslant \|f\|_p \|g\|_q. \qquad \qquad \square$$

Remark 4.61. This corollary allows us to give new proofs of results used at different points in this book, in particular in the proofs of embedding theorems. Indeed, consider, for $p \geqslant 1$, the convolution $g = f * \zeta r^{1-N}$ where $f \in L^p$ and ζ is a regular function with compact support. The function $x \mapsto g(x) = \zeta r^{1-N}$ then belongs to L^q if $(1 - N)(q - 1) > -1$, that is, if $q < N/(N-1)$.

We can therefore apply the corollary, giving us the inclusion $f * g \in L^r$, where $1 + 1/r = 1/p + 1/q$. Since $q < N/(N-1)$, it follows that the exponent r satisfies

$$\frac{1}{r} > \frac{1}{p} + \frac{(N-1)}{N} - 1 = \frac{N-p}{Np}.$$

We thus once more find that the convolution $f * \zeta r^{1-N}$ belongs to L^r for every $r < Np/(N-p)$.

Remark 4.62. In Chapter 6, we will prove the following stronger version of the Riesz–Thorin convexity theorem.

We define the weak-L^1 space to be the set of measurable functions f that satisfy

$$\forall s > 0, \quad |\{x \mid |f(x)| \geqslant s\}| \leqslant \frac{C}{s}.$$

(Note that L^1 is contained in weak-L^1.) Let T be an operator that sends L^1 continuously into weak-L^1 and sends L^2 continuously into L^2; then for $1 < p \leqslant 2$, T sends L^p continuously into itself.

This result is a special case of the Marcinkiewicz interpolation theorem, which we will give later (cf. Theorem 7.34).

Comments

As in the case of trace spaces, we use interpolation spaces when we study fractional Sobolev spaces. The article by Luc Tartar [69] is the best reference for our approach to these spaces, as well as the most agreeable one to read. Let us also mention the articles by J.-L. Lions and Peetre [49] and Uspenski [73].

4.8 Exercises for Chapter 4

Exercise 4.1 (Eigenfunction of the Fourier Transform).
Let $f(x) = \exp(-\pi |x|^2)$ on $\mathbb{R}^N$. Show that f is its own Fourier transform.

Hints. For the case $N = 1$, you can use the first-order differential equation of which f is a solution. You can also use Cauchy's theorem applied to the holomorphic function $z \mapsto \exp(-\pi z^2)$ and a rectangular path with one side equal to the segment $[-R, R]$ on the real axis (subsequently, let R tend to $+\infty$).

For arbitrary N, use the fact that f is a product of exponential functions of the above type.

Exercise 4.2 (Fourier Transform of $x \mapsto 1$).

Compute the Fourier transform of the characteristic function χ_n of $[-n, n]$, where $n \in \mathbb{N}^*$. Prove that the sequence of Fourier transforms $\{\mathcal{F}(\chi_n)\}_n$ converges in $\mathcal{S}'$ to $\mathcal{F}(1)$. Deduce from this that

$$\mathcal{F}(1) = \delta_0.$$

Conclude that

$$\mathcal{F}(e^{2i\pi x_0 t}) = \delta_{x_0}.$$

Exercise 4.3 (Reciprocity Formula for the Fourier Transform).

Demonstrate the reciprocity formula for the Fourier transform for the functions in $\mathcal{S}(\mathbb{R}^N)$. In other words, show that if $\varphi \in \mathcal{S}(\mathbb{R}^N)$, then

$$\overline{\mathcal{F}}\mathcal{F}(\varphi) = \varphi.$$

Deduce the reciprocity formula for tempered distributions from this.

Hints. Let $\gamma = \mathcal{F}(\varphi)$. Note that

$$\mathcal{F}(\varphi_{-a})(\lambda) = e^{2i\pi\lambda a}\gamma(\lambda).$$

Integrate with respect to λ and use the equality $\mathcal{F}(1) = \delta$.

Exercise [∗∗] 4.4 (Fourier Transforms of Homogeneous Distributions).

(1) Let $f \in L^1(\mathbb{R}^N)$. For every $\lambda > 0$, define $H_\lambda(f)$ by setting $H_\lambda(f)(x) = f(\lambda x)$. Prove that if $[f]$ is the distribution associated with the locally summable function f, then

$$\langle [H_\lambda(f)], \varphi \rangle = \lambda^{-N}\langle [f], \varphi(\cdot/\lambda) \rangle.$$

Let T be a distribution on $\mathbb{R}^N$. We extend the previous property by defining $H_\lambda(T)$ to be the distribution defined by

$$\langle H_\lambda(T), \varphi \rangle = \lambda^{-N}\langle T, \varphi(\cdot/\lambda) \rangle.$$

Use $\widehat{f}$ to determine the Fourier transform of $H_\lambda(f)$. Next, prove that the the following formula holds for the tempered distribution T:

(4.63) $$\mathcal{F}(H_\lambda(T)) = \lambda^{-N}H_{\lambda^{-1}}(\mathcal{F}(T)).$$

(2) We call T homogeneous of degree k if

$$\forall \lambda > 0, \quad H_\lambda T = \lambda^k T.$$

We identify T with the radial function f defined by $f(x) = |x|^k$, where $x \in \mathbb{R}^N$ and $|x| = (\sum_i x_i^2)^{1/2}$.

a) We suppose that $-N < k < 0$. Show that T is tempered by noting that it can be written as the sum

$$T = T\chi_{\{|x|<1\}} + T\chi_{\{x||x|\geq 1\}}$$

of a function in L^1 and a function in L^p with $p > -N/k$. Show that its Fourier transform exists and that it is a radial distribution (cf. Exercise 7.12 of Chapter 7).

Show that this Fourier transform is homogeneous of degree $-k - N$

b) We now suppose that $2k < -N$. In this case, T is the sum of a function in L^1 and a function in L^2. Show that $\mathcal{F}(T)$ is a function. Use the positive homogeneity to show that there exists a constant $c(N, k)$ such that

$$\mathcal{F}(T)(\xi) = c(N, k)|\xi|^{k-N}.$$

(3) Use the function $\varphi(x) = e^{-\pi|x|^2}$ to deduce that

$$c(N, k) = \pi^{-k-N/2} \frac{\Gamma((N + k)/2)}{\Gamma(-k/2)},$$

where Γ is the Euler function ([22], [58] or Exercise 3.1 of Chapter 3). We will use these results in Chapter 7 in the case where $k = -N + 1$, which indeed satisfies the condition $2k < -N$ when $N > 2$. There, we will use a derivative with respect to the variable x_i to show that we have

$$\mathcal{F}(x_i/|x|^{N+1}) = \frac{-2i\pi\xi_i}{(N-1)|\xi|} c(N, 1 - N),$$

(cf. the Riesz transform in Chapter 7).

(4) Let us now suppose that $0 > 2k > -N$. Use the reciprocity formula to show that the previous results still hold. Consider the distribution $T = |x|^k$ and set $k' = -N - k$. Prove that we can apply the previous results to the function $x \mapsto |x|^{k'}$. Deduce the Fourier transform of T from this. Study the case $2k = -N$.

Hints. For formula 4.63, it suffices to use the following definitions:

$$\langle \mathcal{F}(H_\lambda(T)), \varphi \rangle = \langle H_\lambda(T), \widehat{\varphi} \rangle$$
$$= \lambda^{-N}\langle T, \widehat{\varphi}(\cdot/\lambda) \rangle = \langle T, \widehat{H_\lambda(\varphi)} \rangle$$
$$= \langle \mathcal{F}(T), H_\lambda(\varphi) \rangle = \lambda^{-N}\langle H_{\lambda^{-1}}(\mathcal{F}(T)), \varphi \rangle.$$

If T is homogeneous of degree k, then we have

$$\mathcal{F}(H_\lambda(T)) = \lambda^{-N} H_{1/\lambda}(\mathcal{F}(T))$$
$$= \lambda^{-N-k} H_{1/\lambda}(H_\lambda(\mathcal{F}(T))) = \lambda^{-N-k}\mathcal{F}(T).$$

In the case where the radial distribution becomes a function, we know that the Fourier transform of T can be identified with the function $\xi \mapsto g(|\xi|)$ (cf. Exercise 7.12 of Chapter 7). For $\lambda > 0$, this leads to the equality $g(\lambda|\xi|) = \lambda^{-k-N} g(|\xi|)$. Use $|\xi| = 1$ to obtain $g(\lambda) = \lambda^{-k-N} g(1)$. Using a constant that we denote by $c(N, k)$, deduce that

$$\mathcal{F}(T) = c(N, k)|\xi|^{-k-N}.$$

Use the function $x \mapsto \exp(-\pi|x|^2)$, which is its own transform, to obtain the equality

$$\int_0^{+\infty} r^{k+N-1} \exp(-\pi r^2)dr = c(N, k) \int_0^{+\infty} r^{-k-1} \exp(-\pi r^2)dr.$$

Introducing the variable $s = \pi r^2$, this becomes

$$\pi^{-(k-N)/2}\Gamma((k+N)/2) = c(N, k)\pi^{k/2}\Gamma(-k/2).$$

Deduce the desired result.

The number k' lies in the interval $]-N, -N/2[$. The previous results gives

$$\mathcal{F}(|x|^{k'})(\xi) = c(N, k')|\xi|^{-N-k'} = c(N, k')|\xi|^{k}.$$

Applying the inverse transformation $\mathcal{F}^{-1}$ to this gives

$$\mathcal{F}(|x|^{k})(\xi) = [c(N, -N-k)]^{-1}|\xi|^{-N-k}.$$

Use the definition of the constant $c(N, k)$ introduced above to show that the coefficient $[c(N, -N-k)]^{-1}$ is equal to this constant. Letting k tend to $-N/2$ also gives $\mathcal{F}(|x|^{-N/2})(\xi) = |\xi|^{-N/2}$ since $|\xi|^{k}$ tends to $|\xi|^{-N/2}$.

Exercise [*] 4.5 (Convergences of Sequences in L^p).

Let u_n be a sequence in L^p, where $p > 1$, that converges either weakly or almost everywhere to u and satisfies $\|u_n\|_p \to \|u\|_p$. Show that u_n converges strongly to u in L^p.

Hints. Reduce to u of norm 1 by dividing by $\|u_n\|_p$, that is, by setting $v_n = u_n/\|u_n\|_p$. The sequence v_n then converges weakly to $v = u/\|u\|_p$ and the norms equal 1. Next, use the semicontinuity of the L^p-norm for the weak topology to show that $\|v_n + v\|_p \to 2$. Moreover, by Minkowski's inequality and the convergence of the norm, we have $\overline{\lim} \|v_n + v\|_p \leqslant 2$. Finally, the norm of $(v_n + v)/2$ tends to 1. Consequently, by the uniform convexity in L^p, we have

$$v_n - v \longrightarrow 0.$$

If, instead of the weak convergence, we have almost everywhere convergence, you can still reduce to a sequence $\{v_n\}$ of norm 1 that converges to v of norm 1 and for which $(v_n + v)/2$ converges almost everywhere to v. In this case, use Fatou's lemma to prove that

$$1 \leqslant \underline{\lim} \left\| \frac{v_n + v}{2} \right\|_p \leqslant \overline{\lim} \left\| \frac{v_n + v}{2} \right\|_p = 1$$

and then use the uniform convexity to conclude.

Exercise [∗] 4.6 (Convolution of a Function in $L^p(\mathbb{R}^N)$ and a Function in $\mathcal{D}(\mathbb{R}^N)$).

Let $f \in L^p(\mathbb{R}^N)$ and let $\zeta \in \mathcal{D}(\mathbb{R}^N)$. Prove that the convolution $f \star \zeta$ belongs to $\mathcal{C}^\infty(\mathbb{R}^N) \cap L^k(\mathbb{R}^N)$ for every $k \geqslant p$.

Hints. Let $k > p$ and $r > 1$ be defined by $1 + 1/k = 1/r + 1/p$. Since $\zeta \in \mathcal{D}(\mathbb{R}^N)$, we have $\zeta \in L^r$ and consequently $\zeta \star f \in L^k$.

Elliptic PDE: Variational Techniques

In this chapter we present a method for solving certain elliptic partial differential equations, namely those of the form $DJ(u) = 0$ where DJ is the differential, in the weak sense, of a functional J that will be convex in most cases. The properties of convex functions allow us to search for a solution of the partial differential equation (PDE) in the form of the minimum of a functional, provided that the functional tends to $+\infty$ at infinity. After quickly presenting the theoretical ingredients that allow us to deduce the existence of a minimum for J, we give a number of classical boundary problems governed by elliptic PDE that may or may not be linear. We will solve these by variational methods. We will then give regularity results for the solutions of the problems. We conclude by presenting other properties in relation with these solutions, in particular those that generalize the maximum principle for harmonic functions.

5.1 Some Useful Results

A sequence $\{u_n\}_{n \in \mathbb{N}}$ is called bounded in $L^p(\Omega)$ if there exists a constant $C > 0$ such that

$$\forall n \in \mathbb{N}, \quad \int_\Omega |u_n|^p(x)dx \leqslant C.$$

For such a sequence, we will use the following notions and results:

- *Owing to the weak compactness of the bounded closed subsets of a reflexive space*: From any bounded sequence in $L^p(\Omega)$ with $1 < p < \infty$, we can extract a weakly convergent subsequence in $L^p(\Omega)$.
- *Owing to the weak-star sequential compactness of the unit ball of the dual of a separable normed space*: From any bounded sequence in $L^1(\Omega)$, we

F. Demengel, G. Demengel, *Functional Spaces for the Theory*
of Elliptic Partial Differential Equations, Universitext,
DOI 10.1007/978-1-4471-2807-6_5,
© Springer-Verlag London Limited 2012

can extract a subsequence that converges vaguely in the sense of measures to a bounded measure on Ω.

- *Owing to the compact embedding theorem in $W^{1,p}(\Omega)$*: Let Ω be a bounded C^1 subset of $\mathbb{R}^N$ and let p be a real number in $]1, N[$. From any bounded sequence in $W^{1,p}(\Omega)$, we can extract a subsequence that converges almost anywhere, converges weakly in $W^{1,p}(\Omega)$, and converges strongly in $L^q(\Omega)$ for $q < Np/(N-p)$.

- *Owing to the uniform boundedness principle (Banach–Steinhaus theorem)*: Let $p \in]1, \infty[$. Every sequence in $L^p(\Omega)$ that converges weakly in $L^p(\Omega)$ is bounded in $L^p(\Omega)$. For every sequence of measures or functions in $L^1_{\text{loc}}(\Omega)$ that converges vaguely to a measure, the integral of the sequence of its absolute values over any compact subset of Ω is bounded uniformly with respect to n.

In this chapter, we will assume Ω connected unless stated otherwise.

5.2 Notions from Convex Analysis

We begin by recalling results on convexity, which we give without proof. The details can be found in the book [23]. From now on, X will denote a Banach space, X' its dual, and $\langle \cdot, \cdot \rangle$ the duality pairing of X with X'. We assume that all functions have values in $\overline{\mathbb{R}} = \mathbb{R} \cup \{+\infty\} \cup \{-\infty\}$.

5.2.1 Convex Spaces, Hausdorff Property, Lower Semicontinuous Functions

Definition 5.1. A subset C of X is called convex if it is closed under convex combinations, that is, if

$$\forall (x,y) \in C^2, \ \forall \lambda \in]0,1[, \quad \lambda x + (1-\lambda)y \in C.$$

Definition 5.2. A hyperplane is a vector subspace of codimension 1, that is, a proper subspace of X for which there exists an $x_0 \in X$ such that the space $[x_0]$ generated by it satisfies $[x_0] \oplus H = X$.

Proposition 5.3. *Let f be a nonzero linear functional on X; then its kernel is a hyperplane that is closed if f is continuous and everywhere dense in X if f is not.*

Definition 5.4. Given two convex sets C_1 and C_2 and an element $b \in X'$, we say that the hyperplane H orthogonal to b, that is, defined by $H = \{x \in X \mid \langle b, x \rangle = a\}$, separates C_1 and C_2 if

$$C_1 \subset E^+ = \{x \in X \mid \langle b, x \rangle \geqslant a\} \quad \text{and} \quad C_2 \subset E^- = \{x \in X \mid \langle b, x \rangle \leqslant a\}.$$

Definition 5.5. We say that C_1 and C_2 are strictly separated by H if there exists an $\varepsilon > 0$ such that

$$C_1 + B(0, \varepsilon) \subset E^+ \quad \text{and} \quad C_2 + B(0, \varepsilon) \subset E^-.$$

The following is a weak form of the Hahn–Banach theorem.

Theorem 5.6. *Let C be a relatively compact convex subset of X and let M be an affine submanifold of X such that $M \cap C = \varnothing$. Then there exists a hyperplane H that separates M and C.*

Definition 5.7. A functional J on X with values in $\overline{\mathbb{R}}$ is called lower semi-continuous (l.s.c.) at x if for every sequence $\{x_n\}$ that converges to x, we have

(5.8) $$J(x) \leqslant \varliminf_{n \to \infty} J(x_n).$$

This property can also be expressed in the following equivalent form:

$\forall \lambda \in \mathbb{R}, \ \lambda < J(x) \implies \{y \mid J(y) > \lambda\}$ is an open subset containing x.

We say that a functional J on X is l.s.c. on X if it is l.s.c. at all points of X. This property can also be expressed as follows:

$\forall \lambda \in \mathbb{R}, \ \forall x \in X, \quad \{x \mid J(x) > \lambda\}$ is an open set.

This semicontinuity can easily be translated into a property of the *epigraph* of the functional.

Proposition 5.9. *A functional J is l.s.c. on X if and only if its epigraph, defined by $\{(x, y) \in X \times \mathbb{R} \mid y \geqslant J(x)\}$, is closed.*

We continue with useful results on the minimization of convex functions.

Definition 5.10. A functional J from X to $\overline{\mathbb{R}}$ is called proper if it is not identically equal to $+\infty$ and does not take on the value $-\infty$. In particular, its domain $\operatorname{dom}(J) = \{x \in X \mid J(x) \in \mathbb{R}\}$ is nonempty.

Theorem 5.11. *If J is convex and bounded in a neighborhood of a point x_0 where $J(x_0)$ is finite, then it cannot take on the value $-\infty$ and it is continuous and even Lipschitz in this neighborhood.*

Theorem 5.12. *If J is convex, l.s.c., and does not take on the value $-\infty$, then it is the upper envelope of the continuous linear functions that bound it from below.*

Corollary 5.13.

- *Every closed convex subset of a Banach space is also weakly sequentially closed.*
- *A convex functional is l.s.c. if and only if it is weakly sequentially l.s.c.*

5.2.2 Subdifferentiability, Gâteaux-differentiability

Definition 5.14. The subdifferential of J at x is the subset of X' defined by

$$\partial J(x) = \{\alpha \in X' \mid \forall y \in \operatorname{dom}(J),\ \langle \alpha, y - x \rangle \leqslant J(y) - J(x)\}.$$

If J is convex, then $\partial J(x)$ is a convex subset of X'. The subdifferential can be empty, for example when the domain of the function is a single point or, more generally, when the interior of the domain of the function is empty.

If J is differentiable in the sense of Fréchet, with derivative $DJ(x)$ at x, then $\partial J(x) = \{DJ(x)\}$. We call a function subdifferentiable at x if its subdifferential at x is nonempty. For example, the function $x \mapsto |x|$ is differentiable everywhere except at 0, where it is nevertheless subdifferentiable. Its subdifferential at this point is the convex set $[-1, 1]$.

Proposition 5.15. *Let J be a convex function from X to $\overline{\mathbb{R}}$ that is finite and continuous at the point $u \in X$; then $\partial J(u) \neq \varnothing$.*

The Gâteaux-differentiable functions are a special case of subdifferentiable functions. Let us recall the notion of directional derivative.

Definition 5.16. Let J be a convex function on X. We define the right derivative of J along $y \in X'$ at the point x to be

$$J'(x, y) = \inf_{\lambda > 0} \frac{J(x + \lambda y) - J(x)}{\lambda}.$$

When f is a function of one variable, then $f'(x, y) = y f'_d(x)$ if $y > 0$ and $f'(x, y) = f'_g(x) y$ if $y < 0$.

It is clear that in the general case, this infimum, which is also a limit, exists. The following theorem links its derivative to the subdifferential.

Theorem 5.17. *If J is continuous and finite at x, or if x is a point in the interior of the domain of J, then*

$$\forall y \in X, \quad J'(x, y) = \sup_{x^* \in \partial f(x)} \langle x^*, y \rangle.$$

The notion of Gâteaux-differentiability can be deduced from that of directional derivative.

Definition 5.18. A convex function J on X is called Gâteaux-differentiable at the point u of X if for every $w \in X$, the map $w \mapsto J'(u, w)$ is an element of X', which we then denote by $J'(u)$. Thus, for every $v \in X$, we have

$$J'(u, v - u) = \langle J'(u), v - u \rangle = \lim_{t \to 0, t > 0} \frac{J((1 - t)u + tv) - J(u)}{t}$$

$$= \lim_{t \to 0, t > 0} \frac{J((u + t(v - u)) - J(u)}{t}.$$

Corollary 5.19 (of Theorem 5.17). *If J is convex and continuous at u, then its subdifferential at the point u is reduced to a singleton in X' if and only if J is Gâteaux-differentiable at u. We then have $\partial J(u) = \{J'(u)\}$.*

Example 5.20 (of Gâteaux-differentiable functions). Let F be defined on $L^p(\Omega)$ with $1 < p < \infty$ by setting $F(u) = 1/p \int_\Omega |u|^p(x)dx$; then F is everywhere Gâteaux-differentiable and

$$F'(u) = p|u|^{p-2}u.$$

Indeed, we first note that $|u|^{p-2}u \in L^{p'}$. Consider the convexity inequality applied to u and h in $L^p(\Omega)$, that is,

$$|u + h|^p(x) - |u|^p(x) \geqslant p|u|^{p-2}u(x)h(x).$$

By integrating this over Ω, we obtain the inclusion $p|u|^{p-2}u \in \partial F(u)$.

Moreover, for almost every $x \in \Omega$, the mean value theorem tells us that there exists a number $\theta_{x,t} \in]0,1[$ such that

$$|u(x) + th(x)|^p - |u(x)|^p - pth(x)|u(x)|^{p-2}u(x)$$
$$= pth(x)\big(|u(x) + t\theta_{x,t}h(x)|^{p-2}(u(x) + t\theta_{x,t}h(x)) - |u(x)|^{p-2}u(x)\big).$$

By continuity, the term between parentheses on the right-hand side tends to 0 almost everywhere in Ω when $t \to 0$. Bounding the right-hand side from above by $2(|u(x)| + |h(x)|)^{p-1}$, we have

$$\left| \frac{|u(x) + th(x)|^p - |u(x)|^p - pth(x)|u(x)|^{p-2}u(x)}{t} \right|$$
$$\leqslant C|h(x)|\big(|u(x)|^p + |h(x)|^p\big)^{(p-1)/p}.$$

Finally, using Hölder's inequality, we see that the integral of this function is bounded from above by $\|h\|_p(\|u\|_p + \|h\|_p)^{p-1}$. We can therefore apply the dominated convergence theorem and conclude that F is Gâteaux-differentiable at u.

Remark 5.21. This example can be generalized to Sobolev spaces as follows.

Let $G \in W^{1,p}(\Omega)$ with $p > 1$ be defined by $G(u) = 1/p \int_\Omega |\nabla u|^p(x)dx$; then G is Gâteaux-differentiable everywhere (cf. Section 5.8):

$$\forall v \in W^{1,p}(\Omega), \quad \langle G'(u), v \rangle = \int_\Omega |\nabla u(x)|^{p-2}\nabla u(x) \cdot \nabla v(x)dx.$$

5.2.3 Minimization of a Convex Function

Definition 5.22. A functional J on a separable Banach space is called coercive if

$$\lim_{\|x\|_X \to +\infty} J(x) = +\infty.$$

We wish to study the minimum of J on a convex closed subset of X. We will use the following results.

Proposition 5.23. *Let J be a convex function on X with values in $\mathbb{R} \cup \{+\infty\}$. The following two properties are equivalent for every $u \in \mathrm{dom}(J)$:*

(1) $J(u) = \inf_{x \in X} J(x)$.
(2) *For every $v \in \mathrm{dom}(J)$, we have $J'(u, v - u) \geqslant 0$.*

Proof of Proposition 5.23.

- If u satisfies (1), then

$$\forall v \in \mathrm{dom}(J), \ \forall t \in \ ]0,1[, \quad \frac{J(u + t(v - u) - J(u)}{t} \geqslant 0.$$

We obtain property (2) by letting t tend to 0.
- Conversely, for every $x \in X$ and every $t \in \ ]0,1[$, we have

$$J(x) - J(u) = \frac{J(u + (x - u)) - J(u)}{1} \geqslant \frac{J(u + t(x - u)) - J(u)}{t}.$$

We obtain the inequality $J(x) - J(u) \geqslant J'(u, x - u) \geqslant 0$ by letting t tend to 0, whence property (1).

$\square$

Proposition 5.24. *If $\inf_{u \in X} J(u)$ is reached for some $u \in X$ and J is Gâteaux-differentiable at u, then the subdifferential at u, which we can write as $\partial J(u) = \{J'(u)\}$, is reduced to zero. Conversely, if J is convex and Gâteaux-differentiable at u with $J'(u) = 0$, then it has a minimum at u.*

Theorem 5.25. *Let X be a reflexive separable Banach space, let U be a convex closed subset of X, and let J be a proper, convex, coercive, lower semicontinuous functional. Then*

$$\inf_{u \in U} J(u)$$

is reached at some u. This minimum is determined by the relations

$$\forall v \in \mathrm{dom}(J) \cap U, \quad J'(u, v - u) \geqslant 0.$$

When $U = X$, this characterization becomes

$$\forall v \in \text{dom}(J), \quad J'(u, v) = 0,$$

or $0 \in \partial J(u)$, once more giving $J'(u) = 0$ if J is Gâteaux-differentiable at u.

In the case of an affine subspace $U = x_0 + Y$, where Y is a closed vector subspace of X, the minimum $x_0 + \tilde{u}$ satisfies

$$\forall \tilde{v} \in Y, \quad x_0 + \tilde{v} \in \text{dom } J \cap U \implies J'(x_0 + \tilde{u}, \tilde{v}) = 0.$$

If J is Gâteaux-differentiable at $x_0 + \tilde{u}$, this characterization becomes $J'(x_0 + \tilde{u}) = 0$.

Proof of Theorem 5.25.

Let us show that the infimum is finite. We assume that it is not, in which case it equals $-\infty$ and there exists a sequence $\{u_n\} \in U^{\mathbb{N}}$ with $J(u_n) \to -\infty$. If $\{u_n\}$ were bounded, then by extracting a subsequence that converges weakly to u, we can show that since J is l.s.c.,

$$J(u) = -\infty,$$

which is absurd. Therefore $\{u_n\}$ is unbounded and there exists a subsequence $\|u_{\sigma(n)}\|_X \to +\infty$, so that the coercivity of J implies that $J(u_{\sigma(n)}) \to +\infty$, giving a contradiction. We conclude that

$$m = \inf_{u \in U} J(u) > -\infty.$$

Let $\{u_n\}$ be a minimizing sequence for the problem; then $J(u_n) \to m$ and, in particular, $\{u_n\}$ is bounded. If not, there would exist a subsequence $\{u_{\sigma(n)}\}$ that tends to infinity and therefore satisfies $J(u_{\sigma(n)}) \to \infty$. Since X is reflexive and U is weakly sequentially closed, we can extract a subsequence from $\{u_n\}$ that converges weakly to u in U. Since J is convex and l.s.c., it is also weakly l.s.c., so that

$$J(u) \leqslant \varliminf_{n \to \infty} J(u_n) = m,$$

proving that u is a solution. The remainder of the theorem follows from the definitions of the directional derivative and of the subdifferential. $\square$

Remark 5.26. If J is strictly convex, then the solution u is unique.

Remark 5.27. If u is an interior point of U, then J is continuous at u and has a nonempty subdifferential at u. Since u is the minimum, we have $0 \in \partial J(u)$ by the previous proposition.

5.3 Solving Elliptic Linear PDE with Dirichlet Boundary Conditions

5.3.1 Introduction

Let us consider the physics problem that consists of studying the equilibrium position of a stretched elastic membrane in a plane. The membrane projects into an open subset Ω of the plane, with its boundary mapping onto the boundary $\partial\Omega$. At each point $x = (x_1, x_2)$, we apply a vertical force defined by a function $x \mapsto f(x)$, giving tension in the membrane. The displacement of the point x can be identified with the height of the membrane $z = u(x)$ at that point. The equations describing the situation in physics lead to an equation for u, namely $-\Delta u = f$ with, moreover, the boundary condition $u = 0$ on $\partial\Omega$. Replacing the boundary condition $u = 0$ by $u = u_0$, where u_0 is a function on $\partial\Omega$, we obtain an inhomogeneous Dirichlet problem.

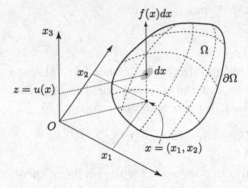

Fig. 5.1.

By modifying the boundary condition, we also find other types of problems such as the Neumann problems, which we will study further on.

5.3.2 The Dirichlet Problem $[\mathcal{D}ir]_{\Delta}^{f}$ in $H^1(\Omega)$ for the Laplacian

Statement of the Dirichlet Problem. For an open subset Ω of $\mathbb{R}^N$, we let Δ be the Laplace operator that sends a distribution $T \in \mathcal{D}'(\Omega)$ to

$$\Delta T = \sum_{1 \leqslant i \leqslant N} \frac{\partial^2 T}{\partial x_i^2}.$$

We begin by considering the so-called *Dirichlet* problem. Let Ω be a bounded open subset of $\mathbb{R}^N$ of class $\mathcal{C}^1$, and let f be a function in $L^2(\Omega)$. We are looking for a solution u of the problem

$$[\mathcal{D}ir]_{\Delta}^{f} : \begin{cases} -\Delta u = f & \text{in } \Omega, \\ u = 0 & \text{on } \partial\Omega. \end{cases}$$

We can also consider the same problem with a nonzero restriction to the boundary, which will need to have a certain degree of regularity. For example, if we are looking for a solution in $H^1(\Omega)$, then the restriction will need to be at least in $H^{1/2}(\partial\Omega)$.

Uniqueness of the Solution in $H^1(\Omega)$ if it exists. Let us suppose that both u and v in $H^1(\Omega)$ satisfy the equation. The difference $u - v$ then satisfies $\Delta(u - v) = 0$. Multiplying this by $u - v$, integrating over Ω, and applying the generalized Green's formula from Chapter 3, we obtain

$$\int_{\Omega} |\nabla(u - v)|^2(x)dx = 0, \quad \text{whence} \quad u - v = \text{constant}.$$

Since $u - v = 0$ on the boundary, the uniqueness of the solution follows.

Existence of a Solution in $H^1(\Omega)$. To show the existence of a solution, we transform the problem into a so-called variational one. We then apply Proposition 5.24 and Theorem 5.25 to a functional J that we will associate to the Dirichlet problem.

Let Ω be a bounded open subset of $\mathbb{R}^N$, let $f \in L^2(\Omega)$, and let J be defined on $H_0^1(\Omega) = W_0^{1,2}(\Omega)$ by setting

$$J(u) = \frac{1}{2} \int_{\Omega} |\nabla u|^2 - \int_{\Omega} fu.$$

Let us suppose that J is convex, continuous, and coercive in $H_0^1(\Omega)$. Theorem 5.25 then ensures us of the existence of a minimum for J. Since J is Gâteaux-differentiable, and even Fréchet-differentiable, at every point $u \in H^1(\Omega)$, with

$$\langle J'(u), v \rangle = \int_{\Omega} \nabla u \cdot \nabla v - \int_{\Omega} fv,$$

it follows that if u is a minimum, then for $v \in \mathcal{D}(\Omega)$, the condition $\langle J'(u), v \rangle = 0$ (Proposition 5.24) gives $-\Delta u = f$. In other words, u is a solution of the Dirichlet problem.

We can easily see that J is convex and continuous, so that it remains to show that J is coercive on $H_0^1(\Omega)$. We will need the following *Poincaré* inequality (cf. its generalization in Exercise 2.9).

Proposition 5.28. *Let Ω be a bounded domain of class C^1; then there exists a constant $C_P > 0$ such that every u in $H_0^1(\Omega)$ satisfies*

$$\|u\|_{H^1(\Omega)} \leqslant C_P \|\nabla u\|_2.$$

Proof of Proposition 5.28. If we assume that the result of the proposition is false, then there exists a sequence $\{u_n\}$ in $H_0^1(\Omega)$ with $\|u_n\|_{H_0^1} = 1$ and $\|\nabla u_n\|_2^2 \leqslant 1/n$. By the compactness of the Sobolev embedding $H^1(\Omega) \hookrightarrow L^2(\Omega)$, we may extract a subsequence from $\{u_n\}$ that converges weakly in $H^1(\Omega)$ and strongly in $L^2(\Omega)$. Let u be its limit. Since we have $\|\nabla u_n\|_2 \to 0$, the lower semicontinuity of the norm in L^2 for the weak topology gives

$$\|\nabla u\|_2 \leqslant \underline{\lim} \|\nabla u_n\|_2 = 0.$$

Consequently, u is a constant that must be zero because it belongs to H_0^1. However, since $\{u_n\}$ converges strongly to u in L^2, we also have

$$\|u\|_2 = \lim \|u_n\|_2 = \lim \|u_n\|_{H_0^1} = 1,$$

giving a contradiction.   □

Let us return to the coercivity of J. Using the constant C_P of Proposition 5.28, we can write

$$\left| \int_\Omega fu \right| \leqslant \|f\|_2 \|u\|_2 \leqslant \|f\|_2 \|u\|_{H^1(\Omega)}$$
$$\leqslant C_P^2 \|f\|_2^2 + \frac{1}{4C_P^2} \|u\|_{H^1(\Omega)}^2.$$

The coercivity then follows from $J(u) \geqslant 1/4C_P^2 \|u\|_{H^1(\Omega)}^2 - \|f\|_2^2$.

We will now generalize this Dirichlet problem to an operator other than Δ.

5.3.3 The Dirichlet Problem $[\mathcal{D}ir]_A^f$ in $H^1(\Omega)$ for an Operator A

Statement of the Problem. Let Ω be a bounded domain of class $\mathcal{C}^1$ and let f be an element of $L^2(\Omega)$. Let $A = (A_{ij})_{ij} \in L^\infty(\Omega, \mathbb{R}^N \times \mathbb{R}^N)$ satisfy the following:

(1) For every i and every j in $[1, N]$, we have $A_{ij} = A_{ji}$.
(2) There exists an $\alpha > 0$ such that

$$\forall x \in \mathbb{R}^N, \quad \sum_{ij} A_{ij} x_i x_j \geqslant \alpha |x|^2.$$

This last property is called the *uniform ellipticity of A*.

We are looking for a solution u of the problem

$$[\mathcal{D}ir]_A^f : \begin{cases} -\sum_{ij} \partial_i (A_{ij} \partial_j u) = f & \text{in } \Omega, \\ u = 0 & \text{on } \partial\Omega. \end{cases}$$

Remark 5.29. This problem can also be written as $-\operatorname{div}(A(x)\nabla u) = f$, that is, as a PDE in *divergence form* (cf. introduction). One of the advantages of writing it this way is that we obtain a variational form of the problem. This problem is a generalization of $[\mathcal{D}ir]_\Delta^f$, which corresponds to the case $A_{ij} = \delta_i^j$.

Existence and Uniqueness of a Solution. Both for the existence and for the uniqueness, it suffices to follow the same arguments as those used for the problem $[\mathcal{D}ir]^f_\Delta$. The functional J that we associate with the problem is

$$J(u) = \frac{1}{2} \int_\Omega A(x)\nabla u(x) \cdot \nabla u(x) dx - \int_\Omega f(x)u(x)dx,$$

where $A(x)X \cdot Y$ denotes the scalar $A_{ij}(\dot{x})X_iY_j$. The variational form of $[\mathcal{D}ir]^f_A$ is therefore the minimization associated with

$$\inf_{u \in H^1_0(\Omega)} \left\{ \frac{1}{2} \int_\Omega A(x)\nabla u \cdot \nabla u \, dx - \int_\Omega fu \, dx \right\}.$$

We can easily demonstrate the convexity and continuity of J. The coercivity follows from the Poincaré inequality and the uniform ellipticity of A. The functional J is Gâteaux-differentiable since its derivative is defined by

$$\langle J'(u), v \rangle = \int_\Omega A(x)\nabla u(x) \cdot \nabla v(x) \, dx - \int_\Omega f(x)v(x) \, dx.$$

Using Green's formula, we can show that the minimum of J on $H^1_0(\Omega)$ is indeed the solution of the problem $[\mathcal{D}ir]^f_A$.

Remark 5.30. Note that we can also replace $f \in L^2$ by $f \in H^{-1}(\Omega)$. In that case, we replace the integral $\int_\Omega fu$ by the duality pairing $\langle f, u \rangle$. The corresponding modification of the previous functional remains continuous and coercive.

This remark will be useful in the section on nonhomogeneous problems, for both the Dirichlet and the Neumann problems.

5.3.4 The Problem $[\mathcal{D}ir]^0_{\Delta,\lambda}$, Eigenvalues and Eigenvectors of $-\Delta$

Let Ω again be a bounded domain of class $\mathcal{C}^1$. The optimal constant $C = C^2_P$ in Proposition 5.28 is given by $1 + 1/\lambda_1$, where

$$\lambda_1 = \inf_{\substack{u \in H^1_0(\Omega) \\ \|u\|_2 = 1}} \int_\Omega |\nabla u|^2(x) dx.$$

We will see that this critical value λ_1 is an eigenvalue of $-\Delta$ and that the associated homogeneous problem, $[\mathcal{D}ir]^0_{\Delta,-\lambda}$, admits nonzero solutions that are eigenvectors of $-\Delta$ for the eigenvalue λ_1. More precisely, we have the following result.

Proposition 5.31. *Let λ_1 be as above; then λ_1 is positive and there exists a $u \geqslant 0$ satisfying $\|u\|_2 = 1$ and $\|\nabla u\|^2 = \lambda_1$. Moreover, u is an eigenvector of $-\Delta$ for the eigenvalue λ_1, that is, u is a solution of $[\mathcal{D}ir]^0_{\Delta,-\lambda_1}$.*

Furthermore, the associated eigenspace has dimension 1 when Ω is connected. In particular, under this assumption, every eigenfunction has constant sign.

Proof.

We begin by showing that $\lambda_1 > 0$. This follows from the Poincaré inequality, but we will give a direct proof for ease of reading.

We have $\lambda_1 \geqslant 0$. Let us assume that $\lambda_1 = 0$. Then there exists a sequence $\{u_n\}$ in $H_0^1(\Omega)$ with $\|u_n\|_2 = 1$ and $\|\nabla u_n\|_2 \to 0$. Since $H_0^1(\Omega)$ is a Hilbert space and therefore reflexive, we can extract a subsequence from $\{u_n\}$ that converges weakly in $H^1(\Omega)$ to a function u. By the compactness of the embedding of H_0^1 in L^2, we have $\|u\|_2 = 1$ and, finally, the strong convergence of $\{u_n\}$ to u in H^1 because it tends to u in L^2 and $\{\nabla u_n\} \to 0$ in L^2. We deduce that $\nabla u = \lim_{n \to +\infty} \nabla u_n = 0$, whence $u = 0$ because $u = 0$ on the boundary, giving a contradiction with $\|u\|_2 = 1$. Consequently, we have $\lambda_1 > 0$.

Next, let $\{u_n\}$ be a minimizing sequence, that is, one satisfying $\|\nabla u_n\|_2^2 \to \lambda_1$ with $\|u_n\|_2 = 1$. The sequence is bounded in H_0^1, so that there exists a subsequence, which we also denote by $\{u_n\}$, satisfying

$$u_n \rightharpoonup u \text{ in } H_0^1, \quad u_n \longrightarrow u \text{ in } L^2.$$

In particular, $\|u\|_2 = 1$, and by the lower semicontinuity of $u \mapsto \|\nabla u\|_2^2$ for the weak topology, we have

$$\lambda_1 \leqslant \int_\Omega |\nabla u|^2(x)dx \leqslant \varliminf \|\nabla u_n\|_2^2 = \lambda_1.$$

Consequently, u satisfies $\|u\|_2 = 1$ and $\|\nabla u\|_2^2 = \lambda_1$. Moreover, by noting that $\|(\nabla|u|)\| = \|\nabla u\|$ (cf. Lemma 5.62 at the end of the chapter), we deduce that there exists a nonnegative solution.

Let us now show that u satisfies the equation $-\Delta u = \lambda_1 u$. Let u be a solution of the variational problem that satisfies $\|u\|_2 = 1$, let $\varphi \in \mathcal{D}(\Omega)$, and let $t \in \mathbb{R}$ satisfy $2|t| < \|\varphi\|_2^{-1}$. Then $\|u + t\varphi\|_2 \neq 0$ and $u + t\varphi \in H_0^1$, so that, by the definition of λ_1,

$$\int_\Omega |\nabla(u + t\varphi)|^2 dx \geqslant \lambda_1 \int_\Omega |u + t\varphi|^2 dx.$$

It follows from the assumptions that

$$2t \int_\Omega \nabla u \cdot \nabla \varphi(x)dx + t^2 \int_\Omega |\nabla \varphi|^2(x)dx \geqslant \lambda_1 \left(2t \int_\Omega u\varphi(x)dx + t^2 \int_\Omega |\varphi|^2(x)dx \right).$$

Dividing by t, which we assume to be positive, and letting t tend to 0, we obtain $\int_\Omega \nabla u \cdot \nabla \varphi dx \geqslant \lambda_1 \int_\Omega u\varphi(x)dx$. When $t < 0$, we either apply the same process or change φ to $-\varphi$ to obtain the opposite inequality, whence

$$\int_\Omega \nabla u \cdot \nabla \varphi dx = \lambda_1 \int_\Omega u\varphi(x)dx.$$

The result follows by using the definition of Δu in the sense of distributions.

Let us show that λ_1 is the smallest eigenvalue. We take a $\lambda \in \mathbb{R}$ and a nonzero $v \in H_0^1$ such that $-\Delta v = \lambda v$. Multiplying by v and applying the generalized Green's formula, we obtain

$$\lambda_1 \|v\|_2^2 \leqslant \int_\Omega |\nabla v|^2 = \lambda \|v\|_2^2,$$

and therefore $\lambda \geqslant \lambda_1$.

Let us now show that the eigenspace corresponding to λ_1 has dimension 1. Let v be an eigenvector for λ_1 and let u be a nonnegative eigenfunction. We showed the existence of such a u earlier on in this proof. We multiply the eigenvalue equation by $v^2/(u + \varepsilon) \in H_0^1$, where $\varepsilon > 0$. This gives

$$\lambda_1 \int_\Omega \frac{v^2 u}{u + \varepsilon} dx = \int_\Omega \nabla u \cdot \nabla \left(\frac{v^2}{u + \varepsilon}\right) dx.$$

The right-hand side satisfies

$$\nabla u \cdot \nabla \left(\frac{v^2}{u + \varepsilon}\right) = 2\frac{v}{u + \varepsilon}\nabla u \cdot \nabla v - \frac{v^2}{(u + \varepsilon)^2}|\nabla u|^2$$

$$= -\left|\frac{v}{u + \varepsilon}\nabla u - \nabla v\right|^2 + |\nabla v|^2.$$

Hence

$$\lambda_1 \int_\Omega \frac{v^2 u}{u + \varepsilon} dx = -\int_\Omega \left|\frac{v}{u + \varepsilon}\nabla u - \nabla v\right|^2 dx + \int_\Omega |\nabla v|^2 dx.$$

Now, by the dominated convergence theorem, the left-hand side tends to $\lambda_1 \int_\Omega v^2(x)dx = \int_\Omega |\nabla v|^2(x)dx$. Consequently,

$$\lim_{\varepsilon \to 0} \int_\Omega \left|\frac{v}{u + \varepsilon}\nabla u - \nabla v\right|^2 = 0,$$

which implies that $\lim_{\varepsilon \to 0} \nabla(v/(u + \varepsilon)) = 0$ strongly in L^2 on any compact set. By the strong maximum principle (cf. Proposition 5.72), $u > 0$ in the interior of Ω. Let Ω_1 be a connected compact subset of Ω and let m_{Ω_1} be a lower bound for u in Ω_1. The sequence $\{v/(u + \varepsilon)\}$ then converges to v/u in $L^2(\Omega_1)$. The previous limit shows that its gradient is zero in Ω_1. We deduce from this that $v = c_{\Omega_1} u$. Finally, by considering connected open sets containing Ω_1, we see that this constant does not depend on Ω_1. Since the open set Ω is connected, we have thus proved the existence of a C such that $v = Cu$ in Ω. At the same time, we have shown that every eigenfunction has constant sign, concluding the proof.   □

Remark 5.32. Instead of this proof, we can also use the regularity of the solutions of Dirichlet problems (see further on) and the Hopf principle stated in Theorem 5.81. In that case, we note that the function v^2/u belongs to H^1, allowing us the avoid the use of the parameter ε (cf. Exercise 5.1).

5.3.5 The Problem $[\mathcal{D}ir]^f_{\Delta, -\lambda}$ with $0 < \lambda < \lambda_1$

We wish to find a solution u of the problem

$$[\mathcal{D}ir]^f_{\Delta, \lambda} : \begin{cases} -\Delta u + \lambda u = f & \text{in } \Omega, \\ u = 0 & \text{on } \partial\Omega. \end{cases}$$

The functional we now wish to minimize is no longer convex but is coercive and weakly l.s.c.. We assume that $0 < \lambda < \lambda_1$. Given a bounded domain Ω in $\mathbb{R}^N$ of class $\mathcal{C}^1$, we wish to find a solution u of $[\mathcal{D}ir]^f_{\Delta, -\lambda}$ in $H^1_0(\Omega)$, where $f \in L^2(\Omega)$.

Existence of a Solution.

The equation leads us to consider the functional on $H^1_0(\Omega)$ defined by

$$J(u) = \frac{1}{2} \int_\Omega |\nabla u|^2(x)dx - \frac{\lambda}{2} \int_\Omega |u|^2(x)dx - \int_\Omega f(x)u(x)dx.$$

This functional is coercive because $\lambda < \lambda_1$. Its minimum therefore belongs to $\mathbb{R}$. Let $\{u_n\}$ be a minimizing sequence for J. It is bounded in H^1_0, whence, after extracting a subsequence, if necessary, it converges to $u \in H^1_0$, converges weakly in H^1, and converges strongly in L^2. It follows that the nonconvex term $-\lambda \int_\Omega |u_n|^2(x)dx$ converges to $-\lambda \int_\Omega |u|^2(x)dx$. Since the gradient of the other term is l.s.c. for the weak topology, we can deduce that u is a solution of

$$J(u) \leqslant \underline{\lim} J(u_n),$$

giving the desired result.

Since J admits a minimum in u, we have $J'(u) = 0$, giving the PDE satisfied by u in $H^1_0(\Omega)$, namely $-\Delta u - \lambda u = f$.

Uniqueness. Since the equation is linear, it suffices to verify that the solution w of $[\mathcal{D}ir]^0_{\Delta, -\lambda}$ vanishes in Ω. Recall that if w is not identically zero, then it is an eigenfunction for an *eigenvalue* $\lambda < \lambda_1$, which is impossible by Proposition 5.31.

5.4 Regularity of the Given Solutions

We will now consider the regularity of the solutions of the Dirichlet problems we have studied above.

5.4.1 The Problem $[\mathcal{D}ir]_A^f$

Theorem 5.33. *Let Ω be a bounded domain of class $\mathcal{C}^2$ and let f be an element of $L^2(\Omega)$. Let $A \in \mathcal{C}^1(\Omega, \mathbb{R}^{N \times N})$ satisfy the following conditions:*

(1) For every i and every j in $[1, N]$, we have $A_{ij} = A_{ji}$.
(2) There exists an $\alpha > 0$ such that

$$\forall x \in \mathbb{R}^N, \quad \sum_{ij} A_{ij} x_i x_j \geqslant \alpha |x|^2.$$

Then the solution u of $[\mathcal{D}ir]_A^f$ in $H_0^1(\Omega)$ belongs to $H^2(\Omega)$.

Proof of Theorem 5.33. Let us begin with an introduction for ease of reading. We will divide the proof into three steps that we will each justify.

Using a partition of unity $\{\varphi_i\}$ associated with the class $\mathcal{C}^2$ cover of Ω, we reduce to showing that every $\varphi_i u$ belongs to $H^2(\Omega)$. Indeed, if φ_k belongs to $\mathcal{D}(\mathbb{R}^N)$, then

$$\mathrm{div}\big(A(x)\nabla(\varphi_k u)\big) \in L^2(\Omega),$$

because the right-hand side of

$$\mathrm{div}\big(A(x)\nabla(\varphi_k u)\big)$$
$$= \sum_i \Big[\partial_i\big(A_{ij}\partial_j \varphi_k u\big) + A_{ij}(\partial_{ij}\varphi_k)u + A_{ij}\partial_j\varphi_k\partial_i u\Big] + \varphi_k \,\mathrm{div}\big(A(x)\nabla u\big)$$

belongs to $L^2(\Omega)$. When $k = 0$, then by the compactness of the support of $\varphi_0 u$ in Ω, we have

$$\mathrm{div}\big(A(x)\nabla(\varphi_0 u)\big) \in L^2(\mathbb{R}^N),$$

thus justifying the first step, which we will now state.

Step 1. We begin by showing the result on $\mathbb{R}^N$, that is, if $u \in H^1(\mathbb{R}^N)$ has compact support and satisfies the equation

$$-\,\mathrm{div}(A(x)\nabla u) = f$$

with $f \in L^2(\mathbb{R}^N)$ and A symmetric, Lipschitz, and coercive, then $u \in H^2(\mathbb{R}^N)$.

For the remaining functions $\varphi_k u$, we must now show that if u has compact support in an open set of the form $\Omega_k \cap \overline{\Omega}$, with boundary condition $\varphi_k u(x', a(x')) = 0$ and, moreover, satisfies $\mathrm{div}\big(A(x)\nabla(\varphi_k u)\big) \in L^2$, then $\varphi_k u \in H^2$. Unless a is the zero function, in which case the boundary is locally straight, we can reduce to this situation by changing the local coordinate systems, as we will show further on. This remark justifies the second step.

Step 2. We extend the result obtained in the first step to the open set $\mathbb{R}^{N-1} \times$ $]0, +\infty[$ with the condition $u = 0$ on $\{x_N = 0\}$.

We will conclude the proof as follows.

Step 3. We use local coordinate systems and partitions of unity to extend the result to Ω.

The difficulty in this step lies in the modification of $A(x)$ when we change the local coordinate systems. We deal with this problem by noting that $A(x)$ is replaced by a matrix $B(x)$ that is also uniformly elliptic. We can therefore conclude using the results we have already obtained on $\mathbb{R}^{N-1} \times]0, +\infty[$.

First Step. Let $u \in H^1(\mathbb{R}^N)$ have compact support. We fix a direction e_i and define the translation $u_h : x \mapsto u(x + he_i)$. Since this is linear in u, we have $\operatorname{div}(A_h \nabla u_h) = f_h$. Consequently, after subtracting the equation for u_h from that for u and multiplying by $u_h - u$, integrating over Ω and applying Green's formula on $H^1 \times W^2(\operatorname{div})$ gives

$$\int_{\mathbb{R}^N} \left(A_h \nabla u_h - A \nabla u \right) \cdot \left(\nabla u_h - \nabla u \right) dx = \int_{\mathbb{R}^N} (f_h - f)(u_h - u) dx.$$

We expand the first factor to $(A_h - A)\nabla u_h + A(\nabla u_h - \nabla u)$, after which we use a translation of the variable in the integral on the right-hand side to deduce that

$$\int_{\mathbb{R}^N} \sum_{i,j} A_{ij}(\partial_i(u_h) - \partial_i u)(\partial_j(u_h) - \partial_j u) \, dx$$

$$+ \int_{\mathbb{R}^N} \sum_{ij} \left((A_{ij})_h - A_{ij} \right) \partial_i(u)_h (\partial_j(u_h) - \partial_j u) \, dx$$

$$= \int_{\mathbb{R}^N} (f_h - f)(u_h - u) dx = \int_{\mathbb{R}^N} f(x)\left(-u_{-h} - u_h + 2u \right) dx.$$

Dividing by h^2 gives

$$\int_{\mathbb{R}^N} \sum_{ij} A_{ij} \left(\frac{\partial_i(u_h) - \partial_i u}{h} \right) \left(\frac{(\partial_j(u_h) - \partial_j u}{h} \right) dx$$

$$= -\int_{\mathbb{R}^N} \sum_{j,i} \frac{(A_{ij})_h - A_{ij}}{h} \partial_i(u_h) \frac{\partial_j(u_h) - \partial_j u}{h} \, dx$$

$$- \int_{\mathbb{R}^N} f(x) \frac{u_{-h} + u_h - 2u}{h^2}(x) \, dx.$$

To bound the second term on the right-hand side, we let $v = (u_h - u)/h$. We then have $(v - v_{-h})/h = (u_h - 2u + u_{-h})/h^2$. Since $v \in H^1(\mathbb{R}^N)$, we can deduce the following inequality from inequality (2.26) of the proof of Proposition 2.23 applied to $\Omega = \mathbb{R}^N$:

$$\|v - v_{-h}\|_2 \leqslant |h| \|\partial_i v\|_2 \leqslant |h| \left\| \frac{\nabla(u_h - u)}{h} \right\|_2.$$

Using, moreover, the uniform ellipticity of A, the previous relation gives

$$\alpha \left\| \frac{\nabla(u_h - u)}{h} \right\|_2^2 \leqslant \|\nabla A\|_\infty \|\nabla u_h\|_2 \left\| \frac{\nabla(u_h - u)}{h} \right\|_2 + \|f\|_2 \left\| \frac{\nabla(u^h - u)}{h} \right\|_2.$$

Finally, we obtain

$$\left\| \frac{\nabla(u^h - u)}{h} \right\|_2 \leqslant \frac{1}{\alpha} \Big(\|\nabla u\|_2 \|\nabla A\|_\infty + \|f\|_2 \Big).$$

Since the right-hand sides does not depend on h, we may use the characterization of the functions in H^1 using finite differences given in Chapter 2 (cf. Proposition 2.23). By choosing a basis of $\mathbb{R}^N$ for the e_i, we obtain that for a solution u of $[\mathcal{D}ir]_A^f$, $\nabla\nabla u$ belongs to L^2 and has norm satisfying

$$\|\nabla\nabla u\|_2 \leqslant \frac{1}{\alpha}(\|\nabla u\|_2 \|\nabla A\|_\infty + \|f\|_2).$$

Second Step: $\mathbb{R}^{N-1} \times]0, +\infty[$. We can repeat the computations given above with $\overrightarrow{h} = he_i$, where $i < N$. Given the vanishing of $u_h - u$ on the boundary, Green's formula applied to the formula obtained by integrating the product $\text{div}(A^h \nabla u_h - A\nabla u)(u_h - u)$ gives us the inclusion

$$\partial_{ij} u \in L^2(\mathbb{R}^{N-1} \times]0, +\infty[),$$

provided that one of the indexes (i, j) is different from N. It remains to show that $\partial_{NN} u \in L^2$. For this, we write the equation as

$$\partial_N(A_{NN}\partial_N u) = f - \sum_{i \leqslant N-1, j} \partial_i(A_{ij}\partial_j u) \in L^2.$$

Setting $A_{NN}\partial_N u = bv$, we reduce to showing the following result.

Lemma 5.34. *If* $b \in W^{1,\infty}(\mathbb{R}^{N-1} \times]0, +\infty[)$ *with* $b \geqslant \alpha > 0$ *and* $v \in L^2(\mathbb{R}^{N-1} \times]0, +\infty[)$ *satisfy* $\partial_N(bv) = V \in L^2(\mathbb{R}^{N-1} \times]0, +\infty[)$ *in the sense of distributions, then* $\partial_N v = (V - (\partial_N b)v)/b$ *belongs to* $L^2(\mathbb{R}^{N-1} \times]0, +\infty[)$.

Proof of Lemma 5.34.

We first assume that b is also of class $\mathcal{C}^1$, in which case the argument is simpler. Indeed, since $\partial_N v$ is a distribution of order $\leqslant 1$, we can differentiate its product with b using the formula $\partial_N(bv) = b\partial_N v + v\partial_N b$, giving us $b\partial_N v \in L^2$. The result now follows from the inclusion $1/b \in L^\infty$.

The result still holds when $b \in W^{1,\infty}$. Indeed, if $\partial_N(bv) \in L^2(\mathbb{R}^{N-1} \times]0,+\infty[)$, then by extending b and v by the reflexion $(x', x_N) \mapsto (x', -x_N)$, that is, by taking $v(x', x_N) = v(x', -x_N)$ and the analogue for b, we obtain $\partial_N(bv) \in L^2(\mathbb{R}^N)$. Consequently, once more using Proposition 2.23, we find the upper bound $\|((bv)_h - bv)/h\|_2 \leqslant C$, where C does not depend on $\overrightarrow{h} = he_N$. It follows that the function $b(v_h - v)/h + v_h(b_h - b)/h$ is uniformly bounded in $L^2(\mathbb{R}^N)$. Since b is Lipschitz, whence $v_h(b_h - b)/h$ is also uniformly bounded in $L^2(\mathbb{R}^N)$, we can deduce that $b(v_h - v)/h$ is uniformly bounded in $L^2(\mathbb{R}^N)$. Finally, since b has a lower bound, $(v_h - v)/h$ is also bounded in $L^2(\mathbb{R}^N)$, giving $\partial_N v \in L^2(\mathbb{R}^N)$. □

Remark 5.35. Let us note that when A either is a diagonal matrix or has coefficients A_{iN} all equal to zero, which is for example the case for the Laplace operator, then we can use the extension $\widetilde{u}(x', x_N) = -\widetilde{u}(x', -x_N)$ that satisfies $\operatorname{div} A(\nabla \widetilde{u})(x', x_N) = \widetilde{f}(x', x_N)$ in $\mathbb{R}^N$, where $\widetilde{f}$ is the antisymmetrization of f.

Third Step. We continue with the case of an open set of class $\mathcal{C}^2$. Let u be the solution of $[\mathcal{D}ir]_A^f$. Let φ_k be a regular function with compact support in $\overline{\Omega} \cap \Omega_k$, where Ω_k has the property that there exists a $\mathcal{C}^2$ function a_k on an open subset $\mathcal{O}'$ of $\mathbb{R}^{N-1}$ such that

$$\Omega \cap \Omega_k \subset \{(x', x_N) \mid x' \in \mathcal{O}', \ x_N > a_k(x')\},$$
$$\partial\Omega \cap \Omega_k = \{(x', a_k(x')) \mid x' \in \mathcal{O}'\}.$$

Let us show that the function $\varphi_k u$ satisfies

$$\operatorname{div}(A(x)\nabla(\varphi_k u)) = g \in L^2(\Omega \cap \Omega_k).$$

Simplifying the notation by writing φ for φ_k and Ω for $\Omega \cap \Omega_k$, we have

$$\operatorname{div}(A(x)\nabla(\varphi u)) = \operatorname{div}(A(x)\varphi\nabla u) + \operatorname{div}\big(A(x)(\nabla\varphi)u\big)$$
$$= \varphi\operatorname{div}(A(x)\nabla u) + \nabla\varphi \cdot A(x)\nabla u + \operatorname{div}(u\,A(x)(\nabla\varphi))$$
$$= \varphi f + h,$$

where $h \in L^2(\Omega)$. Indeed, $A \in L^\infty$ and $\nabla u \in L^2$ imply that $A(x)\nabla u \in L^2$ and $\nabla\varphi \in \mathcal{D}(\mathbb{R}^N)$, so that $A(x)\nabla u\nabla\varphi \in L^2$. Moreover, $(\nabla\varphi)u \in H^1$, so that $uA(x) \cdot \nabla\varphi$ belongs to H^1 since it is the product of a function in $W^{1,\infty}$ and a function in H^1. We have thus reduced the problem to showing the following regularity result.

Lemma 5.36. *Let u have compact support in $\Omega_k \cap \overline{\Omega}$ and satisfy*

$$\operatorname{div}(A(x) \cdot \nabla u) = g \in L^2(\Omega_k \cap \Omega) \quad \text{and} \quad u = 0 \text{ on } \partial\Omega \cap \Omega_k;$$

then $u \in H^2(\mathbb{R}^{N-1} \times]0,+\infty[)$.

Proof of Lemma 5.36.

Let v be defined on $\mathcal{O}' \times \,]0, +\infty[$ by $v(x', x_N) = u(x', a(x') + x_N)$. The regularity of Ω then implies that v belongs to $H^1(\mathcal{O}' \times \,]0, +\infty[)$ and has compact support in $\mathcal{O}' \times [0, +\infty[$. We will show that it satisfies an equation of the type $\mathrm{div}(B(\nabla v)) = h$, where h is an element of L^2 and B is a matrix that we will determine using A.

For a fixed x in $\Omega \cap \Omega_k$, the relations

$$\partial_i u(x', x_N) = \partial_i v(x', x_N - a(x')) - \partial_i a \partial_N v(x', x_N - a(x')),$$
$$\partial_N u(x', x_N) = \partial_N v(x', x_N - a(x')),$$

lead us to associate to $X \in \mathbb{R}^N$ the vector Y defined by

$$\forall i \in [1, N-1], \quad Y_i = X_i - \partial_i a X_N \quad \text{and} \quad Y_N = X_N.$$

We must therefore determine the symmetric matrix B such that for every $X \in \mathbb{R}^N$, we have

$$(*) \qquad\qquad \sum_{ij} B_{ij} X_i X_j = \sum_{ij} A_{ij} Y_i Y_j.$$

Expanding this equality and simplifying, we obtain the relations

$$\forall (i,j) \in [1, N-1]^2, \quad B_{ij} = A_{ij}$$
$$\forall i \in [1, N-1], \quad B_{iN} = A_{iN} - \sum_{j \leqslant N-1} A_{ij} \partial_j a$$
$$B_{NN} = A_{NN} + \sum_{i,j \leqslant N-1} A_{ij} \partial_i a \partial_j a - \sum_{i \leqslant N-1} \partial_i a A_{iN}.$$

The matrix B therefore has coefficients in $W^{1,\infty}$. Our assumptions on a allow us to conclude that the function $(x', x_N) \mapsto h(x', x_N) = f(x', a(x') + x_N)$ belongs to $L^2(\mathcal{O}' \times \,]0, +\infty[)$. Since $v(x', 0) = u(x', a(x'))$, we see that v is a solution of $[\mathcal{D}ir]_B^h$. In order to apply the results of the second step, we still need to show the uniform ellipticity of B.

Let C be the matrix for which $Y = CX$:

$$\forall i \leqslant N-1, \quad C_{ij} = \delta_{ij} - \partial_i a \delta_{Nj}, \quad C_{Nj} = \delta_{Nj}.$$

This matrix is invertible, and $(*)$ corresponds to $B = \,^t CAC$. It is therefore clear that both C and its inverse belong to L^∞ and that, consequently, the matrix B is uniformly elliptic. It follows that v is in the situation of the second step. Hence $v \in H^2(\mathbb{R}^{N-1} \times \,]0, +\infty[)$.

Returning to u, we finally have

$$\varphi_k u \in H^2(\Omega_k \cap \Omega),$$

giving the inclusion stated in the lemma. $\qquad\qquad\qquad\qquad\qquad\qquad\qquad\square$

Since u is the sum of the $\varphi_k u$, it belongs to $H^2(\Omega)$. This concludes the proof of Theorem 5.33.   □

Remark 5.37. When $A = \mathrm{Id}$, that is, for $[\mathcal{D}ir]^f_A$, we can use a regularizing argument in the first step, as follows.

We begin by showing that if $u \in \mathcal{D}(\mathbb{R}^N)$, then

$$\int_{\mathbb{R}^N} |\Delta u|^2 = \int_{\mathbb{R}^N} |\nabla \nabla u|^2.$$

This follows by carrying out two successive integrations by parts:

$$\int_{\mathbb{R}^N} \sum_{ij} \partial_{ij}(u)^2(x)dx = -\sum_{i,j} \int_{\mathbb{R}^N} \partial_{ijj} u(x) \partial_i u(x) dx$$

$$= \sum_{i,j} \int_{\mathbb{R}^N} \partial_{jj} u(x) \partial_{ii} u(x) dx = \int_{\mathbb{R}^N} |\Delta u|^2.$$

We then consider $u_\varepsilon = \rho_\varepsilon \star u$. We have

$$\Delta u_\varepsilon = \rho_\varepsilon \star f$$

and, by the computation above, $\nabla \nabla u_\varepsilon$ is a Cauchy sequence in $L^2(\mathbb{R}^N)$. Since it converges in the sense of $\mathcal{D}'$ to $\nabla \nabla u$, we find that $u \in H^2(\mathbb{R}^N)$.

5.4.2 Higher Order Regularity

Proposition 5.38. *For $m \geqslant 0$, consider a bounded domain Ω of class $\mathcal{C}^{m+2}$ and let $f \in H^m(\Omega)$. Let A be a matrix satisfying the conditions of Theorem 5.33 and the regularity condition $A \in \mathcal{C}^{m+1}(\overline{\Omega})$. Then the solution u of the problem $[\mathcal{D}ir]^f_A$ is an element of $H^{m+2}(\Omega)$.*

Using Sobolev embeddings, we note, in particular, the following consequences of the theorem:

When $2(m + 2) > N$, the solution u is continuous, and when $2m > N$, it is of class $\mathcal{C}^2$.

If $f \in \mathcal{C}^\infty(\Omega)$ and $A \in \mathcal{C}^\infty(\Omega)$, which implies that $f \in \bigcap_m H^m_{\mathrm{loc}}(\Omega)$, then $u \in \bigcap_m H^{m+2}_{\mathrm{loc}}(\Omega) = \mathcal{C}^\infty(\Omega)$.

Proof of Proposition 5.38.

We use induction on m. Let u be the solution of the problem $[\mathcal{D}ir]^f_A$ in $H^1(\mathbb{R}^{N-1} \times]0, +\infty[)$, where $f \in H^m(\mathbb{R}^{N-1} \times]0, +\infty[)$. We suppose that the proposition has been proved at the order $m - 1$. We therefore have

$u \in H^{m+1}(\mathbb{R}^{N-1} \times]0, +\infty[)$. For $k \leqslant N - 1$, differentiating the equation with respect to the variable x_k gives

$$(**) \qquad \sum_{ij} \partial_j \big(A_{ij} \partial_i (\partial_k u) \big) = \partial_k f - \sum_{ij} \partial_j \big((\partial_k A_{ij}) \partial_i u \big).$$

Hence, taking into account the assumptions and the result at the order $m-1$, we see that the right-hand side g of $(**)$ belongs to H^{m-1}. Moreover, on $\partial\Omega$, we have $\partial_k u = 0$ because $u(x', 0) = 0$ implies $\partial_k u(x', 0) = 0$. The relation $(**)$ therefore expresses the fact that $\partial_k u$ is a solution of $[\mathcal{D}ir]_A^g$.

Once again using the induction hypothesis for $\partial_k u$, we see that the inclusion of g in $H^{m-1}(\mathbb{R}^{N-1} \times]0, +\infty[)$ implies that its derivative $\partial_k u$ belongs to $H^{m+1}(\mathbb{R}^{N-1} \times]0, +\infty[)$.

It remains to show that $\partial_N u \in H^{m+1}(\mathbb{R}^{N-1} \times]0, +\infty[)$. Now, since $u \in H^{m+1}(\mathbb{R}^{N-1} \times]0, +\infty[)$, we already have $\partial_N u \in H^m(\mathbb{R}^{N-1} \times]0, +\infty[)$. We have just shown that $\partial_k u \in H^{m+1}(\mathbb{R}^{N-1} \times]0, +\infty[)$, so that we have $\partial_{kN} u \in H^m(\mathbb{R}^{N-1} \times]0, +\infty[)$ for $k \leqslant N - 1$. Moreover,

$$A_{NN} \partial_{NN} u = f - \sum_{(i,j) \neq (N,N)} A_{ij} \partial_{ij} u - \sum_{ij} \partial_j A_{ij} \partial_i u \in H^m(\mathbb{R}^{N-1} \times]0, +\infty[).$$

Finally, by the uniform ellipticity of A, there exists a constant $\alpha > 0$ such that $A_{NN} \geqslant \alpha > 0$. Therefore, since for a function $v \in H^m$ and a nonzero $b \in \mathcal{C}^m$, we have $v/b \in H^m$, we obtain $\partial_{NN} u \in H^m(\mathbb{R}^{N-1} \times]0, +\infty[)$. It follows that $u \in H^{m+2}(\mathbb{R}^{N-1} \times]0, +\infty[)$.

In the above, we could also only assume that A is an element of $W^{m+1,\infty}$.

Let us continue with the general case. We again use the partition of unity and localization. We use the notation from the definition of the $\mathcal{C}^{m+2}$ regularity. We must show that if $\mathrm{div}(A(\nabla u)) \in H^m(\Omega_k \cap \Omega)$, then $\varphi_k u \in H^{m+2}(\Omega_k \cap \Omega)$.

Let v be the function on $\Omega_k \cap \Omega$ defined by

$$v(x', x_N) = (\varphi_k u)(x', a(x') + x_N),$$

where a is a $\mathcal{C}^{m+2}$ function on $\mathcal{O}'$; then v has compact support in $\mathcal{O}' \times [0, \infty[$. For B as in the proof of Proposition 5.33, we have

$$\mathrm{div}(B(\nabla v)) = g$$

with $g \in H^m(\mathcal{O}' \times]0, +\infty[)$. Since $B \in \mathcal{C}^{m+1}(\overline{\Omega \cap \Omega_k})$, the first part of the proposition tells us that $v \in H^{m+2}(\mathcal{O}' \times]0, +\infty[)$. Moreover, since a is $\mathcal{C}^{m+2}$, we find that $\varphi_k u \in H^{m+2}(\Omega_k \cap \Omega)$.

By gluing the local results, we finally conclude that $u \in H^{m+2}(\Omega)$. $\qquad\square$

5.5 Neumann Problems

When, in the physical model of Dirichlet, the boundary condition no longer involves an equality concerning the unknown function but rather one concerning a derivative of that function, we speak of a *Neumann* problem.

5.5.1 Normal Trace and Derivative

Let Ω be a bounded domain of class $\mathcal{C}^1$ and let A be a function in $\mathcal{C}^1(\overline{\Omega})$ with values in the space of symmetric $N \times N$ matrices over $\mathbb{R}$. We suppose that $\sigma \in L^2(\Omega, \mathbb{R}^N)$, so that $x \mapsto A(x)\sigma(x)$ defines a function on Ω with values in $\mathbb{R}^N$. Since Ω is bounded, we have $A\sigma \in L^2(\Omega, \mathbb{R}^N)$, so that if $\operatorname{div}(A\sigma) \in L^2(\Omega)$, then $A\sigma \in W_2^2(\operatorname{div})(\Omega)$ (this space was introduced in Chapter 3, §3.4.3). By the generalized Green's formula 3.58, the symbol $A\sigma \cdot \overrightarrow{n}$ is well defined on $\partial\Omega$. Hence

$$\forall U \in H^1(\Omega), \quad \langle A\sigma \cdot \overrightarrow{n}, \gamma_0 U \rangle = \int_\Omega A\sigma(x) \cdot \nabla U(x)dx + \int_\Omega U(x)\operatorname{div}(A\sigma)(x)dx.$$

Definition 5.39. The linear functional $A\sigma \cdot \overrightarrow{n}$, which belongs to the dual $H^{-1/2}(\partial\Omega)$ of the space of traces $H^{1/2}(\partial\Omega)$, is called the *normal trace* of $A\sigma$ on $\partial\Omega$.

In particular, if $u \in H^1(\Omega)$ and $\operatorname{div}(A\nabla u) \in L^2$, the *normal derivative* or, more precisely, the *A-normal derivative* $A(x)\nabla u \cdot \overrightarrow{n} = A_{ij}\partial_i u\, n_j$ of u belongs to $H^{-1/2}(\partial\Omega)$. Taking the identity matrix for A, we find that if $\Delta u \in L^2(\Omega)$ and $u \in H^1(\Omega)$, then the normal derivative $\partial_n u$ belongs to $H^{-1/2}(\partial\Omega)$.

5.5.2 Homogeneous Neumann Problem $[\mathcal{N}eu]_A^f$

Statement of the Problem. The problem consists in determining u in $H^1(\Omega)$ such that

$$[\mathcal{N}eu]_A^f : \begin{cases} -\operatorname{div}(A(x)\nabla u) = f & \text{in } \Omega, \\ A(\nabla u) \cdot \overrightarrow{n} = 0 & \text{on } \partial\Omega. \end{cases}$$

Remark 5.40. Note that this problem has a solution only if

$$(5.41) \qquad\qquad \int_\Omega f(x)dx = 0.$$

Indeed, if u is a solution, then by applying Green's formula with $\varphi = 1_\Omega$ and $A(x)\nabla u$, which belongs to $W_2^2(\operatorname{div})$, we have

$$\int_\Omega f(x)dx = \int_\Omega -\operatorname{div}\big(A(x)\nabla u(x)\big)dx = \langle A(x)\nabla u \cdot \overrightarrow{n}, 1_\Omega \rangle = 0.$$

We will assume that this condition is satisfied and, moreover, that A satisfies the conditions of Theorem 5.33.

Variational Formulation. As before, the variational form of this problem is
the minimization associated to

$$(5.42) \qquad \inf J(u) = \inf_{u \in H^1(\Omega)} \left\{ \frac{1}{2} \int_\Omega (A(x)\nabla u) \cdot \nabla u \, dx - \int_\Omega f u \, dx \right\}.$$

to this problem. Taking into account the hypothesis $\int_\Omega f(x)dx = 0$, we note
that if u is a solution, then so is $u + $ cte. More generally, the functional J
defined in (5.42) satisfies $J(v + \text{cte}) = J(v) \, \forall v \in H^1(\Omega)$. By identifying
the space of constant functions with $\mathbb{R}$, we can work on the quotient space
$\widetilde{H^1(\Omega)} = H^1(\Omega)/\mathbb{R}$. When endowed with the quotient norm, that is,

$$(5.43) \qquad \|u\|_{\widetilde{H^1(\Omega)}} = \inf_{c \in \mathbb{R}} \|u + c\|_{H^1(\Omega)}$$

(cf. Exercise 1.28), this is a reflexive separable Banach space. To show the co-
ercivity of $\widetilde{J}$, which on $\widetilde{H^1(\Omega)}$ is defined by $\widetilde{J}(\widetilde{v}) = J(v)$, we use an inequality
analogous to that of Poincaré.

Proposition 5.44. *Let Ω be a bounded domain in $\mathbb{R}^N$. For every u in $H^1(\Omega)$,
let $[u]_\Omega = (\mathrm{mes}(\Omega))^{-1} \int_\Omega u(x)dx$.*
   Then there exists a constant $C > 0$ such that

$$\forall u \in H^1(\Omega), \quad \|u\|_{\widetilde{H^1(\Omega)}} \leqslant \|u - [u]_\Omega 1_\Omega\|_{H^1(\Omega)} \leqslant C\|\nabla u\|_2.$$

Proof of Proposition 5.44. If $u = $ cte, the inequality is obvious. Otherwise, for
$u \in H^1(\Omega)$, we set $m(u) = [u]_\Omega 1_\Omega$. Our proof is by contradiction. We therefore
assume that there exists a sequence $\{u_n\} \in H^1$ with nonconstant u_n, such
that

$$\|u_n - m(u_n)\|_{H^1(\Omega)} \geqslant n\|\nabla u_n\|_2.$$

Consider the sequence with terms $v_n = (\|u_n - m(u_n)\|_2)^{-1}(u_n - m(u_n))$.
We have $\|\nabla v_n\|_2 \leqslant 1/n$ and $\|v_n\|_2 = 1$, so that $\{v_n\}$ is bounded in $H^1(\Omega)$.
Since Ω is bounded, we can therefore extract a subsequence, which we de-
note in the same way, that converges weakly in $H^1(\Omega)$ and strongly in $L^2(\Omega)$.
Since $\|\nabla v_n\|_2$ converges to 0, we have strong convergence in $H^1(\Omega)$. In par-
ticular, the chosen subsequence converges to a constant function. However,
as the functional m is linear, we have $m(v_n) = 0$. Since m is clearly continuous for the norm on H^1, it follows that $\{m(v_n)\}$ converges to $m(v)$, which
equals v because v is a constant. Consequently, $v = 0$. Using the equality
$\|v_n\|_{H^1} = 1$ and the strong convergence, we deduce that $\|v\|_{L^2(\Omega)} = 1$, giving
a contradiction. $\qquad \square$

Existence of a Solution. Let us return to the variational form (5.42) of the problem. The convexity of J follows from the convexity of the integral and the linearity of the term $\int_\Omega f(x)u(x)dx$. The continuity is obvious. To deduce the coercivity, we first note that $J(v) \geqslant \alpha\|\nabla v\|_2^2 - \|f\|_2\|v\|_2$ by the ellipticity, and then, that by Proposition 5.44,

$$\widetilde{J}(\widetilde{v}) \geqslant \frac{\alpha}{C^2}\|\widetilde{v}\|_{H^1}^2 - \|f\|_2\|\widetilde{v}\|_{H^1}.$$

We deduce from this the existence of a minimum of $\widetilde{J}$ on $\widetilde{H^1(\Omega)}$. It remains to describe the function u realizing this minimum and to verify that it satisfies the Neumann condition.

Using the differentiability of J, u is characterized by

$$\forall\varphi \in \mathcal{D}(\Omega), \quad \int_\Omega A(x)\nabla u(x) \cdot \nabla\varphi(x)dx - \int_\Omega f(x)\varphi(x)dx = 0.$$

It follows that in Ω, we have the equality

$$\forall x \in \Omega, \quad -\operatorname{div}(A(x)\nabla u(x)) = f(x).$$

Keeping in mind this equality, we apply Green's formula for every $\varphi \in H^1(\Omega)$. This gives

$$\int_\Omega A(x)\nabla u(x) \cdot \nabla\varphi(x)dx - \int_\Omega f(x)\varphi(x)dx = 0 = \int_{\partial\Omega} A(x)\nabla u \cdot \overrightarrow{n}\,\varphi(x)dx.$$

We conclude that $A(x)\nabla u \cdot \overrightarrow{n} = 0$ in the dual $H^{1/2}(\partial\Omega)$. This guarantees the existence of a solution.

Uniqueness in the Quotient Space. Let u and v be two solutions. We will show that their difference w is a constant. Indeed, w satisfies $[\mathcal{N}eu]_A^0$, that is,

$$\forall x \in \Omega, \quad -\operatorname{div}(A(x)\nabla w(x)) = 0 \quad \text{and on } \partial\Omega, \quad A(x)\nabla w \cdot \overrightarrow{n} = 0.$$

By multiplying by w and applying Green's formula, we obtain

$$\int_\Omega A(x)\nabla w(x) \cdot \nabla w(x)dx = \int_{\partial\Omega} w(x)A(x)\nabla w \cdot \overrightarrow{n}\,d\sigma = 0.$$

By the uniform ellipticity, the left-hand side is bounded from below by $\alpha\|\nabla w\|_{L^2(\Omega)}^2$. It follows that $w = \text{cte}$, or, in other words, that $\widetilde{w} = 0$.

Regularity of the Solution. We now assume that Ω is of class $\mathcal{C}^2$, that the function f belongs to $L^2(\Omega)$, and that the matrix function A is $\mathcal{C}^1$ on $\overline{\Omega}$ and, obviously, uniformly elliptic. Finally, let u be the solution of the problem $[\mathcal{N}eu]_A^f$. We will show regularity results analogous to those for the solutions of Dirichlet problems.

Theorem 5.45.

(1) *Under the assumptions stated above, the solution of* $[\mathcal{N}eu]_A^f$ *belongs to* $H^2(\Omega)$.

(2) *If* $f \in H^m(\Omega)$ *and* $A \in \mathcal{C}^{m+1}(\overline{\Omega})$, *where the open set* Ω *is of class* $\mathcal{C}^{m+2}$, *then the solution satisfies* $u \in H^{m+2}(\Omega)$.

Proof of Theorem 5.45. As in the Dirichlet regularity theorem, we divide the proof into several steps.

The first step, on $\mathbb{R}^N$, is the same as in the Dirichlet case.

We proceed to $\mathbb{R}^{N-1} \times]0, +\infty[$.

Let u have compact support in $\mathbb{R}^{N-1} \times [0, \infty[$. We note that, owing to the homogeneous Neumann condition, Green's formula

$$\int_{\mathbb{R}^{N-1}\times]0,\infty[} (A(x)\nabla u) \cdot \nabla v + \int_{\mathbb{R}^{N-1}\times]0,\infty[} fv = 0$$

still holds for every $v \in H^1(\mathbb{R}^{N-1} \times]0, \infty[)$. We can therefore proceed as in the proof of the Dirichlet regularity, using translations in directions other than e_N. We take the difference of the equations satisfied by u and by u_h, multiply by $u_h - u$, and integrate over $\mathbb{R}^{N-1} \times]0, \infty[$. This gives us a uniform estimate that allows us to show that $\partial_{ij}u \in L^2$ provided that at least one index is not N. For the inclusion of $\partial_{NN}u$ in L^2, we conclude as in the proof of the Dirichlet regularity by writing the equation as

$$\partial_N(A_{NN}\partial_N u) = -f - \sum_{i \leqslant N-1, j} \partial_i(A_{ij}\partial_j u) \in L^2,$$

and using Lemma 5.34.

General case. We take the usual elements of the regularity of Ω: the cover, the local coordinate systems, the functions φ_k of the partition of unity, and so on. Reasoning as we did in the Dirichlet case, we see that the function $\varphi_k u$ satisfies

$$\mathrm{div}(A(x)\nabla(\varphi_k u)) = g$$

in $\Omega \cap \Omega_k$, where $g \in L^2(\Omega \cap \Omega_k)$. However, in contrast to the Dirichlet case, the boundary condition $A(x)\nabla(\varphi_k u) \cdot \overrightarrow{n} = 0$ on $\partial\Omega \cap \Omega_k$ may no longer be verified. Nevertheless, by expanding $\nabla(\varphi_k u)$, using the linearity of the normal trace on L^2, and factoring by the real-valued functions, we obtain

$$A\nabla(\varphi_k u) \cdot \overrightarrow{n} = (A\nabla u \cdot \overrightarrow{n})\varphi_k + (A(\nabla\varphi_k) \cdot \overrightarrow{n})u = (A(\nabla\varphi_k) \cdot \overrightarrow{n})u.$$

Let us consider the function A^* on $\partial\Omega$ defined by $x' \mapsto (A(x')\overrightarrow{n}(x') \cdot \overrightarrow{n}(x'))$. It is a class $\mathcal{C}^1$ function and, by the uniform ellipticity condition, does not take on the value zero. Since $\partial\Omega$ is of class $\mathcal{C}^2$, when restricted to this boundary, the function $(1/A^*)A(\nabla\varphi_k) \cdot \overrightarrow{n}\, u$ is the product of the trace $\gamma_0 u \in H^{1/2}(\partial\Omega)$ and a function that is $\mathcal{C}^1$ on $\overline{\Omega}$. Adapting the proof of the local character of $H^{1/2}$ stated in Proposition 4.26 of Chapter 4, we show that this function belongs to $H^{1/2}(\partial\Omega)$. Since Ω is of class $\mathcal{C}^2$, we can then apply the trace theorem 3.79 of Chapter 3 for $m = 2$ and $p = 2$. It states that the map $\gamma = (\gamma_0, \gamma_1)$ from $H^2(\Omega)$ to the product space $H^{3/2}(\partial\Omega) \times H^{1/2}(\partial\Omega)$ that sends v to the pair $(\gamma_0 v, \partial_{\overrightarrow{n}} v)$ is surjective. In our present situation, we can therefore find a $V \in H^2(\Omega)$ such that

$$\begin{cases} V(x) = 0 & \text{if } x \in \partial\Omega, \\ \partial_{\overrightarrow{n}} V = \dfrac{1}{A^*}\Big(A(\nabla\varphi_k) \cdot \overrightarrow{n})\Big)u & \text{if } x \in \partial\Omega. \end{cases}$$

From this, we deduce that

$$A(\nabla V) \cdot \overrightarrow{n} = (A(\nabla\varphi_k) \cdot \overrightarrow{n})u.$$

The function $U = \varphi_k u - V$ therefore satisfies the relation

$$-\operatorname{div}(A(x)\nabla U) = -\operatorname{div}(A(x) \cdot \nabla(\varphi_k u) + \operatorname{div}(A(x)\nabla V) \in L^2$$

with the condition $A(x)\nabla U \cdot \overrightarrow{n} = 0$.

We then define v on $H^1(\mathbb{R}^{N-1} \times\,]0, +\infty[)$ by setting

$$v(x', x_N) = U(x', x_N + a(x')).$$

As in the proof of the Dirichlet regularity, the function v satisfies $\operatorname{div}(B(x)\nabla v) = h$, where h belongs to $L^2(\mathbb{R}^{N-1} \times\,]0, +\infty[)$. We will show that v is the solution of a Neumann problem on $\mathbb{R}^{N-1} \times\,]0, +\infty[)$, allowing us to use the regularity result on that open space.

We recall that

$$\forall\, i \in [1, N-1], \quad B_{iN} = A_{iN} - \sum_{j \leqslant N-1} A_{ij}\partial_j a,$$

$$B_{NN} = A_{NN} + A\nabla a\nabla a - \sum_{j \leqslant N-1} A_{Nj}\partial_j a.$$

We verify the relation

$$(*) \qquad\qquad \sum_{i \leqslant N-1} B_{iN}\partial_i v + B_{NN}\partial_N v = 0.$$

Indeed, taking into account the colinearity of $\overrightarrow{n}$ to $-\nabla a + e_N$ and the relations between the partial derivatives of U and v computed in the previous section, the relation

$$A(x)\nabla U \cdot \overrightarrow{n} = 0$$

can be written as

$$
\begin{aligned}
0 &= \sum_{i,j \leqslant N-1} A_{ij}(\partial_i v - \partial_i a \partial_N v)(-\partial_j a) + \sum_{i \leqslant N-1} A_{iN}(\partial_i v - \partial_i a \partial_N v) \\
&\quad + \sum_{j \leqslant N-1} A_{Nj}\partial_N v(-\partial_j a) + A_{NN}\partial_N v \\
&= -\sum_{ij \leqslant N-1} A_{ij}\partial_i v \partial_j a + A_{iN}\partial_i v + \partial_N v\Big(A_{NN} + A\nabla a\nabla a - \sum_{j \leqslant N-1} A_{Nj}\partial_j a\Big) \\
&= -\sum_1^N B_{iN}\partial_i v - B_{NN}\partial_N v.
\end{aligned}
$$

This proves $(*)$, which shows that the normal trace $B\nabla v \cdot \overrightarrow{e_N}$ vanishes on $\{x_N = 0\}$. The function v is therefore a solution of the problem $[\mathcal{N}eu]_B^h$ in the open set $\Omega = \mathbb{R}^{N-1}\times]0, +\infty[$, as desired. We have thus reduced the problem to showing a regularity result on $\mathbb{R}^{N-1}\times]0, +\infty[$. Now, $v \in H^2(\mathbb{R}^{N-1}\times]0, +\infty[)$, which, using the fact that a is C^2, easily implies that $u \in H^2(\Omega \cap \Omega_k)$.

Higher Order Regularity. Let us show the order H^{m+2} regularity when the boundary of Ω is of class C^{m+2}, $A \in C^{m+1}(\overline{\Omega})$, and $f \in H^m(\Omega)$.

We first consider the case where $\Omega = \mathbb{R}^{N-1} \times]0, +\infty[$, which we will from now on denote by $\mathbb{R}^{N+}$.

We suppose that u satisfies $\mathrm{div}(A(x)\nabla u) = -f$ in $\mathbb{R}^{N+}$ and $\sum_i A_{iN}\partial_i u = 0$ on the boundary $\{x_N = 0\}$. We will use induction on m. Let us therefore suppose shown that if $f \in H^{m-1}$ and $A \in C^m(\overline{\Omega})$, then $u \in H^{m+1}(\mathbb{R}^{N+})$.

Now, let $f \in H^m(\mathbb{R}^{N+})$ and $A \in C^{m+1}(\mathbb{R}^{N+})$. The derivative of u with respect to x_k, where $k \leqslant N - 1$, satisfies

$$
\mathrm{div}(A(x)\nabla(\partial_k u)) = -\partial_k f - \mathrm{div}(\partial_k A(x)\nabla u).
$$

The right-hand side of this equation is an element of H^{m-1}, because $\nabla u \in H^m$ by the induction hypothesis and because $\partial_k A \in C^m$ by a variant of the argument we used to show the local character. The condition on the boundary is not zero, but we have

$$
A(x)\nabla(\partial_k u) \cdot e_N = \partial_k(A\nabla u \cdot e_N) - (\partial_k A)\nabla u \cdot e_N = -(\partial_k A)\nabla u \cdot e_N.
$$

This last function $-(\partial_k A)\nabla u \cdot e_N$ is the trace of a function belonging to $H^m(\mathbb{R}^{N+})$. It is therefore an element of $H^{m-1/2}(\mathbb{R}^{N-1})$. Using the surjectivity of γ, which was shown in Theorem 3.79, we can prove the existence of a $V \in H^{m+1}$ such that $A(x)\nabla V \cdot e_N = (\partial_k A)\nabla u \cdot e_N$. The function $w = \partial_k u - V$ satisfies the relations

$$
\mathrm{div}(A(x)\nabla w) \in H^{m-1}(\Omega), \quad A(x)\nabla w \cdot \overrightarrow{e_N} = 0.
$$

It follows that $w \in H^{m+1}$, and therefore $\partial_k u \in H^{m+1}$.

It remains to show that $\partial_N u \in H^{m+1}(\Omega)$. Since we already have $\partial_{kN}u \in H^m(\Omega)$, it suffices to verify that $\partial_{NN}u \in H^m(\Omega)$. We can show that this holds by writing

$$A_{NN}\partial_{NN}u = -\sum_{ij\neq(N,N)} A_{ij}\partial_{ij}u - \sum_{ij}\partial_i A_{ij}\,\partial_j u \in H^m,$$

as we did in the Dirichlet case.

Next, we consider the case of an open set of class $\mathcal{C}^{m+2}$.

We use localization and modify the function to reduce to $\mathbb{R}^{N-1} \times \,]0, +\infty[$. Let $\{\Omega_k\}$ be open sets of class $\mathcal{C}^{m+2}$ that cover Ω and let $\{\varphi_k\}$ be a partition of unity subordinate to this cover, as in the definition of the $\mathcal{C}^{m+2}$-regularity. The function $\varphi_k u$ satisfies

$$\mathrm{div}\big(A(x)\nabla(\varphi_k u)\big) \in H^m,$$

for some A, but the Neumann boundary condition is not zero. In order to apply the induction hypothesis, we note that

$$A(x)\nabla(\varphi_k u) \cdot \overrightarrow{n} = A(x)(\nabla\varphi_k)u \cdot \overrightarrow{n} \in H^{m+1/2}(\partial\Omega)$$

because $u \in H^{m+1}(\Omega)$. Let V be a function in H^{m+2} that satisfies

(5.46) $\qquad V = 0 \quad$ and $\quad (A(x)n, n)\partial_n V = A(x)(\nabla\varphi_k)u \cdot \overrightarrow{n}$

on $\partial\Omega$. On $\partial\Omega \cap \Omega_k$, the function $\varphi_k u - V$ then satisfies

$$-\,\mathrm{div}(A(x)\nabla(\varphi_k u - V)) \in H^m \quad \text{and} \quad A(x)\cdot\nabla(\varphi_k u - V)\cdot\overrightarrow{n} = 0 \quad \text{on} \quad \partial\Omega.$$

As before, we set
$$v(x', x_N) = u(x', a(x') + x_N)$$

and verify, as in the case of H^2-regularity, that

$$-\,\mathrm{div}(B(x)\nabla v) \in H^m(\mathbb{R}^N \times\,]0, +\infty[) \quad \text{and, on } \{x_N = 0\}, \quad B(x)\nabla v\cdot\overrightarrow{e_N} = 0.$$

The regularity we showed in the case of the half-space now implies that v belongs to $H^{m+2}(\mathbb{R}^{N-1} \times\,]0, +\infty[)$. The regularity of A then allows us to deduce that $\varphi_k u \in H^{m+2}(\Omega\cap\Omega_k)$. Finally, we use the properties of the locally finite cover of Ω to conclude that $u = \sum_k \varphi_k u \in H^{m+2}$. This completes the proof of Theorem 5.45. $\qquad\square$

5.6 Nonhomogeneous Dirichlet and Neumann Problems

5.6.1 Nonhomogeneous Dirichlet Problem

As before, let Ω denote a bounded domain of class $\mathcal{C}^1$. Let $u_0 \in H^{1/2}(\partial\Omega)$. The nonhomogeneous Dirichlet problem $[\mathcal{D}ir]_A^{f,u_0}$ consists in looking for a u in $H^1(\Omega)$ such that

$$[\mathcal{D}ir]_A^{f,u_0} : \begin{cases} -\operatorname{div}(A(x)\nabla u) = f & \text{in } \Omega, \\ u = u_0 & \text{on } \partial\Omega. \end{cases}$$

Existence and Uniqueness. We can show these by considering the corresponding variational problem of determining a u in $H^1(\Omega)$ for which

$$(5.47) \qquad \inf_{\{u \in H^1(\Omega), u = u_0 \text{ on } \partial\Omega\}} \left\{ \frac{1}{2} \int_\Omega A(x)\nabla u(x) \cdot \nabla u(x)dx - \int_\Omega f(x)u(x)dx \right\}$$

is reached. This problem is a minimization on a closed convex set, but we can translate it to a minimization on all of H^1. For this, we note that u_0 belongs to the trace space $H^{1/2}(\partial\Omega)$. We can therefore lift this function to an element U_0 of $H^1(\Omega)$ (cf. Chapter 3). Fixing this lifting and applying the translation $u = U_0 + v$, the above problem becomes to determine a u in $H^1(\Omega)$ where

$$\inf_{v \in H_0^1(\Omega)} \left\{ \frac{1}{2} \int_\Omega A(x)\nabla(U_0 + v)(x) \cdot \nabla(U_0 + v)(x)dx - \int_\Omega f(x)(v + U_0)(x)dx \right\}$$

is reached. Setting $K = 1/2 \int_\Omega A(x)\nabla U_0(x) \cdot \nabla U_0(x)dx - \int_\Omega f(x)U_0(x)dx$, we can also write the infimum as

$$\inf_{v \in H_0^1(\Omega)} \left\{ \int_\Omega A\nabla v \cdot \nabla U_0 dx + \frac{1}{2} \int_\Omega A(x)\nabla v(x) \cdot \nabla v(x)dx - \int_\Omega f(x)v(x)dx + K \right\}.$$

This new functional $v \mapsto J_1(v)$ whose first term is a continuous linear functional, is still convex and continuous on $H^1(\Omega)$. Indeed, using the uniform ellipticity of A, the coercivity of J_1 leads to the inequality

$$|J_1(v)| \geqslant \alpha\|\nabla v\|_2^2 - \|A\nabla U_0\|_2\|\nabla v\|_2 - \|f\|_2\|\nabla v\|_2 - |K|.$$

We may therefore apply Theorem 5.25 and use the strict convexity of J_1 to prove the existence and uniqueness of a solution of the problem associate with (5.47).

Let us continue. The functional J_1 is G-differentiable. Through a computation that is by now classic, we have, for every $\varphi \in \mathcal{D}(\Omega)$,

$$J_1'(v,\varphi) = \int_\Omega A\nabla\varphi \cdot \nabla U_0 dx + \int_\Omega A(x)\nabla v(x) \cdot \nabla\varphi(x)dx - \int_\Omega f(x)\varphi(x)dx.$$

Consequently,

$$J_1'(v) = -\operatorname{div}\big(A(\nabla(v + U_0))\big) - f.$$

By making this derivative vanish at v, we find that the solution $u = v + U_0$ of the problem associated with (5.47) is indeed also the solution of $[\mathcal{D}ir]_A^{f,u_0}$.

Note that we can use the translation $u - U_0$ to directly reduce to a homogeneous Dirichlet problem. In that case, $u - U_0$ must be the solution of

$$-\operatorname{div}(A(x)\nabla v) = f + \operatorname{div}(A(x)\nabla U_0),$$
$$v = 0 \quad \text{on } \partial\Omega.$$

Since it is the divergence of a function in L^2, we have $\operatorname{div}(A(x)\nabla U_0) \in H^{-1}(\Omega)$, which shows that the right-hand side belongs to $H^{-1}(\Omega)$. Remark 5.30 now allows us to conclude the proof.

Regularity Properties.

Proposition 5.48. *Let $m \geqslant 0$. Let Ω be a bounded domain of class $\mathcal{C}^{m+2}$, let $A \in \mathcal{C}^{m+1}(\overline{\Omega})$, let $u_0 \in H^{m+3/2}(\partial\Omega)$, and let $f \in H^m(\Omega)$. The solution u of*

$$\begin{cases} -\operatorname{div}(A(x)\nabla u) = f & in\ \Omega, \\ u = u_0 & on\ \partial\Omega, \end{cases}$$

then is an element of $H^{m+2}(\Omega)$.

Proof of Proposition 5.48.

The proof is obvious when we use a translation. By the trace theorem 3.79, there exists a $U \in H^{m+2}(\Omega)$ with trace u_0 on $\partial\Omega$ because $u_0 \in H^{m+3/2}(\partial\Omega)$. By the properties of A and U, we therefore have

$$-\operatorname{div}\big((A(x)\nabla(u - U)\big) = f + \sum_{i,j}\big(\partial_i(A_{ij})\partial_j U + A_{ij}\partial_{ij} U\big) = g.$$

The regularity assumptions on f, A, and u imply that $g \in H^m(\Omega)$. We obtain the desired conclusion, namely that $u \in H^{m+2}(\Omega)$, using the regularity theorem 5.38 for the problem $[\mathcal{D}ir]_A^g$.   □

5.6.2 Nonhomogeneous Neumann Problem

Let Ω be a bounded domain of class $\mathcal{C}^1$. We begin by supposing that $u_1 \in H^{-1/2}(\partial\Omega)$. We propose to solve the problem

$$[\mathcal{N}eu]_A^{f,u_1} : \begin{cases} -\operatorname{div}(A(x)\nabla u) = f & in\ \Omega, \\ A(\nabla u) \cdot \overline{n} = u_1 & on\ \partial\Omega. \end{cases}$$

Existence and Uniqueness of a Solution.

In order to prove the existence of a solution u in $H^1(\Omega)$, we multiply the equation by an element v of $H^1(\Omega)$. By the generalized Green's formula (cf. Proposition 3.58), we have

$$\int_\Omega A(x)\nabla u(x) \cdot \nabla v(x)dx = \int_\Omega f(x)v(x)dx + \langle A(x)\nabla u \cdot \overrightarrow{n}, v\rangle,$$

which leads us to considering the minimization

$$(5.49) \quad \inf_{v\in H^1(\Omega)} J(v)$$

$$= \inf_{v\in H^1(\Omega)} \left\{ \int_\Omega \frac{1}{2}(A(x)\nabla v(x) \cdot \nabla v(x) - \int_\Omega f(x)v(x)dx - \langle u_1, v\rangle \right\}.$$

Since the constant functions belong to $H^1(\Omega)$, we note that if $\int_\Omega f(x)dx + \langle u_1, 1_\Omega\rangle \neq 0$, then the infimum in the equation is equal to $-\infty$. We therefore suppose that $\int_\Omega f(x)dx + \langle u_1, 1_\Omega\rangle = 0$, which generalizes the assumptions we made for the homogeneous Neumann problem.

The functional $\widetilde{J}$ on the separable and reflexive quotient space $\widetilde{H^1(\Omega)}$ is strictly convex, continuous, and coercive. The existence and uniqueness of a solution of the problem associated with (5.49) follow modulo the constant functions, giving the result for $[\mathcal{N}eu]_A^{f,u_1}$. $\qquad\square$

Regularity Result. As above, we suppose that $\int_\Omega f(x)dx + \langle u_1, 1_\Omega\rangle = 0$.

Theorem 5.50. *If $f \in H^m(\Omega)$ with $m \geqslant -1$, $A \in \mathcal{C}^{m+1}(\overline{\Omega})$, and $u_1 \in H^{m+1/2}(\partial\Omega)$, then the solution u of $[\mathcal{N}eu]_A^{f,u_1}$ belongs to $H^{m+2}(\Omega)$.*

Proof of Theorem 5.50. The proof uses a function V in H^{m+2} for which $(A(x)\nabla V) \cdot \overrightarrow{n} = u_1$, as, for example, in the proof of the homogeneous Neumann case (cf. relation 5.46).

We conclude the proof by noting that $\mathrm{div}(A(x)\nabla V) \in H^m(\Omega)$ and by using the regularity results for the homogeneous Neumann problem. $\qquad\square$

5.7 Elasticity Problem

Elasticity problems are studied in [15].

5.7.1 Linear Elasticity, Small Deformations

In these problems, taking Ω to be a bounded domain of class $\mathcal{C}^1$, we consider the deformation tensor $\varepsilon(u)$ associated with the displacement u in $H^1(\Omega, \mathbb{R}^N)$, which is the variable in this problem. This tensor of order 2 has components $\varepsilon(u)_{ij} = \frac{1}{2}(\partial_j u_i + \partial_i u_j)$ that belong to $L^2(\Omega)$. We define the seminorm $u \mapsto |\varepsilon(u)|_2$ in $H^1(\Omega, \mathbb{R}^N)$ by

$$|\varepsilon(u)|_2^2 = \sum_{i \leqslant j} |\varepsilon(u)_{ij}|_{L^2(\Omega)}^2.$$

This seminorm usually becomes a norm in the space $H_0^1(\Omega, \mathbb{R}^N)$, as we can see using Exercise 2.10.

If the divergence of the tensor $\varepsilon(u)$ is the vector with components $\operatorname{div}(\varepsilon(u)))_i = \sum_j \partial_j(\varepsilon(u)_{ij})$ and if f is a fixed vector in $L^2(\Omega, \mathbb{R}^N)$, then the problem $[\mathcal{E}last]^{f,0}$ consists in finding the solution u of

$$[\mathcal{E}last]^{f,0} : \begin{cases} -\operatorname{div}(\varepsilon(u)) = f & \text{in } \Omega, \\ u = 0 & \text{on } \partial\Omega \end{cases}$$

in $H^1(\Omega, \mathbb{R}^N)$.

Variational Form of the Problem. The variational form of the problem consists in determining a u where

$$\inf_{u \in H_0^1(\Omega, \mathbb{R}^N)} \left\{ \frac{1}{2} \int_\Omega |\varepsilon(u)|^2(x) dx - \int_\Omega (f \cdot u)(x) dx \right\}$$

is reached.

Existence and Uniqueness. Under this form, it is clear that the functional J in the infimum is strictly convex and continuous. To show that it is coercive, we first use the Poincaré inequality, namely

$$\left| \int_\Omega (f \cdot u)(x) dx \right| \leqslant \|f\|_2 \|u\|_2 \leqslant C \|f\|_2 \|\nabla u\|_2,$$

and then Korn's inequality (cf. Chapter 7, Section 7.4). The latter gives the existence of a C' such that

$$\|\nabla u\|_2 \leqslant C' |\varepsilon(u)|_2.$$

From this, we deduce that

$$\left| \int_\Omega (f \cdot u)(x) dx \right| \leqslant \frac{1}{4} |\varepsilon(u)|_2^2 + C^2 C'^2 \|f\|^2.$$

Finally, we have

$$|J(u)| = \left| \frac{1}{2} \int_\Omega |\varepsilon(u)|^2(x) dx - \int_\Omega (f \cdot u)(x) dx \right| \geqslant \frac{1}{4} |\varepsilon(u)|_2^2 - C'^2 \|f\|^2,$$

giving us the coercivity. The existence and uniqueness of a solution u of the variational problem follow. □

We leave it to the reader to study the differentiability of J, which allows us to show that u is also the solution of $[\mathcal{E}last]^{f,0}$.

5.7.2 Extension to the Case where $p \neq 1, \infty$

Let $p > 1$ and let $f \in L^{p'}(\Omega, \mathbb{R}^N)$. We set $|\varepsilon(u)|^p = \left(\sum_{ij} \varepsilon_{ij}(u)^2\right)^{p/2}$ and begin with the variational problem of finding a u where

$$\inf_{u \in W_0^{1,p}(\Omega, \mathbb{R}^N)} \left\{ \frac{1}{p} \int_\Omega |\varepsilon(u)|^p(x)dx - \int_\Omega (f \cdot u)(x)dx \right\}$$

is reached. The system of Euler equations associated with this minimization can be written as

$$\forall i \in [1, N], \quad -\sum_{j=1}^{j=N} \partial_j(|\varepsilon(u)|^{p-2}\varepsilon(u)_{ij}) = f_i.$$

We show the existence and uniqueness of a solution by using the convexity and coercivity of the functional. The latter is a consequence of Korn's inequality (cf. Section 7.4).

Let us now proceed to examples of solutions of nonlinear PDE.

5.8 The Equation of the p-Laplacian

5.8.1 Statement of the p-Laplacian problem

The problem we will now study is obtained by replacing the Laplace operator $\Delta = \operatorname{div}(\nabla)$ by the nonlinear operator Δ_p defined by

$$\Delta_p u = \operatorname{div}(|\nabla u|^{p-2}\nabla u).$$

Let $p > 1$ be a real number, let p' be its conjugate, and let Ω be a bounded domain of class $\mathcal{C}^1$. Given $\lambda \geqslant 0$ and $f \in L^{p'}(\Omega)$, we wish to solve the problem

$$(5.51) \qquad [\mathcal{L}ap]_\lambda^p : \begin{cases} \lambda|u|^{p-2}u - \operatorname{div}(|\nabla u|^{p-2}\nabla u) = f & \text{in } \Omega, \\ u = 0 & \text{on } \partial\Omega. \end{cases}$$

We are looking for a solution u in $W_0^{1,p}(\Omega)$. Note that $|\nabla u|^{p-2}\nabla u$ is the vector function in $L^{p'}(\Omega)$ that is colinear with ∇u and has absolute value $|\nabla u|^{p-1}$. This defines a distribution, so that we may talk of its divergence.

Remark 5.52. We can consider this same problem when f belongs to another space than $L^{p'}$. We will give the details of these other cases further on.

5.8.2 Existence

Proposition 5.53. *The function u is the solution of the problem $[\mathcal{L}ap]_\lambda^p$ if and only if u realizes the minimum of the functional on $W_0^{1,p}(\Omega)$ defined by*

$$(5.54) \qquad J(u) = \frac{1}{p} \left(\int_\Omega |\nabla u|^p(x)dx + \lambda \int_\Omega |u|^p(x)dx \right) - \int_\Omega f(x)u(x)dx.$$

For the proof of this proposition when $\lambda = 0$, we need a generalization of the Poincaré inequality, which we proved on H_0^1.

Proposition 5.55. *Let $1 < p < \infty$ and let Ω be a bounded domain of class C^1 in $\mathbb{R}^N$. Let $\mathcal{N}$ be a continuous seminorm on $W^{1,p}(\Omega)$ that, moreover, is a norm on the constants. Then there exists a constant $C > 0$ such that*

$$(5.56) \qquad \forall u \in W^{1,p}(\Omega), \quad \|\nabla u\|_p + \mathcal{N}(u) \geqslant C(\|u\|_p + \|\nabla u\|_p).$$

We gave the proof of this proposition in Exercise 2.9 and will not repeat it here. Below, we will use the seminorm $\mathcal{N}(u) = \left(\int_{\partial\Omega} |u|^p \right)^{1/p}$. We conclude that in $W_0^{1,p}(\Omega)$, $\|\nabla u\|_p$ is a norm that is equivalent to the norm $\|\cdot\|_{W^{1,p}(\Omega)}$.

Proof of Proposition 5.53. Since treating the questions of coercivity and G-differentiability is more complex than in the elliptic linear PDE case we have already considered, we will give the proof of this equivalence in detail. In the particular case we study explicitly, this will correspond to the proof of Theorem 5.25.

We use minimizing sequences and the extraction of subsequences to show the existence of a solution of the variational form of the problem, which is associated with $\inf_{u \in H_0^1} J(u)$.

Let $\{u_n\}$ be a minimizing sequence, that is, a sequence such that $\{J(u_n)\}$ converges to the infimum of J. By using Hölder's inequality and Proposition 5.55 for $p > 1$, $p < \infty$, we obtain

$$\left| \int_\Omega f(x)u(x)dx \right| \leqslant \|f\|_{p'}\|u\|_p \leqslant C\|f\|_{p'}\|\nabla u\|_p.$$

We then use the convexity inequality $X^\alpha Y^\beta \leqslant \alpha X + \beta Y$, where $\alpha + \beta = 1$, with $X = 2^{-p}\|\nabla u\|_p^p$ and $Y = (2C)^{p'}\|f\|_{p'}^{p'}$. This gives

$$\left| \int_\Omega f(x)u(x)dx \right| \leqslant \frac{1}{p2^p} \left(\int_\Omega |\nabla u|^p(x)dx \right) + \frac{(2C)^{p/(p-1)}}{p'} \|f\|_{L^{p'}(\Omega)}^{p'},$$

from which we deduce the inequality

$$J(u_n) \geqslant \frac{1}{p}(1 - 2^{-p})\|\nabla u_n\|_p^p + \lambda\|u_n\|_p^p + K.$$

Since $\lambda \geqslant 0$, it follows by replacing u_n by u that $\inf J(u) > -\infty$, and, moreover, that $\{u_n\}$ is bounded in $W^{1,p}(\Omega)$. Using the weak compactness of bounded subsets of $L^p(\Omega)$ when $1 < p < \infty$ (cf. Section 5.1) and the lower weak semicontinuity of J for the L^p norm, we find that after extracting a subsequence, if necessary, the sequence converges weakly to u in $W^{1,p}(\Omega)$ and

$$J(u) \leqslant \lim_{n \to \infty} J(u_n).$$

We will now show that $u = 0$ on $\partial\Omega$. Since $\gamma_0 u_n = 0$, it suffices to use the continuity of the trace map from $W^{1,p}(\Omega)$ onto $W^{1-1/p,p}(\partial\Omega)$ for the weak topology on $W^{1,p}$. This is the aim of Exercise 3.2 of Chapter 3. Consequently, the above supplies the first part of the proof.

Let us now show the converse. We suppose that the infimum

$$\inf_{v \in W_0^{1,p}(\Omega)} J(v)$$

is reached at u. The functional J is well defined on $W^{1,p}(\Omega)$. By expressing it in terms of $\|u\|_p^p$ and $\|\nabla u\|_p^p$ and using Hölder's formula, we see that it is continuous on $W_0^{1,p}(\Omega)$. It is convex, because the first term involves integration and the composition of ∇, which is linear, and the convex function $t \mapsto t^p$. For the coercivity, we again use Hölder's formula and Proposition 5.55. Let us show that $J_1 : u \mapsto \int_\Omega |\nabla u(x)|^p dx$ is Gâteaux-differentiable with

$$\langle J_1'(u), v \rangle = p \int_\Omega |\nabla u|^{p-2}(x) \nabla u(x) \cdot \nabla v(x) dx.$$

We proceed as in Example 5.20. By the mean value theorem, we know that for almost all $x \in \Omega$ and for all $t > 0$, there exists a function θ with values in $]0, 1[$ such that we can write

(5.57) $|\nabla u + t\nabla v)(x)|^p - |\nabla u(x)|^p - tp|\nabla u(x)|^{p-2}\nabla u(x) \cdot \nabla v(x)$
$$= tp|\nabla u(x) + \theta(t,x)t\nabla v(x))|^{p-2}(\nabla u(x) + \theta(t,x)t\nabla v(x)) \cdot \nabla v(x)$$
$$- tp|\nabla u(x)|^{p-2}\nabla u(x) \cdot \nabla v(x).$$

Dividing by t, we find that for almost all x,

$$\lim_{t \to 0} \frac{|\nabla(u + tv)(x)|^p - |\nabla u(x)|^p - tp|\nabla u(x)|^{p-2}\nabla u(x) \cdot \nabla v(x)}{t} = 0.$$

We can also bound the right-hand side of equality (5.57) divided by t from above by $h(x) = 2|\nabla v(x)|(\nabla u(x)| + |\nabla v(x)|^{p-1}$. Next, using Hölder's inequality, we have

$$|h| \leqslant C\|\nabla v\|_p(\|\nabla u\|_p^{p-1} + \|\nabla v\|_p^{p-1}).$$

We can therefore apply the dominated convergence theorem and conclude that

$$\langle J_1'(u), v \rangle = p \int_\Omega |\nabla u|^{p-2}(x) \nabla u(x) \cdot \nabla v(x) dx.$$

The second term of J is also G-differentiable, as shown in Example 5.20. Taking this into account, we can write

$$\langle J'(u), v \rangle = \int_\Omega |\nabla u|^{p-2}(x) \nabla u(x) \cdot \nabla v(x) dx$$
$$+ \lambda \int_\Omega |u|^{p-2}u(x)v(x)dx - \int_\Omega f(x)v(x)dx.$$

In particular, using this equality when v belongs to $\mathcal{D}(\Omega)$, which is dense in $W_0^{1,p}(\Omega)$, we deduce the following characterization of the minimum u of J:

$$-\operatorname{div}\Big(|\nabla u|^{p-2}\nabla u\Big) + \lambda|u|^{p-2}u - f = 0,$$

with $u \in W_0^{1,p}(\Omega)$. □

Remark 5.58. The above holds for any $\lambda \geqslant 0$. It still holds when f is a function belonging to $L^{Np/(Np-N+p)}$ if $p < N$, belonging to $L^1(\Omega)$ if $p > N$, or belonging to $L^{1+\varepsilon}$ for some $\varepsilon > 0$ if $p = N$.

It suffices to see that in each of these cases, we can define the integral $\int_\Omega f(x)u(x)dx$ when $u \in W_0^{1,p}(\Omega)$, which follows from the Sobolev embedding theorem of Chapter 2. We leave the details to the reader.

5.8.3 Uniqueness

Theorem 5.59. *The solution of the problem* $[\mathcal{L}ap]_\lambda^p$ *is unique.*

Proof of Theorem 5.59.

Consider two solutions u_1 and u_2. For the sake of simplicity, we use the notation $\sigma_i = (|\nabla u_i|^{p-2}\nabla u_i)$ for $i = 1, 2$. Taking the difference of the two associated equations, multiplying by $(u_1 - u_2)$, and integrating over Ω, we obtain

(5.60)
$$\int_\Omega -\operatorname{div}(\sigma_1 - \sigma_2) \cdot (u_1 - u_2)dx + \lambda \int_\Omega (|u_1|^{p-2}u_1 - |u_2|^{p-2}u_2)(u_1 - u_2)dx = 0.$$

Let us consider the signs of the integrants.

Let X and Y be vectors in $\mathbb{R}^N$. For $p > 1$, we expand the scalar product $U(X, Y) = \big(|X|^{p-2}X - |Y|^{p-2}Y\big) \cdot (X - Y)$. Using $X \cdot Y \leqslant |X| |Y|$, we have $U(X, Y) \geqslant |X|^p + |Y|^p - \big(|X|^{p-2} + |Y|^{p-2}\big)|X| |Y|$, that is,

$$U(X, Y) \geqslant \big(|X|^{p-1} - |Y|^{p-1}\big)\big(|X| - |Y|\big) \geqslant 0.$$

This result also holds for the scalars $X = u_1(x)$ and $Y = u_2(x)$, where $x \in \Omega$. Consequently, $(|u_1(x)|^{p-2}u_1(x) - |u_2(x)|^{p-2}u_2(x))(u_1(x) - u_2(x)) \geqslant 0$, which means that the second integral in (5.60) is positive. Using the generalized Green's formula and the equality $\gamma_0(u_1 - u_2) = 0$, we transform the first integral into

$$\int_\Omega (|\nabla u_1|^{p-2}\nabla u_1 - |\nabla u_2|^{p-2}\nabla u_2) \cdot (\nabla u_1 - \nabla u_2)\, dx.$$

The relation $U(\nabla u_1(x), \nabla u_2(x)) \geqslant 0$ implies that if $\lambda \neq 0$, then almost everywhere on Ω, we have

$$u_1(x) = u_2(x) \quad \text{and} \quad \nabla u_1(x) = \nabla u_2(x).$$

If $\lambda = 0$, then the single conclusion $\nabla u_1 = \nabla u_2$ suffices to prove that $u_1 = u_2$ on Ω, since $u_1 = u_2 = 0$ on the boundary $\partial\Omega$. The uniqueness follows. $\square$

In the appendix, we establish certain results concerning the regularity of the solution of the p-Laplacian problem, using, in particular, a priori error estimates.

5.9 Maximum Principles for Elliptic PDE

We recall the classical maximum principle. A nonconstant function u that is harmonic on a bounded connected subset Ω of $\mathbb{R}^N$ and extends to a continuous function on $\overline{\Omega}$ reaches its maximum and minimum on the boundary $\partial\Omega$. This corresponds to saying that if $u(x) \geqslant m$ on $\partial\Omega$, then $u(x) \geqslant m$ in Ω. Using $u - m$, we reduce the problem to studying the sign of a solution of a PDE based on the sign of its trace on $\partial\Omega$. Let us add, however, that this technique only works for linear PDE. Below, we study principles of the same type that can be associated with solutions of elliptic PDE, which generalize the harmonic functions in the classical case.

5.9.1 Weak Maximum Principle

The Solution of $[Dir]_{A,\lambda}^f$. In this subsection, Ω denotes a bounded domain of class $\mathcal{C}^1$ in $\mathbb{R}^N$. Let us recall the definition of the first eigenvalue of the operator $-\operatorname{div}(A(x)\nabla u)$ on $H_0^1(\Omega)$.

As in Subsection 5.3.5, we study $[Dir]_{A,-\lambda}^0$. Using the inequality defining the uniform ellipticity of A, we find that the real number

$$\lambda_1 = \inf_{\{u \in H_0^1(\Omega)\,|\,|u|_2 = 1\}} \left\{ \int_\Omega A(x)(\nabla u(x)) \cdot \nabla u(x)\, dx \right\},$$

is positive and is the smallest eigenvalue of the operator $-\operatorname{div}(A(\nabla u))$ on $H_0^1(\Omega)$.

Theorem 5.61. *Let λ be a real number satisfying $0 \leqslant \lambda < \lambda_1$ and let $f \geqslant 0$ in Ω. Let $u \in H^1(\Omega)$ be the solution of the problem*

$$-\operatorname{div}(A(x)\nabla u) - \lambda u = f \quad in\ \Omega.$$

Then if $u \geqslant 0$ on $\partial\Omega$, we also have $u \geqslant 0$ in Ω.

Proof of Theorem 5.61. We use the following result on the positive and negative parts of the functions in $W^{1,p}$.

Lemma 5.62. *Let $u \in W^{1,p}(\Omega)$ and let H denote the Heaviside step function satisfying*

$$H(x) = \begin{cases} 1 & if\ x > 0, \\ 0 & if\ x \leqslant 0. \end{cases}$$

Then $u^+, u^-, |u| \in W^{1,p}(\Omega)$ and

$$\nabla(u^+) = H(u)\nabla u,$$
$$\nabla(u^-) = -H(-u)\nabla u,$$
$$\nabla|u| = \nabla u\left(H(u) - H(-u)\right).$$

Proof of Lemma 5.62 (see also [10] or [41]). Clearly, it suffices to show the result for $p = 1$. Indeed, if $p > 1$, then for every open set Ω_1 with compact closure in Ω, we have $\nabla u \in L^1(\Omega_1)$, whence $\nabla(u^+) = H(u)\nabla u$. This equality proves that for arbitrary Ω_1, the distributional gradient $\nabla(u^+)$ belongs to $L^p(\Omega)$.

Let j_ε be the function on $\mathbb{R}$ defined by

$$\forall t > 0, \quad j_\varepsilon(t) = (\varepsilon^2 + t^2)^{1/2} - \varepsilon \quad \text{and} \quad \forall t < 0, \quad j_\varepsilon(t) = 0.$$

We can easily see that j_ε converges uniformly to $j(t) = t^+$ and that $j_\varepsilon'(t)$ converges to $H(t)$ for every t. Let $u \in L^1_{\mathrm{loc}}(\Omega)$. By the dominated convergence theorem, $j_\varepsilon(u)$ converges to $j(u) = u^+$ in $L^1_{\mathrm{loc}}(\Omega)$.

Furthermore, for almost all x in Ω, $\nabla(j_\varepsilon(u)) = (\varepsilon^2 + u^2)^{-1/2}(u^+\nabla u)$ converges to $H(u)\nabla u$ and is dominated by $|\nabla u|$. We deduce that in $L^1(\Omega)$,

$$\lim_{\varepsilon \to 0} \nabla\left(j_\varepsilon(u)\right) = H(u)\nabla u.$$

The conjunction of these two results implies that $H(u) \in W^{1,p}$ and $\nabla H(u) = H(u)\nabla u$. Since $u^- = (-u)^+$, we also have $\nabla(u^-) = H(-u)\nabla(-u)$. $\qquad\square$

We return to the proof of Theorem 5.61. We multiply the equation in Theorem 5.61 by u^-. Since $f \geqslant 0$ in Ω, we obtain

$$\int_\Omega -\operatorname{div}(A\nabla u)(x)u^-(x)dx - \int_\Omega \lambda u(x)u^-(x)dx = \int_\Omega f(x)u^-(x)dx \geqslant 0.$$

Moreover, since $u^- = 0$ on $\partial\Omega$, Green's formula gives

$$\int_\Omega -\operatorname{div}(A\nabla u)(x)u^-(x)dx = \int_\Omega A(x)\nabla u(x) \cdot \nabla(u^-)dx.$$

Now,

$$\int_\Omega A(x)\nabla u(x) \cdot \nabla u^-(x)dx = -\int_\Omega A(x)\nabla u^-(x) \cdot \nabla u^-(x)dx.$$

Hence, using $\int_\Omega f(x)u^-(x)dx \geqslant 0$, we have

$$-\int_\Omega A(x)\nabla u^-(x) \cdot \nabla u^-(x) + \lambda \int_\Omega (u^-)^2(x)dx \geqslant 0.$$

From this, we deduce that

$$\int_\Omega A(x)\nabla u^-(x) \cdot \nabla u^-(x)dx \leqslant \lambda |u^-|^2,$$

which contradicts the definition of λ_1 unless $u^- = 0$. It follows that $u \geqslant 0$ in Ω. $\square$

Of course, the linearity of the equation allows us to show that if $f \leqslant 0$, then $u \leqslant 0$ in Ω if it is $\leqslant 0$ on the boundary of Ω.

We will see the strong maximum principle later. In a more general form, it is due to Vázquez. It states that if u is a solution $\geqslant 0$ of the inequality $-\operatorname{div}(A(x)\nabla u) \geqslant 0$, then in each of the connected components of Ω, u is either identically zero or positive.

The reader can consult [34] and [57] for more general maximum principles.

The Solution of $[\mathcal{L}ap]_\lambda^p$.

Theorem 5.63. *Let $\lambda \geqslant 0$. If u is the solution of*

$$-\operatorname{div}(|\nabla u|^{p-2}\nabla u) + \lambda|u|^{p-2}u = f,$$

$f \geqslant 0$ in Ω, and $u \geqslant 0$ on the boundary of Ω, then $u \geqslant 0$ in Ω.

Proof of Theorem 5.63. As before, we multiply by u^-, giving

$$(5.64) \qquad \int_\Omega \Big[|\nabla u|^{p-2}\nabla u\nabla(u^-) + \lambda|u|^{p-2}u(u^-)\Big]dx = \int_\Omega f(x)(u^-(x))dx.$$

We have two integrals of nonpositive functions on the left-hand side and one integral of a nonnegative function on the right-hand side. From this, we deduce that

$$-\int_\Omega |\nabla u^-|^p dx - \lambda \int_\Omega (u^-)^p dx = \int_\Omega f u^- dx,$$

which implies that

$$|\nabla u^-|^p + \lambda(u^-)^p = 0.$$

Since $\lambda \geqslant 0$, it follows that $\nabla(u^-) = 0$ and therefore $u^- = 0$ because this already holds on the boundary $\partial\Omega$.   □

In Example 5.82, we show the existence of a first eigenvalue, as we did in the Laplacian case. For λ greater than the opposite of the first eigenvalue, the result remains true (cf. [17]).

The following theorem generalizes the maximum principle to a statement concerning the sign of the difference $u_1 - u_2$ of two solutions of the PDE under consideration. We do not need this result when the equation is linear as in the previous section, because the difference of the two solutions is then a solution of the homogeneous equation and we can apply the classical maximum principle.

Comparison of Two Solutions in the Case of Nonlinear Equations.

Theorem 5.65. *Let $\lambda \geqslant 0$. Consider functions u_1 and u_2 satisfying*

$$-\operatorname{div}(|\nabla u_i|^{p-2}\nabla u_i) + \lambda|u_i|^{p-2}u_i = f_i.$$

If $f_1 \geqslant f_2$ in Ω and $u_1 \geqslant u_2$ on $\partial\Omega$, then we have $u_1 \geqslant u_2$ in Ω.

Remark 5.66. In contrast to the Laplacian case, this result cannot be deduced from the maximum principle, since the equation is not linear. We note that the comparison principle is the key argument for Vázquez's strong maximum principle, which we present in the next section. In the case $\lambda > -\lambda_1$, where λ_1 is the first eigenvalue, this comparison result still holds but is more delicate to prove (cf. [17]).

Proof of Theorem 5.65. We multiply the difference of the equations for u_1 and u_2 by $(u_2 - u_1)^+$, integrate over $\partial\Omega$, and use that the boundary term is zero to obtain

$$\int_\Omega \left(|\nabla u_1|^{p-2}\nabla u_1 - |\nabla u_2|^{p-2}\nabla u_2\right) \cdot \nabla((u_2 - u_1)^+)$$

$$+ \lambda \int_\Omega \left(|u_1|^{p-2}u_1 - |u_2|^{p-2}u_2\right)((u_2 - u_1)^+)$$

$$= \int_\Omega (f_1 - f_2)((u_2 - u_1)^+).$$

It follows that the first integral is nonnegative. Now, by the properties of the gradient of $(u_2 - u_1)^+$ we saw earlier, we have

$$(|\nabla u_1|^{p-2}\nabla u_1 - |\nabla u_2|^{p-2}\nabla u_2) \cdot \nabla((u_2 - u_1)^+)$$
$$= -H(u_2 - u_1)(|\nabla u_1|^{p-2}\nabla u_1 - |\nabla u_2|^{p-2}\nabla u_2) \cdot (\nabla u_1 - \nabla u_2),$$

which is nonpositive. Since it vanishes if and only if $\nabla((u_2 - u_1)^+) = 0$, the previous equality implies that $(u_2 - u_1)^+ = $ cte and therefore that $u_2 \leqslant u_1$ because $(u_2 - u_1)^+$ vanishes on the boundary. $\square$

We can generalize this comparison result as follows.

Theorem 5.67. *Let β be a continuous nondecreasing function on $\mathbb{R}$. Let u_1 and u_2 satisfy*

$$- \operatorname{div}(|\nabla u_i|^{p-2}\nabla u_i) + \beta(u_i) = f_i.$$

Then if $f_1 \geqslant f_2$ in Ω and $u_1 \geqslant u_2$ on $\partial\Omega$, we have $u_1 \geqslant u_2$ in Ω.

Proof. The proof is the same as the previous one. $\square$

5.9.2 Strong Maximum Principle

Strong Maximum Principle for the Laplacian. We begin by recalling a result that is certainly well known to a reader who is familiar with the theory of harmonic functions, at least in the case $N = 2$.

Proposition 5.68. *If u is nonnegative and of class $\mathcal{C}^2$ and if $\Delta u = 0$ in a domain Ω, then either u is identically zero or $u > 0$ in Ω.*

Proof of Proposition 5.68. Indeed, the set of points Z where $u = 0$ is closed because u is continuous. Let us show that it is also open. Let $x_0 \in Z$ and $r > 0$ be such that the ball of radius r with center x_0 is contained in Ω. For every $\varepsilon < r$, the mean value property for harmonic functions (cf. Exercise 7.2 of Chapter 7) gives

$$0 = u(x_0) = \frac{1}{w_{N-1}\varepsilon^{N-1}} \int_{\partial B(x_0,\varepsilon)} u(s)\,ds,$$

where w_{N-1} is the $(N-1)$-dimensional surface measure of the unit sphere in $\mathbb{R}^N$. In particular, since $u \geqslant 0$, the continuity of u implies that $u = 0$ on the boundary $\partial B(x_0, \varepsilon)$. Since this property holds for every $\varepsilon \in \,]0, r[$, we deduce that $u = 0$ in $B(x_0, r)$. Consequently, the set Z is open. Since the open set Ω is connected, it follows that either $Z = \varnothing$ or $Z = \Omega$, concluding the proof. $\square$

We now set out to obtain the same property for a function u that is continuous and superharmonic in Ω. The latter means that $-\Delta u \geqslant 0$ in Ω. Before we do this, we need to describe the solutions of class $\mathcal{C}^2$ of the Dirichlet problem explicitly when the boundary function is continuous. We will then use the expression specifying these solutions in an argument involving comparison, in order to obtain the positivity of the superharmonic function.

We first recall the existence and uniqueness result for this so-called *classical* Dirichlet problem, classical in the sense that the solutions must be of class $\mathcal{C}^2$ in the open set under consideration. The proof of this result when the open set is the unit ball $B = B(0,1)$ is given in Exercise 7.5. We use the Poisson kernel $(s,x) \mapsto p(s,x)$ for ∂B, which for $s \in \partial B$ and $x \in B$ is defined by

$$p(s,x) = \frac{1}{w_{N-1}} \frac{1 - |x|^2}{|x - s|^N}.$$

For a function f that is continuous on ∂B, the function Pf defined by

$$\forall x \in \mathbb{R}^N, \quad |x| < 1 \implies Pf(x) = \int_{\partial B} f(s)p(s,x)ds$$

is harmonic on the ball B and admits a continuous extension to the boundary that is identical to f.

Remark 5.69. Using the maximum principle, we can see that the function Pf is the unique solution of class $\mathcal{C}^2$ of the Dirichlet problem associated with the continuous boundary condition f.

Remark 5.70. Using a translation and a homothety, we can easily deduce the solution of the classical Dirichlet problem, namely

$$Pf(x) = \frac{1}{w_{N-1}r^{2-N}} \int_{\partial(B(x_0,1))} f(x_0 + rs) \frac{r^2 - |x - x_0|^2}{|(x - x_0) - rs|^N} ds$$

for the ball $B(x_0, r)$ from the previous result.

Let us now compare the *classical solution* given above, which is of class $\mathcal{C}^2$, to the *solution of the variational problem* on the ball B when the boundary condition is continuous. We have the following result.

Proposition 5.71. *Let* $v \in \mathcal{C}(\partial B) \cap H^{1/2}(\partial B)$. *On the one hand, let* $u \in H^1(B)$ *be the solution of the problem* $[\mathcal{D}ir]_\Delta^{0,v}$, *whose Laplacian* Δu, *taken in the sense of distributions in* B, *is zero and satisfies* $u = v$ *on* ∂B. *On the other hand, let* w *be the* $\mathcal{C}^2$ *solution defined by* $w = Pv$, *which is harmonic in* B *and satisfies* $w = v$ *on* ∂B. *Then* $w = u$ *in* B.

Proof of Proposition 5.71.

By the density of the regular functions in $\mathcal{C}(\partial B) \cap H^{1/2}(\partial B)$, there exists a sequence $\{v_n\}$ in $\mathcal{C}^\infty(\partial B)$ that converges in $\mathcal{C}(\partial B) \cap H^{1/2}(\partial B)$ to the function v. Let us take such a sequence. Let $Pv_n = w_n$ denote the image of v_n in B under the Poisson operator and let u_n denote the solution in $H^1(B)$ of the Dirichlet problem with boundary condition v_n, which, in particular, belongs to $H^{1/2}(\partial B)$. Taking the variational form of the problem, this solution is the minimum of

$$\mathcal{P}_n = \inf_{\substack{u \in H^1(B) \\ u = v_n \text{ on } \partial B}} \frac{1}{2} \int_B |\nabla u(x)|^2 \, dx.$$

We will first show that u_n is of class $\mathcal{C}^\infty$, from which we will then deduce that $u_n = w_n$.

To see that u_n is of class $\mathcal{C}^\infty$, we can use regularity results for the solution of $\Delta u = 0$ when the boundary function is of class $\mathcal{C}^\infty$. Since the boundary is $\mathcal{C}^\infty$, the right-hand side, which is zero, belongs to $H^k(B)$ for every integer k, and the boundary condition v_n belongs to $H^{k+1/2}(\partial B)$, this regularity result tells us that $u_n \in H^k$ for every k. It follows that u_n is of class $\mathcal{C}^\infty$ in B and, consequently, that $u_n = w_n$ in B.

Using the Poisson kernel, it is clear that w_n tends to w in $\mathcal{C}(B)$. Namely, using the positivity of p and the equality $\int_{B(0,1)} p(s) ds = 1$ (cf. Exercise 7.5), this follows from the uniform convergence of v_n to v on ∂B:

$$\int_{\partial B} p(s,x) |v(s) - v_n(s)| \, ds \longrightarrow 0.$$

It remains to show that u_n tends to u, even if only in the sense of distributions. We will in fact show it in the sense of strong convergence in H^1. For this, we show that the infimum

$$\inf_{u = v_n \text{ on } \partial B} \frac{1}{2} \int_B |\nabla u|^2$$

of $\mathcal{P}_n$ converges to $\inf \mathcal{P}$, which is defined to be

$$\inf_{u = v \text{ on } \partial B} \frac{1}{2} \int_B |\nabla u|^2.$$

Let u_n realize the infimum of $\mathcal{P}_n$, then u_n is clearly bounded in H^1. To see this, it suffices to consider a lifting V_n of v_n, that is, an element of $H^1(B)$ with trace v_n on ∂B. By the continuity of the lifting map, there exists a C such that, for every $n \in \mathbb{N}$,

$$\|V_n\|_{H^1(B))} \leqslant C \|v_n\|_{H^{1/2}(\partial B)}.$$

Since the sequence $\{v_n\}$ converges to v in $H^{1/2}$, we deduce from this that the sequence $\{\nabla V_n\}$ is bounded in $L^2(B)$ by a constant K. For the minimum u_n

of $\mathcal{P}_n$, this gives

$$\int_B |\nabla u_n(x)|^2 \, dx \leqslant \int_B |\nabla V_n(x)|^2 dx \leqslant K.$$

Now, since the sequence $\{u_n\}$ is bounded in H^1, we can extract a subsequence that converges to a function $u^* \in H^1$ that equals v on the boundary. Finally, by the lower semicontinuity, we have

$$\int_B |\nabla u^*|^2 \leqslant \underline{\lim} \, \|\nabla u_n\|^2.$$

It remains to show that $\overline{\lim} \inf \mathcal{P}_n \leqslant \inf \mathcal{P}$, from which we will deduce that u^* is a minimum for $\mathcal{P}$. Let $\zeta \in H^1(B)$ with $\zeta = v$ on the boundary. We will show that there exists a sequence $\{\zeta_n\} \in H^1(B)$ with $\zeta_n = v_n$ on the boundary that converges in H^1 to ζ. Indeed, by the continuity of the lifting of $H^{1/2}(\partial B)$ to $H^1(B)$, there exists a ξ_n that tends to 0 in H^1 and equals $v_n - v$ on the boundary. Let $\zeta_n = \xi_n + \zeta$. The sequence $\{\zeta_n\}$ converges to ζ in $H^1(B)$. If we now take ζ to realize the infimum of $\mathcal{P}$, then for n sufficiently large,

$$\inf \mathcal{P}_n \leqslant \int_B |\nabla \zeta_n|^2 \leqslant \inf \mathcal{P} + \varepsilon.$$

As before, $\|\nabla u_n\|_2$ converges to $\|\nabla u\|_2$, which implies the strong convergence of u_n to u in H^1, completing the proof. $\qquad\square$

Let us now return to the positivity of the subharmonic functions.

Proposition 5.72. *Let u be a nonnegative continuous function in H^1 that satisfies the inequality $\Delta u \leqslant 0$ in a connected open set Ω; then either $u > 0$ in Ω or u is identically zero in Ω.*

Proof of Proposition 5.72. By Proposition 5.61, we already know that $u \geqslant 0$ in Ω. It therefore suffices to show that if the set Z of points of Ω where u vanishes is nonempty, then it is open.

Let x_0 satisfy $u(x_0) = 0$ and let $\varepsilon < r$ with $B(x_0, r) \subset \Omega$. Let v be the C^2 solution of the Dirichlet problem in $B(x_0, \varepsilon)$ with boundary condition on $\partial B(x_0, \varepsilon)$ equal to u, which is continuous by assumption. By expressing v using the Poisson kernel, namely $v = Pu$, we see that it is continuous. Moreover, by the weak maximum principle, it is nonnegative. By Proposition 5.68, v is either positive in $B(x_0, \varepsilon)$ or identically zero. Furthermore, the comparison principle implies that, since $u = v$ on $\partial B(x_0, \varepsilon)$ and $-\Delta(u - v) \geqslant 0$, we have $u \geqslant v$ in $B(x_0, \varepsilon)$. In particular, $0 \leqslant v(x_0) \leqslant u(x_0) = 0$, which implies that v is identically zero on $B(x_0, \varepsilon)$ and, consequently, also on the boundary, where it coincides with u. It follows that $u = 0$ on $\partial B(x_0, \varepsilon)$. By letting ε tend to r, we see that u is identically zero on $B(x_0, r)$. The set Z is therefore both open and closed. Using the connectedness of Ω, we finally deduce the desired result.   □

Strong Maximum Principle for More General Dirichlet Problems. We will now show a simplified statement of the strong maximum principle for more general operators than Δ.

Proposition 5.73. *Let u be a solution of class $\mathcal{C}^1$ of the inequality*

$$ -\operatorname{div}(A(x)\nabla u) \geqslant 0 $$

in the bounded domain Ω in $\mathbb{R}^N$. If $u \geqslant 0$ in Ω, then u is either identically zero or positive in Ω.

Proof of the proposition. Let us also note that if Ω were not connected, then we would apply our reasoning to each of the connected components. We suppose that there exist points $m \in \Omega$ such that $u(m) > 0$ as well as points m' such that $u(m') = 0$. Then there exists a ball in Ω in which this same property holds. If this were not the case, then given a ball B in Ω, we would have either $u(x) > 0$ at every point $x \in B$ or $u(x) = 0$ at every point $x \in B$. The union of the balls where the first holds is then an open set Ω^+ and that of the balls where the second holds is then an open set Ω^0. These sets are disjoint, with union Ω, contradicting the connectedness of Ω. We may, and do, therefore assume that $\Omega = B$ is a ball. Hence there exist x_0' and x_1 in B such that $u(x_0') = 0$ and $u(x_1) > 0$. By a similar reasoning using connectedness, we may, and do, assume that x_1 is the center of the ball B, whence $\Omega = B(x_1, R)$, $u(x_1) > 0$, and $|x_0' - x_1| < R$.

Let us first suppose that u is continuous. In this case, there exist balls $B(x_1, r)$ in whose interior we have $u(x) > 0$. We have $r \leqslant |x_1 - x_0'|$. If we set $r_1 = \sup\{r \mid \forall x \in B(x_1, r), u(x) > 0\}$, then the boundary Γ_1 of the ball $B(x_1, r_1)$ contains at least one point x_0 such that $u(x_0) = 0$. If not, we would be able to find neighborhoods of each of the points of Γ_1 in which $u > 0$, and by extracting from these neighborhoods a finite cover of the boundary, we would find a ball $B(x_1, r)$ with $r > r_1$ with the desired property, contradicting the assumption on the supremum.

Let us consider the annulus $G = \{x \mid r_1/2 < |x - x_1| < r_1\}$ in $\mathbb{R}^N$, on which we have $u > 0$. Let m_1 be defined by $m_1 = \inf\{u(x) \mid |x - x_1| = r_1/2\}$. By the continuity of u, we have $m_1 > 0$. Supposing that $R > 3r_1/2$, we also define the annulus $G' = \{x \mid r_1/2 \leqslant |x - x_1| \leqslant 3r_1/2\}$. The main idea of the proof is as follows.

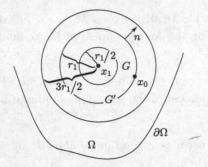

Fig. 5.2. An argument used for the strong maximum principle. We have $u(x_0) = 0$, $u(x_1) > 0$, and $|x_0 - x_1| = r_1$; G and G' are the annuli with center x_1.

We are going to construct a function v, $v > 0$ in G', that satisfies the following conditions:

$$(*) \qquad\qquad \forall x \in G', \quad -\operatorname{div}\Big(A(x)\nabla(u - v)\Big) \geqslant 0,$$

$$(**) \qquad\qquad \forall x \in \partial G', \quad v(x) \leqslant u(x).$$

By using the weak maximum principle, we will see that $u \geqslant v$ in the annulus G', and therefore also in G. Supposing that u is of class $\mathcal{C}^1$, we will obtain the expected contradiction by considering the normal derivative at the point $x_0 \in \partial G$.

We therefore suppose that u is of class $\mathcal{C}^1$ at x_0. Let $0 < \beta < m_1$. We choose the number $c > 0$ sufficiently large that the function $v = \beta(e^{-c|x-x_1|} - e^{-c|x_0-x_1|})$, which vanishes at x_0, satisfies the conditions $(*)$ and $(**)$ stated above.

On the sphere $S_1 = \{|x - x_1| = r_1/2\}$, we have $v = \beta(e^{-cr_1/2} - e^{-cr_1}) < \beta$, whence $v < u$ on S_1 because $\beta < m_1$. On the sphere $S_2 = \{|x - x_1| = 3r_1/2\}$, we have $v = \beta(e^{-3cr_1/2} - e^{-cr_1}) < 0$, whence $v < u$ also holds on S_2 because $u \geqslant 0$ on this sphere. We deduce condition $(**)$ from this, that is, $v < u$ on $\partial G'$.

For condition $(*)$, we set $f(x) = e^{-c|x-x_1|}$ and begin by computing ∇f. From this we deduce $\operatorname{div}(A(x)\nabla v)$, which is none other than $\beta \operatorname{div}(A(x)\nabla f)$.

We have $\partial_j f(x) = -cf(x)(x - x_1)_j/|x - x_1|$ and then

$$\operatorname{div}(A(x)\nabla f) = -c\frac{f(x)}{|x - x_1|}\Big[\sum_{ij} \partial_i\Big(A_{ij}(x)(x - x_1)_j\Big)\Big]$$

$$+ f(x)\Big(\frac{c^2}{|x - x_1|^2} - \frac{c}{|x - x_1|^3}\Big)\Big\langle A(x)(x - x_1), (x - x_1)\Big\rangle$$

$$= -V + U.$$

In U, the term between the parentheses, which we can also write as $[c/|x - x_1|^3](c|x - x_1| - 1)$, is positive if $c > 2/r_1$. Under this condition, the uniform ellipticity of A implies that $U(x) > 0$ in G', giving the lower bound

$$U(x) \geqslant \alpha f(x)\left[c^2 - 2\frac{c}{r_1}\right],$$

where α is the ellipticity constant of A.

By expanding the derivative in the first term $-V$, which is negative, we see that $V \leqslant cf(x)(\|\nabla A\|_\infty + N\|A\|_\infty/r_1)$. Summarizing, we have

$$\mathrm{div}(A(x)\nabla v) \geqslant \beta c e^{-3cr_1/2}\left[\alpha\left(c - \frac{2}{r_1}\right) - \left(\|\nabla A\|_\infty + \frac{N\|A\|_\infty}{r_1}\right)\right].$$

Therefore there exist values of c that are sufficiently large that $\mathrm{div}(A(x)\nabla v) \geqslant 0$ on G', thus giving condition (*).

Since $-\mathrm{div}(A(x)\nabla u) \geqslant 0$, we have $-\mathrm{div}(A(x)\nabla(u - v)) \geqslant 0$. We apply the weak maximum principle (cf. Theorem 5.61) to this situation and deduce that $u \geqslant v$ in G', and therefore also in G. In particular, at the point x_0, we know that $v(x_0) = u(x_0) = 0$. Let $\overrightarrow{n} = (x_0 - x_1)/|x_0 - x_1|$ be the outward-pointing normal to the boundary of G at x_0. For $h > 0$ sufficiently small, we have

$$u(x_0 - h\overrightarrow{n}) - u(x_0) \geqslant v(x_0 - h\overrightarrow{n}) - v(x_0).$$

Applying the mean value theorem to the right-hand side of the inequality gives

$$u(x_0 - h\overrightarrow{n}) - u(x_0) \geqslant \beta ch.$$

Dividing by $-h$ and letting h tend to 0, we obtain

$$\partial_{\overrightarrow{n}} u < -\beta c < 0,$$

which contradict the fact that the $\mathcal{C}^1$ function u takes on its minimum at the point x_0.   □

The Strong Maximum Principle for the p-Laplacian. The previous result is called the strong maximum principle and is due to Vázquez [74]. More generally, Vázquez's strong maximum principle can be applied to equations related to the p-Laplacian. As above, its proof is based on the local comparison to a positive sub-solution. This phenomenon moreover generalizes to other types of operators.

Let us take a continuous function β that is nondecreasing on $[0, +\infty[$, such that $\beta(0) = 0$, and satisfies the condition

$$(5.74) \qquad \exists\, r_1 > 0, \quad \int_0^{r_1} \frac{ds}{(s\beta(s))^{1/p}} = \infty.$$

We let $j(s) = \int_0^s \beta(t)dt$ and note that

$$\frac{s}{2}\beta(s/2) \leqslant j(s) \leqslant s\beta(s),$$

so that condition (5.74) can be written as

$$(5.75) \qquad \int_0^{r_1} \frac{ds}{(j(s))^{1/p}} = +\infty.$$

Theorem 5.76. *Let β be a continuous nondecreasing function with $\beta(0)=0$ that satisfies condition (5.74). Let $u \in \mathcal{C}^1(\Omega)$ be a nonnegative bounded solution of the inequality*

$$-\Delta_p u + \beta(u) \geqslant 0$$

in the bounded domain Ω. Then u is either identically zero or positive in Ω.

Remark 5.77. A solution of the inequality of the theorem is called a super-solution of the PDE $-\Delta_p u + \beta(u) = 0$. In most cases, we use the principle stated in the theorem for solutions of the equation and not only for supersolutions. When it is stated for a solution, the continuous differentiability and boundedness conditions on u may in general be omitted because of regularity results for solutions of elliptic PDE that ensures us that u is bounded and $\mathcal{C}^1$.

For this matter, the reader can consult the introduction to the appendix and the partial results that are established there. For the proofs of the full results concerning the $\mathcal{C}^1$ regularity, one can read Evans [31], Moser [52], Tolksdorff [72], Lewis [46], or Di Benedetto [27].

Proof of Theorem 5.76. We repeat the first part of the previous proof, replacing r_1 by r. Let us consider the annulus $G = \{x \mid r/2 < |x - x_1| < r\}$, on which $u > 0$. We set $m_1 = \inf\{u(x) \mid |x - x_1| = r/2\} > 0$. Since the structure of the proof is the same as in that of the previous proposition, we are going to construct a suitable solution of $-\Delta_p u + \beta(u) \leqslant 0$, that is, a subsolution. We begin with the following result.

Lemma 5.78. *Let k_1, k_2, r_1, and m_1 be positive real numbers, let $p > 1$, and let β be an nondecreasing function with $\beta(0) = 0$. Then there exists a unique function $v = v(r, k_1, k_2, r_1, m_1)$ of class $\mathcal{C}^2$ on $[0, r_1[$ satisfying*

$$\frac{d}{ds}\left[|v'|^{p-2}v'\right] = k_1|v'|^{p-2}v' + k_2\beta(v),$$

$v(0) = 0$, and $v(r_1) = m_1$. Moreover, $v \geqslant 0$, $v' \geqslant 0$, and $0 < v < m_1$ on $]0, r_1[$.

Proof of Lemma 5.78. In this proof, we set

$$W^* = \{u \in W^{1,p}(]0, r_1[) \mid u(0) = 0, \; u(r_1) = m_1\},$$

and we consider the variational problem associated with

$$\inf_{v \in W^*} \left\{ \frac{1}{p} \int_0^{r_1} |v'|^p(s) e^{-k_1 s} ds + k_2 \int_0^{r_1} j(v)(s) e^{-k_1 s} ds \right\}.$$

Since $\exp(-k_1 s) \geqslant \exp(-k_1 r_1)$ and $j \geqslant 0$, we can easily verify the conditions of Theorem 5.25 for the closed convex set W^* in the reflexive separable space $W^{1,p}(]0, r_1[)$ with $p > 1$. Moreover, the functional $v \mapsto J(v)$, whose minimization was the aim of the previous problem, is G-differentiable. By using the expression of the derivative of the functional $u \mapsto 1/p \int_\Omega |\nabla u(x)|^p dx$ obtained in Proposition 5.53, we find that the derivative $J'(v)$ equals the linear functional

$$\langle J'(v), \varphi \rangle = \int_0^{r_1} |v'|^{p-2}(s) v'(s) \cdot e^{-k_1 s} \varphi'(s) ds + k_2 \int_0^{r_1} \beta(v)(s) e^{-k_1 s} \varphi(s) ds.$$

The derivative at the point v is therefore

$$J'(v) = -\left[\frac{d}{ds} \left[|v'|^{p-2} v' \right] - k_1 |v'|^{p-2} v' - k_2 \beta(v) \right] e^{-k_1 s}.$$

Since W^* is an affine space, the equation $J'(v) = 0$ supplies the solution of the problem, namely

$$(5.79) \qquad \frac{d}{ds} \left[|v'|^{p-2} v' \right] = k_1 |v'|^{p-2} v' + k_2 \beta(v).$$

Let us multiply this equation by $v^- \exp(-k_1 s)$ and proceed as in Theorem 5.61. Since $v^- = 0$ at 0 and at r_1, integration gives

$$\int_0^{r_1} \exp(-k_1 s) \left[|v'|^{p-2} v' \right] (v^-)' ds + k_2 \int_0^{r_1} \beta(v) v^- \exp(-k_1 s) ds = 0,$$

which can also be written as

$$-\int_0^{r_1} \exp(-k_1 s) |(v^-)'|^p ds + k_2 \int_0^{r_1} \beta(v)(s) v^-(s) \exp(-k_1 s) = 0.$$

We have $\beta(v) v^- \leqslant 0$ because β is nondecreasing. The negativity of the integral of the first term therefore implies that $v^{-\prime} = 0$. Consequently, since $v(0) = 0$, we have $v^- = 0$, or, in other words, $v \geqslant 0$.

Furthermore, since $k_2 \beta(v) \geqslant 0$, the equation (5.79) implies that the function $|v'|^{p-2} v' \exp(-k_1 s)$ is nondecreasing, and therefore that v' is nondecreasing. Since $v(0) = 0$ and $v \geqslant 0$, we have $v'(0) \geqslant 0$, and since v' is nondecreasing, we find that $v'(r) \geqslant 0$ on $[0, r_1]$.

Let us now show that $v > 0$ and $v' > 0$ on $]0, r_1]$. Let r_0 be the largest r in $]0, r_1[$ for which $v(r) = 0$. We wish to show that $r_0 = 0$. We have $v' > 0$ on $]r_0, r_1[$ since otherwise there would exist an $r \in]r_0, r_1[$ with $v'(r) = 0$. Since v' is nondecreasing, we then have $v' = 0$ on $[r_0, r_1]$ and therefore $v(r_1) = 0$, which contradicts the fact that r_0 is the greatest zero of v.

The function v is therefore bijective from $[r_0, r_1]$ into $[0, m_1]$. We have

$$(*) \qquad \int_{r_0}^{r_1} \frac{v'(t)}{(j(v)(t))^{1/p}} dt = \int_0^{m_1} \frac{1}{(j(s))^{1/p}} ds = +\infty.$$

Let $w = (v')^p$ and $a = p/(p-1)$, so that

$$(\exp(-ak_1 r)w)' = \exp(-ak_1 r)(-ak_1 w + p(v')^{p-1} v'').$$

Now, since $v' \geqslant 0$, we can write equation (5.79) as

$$(p-1)(v')^{p-2} v'' - k_1 (v')^{p-1} = k_2 \beta(v).$$

The choice of a therefore implies that

$$\begin{aligned}
(\exp(-ak_1 r)w)' &= a \exp(-ak_1 r)\left[-k_1 w + (p-1)(v')^{p-1} v''\right] \\
&= ak_2 \exp(-ak_1 r)\beta(v)v'.
\end{aligned}$$

Let us assume that $v'(r_0) = 0$. Then, by integrating this expression from r_0 to r, using the upper bound 1 for the exponential expression and the inequality $j(v(r_0)) \geqslant 0$, we obtain

$$\exp(-ak_1 r)(v')^p(r) = ak_2 \int_{r_0}^{r} \exp(-ak_1 s)\beta(v)(s)v'(s)ds \leqslant ak_2 j(v)(r).$$

From this, we deduce that $(v'(r))((j(v)(r))^{-1/p} \leqslant (ak_2 \exp(ak_1 r))^{1/p}$. This expression is bounded on $[r_0, r_1]$, which implies that the integral of the left-hand side is finite, in contradiction to $(*)$. By continuity, there exists a neighborhood of r_0, namely $[r_0 - \alpha, r_0[$, on which $v' > 0$. Therefore if $r_0 > 0$, we have the inequality $v(s) < 0$ on this interval, once more giving a contradiction. We conclude that $r_0 = 0$ and $v'(0) > 0$.   □

Let us conclude the proof of the theorem. We apply the lemma with the function
$$\widehat{u}(x) = v(r - |x - x_1|, k_1, 1, r/2, m_1)$$

on the annulus G. We first compute $\Delta_p f$ for a function f that is radial in $\mathbb{R}^N$. The gradient satisfies $\partial_i f = x_i f'(r)/r$, whence $|\nabla f| = |f'(r)|$. The p-Laplacian is then

$$\Delta_p(f) = \mathrm{div}\left(|\nabla f|^{p-2}\nabla f\right) = \sum_1^N \left[\partial_i\left(|f'(r)|^{p-2}\frac{f'(r)}{r}x_i\right)\right]$$

$$= \frac{d}{dr}[|f'|^{p-2}f']\sum_1^N \frac{x_i^2}{r^2} + N\frac{|f'|^{p-2}f'}{r} - \frac{|f'|^{p-2}f'}{r^3}\sum_1^N x_i^2$$

$$= \frac{d}{dr}[|f'|^{p-2}f'] + (N-1)\frac{|f'|^{p-2}f'}{r}.$$

It follows that

$$\Delta_p\widehat{u} = \frac{d}{dr}[|v'|^{p-2}v'] + \frac{N-1}{r}|v'|^{p-2}v'.$$

Consequently, by taking $k_1 \geqslant 2(N-1)/r$, since $k_2 = 1$, the resulting function $\widehat{u}$ is the desired subsolution satisfying

(5.80) $$-\Delta_p\widehat{u} + \beta(\widehat{u}) \leqslant 0.$$

Moreover, we have $\widehat{u}(0) = 0$ by construction, so that $u \geqslant \widehat{u}$ on the sphere $|x - x_1| = r$ and $\widehat{u}(x) = m_1 \leqslant u(x)$ on the sphere $|x - x_1| = r/2$. Let us apply Theorem 5.67 to the two equations

$$-\Delta_p u + \beta(u) = f \geqslant 0 \quad \text{and} \quad -\Delta_p\widehat{u} + \beta(\widehat{u}) = \widehat{f} \leqslant 0$$

in G, with $f \geqslant \widehat{f}$ and $u \geqslant \widehat{u}$ on ∂G. We conclude that $u \geqslant \widehat{u}$ in G.

Let us finish our proof by contradiction. Since $v'(0) > 0$, we have

$$\lim_{h\to 0, h>0} \frac{1}{h}u(x_0 + h(x_1 - x_0)) \geqslant \lim_{r_h\to 0} v'(r_h) = v'(0) > 0.$$

This result contradicts the fact that $\nabla u(x_0) = 0$ because the minimum is reached at x_0 and u is of class $\mathcal{C}^1$. Consequently, u cannot take its minimum in Ω. □

Hopf Principle. Let us also suppose that $u \geqslant 0$ is a solution of

$$-\Delta_p u + \beta(u) \geqslant 0, \quad u = 0 \text{ on } \partial\Omega$$

in $\mathcal{C}^1(\overline{\Omega})$. The *Hopf principle* then gives us information on the *sign* of the normal derivatives on the boundary $\partial\Omega$, namely

$$\forall x \in \partial\Omega, \quad \frac{\partial u}{\partial \overrightarrow{n}}(x) < 0.$$

Theorem 5.81. *Let $x_0 \in \partial\Omega$ be such that there exists an $x_1 \in \Omega$ with $\partial B(x_1, |x_1 - x_0|) \cap \partial\Omega = \{x_0\}$. Let $\overrightarrow{n}$ be the outward-pointing normal to $\partial\Omega$ at x_0. Then, under the previous assumptions, there exists a $\gamma > 0$ such that*

$$\lim_{x\to x_0, x\in B} \frac{u(x)}{(x_0 - x)\cdot\overrightarrow{n}} = \gamma.$$

Proof of Theorem 5.81.

Indeed, let $x_0 \in \partial\Omega$ and consider a sphere $B(x_1, |x_1 - x_0|)$ in Ω with $\partial B(x_1, |x_1 - x_0|) \cap \partial\Omega = \{x_0\}$. By the previous result, we know that $u > 0$ in $B(x_1, |x_0 - x_1|)$. Moreover, taking the definitions of $G = \{x \in B \mid |x - x_1| \geqslant |x_0 - x_1|/2\}$, v, and $\widehat{u}$ as before, we have

$$u \geqslant \widehat{u}, \quad \gamma = v'(0) > 0,$$

$$\text{and} \quad \lim_{h \to 0, h > 0} \frac{u(x_0 + h(x_1 - x_0))}{h} \geqslant v'(0). \qquad \square$$

Example 5.82 (of an application). Let λ_1 be the first eigenvalue of the p-Laplacian, that is,

$$\lambda_1 = \inf_{\substack{u \in W_0^{1,p}(\Omega) \\ \|u\|_p = 1}} \left\{ \int_\Omega |\nabla u|^p(x) dx \right\}.$$

We can easily see that the infimum λ_1 is reached and that there exists a nonnegative solution, which satisfies the PDE

$$-\Delta_p u = \lambda_1 |u|^{p-2} u.$$

In particular, $-\Delta_p u \geqslant 0$ and $u \geqslant 0$. Admitting that this u is $\mathcal{C}^1$ (see the introduction of this chapter and that of the appendix) and applying the previous theorem with $\beta = 0$, we find that $u > 0$ in Ω.

5.10 Coercive Problems on Nonreflexive Spaces

5.10.1 A Typical Problem and Calculus of Variations

Given a bounded open set Ω in $\mathbb{R}^N$ of class $\mathcal{C}^1$ and $f \in L^N(\Omega)$, we consider the variational problem associated with

$$(5.83) \qquad \inf_{u \in W_0^{1,1}(\Omega)} \left\{ \int_\Omega |\nabla u| \, dx - \int_\Omega f u \, dx \right\}.$$

The functional

$$J(u) = \int_\Omega |\nabla u| - \int_\Omega f u$$

is convex and well defined, owing to the Sobolev embeddings. It cannot be coercive, because the terms $\int_\Omega |\nabla u|$ and $\int_\Omega f u$ have similar growth and can therefore not cancel each other out. Let C be a constant such that

$$\forall u \in W_0^{1,1}, \quad \|u\|_{L^{N/(N-1)}(\Omega)} \leqslant C \int_\Omega |\nabla u|(x) dx,$$

and let us assume that $\|f\|_{L^N(\Omega)} < 1/C$. The functional J is then coercive on $W^{1,1}(\Omega)$.

Having taken care of this first difficulty, we note that since the space $W^{1,1}$ is not coercive, the minimizing sequence for (5.83), which is bounded in $W^{1,1}$ if we assume that $\|f\|_{L^N(\Omega)} < 1/C$, is not necessarily relatively compact in $W^{1,1}$. However, it it relatively compact in $BV(\Omega)$ for the weak topology (Chapter 6). This latter space *consists of the functions u in $L^1(\Omega)$ for which ∇u belongs to the space of bounded measures $M^1(\Omega)$.* We therefore need to extend the definition of the infimum in (5.83). Let us consider

$$(5.84) \qquad \inf_{u \in BV_0(\Omega)} \left\{ \int_\Omega |\nabla u| \, dx - \int_\Omega fu \, dx \right\}.$$

For the moment, we admit the following density result that we will prove in Chapter 6:

If $u \in BV(\Omega)$ satisfies $u = 0$ on $\partial\Omega$, in other words, if u belongs to $BV_0(\Omega)$, then there exists a sequence $\{u_n\}$ in $W^{1,1}(\Omega)$ with $u_n = u = 0$ on $\partial\Omega$ such that

$$\int_\Omega |\nabla u_n| \longrightarrow \int_\Omega |\nabla u| \quad \text{and} \quad \|u_n - u\|_{L^{N/(N-1)}(\Omega)} \longrightarrow 0.$$

This result implies that

$$\inf(5.83) = \inf(5.84).$$

To conclude we only need to show the existence of a solution in BV of the problem associated with (5.84). Let $\{u_n\}$ be a minimizing sequence, which consequently is bounded in $BV(\Omega)$. We can extract a subsequence that converges weakly in $BV(\Omega)$, strongly in all the L^q with $q < N/(N-1)$, and weakly in $L^{N/(N-1)}(\Omega)$. By the lower semicontinuity of the integral over an open set of a measure that is nonnegative for the vague topology, we have

$$\int_\Omega |\nabla u| \leqslant \varliminf_{n \to \infty} \int_\Omega |\nabla u_n|(x) dx.$$

By the weak convergence of $\{u_n\}$ to u in $L^{N/(N-1)}(\Omega)$, we also have

$$\int_\Omega f u_n \longrightarrow \int_\Omega fu.$$

The only delicate point concerns the behavior of the limit of $\{u_n\}$ on the boundary. In Chapter 6, we will see that the trace map on BV is not weakly continuous. To compensate for this difficulty, we introduce that so-called *relaxed* problem, which is associated with

$$(5.85) \qquad \inf_{u \in BV(\Omega)} \left\{ \int_\Omega |\nabla u| + \int_{\partial\Omega} |u| - \int_\Omega fu \right\}.$$

Note that we have

$$\inf(5.85) = \inf(5.84)$$

by the density theorem for the inclusion of $W^{1,1}(\Omega)$ in $BV(\Omega)$ (cf. Theorem 6.56 of Chapter 6).

We will now show that the problem associated with (5.85) admits a solution. Let $\{u_n\}$ be a minimizing sequence for (5.84). Our previous results show that $\{u_n\}$ is bounded in $BV(\Omega)$. Defining $\widetilde{u}_n$ as the extension of u_n by 0 outside of Ω, we have $\widetilde{u}_n \in BV(\mathbb{R}^N)$ with

$$\nabla(\widetilde{u}_n) = \nabla u_n \chi_\Omega + (0 - u_n)\delta_{\partial\Omega}.$$

From this, we deduce that

$$|\nabla \widetilde{u}_n| = |\nabla u_n|\chi_\Omega + |u_n|\delta_{\partial\Omega}.$$

If $\{u_n\}$ converges weakly to u in $BV(\Omega)$, then $\widetilde{u}_n$ converges weakly to an element v of $BV(\mathbb{R}^N)$. We must then have $v = 0$ in the complement of $\overline{\Omega}$ and $v = u$ in Ω. In particular, $\nabla v = \nabla u \chi_\Omega + (0 - u)\delta_{\partial\Omega}$. By the weak lower semicontinuity, we have

$$\int_{\mathbb{R}^N} |\nabla v| - \int_\Omega fv \leqslant \varliminf_{n\to\infty} \int_{\mathbb{R}^N} |\nabla \widetilde{u}_n| - \int_\Omega fu_n$$

because $\int_\Omega fu_n$ converges to $\int_\Omega fu$. Consequently,

$$\int_\Omega |\nabla u| + \int_{\partial\Omega} |u| - \int_\Omega fu \leqslant \inf(5.85),$$

and therefore, u is the solution of the problem associated with (5.85).

5.11 Minimal Surfaces

5.11.1 Presentation of the Problem

We can describe the problem of minimal surfaces as follows. Consider the set of C^1 scalar functions u on a bounded domain Ω in $\mathbb{R}^N$ that satisfy $u = g$ on $\partial\Omega$ for a given $g \in L^1(\partial\Omega)$. We are looking for an element u of this set such that the hypersurface with Cartesian equation $(x_1, \ldots, x_{N-1}, u(x_1, \ldots, x_{N-1}))$ has a minimal $N - 1$-dimensional surface area.

Variational Formulation of the Problem. This corresponds to determining a function u where

$$\inf_{\substack{u \in ? \\ u = g \text{ on } \partial\Omega}} \left\{ \int_\Omega \sqrt{1 + |\nabla u|^2(x)} \, dx \right\}$$

is reached. The question mark denotes a space in which all quantities that are involved are well defined. We will first define a suitable space. Note that if g is a constant, then the unique solution of the problem is given by $u = $ cte, which corresponds to a plane surface. In that case, we of course find that the infimum equals $|\Omega|$. By the trace theorem, since the function g belongs to the trace space $\gamma_0(W^{1,1})$, we see that $W^{1,1}(\Omega)$ is a "minimal" space on which all quantities are well defined. We therefore wish to determine a function u where

$$\inf_{\substack{u \in W^{1,1}(\Omega) \\ u = g \text{ on } \partial\Omega}} \left\{ \int_\Omega \sqrt{1 + |\nabla u|^2(x)} \, dx \right\}$$

is reached.

Transformation of the Problem. Below, we propose to replace the previous problem by an equivalent so-called *relaxed problem* that consists of a minimization on $BV(\Omega)$.

Because it is not reflexive, we replace the space $W^{1,1}(\Omega)$ by $BV(\Omega)$. Its definition and main properties are studied in Chapter 6.

In order to show the existence of a solution, let us start by reasoning as in the case of a reflexive space. It is clear that the infimum is $\geqslant 1$, hence positive, and that the functional J is convex. The functional J is moreover coercive in $W^{1,1}(\Omega)$, by the Poincaré inequality. Indeed, let U in $W^{1,1}(\Omega)$ be a lifting of $g \in L^1(\partial\Omega)$ in $W^{1,1}(\Omega)$. Then $u - U = 0$ on $\partial\Omega$, whence, by the Poincaré inequality,

$$\|\nabla(u - U)\|_{L^1(\Omega)} \geqslant C\|u - U\|_{W^{1,1}(\Omega)}.$$

The coercivity of $J(u)$ follows because

$$J(u) \geqslant \|\nabla u\|_1 \geqslant \|\nabla(u - U)\|_1 - \|\nabla U\|_1$$
$$\geqslant \|u - U\|_{W^{1,1}} - \|\nabla U\|_1 \geqslant \|u\|_{W^{1,1}} - 2\|U\|_{W^{1,1}}.$$

Let $\{u_n\}$ be a minimizing sequence; it is bounded in $W^{1,1}(\Omega)$ and, consequently, bounded in $BV(\Omega)$. By Proposition 6.52 on the weak compactness of bounded sequences in $BV(\Omega)$, it follows that we can extract a subsequence $\{u_{\sigma(n)}\}$ from $\{u_n\}$ that converges weakly to an element u in $BV(\Omega)$. This means that

$$\int_\Omega |u_{\sigma(n)} - u|(x)dx \longrightarrow 0 \quad \text{and} \quad \forall \varphi \in \mathcal{C}_c(\Omega), \quad \langle \nabla u_{\sigma(n)} - \nabla u, \varphi \rangle \longrightarrow 0,$$

where the last property expresses the vague convergence of $\nabla u_{\sigma(n)}$ to ∇u. However, as in the previous subsection, we do not necessarily have $u = g$ on $\partial\Omega$.

We must therefore both extend the functional $\sqrt{1 + |\nabla u|^2}$ to the functions in BV and compensate for the difficulty that we mentioned in Subsection 5.10.1. For the first problem, we use the theory of convex functions of a measure, which we will develop in Chapter 6, for the bounded measure $\mu = \nabla u$ (cf. Section 6.8 and in particular the example $f(\mu) = \sqrt{1 + |\mu|^2}$, which is worked out in detail). This function f admits an asymptotic function, namely $\lim_{t\to+\infty} f(tx)/t = |x|$. It therefore follows from Chapter 6 that if $\nabla u = \nabla u^{\mathrm{ac}} + \nabla u^S$ is the Lebesgue decomposition of the measure ∇u, then we can define $f(\nabla u)$ (cf. Theorem 6.138) by

$$f(\nabla u) = \sqrt{1 + |(\nabla u)^{\mathrm{ac}}|^2} + |\nabla u^S|.$$

With this extension, the functional $u \mapsto \int_\Omega f(\nabla u)$ is lower semicontinuous for the weak topology on $BV(\Omega)$.

In order to solve the trace problem, we consider a function $G \in W^{1,1}(\mathbb{R}^N \setminus \overline{\Omega})$ with trace g on $\partial(\mathbb{R}^N \setminus \overline{\Omega})$. This extends u outside of Ω, giving a function with $\widetilde{u} \in BV(\mathbb{R}^N)$. Using Exercise 6.18 and the function $f - 1$ with value zero for $x = 0$, we obtain

$$f(\nabla\widetilde{u}) = f(\nabla u)\chi_\Omega + |(u - G)\overrightarrow{n}|\delta_{\partial\Omega} + f(\nabla G)\chi_{\mathbb{R}^N \setminus \overline{\Omega}}.$$

Finally, we have the following density results. First, there exists a sequence $u_n \in \mathcal{C}^\infty(\Omega) \cap W^{1,1}(\Omega)$ such that $u_n \to u$ in $L^1(\Omega)$ and

$$\|\nabla u_n\|_1 \longrightarrow \int_\Omega |\nabla u|, \quad \int_\Omega f(\nabla u_n) \longrightarrow \int_\Omega f(\nabla u)$$

(cf. Theorem 6.144). Second, if $u \in BV(\Omega)$ and $g \in L^1(\partial\Omega)$, then Remark 6.73 shows that there exists a sequence $\{u_n\}$ in $W^{1,1}(\Omega)$ that converges weakly to u in BV with

$$\int_\Omega f(\nabla u_n) \longrightarrow \int_\Omega f(\nabla u) + \int_{\partial\Omega} |u - g|\overrightarrow{n}.$$

The first density result allows us to deduce that the infimum

$$\inf_{\substack{u \in BV(\Omega) \\ \gamma_0 u = g}} \int_\Omega f(\nabla u)$$

coincides with the corresponding infimum on $W^{1,1}$, where we maintain the limit condition $\gamma_0 u = g$.

The second result allows us to show that these infima are also equal to

$$\inf_{u \in BV(\Omega)} \left\{ \int_\Omega f(\nabla u) + \int_{\partial\Omega} |u - g| \right\}.$$

This corresponds to the relaxed problem, for which we will now show the existence of a solution.

5.11.2 Existence of a Solution

Let us fix an element G of $W^{1,1}(\mathbb{R}^N \setminus \overline{\Omega})$ with value g on $\partial\Omega$. Let $\{u_n\}$ be a minimizing sequence in $W^{1,1}(\Omega)$ with $u_n = g$ on $\partial\Omega$; then the extension of u_n by $G \in W^{1,1}(\mathbb{R}^N \setminus \overline{\Omega})$ (which we take with compact support) belongs to $W^{1,1}(\mathbb{R}^N)$. It is therefore bounded in $W^{1,1}(\mathbb{R}^N)$. Consequently, we can extract a subsequence that converges weakly to $V \in BV(\mathbb{R}^N)$. By construction, we have $V = G$ on $\mathbb{R}^N \setminus \overline{\Omega}$. Moreover, by the lower semicontinuity, we have

$$\int_{\mathbb{R}^N} \left(\sqrt{1 + |\nabla V|^2} - 1 \right)$$

$$\leqslant \underline{\lim} \int_\Omega \left(\sqrt{1 + |\nabla u_n|^2} - 1 \right) + \int_{\mathbb{R}^N \setminus \overline{\Omega}} \left(\sqrt{1 + |\nabla G|^2} - 1 \right).$$

Let u be the restriction of V to Ω; then $V = u\chi_\Omega + G\chi_{\mathbb{R}^N \setminus \overline{\Omega}}$. Moreover, since the jump when crossing the boundary $\partial\Omega$ for V is $g - u$, we see that the gradient satisfies

$$\nabla V = \nabla u \chi_\Omega + (g - u)\delta_{\partial\Omega} \overrightarrow{n} + \nabla G \chi_{\mathbb{R}^N \setminus \overline{\Omega}}.$$

Consequently, the relation

$$\sqrt{1 + |\nabla V|^2} = \sqrt{1 + |\nabla u|^2} \chi_\Omega + |g - u|\delta_{\partial\Omega} + \sqrt{1 + |\nabla G|^2} \chi_{\mathbb{R}^N \setminus \overline{\Omega}}$$

gives

$$\int_{\mathbb{R}^N} \left(\sqrt{1 + |\nabla V|^2} - 1 \right) = \int_\Omega \left(\sqrt{1 + |\nabla u|^2} - 1 \right) + \int_{\partial\Omega} |u - g|$$

$$+ \int_{\mathbb{R}^N \setminus \overline{\Omega}} \left(\sqrt{1 + |\nabla G|^2} - 1 \right).$$

because $(G - u)\delta_{\partial\Omega}$ is singular (see Theorem 6.138 and Exercise 6.17).

We then deduce that

$$\int_\Omega \sqrt{1 + |\nabla u|^2} + \int_{\partial\Omega} |u - g| \leqslant \underline{\lim} \int_\Omega \sqrt{1 + |\nabla u_n|^2},$$

and therefore that u is a solution of the relaxed problem, in other words, of the problem stated at the beginning. We do not treat the regularity of this solution in this book. Interested readers can consult the book [35] and the articles [33] and [61].

Comments

The literature on subjects related to elliptic nonlinear partial differential equations is considerable. As a consequence, we can choose between many different directions.

In some cases, the variational approach is not possible and we could expect solutions in the sense of viscosity, as in the book by Barles [3] and the articles by Berestycki, Capuzzo-Dolcetta and Nirenberg [4], Cabré and Caffarelli, [12], and many other authors.

For recent work on the different maximum principles, we mention, by way of example, the articles by Grenon, Murat and Poretta [36], or Casado-Díaz, Murat and Poretta [14].

For problems involving nonlinear terms with critical Sobolev exponent, one may consult the articles by Demengel [18, 21, 20] and Demengel and Hebey [24], the basic articles by P.-L. Lions on the concentration compactness method [50, 51], and finally, the article by M. Struwe [66], which includes methods for solving noncoercive variational problems using supersolutions and subsolutions.

Finally, the book by Ferédéric Hélein [38] provides a complete overview of harmonic maps between two Riemann varieties that is very pleasant to read.

5.12 Exercises for Chapter 5

Exercise 5.1 (Regularity of the Eigenfunctions of the Laplacian).
Show that if Ω is an open subset of $\mathbb{R}^N$ of class $\mathcal{C}^\infty$, then every solution $u \in H_0^1(\Omega)$ of $-\Delta u = \lambda u$, where λ is a real number, is $\mathcal{C}^\infty$ in the interior of Ω.

Hints. By the regularity theorem (cf. Proposition 5.38), we have $u \in H^2(\Omega)$ whence, step by step, we obtain the implication

$$\forall u, \quad u \in H^m(\Omega) \Longrightarrow u \in H^{m+2}(\Omega).$$

Exercise 5.2 (Existence of a First Eigenvalue for the p-Laplacian).
Let p satisfy $1 < p < \infty$ and let Ω be a bounded domain of class $\mathcal{C}^1$ in $\mathbb{R}^N$. We consider

$$\lambda_1 = \inf_{\substack{u \in W_0^{1,p}(\Omega) \\ \|u\|_{L^p}=1}} \left\{ \int_\Omega |\nabla u(x)|^p dx \right\}.$$

Prove that $\lambda_1 > 0$ and that the infimum is reached. Prove that a minimum u satisfies

$$-\Delta_p u = \lambda_1 |u|^{p-2} u.$$

Let μ be a number such that there exists a $v \in W_0^{1,p}$, $v \neq 0$, with $-\Delta_p v = \mu |v|^{p-2} v$. Prove that $\mu \geqslant \lambda_1$. For $p = 2$, this corresponds to the first eigenvalue of the Laplacian.

Hints. Use Proposition 5.55 (the Poincaré inequality) to deduce that, for a constant C given by this proposition, $\lambda_1 \geqslant ((1 - C)/C)^{1/p}$.

Next, let $\{u_n\}$ be a sequence of norm 1 such that $\|\nabla u_n\|_p^p \to \lambda_1$. Deduce the existence of a subsequence that converges weakly to u in $W^{1,p}$ and strongly to u in L^p. In particular, $\|u\|_p = 1$. By the lower semicontinuity for the weak topology of the seminorm, $\|\nabla u\|_p^p \leqslant \lambda_1$. Conclude using $\|\nabla u\|_p^p \geqslant \lambda_1$.

Use the inequality $\|\nabla(u + t\varphi)\|_p^p \geqslant \lambda_1 \|u + t\varphi\|_p^p$ for $t \in \mathbb{R}$ and $\varphi \in \mathcal{D}(\Omega)$ and the mean value theorem (cf. for example Chapter 1) to show that

$$\int_\Omega |\nabla u|^p dx + pt \int_\Omega |\nabla u|^{p-2} \nabla u \cdot \nabla \varphi dx + o(t)$$

$$\geqslant \lambda_1 \int_\Omega |u|^p dx + \lambda_1 pt \int_\Omega |u|^{p-2} u \varphi dx + o(t).$$

Since $\|\nabla u\|_p^p = \lambda_1 \|u\|_p^p$, dividing by $t > 0$ and letting t tend to 0 gives

$$\int_\Omega |\nabla u|^{p-2} \nabla u \cdot \nabla \varphi dx \geqslant \lambda_1 \int_\Omega |u|^{p-2} u \varphi dx.$$

Conclude by replacing φ by $-\varphi$.

Let μ be such that there exists a nonzero $v \in W_0^{1,p}$ with $-\Delta_p v = \mu |v|^{p-2} v$. By the definition of λ_1, it suffices to multiply by v and integrate to obtain the stated property, namely $\mu \geqslant \lambda_1$.

Exercise [∗∗] 5.3 (Regularity of the Eigenfunctions of the Divergence Operator).

Let Ω be an open subset of $\mathbb{R}^N$. Let $A \in \mathcal{C}^k(\Omega)$ with $k \geqslant 1 + [N/2]$ be a symmetric uniformly elliptic matrix. Show that any solution u of $\mathrm{div}(A(x)\nabla u) = \lambda u$ is of class $\mathcal{C}^1$ in the interior of Ω. Use induction to show that $u \in H_{\mathrm{loc}}^{k+1}(\Omega)$. Finally, use the Sobolev embeddings to deduce that $u \in \mathcal{C}_{\mathrm{loc}}^{1,\alpha}$ for some α. Determine α explicitly.

Exercise [∗] 5.4 (Complements to the Strong Maximum Principle: the Hopf Principle).

Let Ω be a domain in $\mathbb{R}^N$ of class $\mathcal{C}^1$ and let $p > 1$ be a real number. Suppose that u is a solution of $-\Delta_p u \geqslant 0$ with $u = 0$ on $\partial\Omega$, and that u is $\mathcal{C}^1$ on $\overline{\Omega}$. Prove that on the boundary, we have

$$\exists m > 0, \ \forall x \in \partial\Omega, \quad \frac{\partial u}{\partial n}(x) \leqslant -m.$$

Exercise [∗∗] 5.5 (Simplicity of the First Eigenvalue of the Laplacian).

We use the notations of Subsection 5.3.4.

(1) Prove that $-\Delta\varphi = \lambda_1 \varphi$, where λ_1 is the first eigenvalue of the Laplacian and φ belongs to $H_0^1(\Omega)$, admits a solution.

(2) Use the strong maximum principle to prove that $\varphi > 0$ in Ω. Prove that for every u and every $v > 0$ in $H_0^1(\Omega)$, we have *Picone's identity*:

$$|\nabla u|^2 - \nabla(u^2/v) \cdot \nabla v \geqslant 0,$$

where equality holds if and only if there exists a $\lambda \in \mathbb{R}$ such that $u = \lambda v$.

(3) Let u and v be nonnegative solution of

$$-\Delta u = \lambda_1 u \quad \text{and} \quad -\Delta v = \lambda_1 v.$$

Prove that u and v are proportional to each other. First use the Hopf principle to establish the existence of an $\varepsilon > 0$ such that $u \geqslant \varepsilon v$ in Ω. From this, deduce that u^2/v belongs to $H_0^1(\Omega)$. Next, multiply the equation in v by u^2/v, integrate, and use Picone's identity to prove the desired result.

Hints.

(1) The function φ is the solution of the minimization associated with

$$\inf_{\substack{u \in H_0^1(\Omega) \\ \|u\|_2 = 1}} \int_\Omega |\nabla u(x)|^2 dx$$

(cf. Exercise 5.1). The existence of a nonnegative solution results from the inequality $|\nabla|u|\,| \leqslant |\nabla u|$.

If $\varphi \geqslant 0$, then $-\Delta\varphi \geqslant 0$. Use Vázquez's maximum principle with $\beta = 0$.

(2) Expand the left-hand side in Picone's identity to obtain

$$|\nabla u|^2 - 2\frac{u}{v}\nabla u \cdot \nabla v + u^2\frac{\nabla v}{v^2} \cdot \nabla u,$$

which corresponds to

$$\left|\nabla u - \frac{u}{v}\nabla v\right|^2.$$

This expression is therefore nonnegative. Moreover, if it is everywhere zero, then we have $\nabla(u/v) = 0$ in Ω.

Conclude that $u/v = $ cte, for a constant $\geqslant 0$.

(3) Since there exists a $C > 0$ such that $u \leqslant Cv$ on the boundary, we have $u^2/v \in H_0^1(\Omega)$.

Multiplying the equation in v by u^2/v and the equation in u by u gives

$$\lambda_1 \int_\Omega v\frac{u^2}{v} dx = \lambda_1 \int_\Omega |u(x)|^2 dx = \int_\Omega -\Delta v\frac{u^2}{v} dx$$

$$= \int_\Omega \nabla v \cdot \nabla(u^2/v) dx \leqslant \int_\Omega |\nabla u|^2 dx = \lambda_1 \|u\|^2,$$

so that the inequalities become equalities everywhere, giving $u = \lambda v$.

Exercise [**] 5.6 (Simplicity of the First Eigenvalue of the p-Laplacian).

Let Ω be a bounded domain of class $\mathcal{C}^1$. Show that if $p > 1$, u and v belong to $W_0^{1,p}(\Omega)$ and satisfy $u \geqslant 0$ and $v > 0$, then we have the following form of Picone's identity, which generalizes that of the previous exercise:

$$|\nabla u|^p - \nabla(u^p/v^{p-1}) \cdot \sigma(v) \geqslant 0,$$

where $\sigma(v) = |\nabla v|^{p-2}\nabla v$. Moreover, show that equality holds if and only if $u = \lambda v$.

Use the strong maximum principle and Picone's identity to show that if u and v are solutions of

$$-\Delta_p u = \lambda_1 |u|^{p-2}u, \quad -\Delta_p v = \lambda_1 |v|^{p-2}v,$$

then there exists a $\lambda \in \mathbb{R}$ such that $u = \lambda v$.

Hints. Expanding the above gives the convexity inequality

$$\frac{1}{p}|\nabla u|^p - \nabla u \cdot \sigma(v)\Big(\frac{u}{v}\Big)^{p-1} + \Big(1 - \frac{1}{p}\Big)\sigma(v) \cdot \nabla v\Big(\frac{u}{v}\Big)^p \geqslant 0,$$

with equality if $\nabla u = (u/v)\nabla v$ because of the strict convexity of $x \mapsto |x|^p$. Conclude.

Multiply the equation in u by u and the equation in v by $u^p/(v^{p-1})$. Since $u^p/(v^{p-1}) \in W_0^{1,p}$ (by the Hopf principle), we have

$$\lambda_1 \int_\Omega |u|^p = -\int_\Omega \Delta_p v \frac{u^p}{v^{p-1}} = \int_\Omega \sigma(v) \cdot \nabla\Big(\frac{u^p}{v^{p-1}}\Big) \leqslant \int_\Omega |\nabla u|^p = \lambda_1 \int_\Omega |u|^p,$$

so that the inequalities turn into equalities everywhere. In particular, in Picone's identity, this implies that $u = \lambda v$.

Exercise [**] 5.7 (Eigenfunctions of ∇^2 in H_0^2).

Let Ω be a bounded domain of class $\mathcal{C}^2$ in $\mathbb{R}^N$. Recall that $\nabla\nabla u$ is the vector in $\mathbb{R}^{N^2}$ with components $\partial_{ij}u$ and that

$$H_0^2(\Omega) = \{u \in L^2(\Omega, \mathbb{R}) \mid \nabla u \in L^2(\Omega, \mathbb{R}^N),$$
$$\nabla\nabla u \in L^2(\Omega, \mathbb{R}^{N^2}), \, u|_{\partial\Omega} = \partial u/\partial n|_{\partial\Omega} = 0\}.$$

Consider the variational problem associated with

$$\lambda = \inf_{\substack{u \in H_0^2(\Omega) \\ \int_\Omega |u|^2 dx = 1}} \Big\{\int_\Omega |\nabla\nabla u(x)|^2 dx\Big\}.$$

Prove that $\lambda > 0$ and that this problem admits a unique solution. Prove that if u is this solution, then $\Delta^2 u = \lambda u$.

Hints. The value λ is positive because of the following generalization of the Poincaré inequality:

$$\forall u \in H_0^2(\Omega), \quad \|u\|_2 \leqslant C\|\nabla\nabla u\|_2.$$

Prove this by contradiction, using a sequence $\{u_n\}$ with $\|\nabla\nabla u_n\|_2 \leqslant 1/n\|u_n\|_2$. Divide by the norm $\sqrt{\|u_n\|_2 + \|\nabla u_n\|_2}$ to obtain $\|v_n\|_{H^1} = 1$ and $\|\nabla\nabla v_n\|_2 \leqslant 1/n$.

Extract a subsequence and use the compactness of the embedding of H^2 into H^1 to prove the existence of a subsequence $\{v_n\}$ that converges strongly to v in H^1 while $\{\nabla\nabla v_n\}$ converges weakly to $\nabla\nabla v$. By the lower semicontinuity of the seminorm, we have $\nabla\nabla v = 0$. In particular, v is a linear polynomial. However, since $v = 0 = \partial v/\partial n = 0$ on $\partial\Omega$, we must have $v = 0$, contradicting the equality $\|v\|_{H^1}^2 = \lim \|v_n\|_{H^1}^2 = 1$.

Next, let $\{v_n\}$ be a minimizing sequence for the value λ. The sequence $\|\nabla\nabla v_n\|_2$ is bounded, whence, by using Green's formula and the equality $\partial_{\vec{n}} v_n = 0$ on $\partial\Omega$, we have

$$\|\nabla v_n\|_2^2 = \left| -\int_\Omega v_n \operatorname{div}(\nabla v_n) \right| \leqslant \|v_n\|_2 \|\nabla\nabla v_n\|_2,$$

which implies that v_n is bounded in H^1. Extract a subsequence that converges weakly to v in H^2 and strongly in H^1. The lower semicontinuity then gives $\|\nabla\nabla v\|_2 \leqslant \underline{\lim} \|\nabla\nabla v_n\|_2 = \lambda$ and $\|v\|_2 = \lim \|v_n\|_2 = 1$.

Now, v is the solution of the problem defining λ. Let $t \in \mathbb{R}^+$ and let $\varphi \in \mathcal{D}(\Omega)$. Write

$$\|\nabla\nabla(u + t\varphi)\|^2 \geqslant \lambda\|u + t\varphi\|^2.$$

Using the notation $\nabla\nabla u : \nabla\nabla\varphi = \sum_{i,j} \partial_{ij} u \partial_{ij}\varphi$, expanding gives

$$2t \int_\Omega \nabla\nabla u : \nabla\nabla\varphi + O(t^2) \geqslant \lambda 2t \int_\Omega u\varphi + O(t^2).$$

Integrating by parts then gives

$$2t \int_\Omega (\Delta^2 u)\varphi \geqslant 2t\lambda \int_\Omega u\varphi + O(t^2),$$

from which the result follows by dividing by t and setting $t = 0$. Replace φ by $-\varphi$ to obtain the equality $\Delta^2 u = \lambda u$.

Indeed,

$$\int_\Omega \partial_{ij} u \partial_{ij}\varphi = -\int_\Omega \partial_{ijj} u \partial_i\varphi = \int_\Omega \partial_{iijj} u\varphi = \int_\Omega \Delta^2 u\varphi.$$

Exercise [∗∗] 5.8 (Eigenfunctions for $\Delta^2 - \Delta$).

Let Ω be a bounded domain of class $\mathcal{C}^2$ in $\mathbb{R}^N$. We consider the variational problem associated with

$$\lambda = \inf_{\substack{u \in H_0^1(\Omega) \cap H^2(\Omega) \\ \int_\Omega |u|^2 = 1}} \left\{ \int_\Omega |\nabla\nabla u|^2 + \int_\Omega |\nabla u|^2 \right\}.$$

Show that this problem admits a solution and that the infimum is positive. Show that a solution u satisfies

$$(5.86) \qquad \Delta^2 u - \Delta u = \lambda u, \quad \frac{\partial^2 u}{\partial n^2} = u = 0 \text{ on } \partial\Omega.$$

Hints. To show the positivity of the infimum, use the Poincaré inequality $\|u\|_2 \leqslant C\|\nabla u\|_2$ if $u = 0$ on the boundary. For a reasoning by contradiction, assume that the infimum is zero. Then there exists a sequence $\{u_n\}$ such that $\|u_n\|_2 = 1$, $u_n = 0$ on the boundary, and $\|u_n\|_2 + \|\nabla\nabla u_n\|_2 \leqslant 1/n$. Extracting a subsequence, we see that $\{u_n\}$ converges strongly to u in H^1 with $\|u\|_2 = \lim \|u_n\|_2 = 1$ and $\|\nabla u\|_2 + \|\nabla\nabla u\|_2 \leqslant 0$ by the lower semicontinuity of the seminorm. Since u is zero on the boundary, it follows that $u = 0$, contradicting $\|u\|_2 = 1$.

Show the existence of a solution in a similar manner. Use $u + t\varphi$ and

$$\int_\Omega |\nabla(u + t\varphi)|^2 + |\nabla\nabla(u + t\varphi)|^2 \geqslant \lambda \int_\Omega (u + t\varphi)^2.$$

Expand to obtain

$$2t \int_\Omega \nabla\varphi \cdot \nabla u + 2t \int_\Omega \nabla\nabla u : \nabla\nabla\varphi + O(t^2) = \lambda 2t \int_\Omega u\varphi + O(t^2),$$

with notation $\nabla\nabla u : \nabla\nabla\varphi = \sum_{i,j} \partial_{ij} u \partial_{ij}\varphi$, as before. By the definition of $\Delta^2 u$ in the sense of distributions, this gives

$$\int_\Omega \Delta^2 u\varphi - \int_\Omega \Delta u\varphi = \lambda \int_\Omega u\varphi,$$

that is, the first equation in (5.86). Show the limit condition by taking φ in H^2 with $\varphi = 0$ on $\partial\Omega$. This gives

$$\int_\Omega \nabla\nabla u : \nabla\nabla\varphi = -\int_\Omega \partial_{ijj} u \partial_i\varphi + \int_{\partial\Omega} \partial_{ij} u \partial_i\varphi n_j$$

$$= \int_\Omega \partial_{iijj} u\varphi - \int_{\partial\Omega} \partial_{ijj} u\varphi n_j + \int_{\partial\Omega} \partial_{ij} u \partial_i\varphi n_j$$

$$= \int_\Omega \Delta^2 u\varphi + \int_{\partial\Omega} \partial_{ij} u \partial_i\varphi n_j$$

and
$$\int_\Omega \nabla u \cdot \nabla\varphi = -\int_\Omega \Delta u\varphi + 0.$$

Finally, use equation (5.86) to obtain $\int_{\partial\Omega} \partial_{ij} u \partial_i\varphi n_j = 0$. Note that $\partial_{nn} u \in H^{-1/2}(\partial\Omega)$.

Recall that the surjectivity of the trace map we proved in Chapter 4 implies that for every $(0, v) \in H^{3/2} \times H^{1/2}(\partial\Omega)$, there exists a $\varphi \in H^2(\Omega)$ such that $\varphi = 0$ on $\partial\Omega$ and $\partial_n\varphi = v$ on $\partial\Omega$. Using the equality $\partial_i\varphi = vn_i$ that holds on $\partial\Omega$, deduce that $\int_{\partial\Omega} \partial_{ij} u v n_i n_j = 0$. This implies that $\partial^2 u/\partial n^2 = 0$ because v is arbitrary in $H^{1/2}(\partial\Omega)$.

Exercise [∗∗] 5.9 (Solving a PDE by a Variational Method).

Let Ω be a bounded domain of class $\mathcal{C}^1$. Consider the equation

$$\begin{cases} -\Delta u + |u|^{p-2} u = f, \\ u = 0 \text{ on } \partial\Omega, \end{cases}$$

where f belongs to $L^2(\Omega)$, p is a real number satisfying $1 < p < 2N/(N-2)$, and p' is the conjugate of p.

(1) Prove the existence of a solution by considering the problem associated with

$$\inf_{u \in H_0^1(\Omega)} \left\{ \frac{1}{2} \int_\Omega |\nabla u|^2 \, dx + \frac{1}{p} \int_\Omega |u|^p \, dx - \int_\Omega fu \, dx \right\}.$$

(2) Prove that if $f \geqslant 0$ in Ω, then every solution u of

$$\begin{cases} -\Delta u + |u|^{p-2}u = f, \\ u = 0 \quad \text{on } \partial\Omega \end{cases}$$

satisfies $u \geqslant 0$ in Ω.

(3) Prove the uniqueness of the solution. If Ω is C^2, then prove that if $p < 2(N-1)/(N-2)$, then $u \in H^2$. Moreover, if Ω is C^3, then prove that under this same condition on p, if $f \in H^1$, then $u \in H^3$.

Hints. Under the given conditions, the functional stated in the problem is convex, continuous, and coercive. By considering $u + t\varphi$, it is clear that u satisfies

$$t \int_\Omega \nabla u \cdot \nabla \varphi + t \int_\Omega |u|^{p-2}u\varphi - t \int_\Omega f\varphi + o(t) \geqslant 0.$$

Use a classical argument to obtain the PDE.

For the uniqueness, take the difference of the equations in u_1 and in u_2, multiply this by $u_1 - u_2$, and integrate over Ω. Applying Green's formula then gives

$$\int_\Omega |\nabla(u_1 - u_2)|^2 + \int_\Omega (|u_1|^{p-2}u_1 - |u_2|^{p-2}u_2)(u_1 - u_2) = 0,$$

which implies that $(|u_1|^{p-2}u_1 - |u_2|^{p-2}u_2)(u_1 - u_2)$ is nonnegative, whence $u_1 = u_2$.

Show that $|u|^{p-2}u \in L^2$ if $p < 2(N-1)/(N-2)$. Indeed, $2(p-1) \leqslant 2N/(N-2)$. Use Theorem 5.33 to deduce from this that $u \in H^2$ because $f - |u|^{p-2}u \in L^2$. Use $\nabla(|u|^{p-2}u) = (p-1)|u|^{p-2}\nabla u$ to show that if $N > 4$, then the inclusion $u \in H^2$ implies that $u \in L^{2N/(N-4)}$, and therefore $u \in L^{(p-2)N}$. If $N \leqslant 4$, then the inclusion in all L^q gives the result. We conclude that $|u|^{p-2}u \in H^1$. Hence, if $f \in H^1$, then by Proposition 5.38, $-\Delta u \in H^1$, so that $u \in H^3$.

To see that $u \geqslant 0$, multiply the equation by u^-, which belongs to $H_0^1(\Omega)$. When $f \geqslant 0$, this gives the inequality

$$-\int_\Omega |\nabla u^-|^2 - \int_\Omega |u^-|^p = \int_\Omega fu^- \geqslant 0,$$

and therefore $u^- = 0$.

Exercise [∗] 5.10 (Variational Problem and p-Laplacian with Constraint).

Let Ω be a bounded domain of class C^1 in $\mathbb{R}^N$. Let C be a Poincaré constant, that is, a constant $C > 0$ such that for every $u \in W_0^{1,p}(\Omega)$, we have $\int_\Omega |\nabla u|^p \geqslant C \int_\Omega |u|^p$.

Let $0 < c < C$ and let f be a continuous function that is nonnegative at at least one point. For $p < N$ and $p < q < p^* = pN/(N-p)$, we consider the problem associated with

$$\inf_{\substack{u \in W_0^{1,p}(\Omega) \\ \int_\Omega f(x)|u|^q(x)dx=1}} \left\{ \int_\Omega |\nabla u|^p - c \int_\Omega |u|^p \right\}.$$

(1) Prove that this problem admits a solution by noting that the functional that we minimize is coercive. Prove that there exists a nonnegative solution and that a solution u satisfies the Euler equation

$$-\Delta_p u - c|u|^{p-2}u = \lambda f |u|^{q-2}u,$$

where λ is a constant equal to the previous infimum.

(2) Use a suitable scalar to prove that the equation

$$-\Delta_p u - cu^{p-1} = fu^{q-1}, \quad u \geqslant 0, \quad \text{and } u = 0 \quad \text{on } \partial\Omega$$

admits a solution.

(3) Write the equation as

$$-\Delta_p u + \|f\|_\infty u^{q-1} = (\|f\|_\infty + f)u^{q-1} + cu^{p-1} \geqslant 0.$$

Suppose that u is C^1 and use Vázquez's strong maximum principle with $\beta(u) = \|f\|_\infty u^{q-1}$ to deduce that $u > 0$ in Ω.

Hints. The functional is coercive. It is not convex, but it is l.s.c.

Let $\{u_n\}$ be a minimizing sequence. It is bounded in $W^{1,p}(\Omega)$, hence has a subsequence that converges to $u \in W_0^{1,p}$. Use the weak lower semicontinuity of the seminorm $\|\nabla u\|_p$ and the strong convergence in L^q, which follows from the compactness theorem in L^q, to prove that $\int_\Omega f(x)|u(x)|^q = 1$. Consequently, u realizes the infimum. Moreover, if u is a solution, then so is $|u|$, because the functional is even.

Use the inequality

$$J(u + t\varphi) \geqslant \left(\int_\Omega f(x)(|(u + t\varphi)(x)|^q dx \right)^{p/q} J(u),$$

where u is a solution, $\varphi \in \mathcal{D}(\Omega)$, and t is sufficiently small that

$$\int_\Omega f(x)(|u + t\varphi|^q)dx \neq 0.$$

The homogeneity ensures the existence of t. Expanding this, a classical computation gives

$$J(u) + tp \int_\Omega |\nabla u|^{p-2}\nabla u \cdot \nabla \varphi - tcp \int_\Omega |u|^{p-2}u\varphi + o(t)$$

$$= \left(1 + tq \int_\Omega f |u|^{q-2}u\varphi + o(t) \right)^{p/q} J(u).$$

Therefore, there exists a constant $\mu > 0$ such that

$$-\Delta_p u - c|u|^{p-2}u = \mu f|u|^{q-2}u$$

in Ω. In order to obtain a solution when we replace μ by 1, let $v = \mu^{1/(p-q)}u$.

Exercise [**] 5.11 (The Equation $-\Delta_p u + u^{p-1} = 0$ with a Neumann Boundary Condition).

Let Ω be a bounded domain of class $\mathcal{C}^1$ and let $p > 1$ be a real number. Consider the problem associated with

$$\lambda_1 = \inf_{\substack{u \in W^{1,p}(\Omega) \\ \int_{\partial\Omega} |u|^p = 1}} \left\{ \int_\Omega |\nabla u|^p + \int_\Omega |u|^p \right\}.$$

Show that λ_1 is nonnegative and that the infimum is reached. Show that there exists a nonnegative solution and that such a solution satisfies

$$-\Delta_p u + u^{p-1} = 0 \quad \text{in } \Omega$$

and
$$-\sigma \cdot \vec{n} + \lambda_1 u^{p-1} = 0 \quad \text{on } \partial\Omega,$$

with $\sigma \cdot \vec{n} = \partial_n u(|\nabla u|^{p-2})$. Suppose that u is $\mathcal{C}^1$ on $\overline{\Omega}$ and use the strong maximum principle and Hopf principle to show that $u > 0$ on $\overline{\Omega}$.

Hints. The continuity of the trace, namely $\|\gamma_0 u\|_{L^p(\partial\Omega)} \leqslant C\|u\|_{W^{1,p}}$, implies that the infimum is > 0. Moreover, the continuity of γ_0 for the weak topology on $W^{1,p}$ implies that the infimum is reached. Indeed, if $\{u_n\}$ is a minimizing sequence with $\|\gamma_0 u_n\|_{L^p(\partial\Omega)} = 1$, then it is bounded in $W^{1,p}$. By the lower semicontinuity, we can extract a convergent subsequence, giving $u_n \to u$ where u satisfies $\|u\|_{W^{1,p}} \leqslant \lim J(u_n)$. Consider $u + t\varphi$ with, in first instance, $\varphi \in \mathcal{D}(\Omega)$, to conclude that $-\Delta_p u + |u|^{p-2}u = 0$.

In the second instance, when $\varphi \in \mathcal{D}(\overline{\Omega})$, use

$$\left[\frac{d}{dt} \frac{\|\nabla(u + t\varphi)\|_p^p + \|u + t\varphi\|_p^p}{\|\gamma_0(u + t\varphi)\|_{L^p(\partial\Omega)}^p} \right]_{t=0} = 0,$$

which shows that

$$p \int_\Omega t|\nabla u|^{p-2}\nabla u \cdot \nabla\varphi + pt \int_\Omega |u|^{p-2}u\varphi + \int_\Omega |\nabla u|^p + \int_\Omega |u|^p + o(t)$$
$$\geqslant \lambda_1\left(1 + pt \int_{\partial\Omega} |u|^{p-2}u\varphi + o(t)\right).$$

Use Green's formula on the left-hand side, divide by t, and let t tend to 0 to obtain

$$\int_{\partial\Omega} \sigma \cdot \vec{n}\,\varphi\,dx = \lambda_1 \int_{\partial\Omega} |u|^{p-2}u\varphi\,dx.$$

Exercise [*] 5.12 (Variational Problem in $W^{1,p}$ with a Neumann Boundary Condition).

Let Ω be a bounded domain of class $\mathcal{C}^1$ and let f be a function that is continuous on $\partial\Omega$ and admits at least one point where it is positive. We admit that by the continuity of the trace map from $W^{1,p}$ to $L^p(\partial\Omega)$, there exists a constant $c > 0$ such that for $u \in W^{1,p}(\Omega)$ we have

$$\int_\Omega |\nabla u|^p + \int_\Omega |u|^p \geqslant c \int_{\partial\Omega} |u|^p.$$

Let g be a continuous function on $\partial\Omega$ such that $\|g\|_\infty < c$. Finally, let $p < N$ and let $q < (N-1)p/(N-p)$. We consider the problem associated with

$$\inf_{\substack{u \in W^{1,p}(\Omega) \\ \int_{\partial\Omega} f|u|^q = 1}} \left\{ \int_\Omega |\nabla u|^p + \int_\Omega |u|^p + \int_{\partial\Omega} g|u|^p \right\}.$$

(1) Show that this problem admits a solution, and, moreover, that there exist nonnegative solutions.

(2) Show that such a solution satisfies

$$-\Delta_p u + u^{p-1} = 0 \quad \text{in } \Omega$$

and $\qquad\qquad \sigma(u) \cdot \overrightarrow{n} + g u^{p-1} = \lambda_1 f u^{q-1} \quad \text{on } \partial\Omega.$

Use multiplication by a scalar to show that

$$-\Delta_p u + u^{p-1} = 0 \text{ in } \Omega \quad \text{and} \quad \sigma(u) \cdot \overrightarrow{n} + g u^{p-1} = f u^{q-1} \text{ on } \partial\Omega$$

admits a nonnegative solution.

Exercise 5.13 (Nonconvex Variational Problem).

Let Ω be a bounded domain of class $\mathcal{C}^1$ in $\mathbb{R}^N$. Let $p > 1$, $p < N$, let $k < p$, let $q < p^* = Np/(N-p)$, and let $f \in L^{p'}(\Omega)$. We consider the variational problem associated with

$$\inf_{u \in W_0^{1,p}(\Omega)} \left\{ \frac{1}{p} \int_\Omega |\nabla u|^p - \left(\int_\Omega |u|^q \right)^{k/q} - \int_\Omega fu \right\}.$$

(1) Prove that the infimum is finite. After taking a minimizing sequence and showing that it is bounded, extract a subsequence to deduce the existence of a u that realizes the minimum.

(2) Give the differential equation verified by a solution u. Is it unique?

Exercise [*] 5.14 (Variational Problem and Best Constant for a Critical Sobolev Embedding).
We admit that if $p < N$, then there exists a best constant for the critical Sobolev embedding on $\mathbb{R}^N$,

$$K(N,p)^p = \inf_{\substack{u \in W^{1,p}(\mathbb{R}^N) \\ |u|_{p^*} = 1}} \int_{\mathbb{R}^N} |\nabla u|^p,$$

and that this constant is reached for functions of the form $u(x) = (\lambda^p + r^p)^{(p-N)/p}$. Let Ω be a bounded domain of class $\mathcal{C}^1$. We consider a continuous function a such that $a(x) > -\lambda_1$, where λ_1 is the first eigenvalue of the p-Laplacian on Ω. Let f be a non-identically zero nonnegative continuous function that reaches its supremum inside Ω.

We consider the problem associated with

$$\inf_{\substack{u \in W_0^{1,p}(\Omega) \\ \int_\Omega f|u|^{p^*} = 1}} \left\{ \int_\Omega |\nabla u|^p + \int_\Omega a|u|^p \right\}.$$

Use a point x_0 where f reaches it supremum and a function of the form

$$u_\varepsilon(x) = \left(1 + \left| \frac{x - x_0}{\varepsilon} \right|^{p/(p-1)} \right)^{(p-N)/p} \varphi(x),$$

where φ has compact support and equals 1 in a neighborhood of x_0, to show that we have

$$\inf_{\substack{u \in W_0^{1,p}(\Omega) \\ \int_\Omega f|u|^{p^*} = 1}} \left\{ \int_\Omega |\nabla u|^p + \int_\Omega a|u|^p \right\} \leqslant \|f\|_\infty^{-p/p^*} K(N,p)^p.$$

Exercise [*] 5.15 (Extrema for Sobolev Embeddings in $H^1(\mathbb{R}^N)$).
Consider the equation

$$-\Delta u = \mu u^{2^* - 1}$$

on $\mathbb{R}^N$, where u is nonnegative, $N \geqslant 5$, $2^* = 2N/(N-2)$ is the critical Sobolev exponent, and $\mu > 0$ is given.

(1) Show that if there exists a nontrivial solution, then $\mu > 0$. Determine how we can pass from a solution of the equation with $\mu = 1$ to a solution with arbitrary μ.

(2) Let $r^2 = \sum_i x_i^2$ and let

$$u(r) = (\lambda^2 + r^2)^{1-N/2}$$

for $\lambda \neq 0$ in $\mathbb{R}$. Show that u is a solution of the equation (first verify that $u \in H^1(\mathbb{R}^N)$) by choosing λ as a function of μ.

Exercise 5.16 (Extrema for Critical Sobolev Embeddings in $W^{1,p}(\mathbb{R}^N)$, Generalization).
Consider the equation

$$-\Delta_p u = \mu u^{p^*-1}$$

on $\mathbb{R}^N$, where u is nonnegative, $N \geqslant p^2$, $p^* = pN/(N-p)$ is the critical exponent for the Sobolev embedding of $W^{1,p}$ into L^q, and $\mu > 0$ is given.

(1) Show that if there exists a nontrivial solution, then $\mu > 0$. Determine how we can pass from a solution of the equation with $\mu = 1$ to a solution with arbitrary μ.

(2) Show that the p-Laplacian for a radial function can be written as

$$\Delta_p(u(r)) = \frac{1}{r^{N-1}} \partial_r \left(r^{N-1} |u'|^{p-2} u' \right).$$

(3) Show that the functions

$$u(r) = \left(\lambda^{p/(p-1)} + r^{p/(p-1)} \right)^{1-N/p}$$

belong to $W^{1,p}(\mathbb{R}^N)$ and are solutions of the equation (give λ explicitly as a function of μ).

Exercise 5.17 (Using the Pohozaev Identity).
Consider the equation

$$-\Delta u = u^{2^*-1}, \quad u = 0 \text{ on } \partial B$$

in a Euclidean ball in $\mathbb{R}^N$, where u is nonnegative and not identically zero. We wish to prove that no solution of class $\mathcal{C}^2$ exists with these properties. Recall that if u is not identically zero, then $\partial u/\partial n > 0$ on ∂B.

(1) Multiply by u and integrate over B to find a first energy identity.
(2) Multiply by $x \cdot \nabla u$ and integrate by parts several times to obtain the identity

$$\int_{\partial B} x \cdot \vec{n} \left(\frac{\partial u}{\partial n} \right)^2 = 0.$$

Conclude using the Hopf principle.

Exercise [∗] 5.18 (Existence of Solutions Using Supersolutions and Subsolutions).
Let Ω be a bounded domain of class $\mathcal{C}^1$ in $\mathbb{R}^N$. Let $p > 1$ and let $\overline{u}$ and $\underline{u}$ be two bounded functions in $W_0^{1,p}(\Omega)$ with $0 \leqslant \underline{u} \leqslant \overline{u}$ in Ω. Let f be a nonnegative function in L^∞ and let $q \geqslant 1$. We suppose that

$$-\Delta_p \overline{u} \geqslant f\overline{u}^q \quad \text{and} \quad -\Delta_p \underline{u} \leqslant f\underline{u}^q.$$

Show that there exists a function u in $W_0^{1,p}(\Omega)$ with $\underline{u} \leqslant u \leqslant \overline{u}$ that is a solution of $-\Delta_p u = fu^q$.

Hints. Use induction to construct a sequence $\{u^{(k)}\}$. Start with $\underline{u}$. The function $u^{(k)}$ is then defined by

$$u^{(k)} \in W_0^{1,p}(\Omega) \quad \text{is a solution of } -\Delta_p u^{(k)} = f(u^{(k-1)})^q.$$

The maximum principle and comparison theorem imply the following properties: $u^{(k)} \geqslant 0$, $\{u^{(k)}\}$ is increasing, and $\underline{u} \leqslant u^{(k)} \leqslant \overline{u}$. Deduce from this that $\{u^{(k)}\}$ converges to u. Note that it also converges weakly in $W^{1,p}$ because

$$\int_\Omega |\nabla u^{(k)}|^p dx = \int_\Omega f(x)(u^{(k-1)})^q(x)u^{(k)}(x)dx \leqslant \|f\|_\infty \big(\sup_{\overline{\Omega}} \overline{u}\big)^{q+1}.$$

Extract a weakly converging subsequence in $W^{1,p}$ to show that $|\nabla u^{(k)}|^{p-2}\nabla u^{(k)} = \sigma^{(k)}$ admits a weak limit σ up to a subsequence. Taking the limit in

$$-\operatorname{div}\sigma^{(k)} = (u^{(k-1)})^q f,$$

then gives

$$-\operatorname{div}\sigma = u^q f.$$

We wish to show that $\sigma = |\nabla u|^{p-2}\nabla u$. To do this, prove the convergence $\int_\Omega |\nabla u^{(k)}|^p dx \to \int_\Omega |\nabla u|^p dx$, which implies the strong convergence in $W^{1,p}$ because $p > 1$. Consequently, by extracting a subsequence, we obtain $\nabla u^{(k)} \to \nabla u$ almost everywhere.

To prove the desired result note that, by the dominated convergence theorem and the pointwise convergence of the sequence $\{u^{(k)}\}$, we have

$$\int_\Omega f(x)(u^{(k-1)}(x))^q u^{(k)}(x)dx \longrightarrow \int_\Omega u^{q+1}(x)f(x)dx,$$

whence

$$\int_\Omega \sigma^{(k)} \cdot \nabla u^{(k)} \longrightarrow \int_\Omega u^{q+1}(x)f(x)dx \quad \text{and} \quad \int_\Omega \sigma \cdot \nabla u = \int_\Omega u^{q+1}(x)f(x)dx.$$

Consequently,

$$\overline{\lim} \int_\Omega |\nabla u^{(k)}|^p dx = \int_\Omega \sigma \cdot \nabla u \, dx \leqslant \underline{\lim} \|\nabla u^{(k)}\|_p^{p-1}\|\nabla u\|_p$$

$$\leqslant \overline{\lim}\Big(\int_\Omega |\nabla u^{(k)}(x)|^p dx\Big)^{1-1/p}\|\nabla u\|_p.$$

Dividing by $\overline{\lim}\int_\Omega |\nabla u^{(k)}|^p dx$ leads to the inequality

$$\Big(\overline{\lim}\int_\Omega |\nabla u^{(k)}(x)|^p dx\Big)^p \leqslant (\|\nabla u\|_p)^p,$$

which implies the result since by the lower semicontinuity for the weak topology in L^p, we already have $\|\nabla u\|_p \leqslant \underline{\lim} \int_\Omega |\nabla u^{(k)}(x)|^p dx$.

6

Distributions with Measures as Derivatives

In this chapter, we study the properties of function spaces that present strong analogies to Sobolev spaces, namely spaces of functions with certain derivatives belonging to either $L^1(\Omega)$ or to the space $M^1(\Omega)$ of bounded measures on an open subset Ω of $\mathbb{R}^N$. The properties of Sobolev spaces extend to most of these spaces, but not all. For example, the space $BV(\Omega)$ of functions in $L^1(\Omega)$ with derivatives in $M^1(\Omega)$ is embedded in all of the $L^p(\Omega)$ with $p \leqslant N/(N-1)$. Moreover, for $p < N/(N-1)$, the embeddings are compact when Ω is bounded.

In Chapter 3, we showed that the functions of $W^{1,1}(\Omega)$ have a *trace* on every regular hypersurface Σ inside Ω as well as a "boundary value". Both are obtained by taking a limit. The *trace* belongs to $L^1(\Sigma)$, while the boundary value belongs to $L^1(\partial\Omega)$. In this chapter, we will show that this property partially extends to functions in $BV(\Omega)$, with the exception that, as in dimension 1, a function in BV has limits on both sides of the hypersurface Σ inside Ω and that these limits may be distinct. When we consider the trace of a function in BV on the boundary $\partial\Omega$, there is no ambiguity because Ω is of class $\mathcal{C}^1$ and therefore locally only lies on one side of its boundary.

To better understand this phenomenon, the reader can consider the Heaviside step function H on $]-1,1[$. When defined as in this book, the trace of $H \in BV(]-1,1[)$ at 0 is 0 on the left and 1 on the right.

We will see in this chapter that the existence of certain embeddings and the compactness of $W^{1,1}(\Omega)$ in larger Sobolev spaces extend to the space $BV(\Omega)$.

F. Demengel, G. Demengel, *Functional Spaces for the Theory of Elliptic Partial Differential Equations*, Universitext, DOI 10.1007/978-1-4471-2807-6_6,
© Springer-Verlag London Limited 2012

6.1 Results on Measures, Convergence

6.1.1 General Results on Measures

Let Ω be an open subset of $\mathbb{R}^N$, where $N \geqslant 2$.

Definition 6.1. A complex measure on Ω is a complex distribution that extends to a continuous linear functional on the space $\mathcal{C}_c(\Omega, \mathbb{C})$. The measure spaces, which we denote by $M(\Omega)$, can therefore be identified with the dual of $\mathcal{C}_c(\Omega, \mathbb{C})$. It follows that to every compact subset K of Ω, we can associate a constant C_K such that

$$\forall \varphi \in \mathcal{C}_c(\Omega, \mathbb{C}), \quad \operatorname{supp} \varphi \subset K \implies |\langle \mu, \varphi \rangle| \leqslant C_K \|\varphi\|_\infty.$$

Definition 6.2. The constant C_K does not necessarily depend on the compact subset K of Ω. When it does not, we call the measure μ *bounded* on Ω. In this case, there exists a constant C such that

$$\forall \varphi \in \mathcal{C}_c(\Omega), \quad |\langle \mu, \varphi \rangle| \leqslant C \|\varphi\|_\infty.$$

We denote the vector space of bounded measures on Ω by $M^1(\Omega)$.

Definition 6.3. Let μ be a measure on Ω. The conjugate measure, denoted by $\overline{\mu}$, is the linear functional on $\mathcal{C}_c(\Omega, \mathbb{C})$ defined by

$$\langle \overline{\mu}, \varphi \rangle = \overline{\langle \mu, \overline{\varphi} \rangle}.$$

Definition 6.4. A measure μ on Ω is called real if

$$\forall \varphi \in \mathcal{C}_c(\Omega, \mathbb{R}), \quad \langle \mu, \varphi \rangle \in \mathbb{R}.$$

This corresponds to saying that $\mu = \overline{\mu}$.

Definition 6.5. A real measure μ on Ω is called positive if

$$\forall \varphi \in \mathcal{C}_c(\Omega, \mathbb{R}), \quad \varphi \geqslant 0 \implies \langle \mu, \varphi \rangle \geqslant 0.$$

Proposition 6.6. *A nonnegative distribution on Ω can be extended to a positive measure on Ω.*

Proof of Proposition 6.6.

Recall that a nonnegative distribution is one that satisfies

$$\forall \varphi \in \mathcal{D}(\Omega), \quad \varphi \geqslant 0 \implies \langle T, \varphi \rangle \geqslant 0.$$

Let K be a compact subset of Ω and let Ω_1 be an open subset of K with $K_1 = \overline{\Omega_1}$. Let ψ be a function in $\mathcal{D}(\Omega)$ with $\psi = 1$ on K. If $\varphi \in \mathcal{D}(\Omega)$ has compact support in K, then $|\varphi|_\infty \psi \pm \varphi$ is a nonnegative function and therefore

$$\langle T, \varphi \rangle \leqslant \|\varphi\|_\infty \langle T, \psi \rangle$$

and

$$-\langle T, \varphi \rangle \leqslant \|\varphi\|_\infty \langle T, \psi \rangle.$$

In particular, for $\varphi \in \mathcal{C}_c(\Omega)$ with support in K_1, let $\{\varphi_n\} \subset \mathcal{D}(\Omega)$ be a sequence with support in K that converges uniformly to φ in K_1. The sequence $\langle T, \varphi_n \rangle$ is then a Cauchy sequence by the inequality above; it converges to a real number that we will denote by $\langle T, \varphi \rangle$. We leave it to the reader to verify that this constant does not depend on the chosen sequence φ_n and that the resulting extension of T to the continuous functions with compact support is linear and continuous. □

6.1.2 Absolute Value of a Measure, Bounded Measure

Proposition 6.7. *If μ is a measure with real or complex values, then we can define its absolute value, denoted by $|\mu|$, as the map with real values such that*

$$\forall \psi \in \mathcal{C}_c(\Omega, \mathbb{R}), \ \psi \geqslant 0, \quad \langle |\mu|, \psi \rangle = \sup_{\substack{\varphi \in \mathcal{C}_c(\Omega, \mathbb{C}) \\ |\varphi| \leqslant \psi}} \{|\langle \mu, \varphi \rangle|\}.$$

The map $|\mu|$ is the restriction of a positive measure to the functions in $\mathcal{C}_c(\Omega, \mathbb{R}^+)$. It is bounded if μ is a bounded measure.

The proof of this proposition is left to the reader, who may also consult [22].

Proposition 6.8 (and Definition). *Let μ be a positive bounded measure on Ω. We define its total variation, denoted by $|\mu|_\Omega$ or $\int_\Omega \mu$, to be*

$$|\mu|_\Omega = \sup_{\substack{\varphi \in \mathcal{C}_c(\Omega) \\ 0 \leqslant \varphi \leqslant 1}} \langle \mu, \varphi \rangle.$$

(1) *If $\{\psi_n\}$ is an increasing sequence of functions with compact support, values in $[0,1]$, and value 1 on*

$$K_n = \{x \in \Omega \mid d(x, \partial\Omega) \geqslant 1/n\},$$

then the sequence $\{\langle \mu, \psi_n \rangle\}$ converges to $|\mu|_\Omega$, which we also denote by $\langle \mu, 1_\Omega \rangle$.

(2) *Moreover, for every $\varepsilon > 0$, there exists an N_0 such that if $n \geqslant N_0$, then*

$$\langle \mu, 1_{\Omega \smallsetminus K_n} \rangle < \varepsilon.$$

Proof of Proposition 6.8.

(1) The sequence $\{\langle \mu, \psi_n \rangle\}$ is nondecreasing and bounded from above by $|\mu|_\Omega$. It follows that it converges and

$$\lim_{n \to +\infty} \langle \mu, \psi_n \rangle \leqslant |\mu|_\Omega.$$

Let $\varepsilon > 0$ and let $\varphi \in \mathcal{C}_c(\Omega)$ with $0 \leqslant \varphi \leqslant 1$ and $\langle \mu, \varphi \rangle > |\mu|_\Omega - \varepsilon$. Let K be the compact support of φ. Then for sufficiently large n, $K \subset K_n$ and $\langle \mu, \varphi \rangle \leqslant \langle \mu, \psi_n \rangle$ because $\psi_n = 1$ on K_n.
By taking the limit, we deduce that $\lim_{n \to +\infty} \langle \mu, \psi_n \rangle \geqslant |\mu|_\Omega - \varepsilon$, which implies the result since ε is arbitrary.

(2) Let $\{\varphi_n\}$ be a sequence of functions in $\mathcal{D}(\mathbb{R}^N)$ equal to 1 on K_n that converge to 1_Ω. Let N_0 be sufficiently large that for $n \geqslant N_0$, we have $\langle \mu, \varphi_n - \varphi_{N_0} \rangle \leqslant \varepsilon$. Let φ be a function with values between 0 and 1 and with compact support in $\Omega \smallsetminus K_{N_0}$. Let $n > N_0$ be sufficiently large that $\text{supp } \varphi \subset K_n$. We then have $\varphi = \varphi(\varphi_n - \varphi_{N_0})$, whence

$$\langle \mu, \varphi \rangle \leqslant \varepsilon.$$

By taking the supremum among all such φ, it follows that $\langle \mu, 1_{\Omega \smallsetminus K_{N_0}} \rangle \leqslant \varepsilon$, concluding the proof. $\qquad \square$

Proposition 6.9. *Let μ be a positive bounded measure on Ω. Let $\varphi \in \mathcal{C}_b(\Omega)$ be nonnegative. Let $\{\psi_n\}$ be a nondecreasing sequence in $\mathcal{C}_c(\Omega)$ with $0 \leqslant \psi_n \leqslant 1$ that converges to 1. Then $\langle \mu, \psi_n \varphi \rangle$ converges to a nonnegative real number that we denote by $\langle \mu, \varphi \rangle$.*

Proof of Proposition 6.9.

The sequence $\langle \mu, \psi_n \varphi \rangle$ is nondecreasing and bounded by $C\|\varphi\|_\infty$. It therefore converges. We let $\langle \mu, \varphi \rangle$ denote the limit, which we can show to be independent of the sequence ψ_n. $\qquad \square$

Definition 6.10. For $\varphi \in \mathcal{C}_b(\Omega, \mathbb{R})$ and μ a positive measure in $M^1(\Omega)$, we set

$$\langle \mu, \varphi \rangle = \langle \mu, \varphi_1 - \varphi_2 \rangle,$$

where $\varphi_1 - \varphi_2$ is a decomposition of φ as the difference of two bounded continuous functions with nonnegative values.

We can verify that this definition does not depend on the choice of the two nonnegative functions. In particular, we will often use the positive and negative parts φ^+ and φ^- of φ for φ_1 and φ_2, respectively.

Definition 6.11. If μ is a complex measure, then we can define its real and imaginary parts as follows:

$$\Re(\mu) = \frac{\mu + \overline{\mu}}{2}, \quad \Im(\mu) = \frac{\mu - \overline{\mu}}{2i}.$$

If the measure μ is real, then we can define its positive and negative parts as follows:

$$\mu^+ = \frac{\mu + |\mu|}{2}, \quad \mu^- = \frac{|\mu| - \mu}{2}.$$

Definition 6.12. If μ is a real bounded measure, not necessarily positive, then we extend μ to the functions in $\mathcal{C}_b(\Omega)$ by setting

$$\langle \mu, \varphi \rangle = \langle \mu^+, \varphi \rangle - \langle \mu^-, \varphi \rangle.$$

We can furthermore extend the definition of μ with complex values to bounded continuous functions φ with complex values by using the real and imaginary parts.

Definition 6.13. Let $\overrightarrow{\mu} = (\mu_1, \mu_2, \ldots, \mu_N) \in M(\Omega, \mathbb{C}^N)$ be a vector-valued measure. We define the functional $|\overrightarrow{\mu}|$ by setting

$$\forall \psi \in \mathcal{C}_c(\Omega), \psi \geqslant 0, \quad \langle |\overrightarrow{\mu}|, \psi \rangle = \sup_{\substack{\overrightarrow{\phi} \in \mathcal{C}_c(\Omega, \mathbb{C}^N) \\ \sum_1^N |\varphi_i|^2 \leqslant \psi^2}} |\langle \overrightarrow{\mu}, \overrightarrow{\phi} \rangle|,$$

where $\langle \overrightarrow{\mu}, \overrightarrow{\phi} \rangle = \sum_1^N \mu_i \varphi_i$.

We then show that $|\overrightarrow{\mu}|$ is the restriction of a positive measure on Ω to $\mathcal{C}_c(\Omega, \mathbb{R}^+)$ (cf. [22]).

6.1.3 Vague and Tight Convergence

Definition 6.14. We say that a sequence of measures $\mu_n \in M(\Omega)$ converges vaguely to $\mu \in M(\Omega)$ if for every $\varphi \in \mathcal{C}_c(\Omega)$, we have

$$|\langle \mu_n - \mu, \varphi \rangle| \longrightarrow 0.$$

Proposition 6.15. *If $\{\mu_n\}$ is a sequence of measures that converges vaguely to a measure μ, then we have the following inequality in $\mathbb{R} \cup +\infty$:*

$$\int_\Omega |\mu| \leqslant \varliminf_{n \to +\infty} \int_\Omega |\mu_n|.$$

Proof of Proposition 6.15.

The inequality is trivial if $\varliminf_{n \to +\infty} \int_\Omega |\mu_n| = +\infty$.

Let us therefore assume that this limit is finite and consider a suitable subsequence $\{\sigma(n)\}$ with $\varliminf \int_\Omega |\mu_n| = \lim \int_\Omega |\mu_{\sigma(n)}|$. Note that in this case, for every $\varphi \in \mathcal{C}_c(\Omega)$ satisfying $|\varphi| \leqslant 1$, we have

$$|\langle \mu, \varphi \rangle| = |\lim \langle \mu_{\sigma(n)}, \varphi \rangle| \leqslant \varliminf \int_\Omega |\mu_n|,$$

which implies that the measure μ is bounded. Let $\varepsilon > 0$ and let $\varphi \in \mathcal{C}_c(\Omega)$ satisfy $|\varphi| \leqslant 1$ and $\int_\Omega |\mu| \leqslant \int_\Omega \mu\varphi + \varepsilon$. Let N_0 satisfy

$$\forall n \geqslant N_0, \quad \left| \int_\Omega (\mu_n - \mu)\varphi \right| \leqslant \varepsilon.$$

Then, for every $n \geqslant N_0$, we have

$$\int_\Omega |\mu| \leqslant \int_\Omega \mu\varphi + \varepsilon \leqslant \varliminf \int_\Omega \mu_n\varphi + 2\varepsilon \leqslant \varliminf \int_\Omega |\mu_n| + 2\varepsilon. \qquad \square$$

Remark 6.16. Note that if $\mu_n \geqslant 0$ converges vaguely to μ, then we do not necessarily have $\int_\Omega \mu_n \to \int_\Omega \mu$. Indeed, the sequence in $B(0,1)$ defined by $\mu_n = n(\chi_{B(0,1)} - \chi_{B(0,1-1/n)})$ converges vaguely to 0 in $B(0,1)$ while for every n, the total variation is equal to the volume ω_{N-1} of the unit ball in $\mathbb{R}^N$.

Definition 6.17. We say that a sequence of bounded measures $\mu_n \in M^1(\Omega)$ converges tightly to $\mu \in M^1(\Omega)$ if

$$\forall \varphi \in \mathcal{C}_b(\Omega), \quad |\langle \mu_n - \mu, \varphi \rangle| \longrightarrow 0.$$

Proposition 6.18. *If $\{\mu_n\}$ is a sequence of bounded positive measures that converges vaguely to μ in $M^1(\Omega)$, then the following statements are equivalent:*

(1) *The sequence $\{\mu_n\}$ converges tightly to μ.*
(2) $\int_\Omega \mu_n \to \int_\Omega \mu$.
(3) *For every $\varepsilon > 0$, there exists a compact subset K of Ω such that*

$$\int_{\Omega \setminus K} \mu_n \leqslant \varepsilon.$$

Remark 6.19. It is clear that if the sequence $\{\mu_n\}$ of bounded measures converges vaguely to μ, then this sequence cannot converge tightly to a measure other than μ.

Proof of Proposition 6.18.

We will show that (1) implies (2), which in turn implies (1).

Since μ_n is positive, we use the bounded continuous function 1_Ω in statement (1). We then have

$$\int_\Omega \mu_n \longrightarrow \int_\Omega \mu.$$

Let K_1 be a compact set such that $\int_{\Omega \setminus K_1} \mu \leqslant \varepsilon$ and let Ω_1 be an open set with compact closure $K = \overline{\Omega_1}$ containing K_1. Let φ have compact support in Ω_1 and be equal to 1 on K_1 with, moreover,

$$\int_{\Omega \setminus K_1} \mu \leqslant \langle \mu, (1 - \varphi) \rangle + \varepsilon.$$

Every continuous function with compact support in $\Omega \setminus K$ and values between 0 and 1 is lesser than $1 - \varphi$. It follows that

$$\overline{\lim} \int_{\Omega \setminus K} \mu_n \leqslant \overline{\lim} \langle \mu_n, 1 - \varphi \rangle = \overline{\lim} \int_\Omega \mu_n - \lim \langle \mu_n, \varphi \rangle$$

$$= \int_\Omega \mu - \langle \mu, \varphi \rangle \leqslant 2\varepsilon.$$

The result follows.

Let us now show that (2) implies (1). Let $\varphi \in \mathcal{C}_b(\Omega)$ and, given $\varepsilon > 0$, let K be a compact set such that for every n, $\int_{\Omega \setminus K} \mu_n \leqslant \varepsilon$. Let $\psi \in \mathcal{C}_c(\Omega)$ equal 1 on K and have values between 0 and 1, and let N_0 be sufficiently large that the vague convergence of $\{\mu_n\}$ to μ implies that $|\langle \mu_n - \mu, \varphi \psi \rangle| \leqslant \varepsilon$. We then have

$$|\langle \mu_n - \mu, \varphi \rangle| \leqslant |\langle \mu_n - \mu, \varphi \psi \rangle| + \|\varphi\|_\infty \int_{\Omega - K} (\mu + \mu_n) \leqslant \varepsilon(1 + 2\|\varphi\|_\infty). \qquad \square$$

Proposition 6.20. *Let $\{\mu_n\}$ be a sequence of bounded measures such that there exists a constant C with $\int_\Omega |\mu_n| \leqslant C$. We can then extract a subsequence of measures from $\{\mu_n\}$ that converges vaguely to a bounded measure.*

Proof of Proposition 6.20.

This is obvious because the unit ball of the dual of the separable normed space $\mathcal{C}_c(\Omega)$ is relatively weak-star sequentially compact. $\qquad \square$

Proposition 6.21. *Let $\mu \in M^1(\Omega)$. There exists a sequence $\{u_n\}$ in $\mathcal{C}_c^\infty(\Omega)$ such that*

$$\int_\Omega |u_n| \longrightarrow \int_\Omega |\mu|.$$

Proof of Proposition 6.21.

Let $\varepsilon > 0$, let K be a compact subset of Ω such that $\int_{\Omega \smallsetminus K} |\mu| \leqslant \varepsilon$, and let φ be a function in $\mathcal{C}_c(\Omega)$ with $0 \leqslant \varphi \leqslant 1$ and $\varphi = 1$ on K. Let N_0 be sufficiently large that $1/N_0 < d(K, \partial\Omega)$, and let ρ be an even regularizing function. Then for $n \geqslant N_0$, the sequence $\{\rho_{1/n} \star (\varphi\mu)\}$ converges tightly to $\varphi\mu$, as does its absolute value. Indeed, let us first show that this sequence converges vaguely to $\varphi\mu$. Let $\psi \in \mathcal{C}_c(\Omega)$. For n sufficiently large, the uniform continuity of ψ gives

$$\|\rho_{1/n} \star \psi - \psi\|_\infty \leqslant \frac{\varepsilon}{\int_\Omega |\mu|}.$$

We note that the measure $\varphi\mu$ has compact support in Ω. For n sufficiently large, we use the definition of the convolution of two distributions $\varphi\mu$ and $[\rho_{1/n}]$ with compact support in Ω and the fact that this convolution is a distribution of order $\leqslant 0$, which allows us to apply this convolution to the function ψ. Therefore, since ρ is an even function, we have

$$\int_\Omega \big(\rho_{1/n} \star (\varphi\mu)\big)\psi \, dx = \big\langle (\varphi\mu)_x \otimes (\rho_{1/n})_y, \psi(x+y) \big\rangle$$

$$= \big\langle (\varphi\mu), \rho_{1/n} \star \psi \big\rangle.$$

Moreover, since

$$|\langle \varphi\mu, \rho_{1/n} \star \psi - \psi \rangle| \leqslant \left(\int_\Omega |\mu| \right) \|\rho_{1/n} \star \psi - \psi\|_\infty \leqslant \varepsilon,$$

the previous equality implies that

$$\int_\Omega \big(\rho_{1/n} \star (\varphi\mu)(x)\big)\psi(x) \, dx \longrightarrow \langle \varphi\mu, \psi \rangle.$$

In particular, by Proposition 6.15, it follows that $\int_\Omega |\varphi\mu| \leqslant \varliminf \int_\Omega |\rho_{1/n} \star (\varphi\mu)|$.

Let us now show that $\int_\Omega |\rho_{1/n} \star (\varphi\mu)| \leqslant \int_\Omega |\mu|$. Indeed, since the distribution $\varphi\mu$ has compact support, we see that the convolution on the left-hand side is a function with compact support that can be written as

$$(6.22) \qquad \big(\rho_{1/n} \star (\varphi\mu)\big)(x) = \langle \varphi\mu, \rho_{1/n}(x - \cdot) \rangle.$$

Since the integral of $\rho_{1/n}$ over $\mathbb{R}^N$ is 1, we have

$$\left\langle |\varphi\mu|, \int_{\mathbb{R}^N} \rho_{1/n}(x - \cdot)dx \right\rangle = \int_\Omega |\varphi\mu|.$$

By the definition of the absolute value of a measure and Fubini's formula, integrating equality (6.22) with respect to x over $\mathbb{R}^N$ gives

$$\int_{\mathbb{R}^N} |\rho_{1/n} \star (\varphi\mu)|dx \leqslant \left\langle |\varphi\mu|, \int_{\mathbb{R}^N} \rho_{1/n}(x - \cdot)dx \right\rangle \leqslant \int_\Omega |\varphi\mu|,$$

which implies the result because of the vague convergence and Proposition 6.18 (the equivalence (1) $\Leftrightarrow$ (2)). $\qquad\qquad\square$

6.2 Extension of a Positive Measure

The notions that we introduce in this section are meant to help understand the properties of bounded measures related to absolute continuity and singularity with respect to the Lebesgue measure.

For most of the definitions and properties that we set out we give only a short proof. For example, our presentation of the theory of the integration of arbitrary functions with respect to a positive measure is very concise. We do not state Lebesgue's theorems and say only a few words about μ-measurability and μ-integrability.

We will frequently invoke the Lebesgue–Radon–Nikodym theorem, which we state and prove succinctly. Readers interested in more details can consult references dealing with the theory of Radon measures, in particular [8] and [29].

Below, Ω is an open subset of $\mathbb{R}^N$ and μ is a positive measure.

6.2.1 Extension to l.s.c. and u.s.c. Functions

When μ is a positive measure, we can extend its definition to a class of functions larger than that of the continuous functions. We will assume known the definitions of lower semicontinuous functions (denoted by the symbol *s.c.i.*) and of upper semicontinuous functions (*u.s.c.*). We admit that any function f with positive values that are either finite or not is the upper envelope for the relation $\leqslant$ of the functions $\varphi \in \mathcal{C}_c^+(\Omega)$ with $\varphi \leqslant f$. We let $\mathcal{I}(\Omega)$ denote the set of l.s.c. functions on Ω that are bounded from below by a function in $\mathcal{C}_c(\Omega)$. This set contains the nonnegative l.s.c. functions. Likewise, we let $\mathcal{I}'(\Omega)$ denote the set of u.s.c. functions on Ω that are bounded from above by a function in $\mathcal{C}_c(\Omega)$.

Definition 6.23. Let $f \in \mathcal{I}(\Omega)$ and let μ be a positive measure on Ω. We define the extension μ^* of the measure μ to the function f to be

$$\langle \mu^*, f \rangle = \sup_{\substack{\varphi \in \mathcal{C}_c(\Omega) \\ \varphi \leqslant f}} \langle \mu, \varphi \rangle.$$

When this supremum is finite, we say that the function f is μ-integrable.

For $f \in \mathcal{I}'(\Omega)$, we can also define

$$\langle \mu_\star, f \rangle = \inf_{\substack{\varphi \in \mathcal{C}_c(\Omega) \\ f \leqslant \varphi}} \langle \mu, \varphi \rangle.$$

The sum $f_1 + f_2$ of the two functions in $\mathcal{I}$ is well defined since these do not take on the value $-\infty$; we have $f_1 + f_2 \in \mathcal{I}$. We admit the following additivity property.

Proposition 6.24. *For two functions f_1 and f_2 in $\mathcal{I}$, we have*

$$\mu^*(f_1 + f_2) = \mu^*(f_1) + \mu^*(f_2).$$

6.2.2 Extension to Arbitrary Functions and to Subsets of Ω

Results on μ-integrability. From the above, we deduce the notion of integrability for functions h on Ω with values in $\overline{\mathbb{R}}$. Since there exist functions f in $\mathcal{I}$ with $f \geqslant h$, for example $f = +\infty$, we can also extend μ, which we assume to be positive, in order to obtain the upper and lower integrals of h.

Definition 6.25. For an arbitrary function h on Ω, we set

$$\langle \mu^*, h \rangle = \inf_{\substack{f \in \mathcal{I} \\ f \geqslant h}} \langle \mu^*, f \rangle \quad \text{and} \quad \langle \mu_\star, h \rangle = \sup_{\substack{f \in \mathcal{I}' \\ f \leqslant h}} \langle \mu_\star, f \rangle.$$

We have $\mu_\star(h) = -\mu^*(-h)$ and $\mu_\star(h) \leqslant \mu^*(h)$. We say that h is μ-integrable if $\mu_\star(h) = \mu^*(h)$, where the common value of both sides is finite. We denote this value by $\mu(h)$.

One can show the following characterization of μ-integrability.

Proposition 6.26. *A function h is μ-integrable if and only for every $\varepsilon > 0$, there exist $f \in \mathcal{I}$ and $g \in \mathcal{I}'$ with $g \leqslant h \leqslant f$ satisfying $\mu^*(f - g) \leqslant \varepsilon$.*

Proposition 6.27. *If f is μ-integrable, then the same holds for f^+, f^-, and $|f|$, and we have $|\mu(f)| \leqslant \mu(|f|)$. If f and g are μ-integrable, then the same holds for $f + g$, $\sup(f, g)$, and $\inf(f, g)$.*

We extend the measure μ to subsets A of Ω by introducing the characteristic functions χ_A.

Definition 6.28. Let K be a compact subset of Ω; then $\chi_K \in \mathcal{I}'$, which justifies the decision to define the measure of K to be the real number $\mu_\star(\chi_K)$, that is,

$$\mu_\star(K) = \inf_{\substack{\varphi = 1 \text{ on } K \\ 0 \leqslant \varphi \leqslant 1 \\ \varphi \in \mathcal{C}_c(\Omega)}} \langle \mu, \varphi \rangle.$$

Let O be an open subset of Ω; then χ_O belongs to $\mathcal{I}$ and we set

$$\mu^*(O) = \sup_{\substack{\varphi \in \mathcal{C}_c^+(\Omega) \\ \varphi \leqslant 1 \text{ on } \Omega}} \langle \mu, \varphi \rangle.$$

Every compact subset K of Ω is μ-integrable. Every open subset O of Ω is μ-integrable provided that $\mu^*(O)$ is finite. This holds, for example, for every relatively compact open subset.

Definition 6.29. We say that a subset E of Ω is μ-integrable if for every $\varepsilon > 0$, there exist an open subset O of Ω and a compact subset K with $K \subset E \subset O$, such that

$$\mu^*(O) - \mu_\star(K) \leqslant \varepsilon.$$

It is clear that E is μ-integrable if and only if its characteristic function is μ-integrable. This corresponds to saying that the numbers $\mu^*(E)$ and $\mu_\star(E)$ are finite and equal. We denote their common value by $\mu(E)$ and call it the measure of E.

If A and B are two μ-integrable sets, then we can show that the sets $A \cup B$, $A \cap B$, and $A \cap (\Omega \smallsetminus B)$ are all μ-integrable. In particular, both compact sets and finite intersections of a compact set with open sets are universally integrable, that is, integrable for every positive measure μ.

Definition of μ-measure 0.

Definition 6.30. A set A is said to be of μ-measure 0 if $\mu^*(A) = 0$. We admit that if this is the case, then A is μ-integrable so that the condition becomes $\mu(A) = 0$.

A function f is said to be of $|\mu|$-measure 0 if $\mu^*(|f|) = 0$.

If two functions f and g are equal outside of a set of measure 0, then we call them μ-equivalent and we have $\mu^*(f) = \mu^*(g)$. By defining the associated equivalence classes, this notion leads to the definitions of the vector spaces $L^p(\Omega, \mu)$.

Properties of μ-measurability and μ-integrability.

Definition 6.31. A function f on Ω is μ-measurable if there exist a set N of μ-measure 0 and a partition of $\Omega \smallsetminus N$ in the form of a sequence of compact subsets K_n such that for every n, the restriction of f to K_n is continuous. A subset A of Ω is μ-measurable if its characteristic function is.

We can show that a μ-integrable subset is μ-measurable. The converse is false, but we do have the following result.

Proposition 6.32. *A set A is μ-measurable if and only if for every compact set K, the set $A \cap K$ is μ-integrable. A function f from Ω to $\overline{\mathbb{R}}$ is μ-measurable if and only if for every compact set K, the function $f\chi_K$ is μ-integrable.*

The following characterization of μ-integrability follows from Egoroff's theorem, which we do not state.

Proposition 6.33. *A function f from Ω to $\overline{\mathbb{R}}$ is μ-integrable if and only if f is μ-measurable and, moreover, the upper integral $\mu^*(|f|)$ is finite.*

This leads to the following result.

Proposition 6.34. *If f is μ-integrable, then so is $f\chi_A$ for every measurable set A, and in particular for every compact set.*

Definition 6.35. Let A be a μ-measurable set. We define $\mu\chi_A$ to be the map that sends an element φ of $\mathcal{C}_c(\Omega)$ to the number

$$\langle \mu, \varphi\chi_A \rangle.$$

This is well defined because $\chi_A\varphi$ is μ-integrable.

Local Integrability.

Definition 6.36. A map f from Ω to $\overline{\mathbb{R}}$ is called *locally μ-integrable* if every point x of Ω admits a neighborhood V such that $f\chi_V$ is μ-integrable.

Proposition 6.37. *Let f be a map from Ω to $\overline{\mathbb{R}}$; then f is locally μ-integrable if and only if f is μ-measurable and for every compact set K, we have $\mu^*(|f|\chi_K) < \infty$.*

Proof of Proposition 6.37.

Let f be locally μ-integrable and let K be compact. By decomposing f into its positive and negative parts, we may, and do, assume that $f \geqslant 0$. We can cover K by a finite number of open sets V_j such that $f\chi_{V_j}$ is μ-integrable for every j. The function $\sup_j(f\chi_{V_j})$ is then μ-integrable (cf. Proposition 6.27). Since $f\chi_K = \chi_K \sup_j(f\chi_{V_j})$, it follows from Proposition 6.34 that $f\chi_K$ is integrable, and in particular measurable. Since this is true for every compact set K, we see that f is measurable (cf. Proposition 6.32). Proposition 6.33 moreover gives us the finiteness of $\mu^*(|f|\chi_K)$.

Conversely, let $x \in \Omega$. Consider a function $\varphi \in \mathcal{C}_c(\Omega)$ with values between 0 and 1 that equals 1 in a compact neighborhood V of x. Then the function $f\varphi$ is integrable by Proposition 6.33. Consequently, the same holds for $f\chi_V = f\varphi\chi_V$, by Proposition 6.34.   □

Definition 6.38. We say that a locally μ-integrable set A supports the positive measure μ if $\mu(\Omega \smallsetminus A) = 0$.

6.2.3 Absolute Continuity

In this subsection, μ and ν are two positive measures on Ω.

Definition 6.39. We call μ *absolutely continuous* with respect to ν if the following implication holds:

$$\forall A \subset \Omega, \quad \nu(A) = 0 \implies \mu^*(A) = 0.$$

This relation between positive measures is often denoted by $\mu \ll \nu$. We also say that μ *is dominated by* ν.

This notion can also be expressed in the following manner. Let h be a locally μ-integrable function; then for every $\varphi \in \mathcal{C}_c(\Omega)$, the function $h\varphi$ is μ-integrable. Moreover, the map that sends a function $\varphi \in \mathcal{C}_c(\Omega)$ to the integral $\mu^*(h\varphi)$, which we also denote by $\int_\Omega h\varphi d\mu$, is a linear functional. It is a measure on Ω. Indeed, for every compact subset K of Ω and for every continuous function φ with support in K, we have the inequality

$$\left| \int_\Omega h\varphi d\mu \right| \leqslant \|\varphi\|_\infty \int_\Omega |h\chi_K| d\mu.$$

Definition 6.40. The measure defined above is denoted by $h \cdot \mu$. We call it the *measure with density h with respect to μ*.

Proposition 6.41. *Let $\nu = h \cdot \mu$, where h is locally μ-integrable. Then $\nu^*(f) = \mu^*(fh)$ for every function f from Ω to $\overline{\mathbb{R}}$, where the product fh is zero by definition whenever one of the factors is zero.*

We admit the proposition without proof (cf. [29, chap. 13, §14]).

We can deduce from it that if $\nu(A) = 0$, then $\mu(A) = 0$. In other words, the measure μ is dominated by ν. This property and its converse are part of the Lebesgue–Nikodym theorem. The following result is a corollary of that theorem.

Proposition 6.42. *A measure $\mu \geqslant 0$ is absolutely continuous with respect to $\nu \geqslant 0$ if and only if there exists a locally ν-integrable function g such that $\mu = g \cdot \nu$.*

6.2.4 Singular Measures

Definition 6.43. We say that μ is singular with respect to ν if there exist disjoint subsets A and B of Ω that are locally μ-integrable and locally ν-integrable, respectively, such that μ is supported by A while ν is supported by B. This relation between the two positive measures is denoted by $\mu \perp \nu$. We then have

$$\mu = \mu\chi_A \quad \text{and} \quad \nu = \nu\chi_B.$$

Under these conditions, we can show that A and B may be chosen universally measurable. We will admit this result (cf. [29]).

Definition 6.44. The measure $\mu \geqslant 0$ is called *singular* if it is singular with respect to the Lebesgue measure.

Proposition 6.45. *A measure $\mu \geqslant 0$ is singular with respect to $\nu \geqslant 0$ if and only if* $\inf(\mu, \nu) = 0$

Proof of Proposition 6.45.

Suppose that μ is singular with respect to ν. Let A and B be two disjoint universally measurable sets such that $\mu = \mu \chi_A$ and $\nu = \nu \chi_B$. If $\varphi \in \mathcal{C}_c(\Omega)$, then we have

$$\inf(\mu, \nu)(\varphi) = \inf\big(\langle \mu, \chi_A \varphi \rangle, \langle \nu, \chi_B \varphi \rangle\big) = 0.$$

For the converse, we use Proposition 6.42. Consider the measure $\rho = \mu + \nu$. By Definition 6.39, both μ and ν are absolutely continuous with respect to ρ. Therefore there exist locally ρ-integrable g and h such that $\mu = g \cdot \rho$ and $\nu = h \cdot \rho$ (cf. Proposition 6.42). Since $\inf(\mu, \nu) = \inf(g, h)\rho = 0$, it follows that $\inf(g, h)$ is of ρ-measure 0. Next, let $M = \{x \mid g(x) \neq 0\}$ and let $N = \{x \mid h(x) \neq 0\}$. These sets are locally ρ-integrable and, by the above, we have $\rho(M \cap N) = 0$. Let $A = M \setminus (M \cap N)$ and let $B = N \setminus (M \cap N)$. These sets are locally ρ-integrable and we have $g = \chi_A g$ and $h = \chi_B h$ outside of a set of measure zero for ρ. $\square$

6.2.5 Canonical Decomposition of a Positive Measure

Theorem 6.46 (Lebesgue decomposition). *Let μ be a positive measure; then there is a unique way to write μ as the sum of a measure that is absolutely continuous with respect to the Lebesgue measure and a singular measure.*

Proof of Theorem 6.46.

The uniqueness is obvious. Indeed, suppose that μ' and μ'' are absolutely continuous with respect to the Lebesgue measure and that ν' and ν'' are two singular measures with

$$\mu = \mu' + \nu' = \mu'' + \nu''.$$

We then have

$$\mu' - \mu'' = \nu'' - \nu'.$$

Both sides of the equation are measures that are absolutely continuous with respect to the Lebesgue measure and singular; they are therefore both zero.

To prove the existence, we set

$$\nu = \sup_n \inf(\mu, n dx).$$

Note that ν is a measure. Indeed, since $\nu \leqslant \mu$, we have the inequality $\nu \varphi \leqslant \mu \varphi \leqslant C_K \|\varphi\|_\infty$ for every nonnegative function φ with compact support in K.

We must also verify the additivity and positive homogeneity, that is, if $\varphi_i \geqslant 0$ and $\lambda_i \geqslant 0$, then we must verify that

$$\langle \nu, \lambda_1 \varphi_1 + \lambda_2 \varphi_2 \rangle = \sum_1^2 \lambda_i \langle \nu, \varphi_i \rangle.$$

Let φ_1 and φ_2 be elements of $\mathcal{C}_c(\Omega)$ and let $n_0 \geqslant n_1, n_2$ with $n_i \int \varphi_i \geqslant \mu(\varphi_i)$ for $i = 1, 2$. We then have

$$\nu(\varphi_i) = \sup_{n \leqslant n_0} \inf \left(\mu(\varphi), n \int \varphi_i dx \right).$$

It follows that

$$n_0 \int (\lambda_1 \varphi_1 + \lambda_2 \varphi_2) dx \geqslant n_1 \int \lambda_1 \varphi_1 + n_2 \int \lambda_2 \varphi_2 \geqslant \mu\left(\sum_1^2 \lambda_i \varphi_i \right).$$

Hence

$$\nu\left(\sum_1^2 \lambda_i \varphi_i \right) = \sup_{n \leqslant n_0} \inf \left(\mu\left(\sum_1^2 \lambda_i \varphi_i \right), n \int \left(\sum_1^2 \lambda_i \varphi_i \right) dx \right).$$

Since this reduces the problem to computing the supremum of the infimum of a finite number of measures, we indeed have the stated additivity.

Let us now show that the measure ν is absolutely continuous with respect to the Lebesgue measure.

Indeed, if A is a set with Lebesgue measure zero, that is, $\int_A dx = 0$, then the infima of $\nu(A)$ and of $n \int_A dx$ are zero. Consequently, we have $\nu(A) = 0$. The measure ν is therefore absolutely continuous with respect to the Lebesgue measure.

Finally, let us show that the measure $\mu - \nu$ is singular with respect to the Lebesgue measure.

We will show, by contradiction, that if $(\mu - \nu)(A) > 0$, then $\int_A dx = 0$. Let us therefore suppose that $\int_A dx > 0$. Then for n_0 sufficiently large, we have $n_0 \int_A dx > \mu(A)$, whence $\nu(A) = \mu(A)$, that is, $(\mu - \nu)(A) = 0$. $\square$

6.2.6 Complex Measures and Vector Measures

For a real measure μ, the results presented above apply to the positive part μ^+ and to the negative part μ^-. Likewise, if μ is a complex measure, then we consider the real and imaginary parts of this measure, allowing us to restrict ourselves to considering positive measures.

Let us briefly study the Lebesgue decomposition of a vector measure in finite dimension.

Definition 6.47. Let $\overrightarrow{\mu}$ be a measure with vector values and let ν be a positive measure. We call $\overrightarrow{\mu}$ absolutely continuous with respect to ν if $|\overrightarrow{\mu}| \ll \nu$ (cf. Definition 6.39).

We call two vector measures $\overrightarrow{\mu}$ and $\overrightarrow{\nu}$ mutually singular if $|\overrightarrow{\mu}|$ and $|\overrightarrow{\nu}|$ are mutually singular.

We state the decomposition theorem in a specific case.

Theorem 6.48. *Let $\overrightarrow{\mu}$ belong to $\mathcal{M}^1(\Omega, \mathbb{R}^N)$; then there exist a function h in $L^1(\Omega, \mathbb{R}^N)$ and a vector measure $\overrightarrow{\nu}$ that is singular with respect to the Lebesgue measure dx on Ω with*

$$\overrightarrow{\mu} = \overrightarrow{\nu} + \overrightarrow{h}\,dx.$$

Proof of Theorem 6.48. We apply Theorem 6.46 to the positive and negative parts of each of the components μ_i of $\overrightarrow{\mu}$, giving

$$\mu_i^+ = h_i dx + \nu_i, \quad \mu_i^- = g_i dx + \lambda_i.$$

From this, we deduce that $\mu_i = (h_i - g_i)dx + \nu_i - \lambda_i$. We then have

$$\overrightarrow{\mu} = \Big[\sum_1^N (h_i - g_i)e_i\Big]dx + \Big[\sum_1^N (\nu_i - \lambda_i)e_i\Big],$$

where the last sum represents a measure that is singular with respect to dx, or rather, whose components are all singular with respect to dx.   □

6.3 The Space of Functions with Bounded Variation

Definition 6.49. We say that $u \in BV(\Omega)$ if $u \in L^1(\Omega)$ and $\nabla u \in M^1(\Omega)$. We can also define $BV(\Omega)$ as the set of u in $L^1(\Omega)$ such that

$$\int_\Omega |\nabla u|dx = \sup\Big\{\int_\Omega u \operatorname{div} g \mid g \in \mathcal{C}_c^1(\Omega, \mathbb{R}^N),\ |g| \leqslant 1\Big\} < +\infty.$$

Namely, we have

$$\int_\Omega |\nabla u|dx = \sup_{\substack{\varphi \in \mathcal{C}_c(\Omega,\mathbb{R}^N) \\ |\varphi| \leqslant 1}} \int_\Omega \nabla u \cdot \varphi dx = \sup_{\substack{\varphi \in \mathcal{C}_c^1(\Omega,\mathbb{R}^N) \\ |\varphi| \leqslant 1}} \Big\{-\int_\Omega u \operatorname{div} \varphi(x)dx\Big\},$$

while the opposite inequality follows by a density argument.

Remark 6.50. Clearly $W^{1,1}(\Omega) \subset BV(\Omega)$, but the inclusion in the other direction does not hold. To see this, we can, for example, consider the characteristic function $\chi_{B(0,R)}$ of a Euclidean ball. This belongs to $L^1(\mathbb{R}^N)$ and has gradient $\nabla(\chi_{B(0,R)}) = -(x/|x|)\delta_{|x|=R}$. Indeed, if $\varphi \in \mathcal{D}(\mathbb{R}^N, \mathbb{R}^N)$, then the classical Green's formula gives

$$- \int_{\mathbb{R}^N} \nabla(\chi_{B(0,R)}) \cdot \varphi = \int_{B(0,R)} \operatorname{div} \varphi(x) \, dx$$

$$= \int_{|x|=R} \varphi(x) \cdot \vec{n} \, dx = \int_{|x|=R} \frac{x}{|x|} \cdot \varphi(x) \, dx.$$

This proves that the characteristic function belongs to $BV(\mathbb{R}^N)$, but not to $W^{1,1}(\mathbb{R}^N)$.

Definition 6.51. We say that a sequence $\{u_n\}$ in $BV(\Omega)$ converges weakly to $u \in BV(\Omega)$ if

$$\int_\Omega |u_n - u| dx \longrightarrow 0 \quad \text{and} \quad \nabla u_n \text{ converges vaguely to } \nabla u.$$

The following result is a consequence of the theorem on the weak compactness of sequences of measures with bounded integrals.

Proposition 6.52. Let $\{u_n\}$ be a bounded sequence in $BV(\Omega)$; then we can extract a subsequence from $\{u_n\}$ that converges weakly in $BV(\Omega)$.

Remark 6.53. We will see further on that when the open set Ω is sufficiently regular, the space $BV(\Omega)$ is embedded in $L^p(\Omega)$ for every $p \leqslant N/(N-1)$. If Ω is moreover bounded, then the embedding in $L^q(\Omega)$ is compact for every $q < N/(N-1)$. These properties immediately give the strong convergence of $\{u_n\}$ to u in every $L^q(\Omega)$ with $q < N/(N-1)$ and the weak convergence in $L^{N/(N-1)}(\Omega)$.

Proposition 6.54. Let Ω be an open subset of $\mathbb{R}^N$. Let $\{u_n\}$ be a sequence of functions that converges to u in $L^1_{\text{loc}}(\Omega)$. Then

$$\int_\Omega |\nabla u| dx \leqslant \lim_{n \to +\infty} \int_\Omega |\nabla u_n|.$$

Proof of Proposition 6.54.

If we know that ∇u_n is a measure, then we can apply Proposition 6.15. In the general case, since u_n tends to u in $L^1_{\text{loc}}(\Omega)$, we know that for every $g \in \mathcal{C}^1_c(\Omega)$, we have

$$\int_\Omega u_n(x) \operatorname{div} g(x) dx \longrightarrow \int_\Omega u(x) \operatorname{div} g(x) dx.$$

This implies the result by taking the upper bound when $|g| \leqslant 1$ (cf. Definition 6.49).   □

Remark 6.55. Suppose that $\{u_n\}$ converges strongly to u in $L^1(\Omega)$ and that $\{\nabla u_n\}$ converges weakly to ∇u; then we do not necessarily have $\int_\Omega |\nabla u_n| \to \int_\Omega |\nabla u|$.

Let us take a very simple example to illustrate this. Consider, in dimension 1, the sequence of functions $\{u_n\}$ with general term $u_n = nx\chi_{]0,1/n[} + \chi_{[1/n,1[}$. This sequence converges to 1 on $]0,1[$ but $\int_0^1 |u_n'(t)|dt = 1$, so it does not tend to $\int_0^1 |u'(t)|dt$, which equals 0.

6.3.1 Density Results

Theorem 6.56. *The space $C^\infty(\Omega) \cap W^{1,1}(\Omega)$ is dense in $BV(\Omega)$ for the intermediate topology described above. This topology is finer than that of weak convergence, and is related to the tight convergence of measures. Let $u \in BV(\Omega)$. There exists a sequence $\{u_n\} \subset C^\infty(\Omega) \cap W^{1,1}(\Omega)$ such that*

$$u_n \longrightarrow u \text{ in } L^1(\Omega) \quad and \quad \int_\Omega |\nabla u_n| \longrightarrow \int_\Omega |\nabla u|.$$

Remark 6.57. From now on, we will say that a sequence u_n of functions in $BV(\Omega)$ converges tightly to u in $BV(\Omega)$ if

$$\int_\Omega |u_n - u| + \left| \int_\Omega |\nabla u_n| - \int_\Omega |\nabla u| \right| \longrightarrow 0.$$

Proof of Theorem 6.56.

We use the notation of Proposition 2.12. Let Ω_j be an increasing sequence in Ω with union Ω. Consider the open sets A_j defined by

$$A_j = \Omega_{j+2} \setminus \overline{\Omega_{j-1}}, \quad \text{where} \quad \Omega_{-1} = \Omega_0 = \varnothing$$

and let $\{\varphi_j\}$ be the partition of unity subordinate to the cover $\{A_j\}$ of Ω:

$$(6.58) \qquad \varphi_j \in C_0^\infty(A_j), \quad \sum_0^\infty \varphi_j = 1, \quad 0 \leqslant \varphi_j \leqslant 1.$$

Next, let $\{\eta_j\}$ be a nonincreasing sequence of nonnegative real numbers tending to 0 such that

$$A_j + B(0, \eta_j) \subset A_{j-1} \cup A_j \cup A_{j+1} \quad \text{for } j \geqslant 2$$

and such that, for a given $\delta > 0$,

$$(6.59) \qquad \left| \int_\Omega |\rho_{\eta_j} * (\varphi_j \nabla u)| - \int_\Omega |(\varphi_j \nabla u)| \right| < \delta 2^{-j-2},$$

$$(6.60) \qquad \int_\Omega |\rho_{\eta_j} * (\varphi_j u) - (\varphi_j u)| < \delta 2^{-j-1},$$

$$(6.61) \qquad \int_\Omega |\rho_{\eta_j} * (\nabla(\varphi_j)u) - (\nabla(\varphi_j)u)| < \delta 2^{-j-2}.$$

We then set

$$(6.62) \qquad u_\delta = \sum_0^\infty \rho_{\eta_j} * (\varphi_j u).$$

The existence of a sequence satisfying inequality (6.59) follows from Proposition 6.21.

We thus obtain a $\mathcal{C}^\infty$ function on Ω. Indeed, the resulting "sequence" $\{u_\delta\}$ whose general term is a $\mathcal{C}^\infty$ function, is locally finite on every compact subset K of Ω, because there always exists a j_0 sufficiently large that $A_{j-1} \cap K = \varnothing$ for $j > j_0$. It follows that the terms with indexes $> j_0$ are zero, because their supports lie in $A_{j-1} \cup A_j \cup A_{j+1}$.

We will first show that $\|u_\delta - u\|_{L^1(\Omega)} \leqslant \delta$, which implies that $u_\delta \in L^1(\Omega)$. Next, we will show that $\left| \int_\Omega |\nabla u_\delta| - \int_\Omega |\nabla u| \right| \leqslant 2\delta$, which implies that $\nabla u_\delta \in L^1(\Omega)$, and even that $\int_\Omega |\nabla u_\delta| \leqslant C$. Together, these upper bounds imply that the "sequence" of functions $\{u_\delta\}$ satisfies the property stated in the theorem.

By (6.60), we have,

$$\int_\Omega |u_\delta - u| = \int_\Omega \left| \sum_0^\infty \rho_{\eta_j} * (\varphi_j u) - (\varphi_j u) \right| \leqslant \sum_0^\infty 2^{-j-1}\delta = \delta.$$

Let us write $A = |\sum_0^\infty \rho_{\eta_j} * \nabla(\varphi_j u)|$ as follows:

$$A = \left| \sum_0^\infty \rho_{\eta_j} * (u \nabla \varphi_j + \varphi_j \nabla u) \right|$$

$$\leqslant \left| \sum_0^\infty \left[\rho_{\eta_j} * (u \nabla \varphi_j) - (u \nabla \varphi_j) \right] \right| + \left| \sum_0^\infty u \nabla \varphi_j \right| + \left| \sum_0^\infty \rho_{\eta_j} * (\varphi_j \nabla u) \right|.$$

Then, since $\sum_0^\infty \nabla \varphi_j = 0$ and $|\nabla u| = \sum_0^\infty \varphi_j |\nabla u|$, we have

$$\left| \int_\Omega (|\nabla u_\delta| - |\nabla u|) \right| \leqslant \sum_0^\infty \left| \int_\Omega \left(\rho_{\eta_j} * (u \nabla \varphi_j) - (u \nabla \varphi_j) \right) \right|$$

$$+ \sum_0^\infty \left| \int_\Omega |\rho_{\eta_j} * (\varphi_j \nabla u)| - \int_\Omega |\varphi_j \nabla u| \right|.$$

By (6.59) and (6.60), it now follows that

$$\left| \int_\Omega |\nabla u_\delta| - \int_\Omega |\nabla u| \right| < 2\delta. \qquad \square$$

After proving the trace theorem, we will see that the sequence $\{u_\delta\}$ has the same trace as u when Ω is of class $\mathcal{C}^1$. These density theorems for a topology intermediate between the weak topology and the norm topology allow us to extend the embedding and compact embedding results concerning $W^{1,1}(\Omega)$ to the space $BV(\Omega)$.

Remark 6.63. Using the previous theorem, we can prove the following property for the absolutely continuous and singular parts (cf. Theorem 6.46) of the terms of the sequence $\{\nabla u_n\}$:

$$\int_\Omega |\nabla u_\delta - (\nabla u)^{\mathrm{ac}}| \longrightarrow \int_\Omega |\nabla u^S|.$$

We will use this property when we study functions of a measure in Section 6.10. Exercise 6.3 contains a proof of this result.

6.3.2 Embedding Results

Theorem 6.64. *Let Ω be a Lipschitz open subset of $\mathbb{R}^N$; then the space $BV(\Omega)$ is embedded in $L^p(\Omega)$ for every $p \leqslant N/(N-1)$. If $p < N/(N-1)$ and Ω is bounded, then the embedding is compact.*

Proof of Theorem 6.64, existence of embeddings.

We will use the density of $W^{1,1}(\Omega)$ in $BV(\Omega)$ (Theorem 6.56). Let u be an element of $BV(\Omega)$. There exists a sequence $\{u_n\}$ in $W^{1,1}(\Omega)$ such that

$$u_n \longrightarrow u \text{ in } L^1(\Omega) \quad \text{and} \quad \int_\Omega |\nabla u_n| \longrightarrow \int_\Omega |\nabla u|.$$

Using the existence of the embedding of $W^{1,1}(\Omega)$ in $L^p(\Omega)$ for all $p \leqslant N/(N-1)$, we see that there exists a constant C that does not depend on n such that

$$\|u_n\|_p \leqslant C(\|u_n\|_1 + \|\nabla u_n\|_1).$$

Since for $1 < p < \infty$, every bounded sequence in $L^p(\Omega)$ is relatively weakly compact in $L^p(\Omega)$, we deduce that we can extract a subsequence that converges weakly to an element $v \in L^p(\Omega)$. We of course have $u = v$, and by the lower semicontinuity of the norm in $L^p(\Omega)$,

$$\begin{aligned}
\|u\|_p &\leqslant \lim_{n\to\infty} \|u_n\|_p \\
&\leqslant C \lim_{n\to\infty} (\|u_n\|_1 + \|\nabla u_n\|_1) \\
&= C\Big(\|u\|_1 + \int_\Omega |\nabla u|\Big),
\end{aligned}$$

giving the existence of the embeddings. $\qquad\square$

Proof of Theorem 6.64, compactness.

Let us show the result for $p = 1$. Let K be a bounded subset of $BV(\Omega)$. We use the description of the compact subsets of L^1 (cf. Theorem 1.95 of Chapter 1) to show that K is relatively compact in $L^1(\Omega)$. Let $\varepsilon > 0$ and let G be a compact subset of Ω such that $|\Omega - G|^{1/N} \leqslant \varepsilon$. Then by using Hölder's formula for every $u \in K$, the embedding of $BV(\Omega)$ in $L^{N/N-1}(\Omega)$, and the boundedness of K in BV, we have

$$\int_{\Omega-G} |u| \leqslant \varepsilon \|u\|_{L^{N/(N-1)}(\Omega\setminus G)} \leqslant \varepsilon \|u\|_{L^{N/(N-1)}(\Omega)} \leqslant C\varepsilon.$$

Next, we must show that

$$0 < |h| < d(G, \partial\Omega) \implies \int_G |\tau_h u - u| \leqslant |h| \int_\Omega |\nabla u|.$$

To do this, let $\{u_n\}$ be a sequence in $W^{1,1}(\Omega)$ with

$$\int_\Omega |\nabla u_n(x)| dx \longrightarrow \int_\Omega |\nabla u| \quad \text{and} \quad \int_\Omega |u_n - u|(x) dx \longrightarrow 0.$$

Let N_0 be sufficiently large that for $n \geqslant N_0$,

$$\left| \int_\Omega |\nabla u_n|(x) dx - \int_\Omega |\nabla u| \right| \leqslant \varepsilon \quad \text{and} \quad \int_\Omega |u_n - u|(x) dx \leqslant \varepsilon.$$

The last inequality implies that for $n \geqslant N_0$ and for $h < d(G, \partial\Omega)$, we have

$$\int_G |\tau_h u - \tau_h u_n|(x) dx \leqslant \varepsilon.$$

The proof of Theorem 2.23 in the case $p = 1$ ensures us that $\int_G |\tau_h u_n - u_n| dx \leqslant h \int_\Omega |\nabla u_n|(x) dx$ because u_n belongs to $W^{1,1}(\Omega)$. It follows that

$$\int_G |\tau_h u - u|(x) dx \leqslant \int_G |\tau_h u - \tau_h u_n|(x) dx + \int_G |\tau_h u_n - u_n|(x) dx$$
$$+ \int_G |u_n - u|(x) dx$$
$$\leqslant h \int_\Omega |\nabla u_n|(x) dx + 2\varepsilon \leqslant h \int_\Omega |\nabla u| + 3\varepsilon,$$

giving the result because ε is arbitrary.

Next, let $p > 1$. We consider the bounded sequence $\{u_n\}$ in $BV(\Omega)$. By the relative compactness proved earlier, we can extract a subsequence $\{u_{\sigma(n)}\}$ that converges in $L^1(\Omega)$. By the continuity of the embedding $BV \hookrightarrow L^{N/(N-1)}$, this sequence is bounded in $L^{N/(N-1)}$. This situation allows us to apply Lemma 2.82 of Chapter 2. We thus obtain that $\{u_{\sigma(n)}\}$ converges in every L^q with $q < N/(N-1)$. $\qquad\square$

6.3.3 Trace Results

Before stating the existence theorem for a trace on the boundary, we first need the following result.

Lemma 6.65. *Let μ be a bounded measure on the open subset Ω of $\mathbb{R}^N$. There exists a number of α, at most countable, such that μ charges $\Omega \cap \{x_N = \alpha\}$, that is, such that $\mu(\Omega \cap \{x_N = \alpha\}) > 0$.*

Proof of Lemma 6.65.

By Fubini's theorem, we can write

$$|\mu|(\Omega) = \int_{\mathbb{R}} |\mu|(\Omega \cap \{x_N = \alpha\}) d\alpha.$$

Let φ be defined by

$$\varphi(\alpha) = \int_{\beta \leqslant \alpha} |\mu|(\Omega \cap \{x_N = \beta\}) d\beta.$$

The function φ is nondecreasing, it therefore has at most countably many discontinuities. Now, by definition, these discontinuities are precisely the real numbers α for which

$$\lim_{\varepsilon \to 0} \mu(\Omega \cap \{x_N = \alpha + \varepsilon\}) - \mu(\Omega \cap \{x_N = \alpha - \varepsilon\}) \neq 0. \qquad \square$$

Proposition 6.66. *Let $\{\mu_n\}$ be a sequence of positive measures that converges tightly to μ on Ω. Then if $\Omega_1 \subset \overline{\Omega_1} \subset \Omega$ satisfies $\int_{\partial \Omega_1} \mu = 0$, we have*

$$\int_{\Omega_1} \mu_n \longrightarrow \int_{\Omega_1} \mu.$$

Exercise 6.1 provides the proof with a number of hints.

Theorem 6.67. *Let Ω be an open set of class $\mathcal{C}^1$. There exists a surjective continuous linear map from $BV(\Omega)$ onto $L^1(\partial \Omega)$ that coincides with the usual restriction map on the boundary when $u \in BV(\Omega) \cap \mathcal{C}(\overline{\Omega})$ and with the trace map studied in Chapter 3 when $u \in W^{1,1}(\Omega)$.*

Proof of Theorem 6.67.

We use a cover of $\partial \Omega$ by bounded open sets Ω_i that, after changing the coordinate system, if necessary, satisfy

$$\Omega_i \cap \Omega \subset \{(x', x_N) \mid a(x') < x_N, \, x' \in \mathcal{O}'\},$$
$$\partial \Omega \cap \Omega_i = \{(x', a(x')) \mid x' \in \mathcal{O}'\},$$

where $\mathcal{O}'$ is an open subset of $\mathbb{R}^{N-1}$ and $a \in \mathcal{C}^1(\mathcal{O}')$. We moreover suppose that u has compact support in $\Omega_i \cap \overline{\Omega}$. Now, let $\alpha > 0$ satisfy

$$|\nabla u|\{(x', a(x') + \alpha)\} = 0$$

(cf. Lemma 6.65). Let $\{u_n\}$ be a sequence in $W^{1,1}$ given by the density theorem. We have

$$u_n(x', a(x') + \alpha) - u_n(x', a(x') + \alpha') = \int_{\alpha'}^{\alpha} \partial_N u_n(x', a(x') + s)ds.$$

Let g_α^n denote the function $x' \mapsto u_n(x', a(x') + \alpha)$ and let

$$\mathcal{A}_\alpha = \{(x', x_N) \in \Omega \mid x_N < a(x') + \alpha\}.$$

By integrating the equality over $\mathcal{O}'$, we find that for $0 < \alpha < \alpha'$,

$$\|g_\alpha^n - g_{\alpha'}^n\|_{L^1(\mathcal{O}')} \leqslant \int_\alpha^{\alpha'} \int_{\mathcal{O}'} \left|\frac{\partial u_n}{\partial x_N}(x', a(x') + s)\right| dx' ds$$

$$\leqslant c \int_{\mathcal{A}_{\alpha'} \smallsetminus \mathcal{A}_\alpha} \left|\frac{\partial u_n}{\partial x_N}(x', a(x') + x_N)\right| dx.$$

The convergence of u_n to u in $L^1(\Omega)$ implies that the left-hand side tends to $\|g_\alpha - g_{\alpha'}\|_{L^1(\mathcal{O}')}$ when n tends to infinity. Applying Proposition 6.66 to the right-hand side, we find that its limit is

$$\int_{\mathcal{A}_{\alpha'} \smallsetminus \mathcal{A}_\alpha} \left|\frac{\partial u}{\partial x_N}(x', a(x') + x_N)\right| dx.$$

From this, we deduce that the inequality

$$\|g_\alpha - g_{\alpha'}\|_{L^1(\mathcal{O}')} \leqslant \int_{\mathcal{A}_{\alpha'} \smallsetminus \mathcal{A}_\alpha} |\partial_N u|$$

for the functions in $W^{1,1}$ extends to the functions in BV when $\partial \mathcal{A}_\alpha$ and $\partial \mathcal{A}_{\alpha'}$ have measure 0 for $\partial_N u$.

Since $|\partial u / \partial x_N|$ is a bounded measure on Ω, the limit above is zero when α and α' tend to 0 from above. In particular, since $\{g_\alpha\}$ is a Cauchy sequence in $L^1(\mathcal{O}')$, it converges to a function in $L^1(\mathcal{O}')$ that we denote by $u_{(i)}(x', a(x'))$. Using the usual gluing process that is compatible with the used cover of Ω, the sum of the resulting limit functions gives what we will call the trace of u on the boundary of Ω. $\qquad \square$

Theorem 6.68. *Let Ω be an open set of class $\mathcal{C}^1$. The trace map is continuous for the intermediate topology described in Theorem 6.56.*

More precisely, if $u_n \to u$ in $L^1(\Omega)$ and if $\int_\Omega |\nabla u_n| \to \int_\Omega |\nabla u|$, then

$$|\gamma_0(u_n) - \gamma_0(u)|_{L^1(\partial \Omega)} \longrightarrow 0.$$

Proof of Theorem 6.68.

Since the trace map γ_0 is continuous, there exists a constant C depending only on Ω, such that

$$\forall u \in BV(\Omega), \quad \int_{\partial\Omega} |u| \leqslant C\Big(\int_\Omega |\nabla u(x)| dx + \int_\Omega |u(x)| dx \Big).$$

Let $\{u_n\}$ converge tightly to u in BV, that is, satisfy $\|u_n - u\|_1 \to 0$ and $\int_\Omega \psi |\nabla u_n| \to \int_\Omega \psi |\nabla u|$ for every $\psi \in \mathcal{C}_b(\Omega)$. Let $\varepsilon > 0$ be given. Let Ω_0 be a relatively compact open subset of Ω and let φ_0 be a function with compact support in Ω, equal to 1 on Ω_0, and satisfying $0 \leqslant \varphi_0 \leqslant 1$ and $\int_\Omega (1 - \varphi_0)|\nabla u| \leqslant \varepsilon$. By the tight convergence, there then exists an N_0 such that

$$\forall n > N_0, \quad \int_\Omega (1 - \varphi_0)|\nabla u_n| \leqslant 2\varepsilon.$$

We may, and do, suppose N_0 sufficiently large that for $n \geqslant N_0$,

$$\int_\Omega |u_n - u| dx \leqslant \frac{\varepsilon}{1 + \|\nabla \varphi_0\|_\infty}.$$

Using the continuity of the trace map and the equality $1 - \varphi_0 = 1$ on $\partial\Omega$, we then have for $n > N_0$:

$$\int_{\partial\Omega} |u_n - u| \leqslant C\Big[\int_\Omega |\nabla((u_n - u)(1 - \varphi_0))| dx + \int_\Omega |u_n - u|(1 - \varphi_0) dx \Big]$$

$$\leqslant C\Big[\int_\Omega |\nabla u_n|(1 - \varphi_0) + \int_\Omega |\nabla u|(1 - \varphi_0)$$

$$+ \int_\Omega |u_n - u| \cdot |\nabla \varphi_0| dx + \int_\Omega |(u_n - u)(1 - \varphi_0)| dx \Big]$$

$$\leqslant C\Big[4\varepsilon + \int_\Omega |u_n - u|(1 + \|\nabla \varphi_0\|_\infty) dx \Big] \leqslant 5C\varepsilon. \qquad \square$$

Remark 6.69. The sequence $\{u_\delta\}$ of Theorem 6.56 satisfies $\gamma_0(u_\delta) = \gamma_0(u)$. Indeed, $u - u_\delta$ is the strong limit in BV of

$$v_\delta^n = \sum_0^n \big(\rho_{n_j} * (\varphi_j u) - \varphi_j u \big),$$

a sequence whose general term has compact support in $\partial\Omega$ for every n, and therefore vanishes on the boundary.

Theorem 6.70. *Let Ω be an open subset of $\mathbb{R}^N$ of class $\mathcal{C}^1$ and let $u \in BV(\Omega)$. Then there exists a sequence $\{u_n\}$ of functions in $\mathcal{C}_c^\infty(\Omega)$ such that*

$$\|u_n - u\|_1 \longrightarrow 0 \quad and \quad \int_\Omega |\nabla u_n| \longrightarrow \int_\Omega |\nabla u| + \int_{\partial\Omega} |u|.$$

Proof of Theorem 6.70.

We begin by covering Ω with a countable family of open sets (finite if Ω is bounded), where Ω_0 satisfies $d(\Omega_0, \partial\Omega) > 0$ and, after changing the coordinate system, if necessary, the Ω_i with $i \geqslant 1$ satisfy

$$\Omega_i \cap \Omega \subset \{(x', x_N) \mid x' \in \mathcal{O}_i, x_N > a_i(x')\},$$

for a class $\mathcal{C}^1$ function a_i on the bounded open subset $\mathcal{O}_i$ of $\mathbb{R}^{N-1}$. Let $\{(\varphi_i)_i\}$ be a partition of unity subordinate to this cover. We begin by showing the result for $\varphi_i u$ with fixed index i. We extend $\varphi_i u$ by 0 outside of $\Omega \cap \Omega_i$. The resulting function $\widetilde{\varphi_i u}$ belongs to $BV(\mathbb{R}^N)$ and satisfies

$$(6.71) \qquad \int_{\mathbb{R}^N} |\nabla(\widetilde{\varphi_i u})| = \int_{\Omega \cap \Omega_i} |\nabla(\varphi_i u)| + \int_{\partial\Omega \cap \Omega_i} |\varphi_i u|.$$

As in the proof of Proposition 3.57, we use the inclusion of $\Omega_i \cap \Omega$ in $U_i = \{(x', x_N) \mid x' \in \mathcal{O}'_i, x_N > a_i(x')\}$, which is star-convex with respect to one of its points. Consider the map $x \mapsto h_\lambda(x) = x_i + \lambda(x - x_i)$. If $\lambda_m(i)$ is a sequence of nonnegative real numbers < 1 that tend to 1, then $\widetilde{\varphi_i u} \circ h_{\lambda_m(i)}^{-1}$ has compact support in Ω and converges tightly to $\widetilde{\varphi_i u}$ in $BV(\mathbb{R}^N)$. Let $\varepsilon_{m(i)} = d(\partial\Omega, \partial(h_\lambda(\Delta_i)))/2$ and let ρ be a regularizing function; then $\rho_{\varepsilon_{m(i)}} \star (\widetilde{\varphi_i u} \circ h_{\lambda_m(i)}^{-1})$ belongs to $\mathcal{D}(\Omega)$ and converges tightly to $\widetilde{\varphi_i u}$ in $BV(\mathbb{R}^N)$ when λ tends to 1. We thus obtain a sequence of functions in $\mathcal{C}_c^\infty(\Omega_i \cap \Omega)$ that tends tightly to $\widetilde{\varphi_i u}$ in $BV(\mathbb{R}^N)$ when $\lambda_m(i)$ tends to 1. In particular,

$$D(m, i) = \int_{\mathbb{R}^N} |\nabla(\rho_{\varepsilon_{m(i)}} \star (\widetilde{\varphi_i u} \circ h_{\lambda_m(i)}^{-1}))| - \int_{\Omega_i \cap \Omega} |\nabla(\varphi_i u)| - \int_{\partial\Omega \cap \Omega_i} |\varphi_i u| \longrightarrow 0.$$

Next, imposing that $\lambda_{m(i)}$ is sufficiently near 1 to have $|D(m, i)| \leqslant \eta 2^{-i}$, we can complete the proof by using the properties of the cover of $\partial\Omega$ by the $\Omega_i \cap \partial\Omega$ for $i > 1$ and the properties of the partition of unity $\{\varphi_i\}$. $\qquad \square$

Remark 6.72. By extending $\varphi_i u$ outside of Ω by a function $G \in W^{1,1}(\mathbb{R}^N \setminus \overline{\Omega})$ instead of by 0, the same process allows us to construct a sequence $\{\widetilde{v_n}\}$ in $W^{1,1}(\mathbb{R}^N)$ that equals $g = \gamma_0 G$ on $\partial\Omega$ and satisfies

$$(6.73) \qquad \int_\Omega |\nabla v_n| \longrightarrow \int_\Omega |\nabla u| + \int_{\partial\Omega} |(u - g)\overrightarrow{n}| d\sigma.$$

We used this remark when studying minimal surfaces in Chapter 5.

6.4 Distributions with Gradient in L^p

We will use the notion of an open set of class $\mathcal{C}^1$ given in Chapter 2.

Theorem 6.74. *Let T be a distribution on an open subset Ω of $\mathbb{R}^N$; then*

$$\nabla T \in L^p_{loc}(\Omega) \implies T \in W^{1,p}_{loc}(\Omega).$$

If Ω is moreover bounded and of class $\mathcal{C}^1$, then we have

$$\nabla T \in L^p(\Omega) \implies T \in W^{1,p}(\Omega).$$

Proof of Theorem 6.74 (see also [70]).

Let ω be a relatively compact open subset of Ω. We will show that the restriction $T \mid \omega$ belongs to $L^p(\omega)$. Let $\eta > 0$ be such that $\omega + B(0, 2\eta) \Subset \Omega$. Let γ be a regular function that equals 1 in a neighborhood of zero and has compact support in $B(0, \eta)$. We let E denote the fundamental solution of the Laplacian, that is, the function

$$(6.75) \qquad E(r) = \begin{cases} \dfrac{\ln r}{2\pi} & \text{if } N = 2, \\ k_N r^{2-N} & \text{if } N \geqslant 3, \end{cases}$$

where $r = \left(\sum_i |x_i|^2\right)^{1/2}$ and k_N is the constant given in Chapter 2. We have

$$\Delta(\gamma E) = \gamma \Delta E + \zeta = \delta_0 + \zeta,$$

where $\zeta = (\Delta\gamma)E + 2\nabla\gamma \cdot \nabla E$ is a function in $\mathcal{D}(B(0, \eta))$. The convolution $T \star \zeta$ belongs to $\mathcal{C}^\infty(\omega + B(0, \eta))$, and therefore to $L^p(\omega)$ for every p. We have

$$T = T \star \delta_0 = T \star \Delta(\gamma E) - T \star \zeta.$$

It therefore suffices to study the regularity of $T \star \Delta(\gamma E)$ on ω. Let us write

$$T \star \Delta(\gamma E) = \sum_i \partial_i T \star \partial_i(\gamma E) = \sum_i \partial_i T \star \gamma \partial_i E + \sum_i \partial_i T \star \partial_i(\gamma)E.$$

Since $\nabla(\gamma)E$ is $\mathcal{C}^\infty$ with compact support in $B(0, \eta)$, the convolution $\nabla T \star \nabla(\gamma)E$ is an element of $\mathcal{C}^\infty(\omega + B(0, \eta))$, hence belongs to $L^p(\omega)$ for every p. Let φ be a function that equals 1 on $\omega + B(0, \eta)$ and has compact support in Ω. When restricted to ω, the convolution $\varphi\nabla T \star \gamma\nabla E$ on $\mathbb{R}^N$ coincides with $\nabla T \star \gamma\nabla E$. We now use the inclusions $\varphi\nabla T \in L^p$ and $\gamma\nabla E \in L^1$, which imply that the convolution belongs to $L^p(\omega)$. To obtain a better result, we note that $\gamma\nabla E \in L^k$ for every $k < N/(N-1)$. It follows that $T \in L^r_{loc}(\Omega)$ for every r with $1 + 1/r > 1/p + (N-1)/N$ or, equivalently, with $r < pN/(N-p)$. This completes the proof that $T \in L^p_{loc}(\Omega)$.

Let us now suppose that Ω is a bounded open set of class $\mathcal{C}^1$ and that $\nabla u \in L^p(\Omega)$. We already know that $u \in L^p_{loc}(\Omega)$. Since Ω is of class $\mathcal{C}^1$, we can cover it with a finite number of bounded open subsets Ω_i such that, after changing the coordinate system in such a way that $\vec{n} \cdot e_N \neq 0$, if necessary, we can write

$$\Omega_i \cap \Omega \subset \{(x', x_N) \mid x' \in \Omega_i', \, x_N > a_i(x')\},$$
$$\Omega_i \cap \partial\Omega = \{(x', a_i(x')) \mid x' \in \Omega_i'\},$$

where Ω_i' is a bounded open subset of $\mathbb{R}^{N-1}$ and a_i is a $\mathcal{C}^1$ function on Ω_i'. Let φ_0 be the first element of the partition of unity subordinate to the cover $\{\Omega_i\}$ of Ω. This function has compact support in Ω_0. Since $\Omega_0 \Subset \Omega$, we have $\varphi_0 u \in L^p(\Omega)$. Let us show that, likewise, $\varphi_i u \in L^p(\Omega_i \cap \Omega)$. Let B_n be the strip in $\Omega_i \cap \Omega$ defined by

$$B_n = \{(x', x_N) \mid x' \in \Omega_i', \, x_N = a_i(x') + \lambda, \, \lambda \in [1/n, 1]\}.$$

Using the upper bound we give below, we show that $\lim_{n \to +\infty} \|\varphi_i u\|_{L^p(B_n)}$ is finite, thus proving the finiteness of $\|\varphi_i u\|_{L^p(B_\infty)}$. Together with the inclusion $\varphi_i u \in L^p_{\text{loc}}$, this will give the desired conclusion, namely that $\varphi_i u \in L^p(\Omega_i \cap \Omega)$. Indeed, since $\varphi_i u(x', a_i(x') + \lambda_0) = 0$ for sufficiently large λ_0, we see that the function $\lambda \mapsto \varphi_i u(x', a_i(x') + \lambda)$ can be obtained as an integral over $[\lambda, \lambda_0]$. More precisely,

$$\|\varphi_i u\|_{L^p(B_n)}^p = \int_{\Omega_i'} \int_{1/n}^1 |\varphi_i u|^p (x', a_i(x') + \lambda) \, d\lambda \, dx'$$
$$= \int_{\Omega_i'} \int_{1/n}^1 \left| \int_\lambda^{\lambda_0} \partial_N(\varphi_i u)(x', a_i(x') + s) ds \right|^p d\lambda \, dx',$$

whence, by Hölder's formula,

$$\|\varphi_i u\|_{L^p(B_n)}^p \leqslant (1 - 1/n)\lambda_0^{p-1} \int_{\Omega_i'} \int_0^{\lambda_0} |\nabla(\varphi_i u)|^p (x', a_i(x') + s) \, ds \, dx'$$
$$\leqslant \lambda_0^{p-1} \|\nabla(\varphi_i u)\|_{L^p(\Omega)}^p.$$

As stated above, we therefore have $\varphi_i u \in L^p(\Omega \cap \Omega_i)$. We conclude by writing $\int_\Omega |u|^p \leqslant \sum_i \int_{\Omega_i} |u|^p$, where the sum on the right-hand side is finite. $\qquad \square$

In Exercise 6.14, we treat one of the consequences of this theorem. Let Ω be an open subset of $\mathbb{R}^N$ of class $\mathcal{C}^1$ and let m be an integer with $m \geqslant 1$. For $p \geqslant 2$, we define the space

$$(6.76) \qquad X_m(\Omega) = \{u \in L^p(\Omega) \mid D^m u \in L^p(\Omega)\}.$$

Using Theorem 6.74, we see that it is of local type, which means that if $u \in X_m(\Omega)$, then for every $\varphi \in \mathcal{C}_c^\infty(\Omega)$, we have $\varphi u \in X_m(\Omega)$. Exercise 6.14 contains other properties of these spaces.

6.5 Distributions with Gradient in M^1

Theorem 6.77. *If $T \in \mathcal{D}'(\Omega)$ and $\nabla T \in M^1(\Omega)$, then $T \in BV_{\text{loc}}(\Omega)$. If Ω is moreover of class $\mathcal{C}^1$ and bounded, then $T \in BV(\Omega)$.*

Proof of Theorem 6.77.

The proof is analogous to that of Theorem 6.74. It suffices to verify that if E is the fundamental solution of the Laplacian and μ is a bounded measure on $\mathbb{R}^N$, then the convolution $\mu \star \zeta \nabla E$ belongs to L^p for $p < N/(N-1)$. We will show, more generally, that if $\mu \in M^1(\mathbb{R}^N)$ and $f \in L^p$ with $p > 1$ has compact support, then $f \star \mu$ belongs to L^p and satisfies

$$|f \star \mu|_p \leqslant \|f\|_p \int_{\mathbb{R}^N} |\mu|.$$

This is true even when f does not have compact support, but in that case, we need to define the convolution $f \star \mu$, for which we need generalized convolutions (cf. [22]). Let $\{u_n\}$ be a sequence of functions in $L^1(\mathbb{R}^N)$ that converges vaguely to μ. For example, we can take $u_n = \rho_{1/n} \star \mu$ where ρ is a function in $\mathcal{D}(\mathbb{R}^N)$ with $\int_{\mathbb{R}^N} \rho(x)dx = 1$ and $\rho_{1/n} = n^N \rho(nx)$. We then know that $|u_n|$ converges tightly to $|\mu|$ on $\mathbb{R}^N$. By a well-known property of convolutions, we have

$$\|u_n \star f\|_p \leqslant \|u_n\|_1 \|f\|_p.$$

The sequence $u_n \star f$ is therefore bounded in L^p and, by the weak compactness of the bounded subsets of L^p, we can extract a subsequence that converges weakly in L^p. In the sense of generalized convolutions, its limit is $\mu \star f$. Finally, $\mu \star f \in L^p$ and by the lower semicontinuity of the norm on $L^p(\mathbb{R}^N)$ for the weak convergence, we have

$$\|\mu \star f\|_p \leqslant \lim \|u_n\|_1 \|f\|_p = \left(\int_\Omega |\mu| \right) \|f\|_p. \qquad \square$$

6.6 Functions with Deformations in L^p for $1 < p < \infty$

This section is linked to Section 7.4, which is devoted to Korn's inequality.

Definition 6.78. Let T be a distribution with values in $\mathbb{R}^N$. We denote the components of T by T_i and define the deformation distribution of T to be a symmetric matrix whose coefficients are the distributions

$$(6.79) \qquad \varepsilon_{ij}(T) = \frac{\partial_j T_i + \partial_i T_j}{2}, \quad i, j \in [1, N].$$

For $p > 1$, we define the space

$$Y_p(\Omega) = \{u \in L^p(\Omega, \mathbb{R}^N) \mid \forall i, j \in [1, N]^2, \varepsilon_{ij}(u) \in L^p(\Omega, \mathbb{R})\}.$$

We endow this space with the norm

$$\|u\|_{Y_p} = \left(\|u\|^p_{L^p(\Omega)} + \int_\Omega |\varepsilon(u)(x)|^p(x)dx \right)^{1/p},$$

where $|\varepsilon(u)| = \left(\sum_{ij} |\varepsilon_{ij}(u)|^2 \right)^{1/2}$.

Note that if $u \in W^{1,p}(\Omega, \mathbb{R}^N)$, then the derivatives of the components u_i are in $L^p(\Omega)$, which implies that $\varepsilon(u) \in L^p(\Omega, \mathbb{R}^{N^2})$ and gives $u \in Y_p(\Omega)$. For many reasons, a crucial question is whether the converse implication holds, which would imply the equality $W^{1,p}(\Omega, \mathbb{R}^N) = Y_p(\Omega)$ or, equivalently, the existence of a constant C such that

$$\forall u \in Y_p(\Omega), \quad \|\nabla u\|_p \leqslant C\|u\|_{Y_p(\Omega)}.$$

In analogy to the case $p = 2$, this last relation can be called *Korn's inequality*. Its proof is set up in Chapter 7 and carried out in Section 7.4 for regular open sets. In this section, we content ourselves with three useful results.

Proposition 6.80. *The space* $Y_p(\Omega)$ *endowed with the norm mentioned above is a Banach space.*

The proof is left to the reader.

Proposition 6.81. *The space* $Y_p(\Omega)$ *is of local type, which means that*

$$\forall \varphi \in \mathcal{D}(\Omega), \ \forall u \in Y_p(\Omega), \quad \varphi u \in Y_p(\Omega).$$

Proof of Proposition 6.81.
    First, we have $u_i\varphi \in L^p(\Omega)$ for every i. It follows that $u\varphi \in L^p(\Omega, \mathbb{R}^N)$. Second,

$$\begin{aligned}
2\varepsilon_{ij}(u\varphi) &= \partial_i((u\varphi)_j) + \partial_j((u\varphi)_i) \\
&= \partial_i(u_j\varphi) + \partial_j(u_i\varphi) \\
&= (\partial_i u_j + \partial_j u_i)\varphi + u_j\partial_i\varphi + u_i\partial_j\varphi,
\end{aligned}$$

so that

$$(6.82) \qquad \varepsilon_{ij}(u\varphi) = \varphi\varepsilon_{ij}(u) + \frac{u_j\partial_i\varphi + u_i\partial_j\varphi}{2}.$$

The component $\varepsilon_{ij}(u\varphi)$ belongs to $L^p(\Omega)$ because it is a sum of products of functions in L^p, giving the stated result. $\square$

We can now deduce the following density result.

Proposition 6.83. *Let* Ω *be an open subset of* $\mathbb{R}^N$ *of class* $\mathcal{C}^1$; *then* $\mathcal{C}^\infty(\Omega) \cap Y_p(\Omega)$ *is dense in* $Y_p(\Omega)$.

Proof of Proposition 6.83.

Let Ω_k and A_k be as in the proof of Proposition 6.56. Let $\{\varphi_k\}$ be a partition of unity subordinate to the cover of Ω by the A_k. Finally, let $\eta > 0$, let ρ be a regularizing function, and let η_k be sufficiently small that

$$(6.84) \qquad \|\rho_{\eta_k} \star (\varphi_k u) - \varphi_k u\|_p \leqslant \eta 2^{-(k+1)},$$

$$(6.85) \qquad \|\rho_{\eta_k} \star (\nabla(\varphi_k)u) - \nabla(\varphi_k)u\|_p \leqslant \eta 2^{-(k+1)},$$

$$(6.86) \qquad \|\rho_{\eta_k} \star (\varphi_k \varepsilon(u)) - \varphi_k \varepsilon(u)\|_p \leqslant \eta 2^{-(k+1)}.$$

As in the proof of Theorem 6.56, we show that the sequence defined by $v_\eta = \sum_k \rho_{\eta_k} \star (\varphi_k u)$ lies in $\mathcal{C}^\infty(\Omega)$. Every term v_η of the sequence belongs to $Y_p(\Omega)$. To see this, it suffices to note that $\varepsilon_{ij}(\rho_{\eta_k} \star (\varphi_k u)) = \rho_{\eta_k} \star \varepsilon_{ij}(\varphi_k u)$ and to apply formula (6.82) to $\varepsilon_{ij}(\varphi_k u)$.

Finally, let us show that u_η converges to u in $Y_p(\Omega)$, which at the same time shows that u_η is an element of $Y_p(\Omega)$. To begin, by (6.84), we have

$$\int_\Omega |u_\eta - u|^p \leqslant \int_\Omega \Big[\sum |\rho_{\eta_k} \star (\varphi_k u) - (\varphi_k u)|\Big]^p \leqslant \eta^p.$$

We also have

$$\varepsilon_{ij}(u_\eta - u) = \varepsilon_{ij}\Big[\sum_0^{+\infty}(\rho_{\eta_k} \star (\varphi_k u) - \varphi_k u)\Big],$$

and owing to the properties of convolutions, the right-hand side can be written as the sum of the sequence with general term $\rho_{\eta_k} \star \varepsilon_{ij}(\varphi_k u) - \varepsilon_{ij}(\varphi_k u)$. By (6.82), it can also be written as the sum of the two terms

$$U_{ij} = \rho_{\eta_k} \star (\varphi_k \varepsilon_{ij}(u)) - \varphi_k \varepsilon_{ij}(u),$$

$$V_{ij} = \frac{1}{2}\Big[\rho_{\eta_k} \star (u_j \partial_i \varphi_k + u_i \partial_j \varphi_k) - (u_j \partial_i \varphi_k + u_i \partial_j \varphi_k)\Big].$$

By applying Minkowski's inequality to the norms of these two terms in $L^p(\Omega)$ and using the relations (6.85) and (6.86), we obtain the result

$$\int_\Omega |\varepsilon(u_\eta - u)|^p dx \leqslant K\eta^p. \qquad \qquad \Box$$

6.7 Spaces of Functions with Deformations in L^1

When $p = 1$, the space Y_1 is denoted by[1] $LD(\Omega)$. One can show that Korn's inequality does not extend to the case $p = 1$, [55]. In particular, $Y_1(\Omega) \neq W^{1,1}(\Omega)$.

---

[1] The name of the space $LD(\Omega)$ is an abbreviation of "Lebesgue deformation", that is, with deformations in $L^1(\Omega)$.

Definition 6.87.

$$LD(\Omega) = \{u \in L^1(\Omega, \mathbb{R}^N) \mid \varepsilon(u) \in L^1(\Omega, \mathbb{R}^{N^2})\} = Y_1(\Omega).$$

It is clear that $LD(\Omega)$ endowed with the norm

(6.88) $$\|u\|_{LD(\Omega)} = \|u\|_1 + \|\varepsilon(u)\|_1,$$

is a Banach space.

Theorem 6.89. *If T is a distribution on an open set Ω with values in $\mathbb{R}^N$ such that $\varepsilon(T) \in L^1_{\mathrm{loc}}(\Omega, \mathbb{R}^{N^2})$, then $T \in L^1_{\mathrm{loc}}(\Omega, \mathbb{R}^N)$. If Ω is, moreover, bounded and of class $\mathcal{C}^1$ and if $T \in \mathcal{D}'(\Omega, \mathbb{R}^N)$ satisfies $\varepsilon(T) \in L^1(\Omega, \mathbb{R}^{N^2})$, then $T \in L^1(\Omega, \mathbb{R}^N)$.*

Proof of Theorem 6.89 (see also [70]).

To prove the theorem, we use the following characterization of $LD(\Omega)$:

(6.90) $\quad \forall u \in L^1(\Omega), \quad u \in LD(\Omega) \iff \forall \alpha \in \mathbb{R}^N, \ (\alpha \cdot \nabla(\alpha \cdot u)) \in L^1(\Omega).$

We obtain the implication $\Leftarrow$ by taking $\alpha = e_i$, followed by $\alpha = (e_i + e_j)/2$. Conversely, if $u \in LD(\Omega)$, then

$$\alpha \cdot \nabla(\alpha \cdot u) = \alpha_i \alpha_j u_{i,j} = \alpha_i \alpha_j \varepsilon_{ij}(u),$$

which concludes the proof. Now that we have this result, given a vector α, we introduce a solution of the equation in the sense of distributions, namely

(6.91) $$\Delta E_\alpha + \nabla(\mathrm{div}\, E_\alpha) = \alpha \delta_0.$$

We can verify that the function E_α defined by

$$E_\alpha = \begin{cases} \dfrac{3\alpha}{8\pi} \ln r - x \dfrac{\alpha \cdot x}{8\pi} & \text{if } N = 2, \\[2mm] k_N \dfrac{3\alpha}{4r^{N-2}} + k_N \left(\dfrac{N-2}{4}\right) \dfrac{x(x \cdot \alpha)}{r^N} & \text{if } N > 2, \end{cases}$$

(cf. Exercise 6.4) satisfies the equation. Moreover, the derivatives of E_α clearly belong to $L^p_{\mathrm{loc}}(\mathbb{R}^N)$ for every $p < N/(N-1)$. We want to show that $u \in L^p_{\mathrm{loc}}$ if u is a distribution on Ω with $\varepsilon(u) \in L^p$. Let ω be a relatively compact open subset of Ω and let η be such that $\omega + B(0, 2\eta) \subset \Omega$. Let $\gamma \in \mathcal{D}(B(0, \eta))$ equal 1 in a neighborhood of 0. We compute the jth component of $(\Delta + \nabla \,\mathrm{div})(\gamma E_\alpha)$:

$$\Delta(\gamma E_{\alpha j}) + \partial_j\big(\mathrm{div}(\gamma \overrightarrow{E}_\alpha)\big) = \gamma \Delta E_{\alpha j} + 2\nabla\gamma \cdot \nabla E_{\alpha j} + E_{\alpha j}\Delta\gamma + \gamma\partial_j \,\mathrm{div}\, \overrightarrow{E}_\alpha$$
$$+ (\partial_j \gamma)(\mathrm{div}\, \overrightarrow{E_\alpha}) + \nabla(\partial_j \gamma) \cdot \overrightarrow{E}_\alpha$$
$$= \alpha_j \delta_0 + \zeta_j,$$

where ζ_j is a function in $\mathcal{D}(B(0,\eta))$. In particular, the convolution of u_j and ζ_j is a function in $\mathcal{C}^\infty(\omega + B(0,\eta))$, and therefore lies in $L^p(\omega)$ for every $p \leqslant \infty$. Let us show that for every α, we have $\alpha \cdot u \in L^p$. For this, we take the convolution of the previous equality with u_i. Simplifying the notation E_α to E, this gives

$$\alpha \cdot u = \sum_1^N \alpha_j u_j = \sum_1^N u_j \star (\Delta(\gamma E_j) + \partial_j(\mathrm{div}(\gamma E)) + \sum_1^N u_j \star \zeta_j,$$

whence, by setting $u \overrightarrow{\star} \zeta = \sum_1^N u_i \zeta_i$, we obtain

$$\alpha \cdot u - u \overrightarrow{\star} \zeta = \sum_{1 \leqslant i,j,k \leqslant N} \partial_i u_j \star \partial_i(\gamma E_j) + \partial_k u_i \partial_i(\gamma E_k)$$

$$= \sum_{1 \leqslant i,j \leqslant N} \partial_j u_i \star (\partial_j(\gamma E_i) + \partial_i(\gamma E_j))$$

$$= 2 \sum_{1 \leqslant i,j \leqslant N} \varepsilon_{ij}(u) \star \varepsilon_{ij}(\gamma E).$$

This last function restricted to ω coincides with the product $2(\varphi \varepsilon_{ij}(u)) \star \varepsilon_{ij}(\gamma E)$, where φ is a function in $\mathcal{D}(B(0,2\eta) + \omega)$ that equals 1 on $\omega + B(0,\eta)$. Since $2\varepsilon(\gamma E) \in L^p$ for every $p < N/(N-1)$ and $\varphi\varepsilon(u) \in L^1$, we find that u belongs to $L^p(\omega)$ for $p < N/(N-1)$.

We now wish to show that $u \in L^p(\Omega)$ when Ω is bounded and of class $\mathcal{C}^1$. We once more use the usual cover of Ω and the associated partition of unity. We note that a derivative of the type $\partial_i u_i$, which lies on the diagonal of the matrix $(\varepsilon_{ij}(u))$, is an element of $L^1(\Omega)$. Consider the open set $\Omega_k \cap \Omega$ for $k \geqslant 1$. There exists an index i such that the outward-pointing normal $\overrightarrow{\nu}$ to the boundary $\partial\Omega \cap \Omega_k$ satisfies $\overrightarrow{\nu} \cdot e_i \neq 0$ almost everywhere. We can then write

$$\Omega \cap \Omega_k \subset \{(\breve{x}_i, x_i) \mid \breve{x}_i \in \mathcal{O}_k, a_k(\breve{x}_i) < x_i\},$$

where $\mathcal{O}_k$ is an open subset of $\mathbb{R}^{N-1}$, a_k is a $\mathcal{C}^1$ function on $\mathcal{O}_k$, and the boundary is defined by

$$\partial\Omega \cap \Omega_k = \{(\breve{x}_i, a_k(\breve{x}_i)) \mid \breve{x}_i \in \mathcal{O}_k\}.$$

Given this, the same computation as in the proof of Theorem 6.74 shows that $u_i \in L^p(\Omega \cap \Omega_k)$ because of the inclusion $\partial u_i/\partial x_i \in L^1(\Omega)$.

The same reasoning can be applied to every other component u_j with $j \neq i$ for which $\overrightarrow{\nu} \cdot e_j \neq 0$ almost everywhere on $\partial\Omega \cap \Omega_k$. If this is not the case, then we still have $\overrightarrow{\nu} \cdot ((e_i + e_j)/\sqrt{2}) \neq 0$ almost everywhere. This suggests that we reduce to considering the function v defined by $v = u_i + u_j$ and change the variables so that we can use a derivative of v that belongs to $L^1(\Omega)$ (see

Exercise 6.8 for the details). By applying the same reasoning as before, we find that $v \in L^p(\Omega \cap \Omega_k)$. Since $v = u_i + u_j$ and $u_i \in L^p(\Omega \cap \Omega_k)$, it follows that $u_j \in L^p(\Omega \cap \Omega_k)$.

We use the partition of unity to deduce from the above that every component u_i belongs to $L^p(\Omega)$, and therefore that $u \in L^p(\Omega)$.   □

6.7.1 Trace Results

Theorem 6.92. *Let Ω be an open subset of $\mathbb{R}^N$ of class $\mathcal{C}^1$. Then there exists a continuous surjective linear map from $LD(\Omega)$ onto $L^1(\partial\Omega, \mathbb{R}^N)$ that coincides with the trace operator as defined in the classical sense, that is, on $LD(\Omega) \cap \mathcal{C}(\overline{\Omega}, \mathbb{R}^N)$ or on $W^{1,1}(\Omega, \mathbb{R}^N)$.*

Proof of Theorem 6.92. We take up the arguments of P. Suquet [67] and of R. Temam [70].

We begin by assuming that we are in the neighborhood of a point of the boundary where there exists a system of coordinates that allows us to write the boundary in the form $\{x_N = a_i(x') \mid x' \in \mathcal{O}'\}$. We also assume that u has compact support in $\overline{\Omega_i \cap \Omega}$, while

$$\Omega_i \cap \Omega \subset \{(x', x_N) \mid x_N > a_i(x'),\, x' \in \mathcal{O}'\},$$

where $\mathcal{O}'$ is an open subset of $\mathbb{R}^{N-1}$ and the function a_i is $\mathcal{C}^1$ on $\mathcal{O}'$. We show that in the neighborhood of such a point, we can define a trace $u_N(x', a_i(x'))$. The usual reasoning that uses a cover of Ω and the associated partition of unity then allows us to construct the trace $\gamma_0 u_N$ in $L^1(\partial\Omega)$, starting with this neighborhood. We recall that $\partial_N u_N \in L^1(\Omega)$ and for a pair (α, α') with $0 < \alpha < \alpha'$, we write the equality

$$u_N(x', a_i(x') + \alpha') - u_N(x', a_i(x') + \alpha)) = \int_\alpha^{\alpha'} \partial_N u_N(x', a_i(x') + y) dy.$$

To simplify the notation, we set $g_\alpha(x') = u_N(x', a_i(x') + \alpha)$. By integrating $|g_\alpha - g_{\alpha'}|$ over the hypersurface $\Sigma = \partial\Omega \cap \Omega_i$, we obtain
(6.93)
$$\int_\Sigma |g_\alpha - g_{\alpha'}|(x') d\sigma \leqslant \int_{\mathcal{O}'} \int_{a_i(x') + \alpha}^{a_i(x') + \alpha'} |\partial_N u_N(x', s)|\, |\nu_N^{-1}|(x', a_i(x')) ds\, dx',$$

where $\nu_N(x', a_i(x')) = -1/\sqrt{1 + \|\nabla a_i(x')\|^2}$ is the Nth component of the unit outward-pointing normal vector to $\partial\Omega$ at $(x', a_i(x'))$. Using the assumptions on ∇a_i and setting $\mathcal{A}_\alpha = \{(x', x_N) \in \Omega \mid x_N < a_i(x') + \alpha,\, x' \in \mathcal{O}'\}$, we deduce that

(6.94)
$$\int_\Sigma |g_\alpha - g_{\alpha'}|(x') d\sigma \leqslant C_1 \int_{\mathcal{A}_{\alpha'} \setminus \mathcal{A}_\alpha} |\partial_N u_N|(x) dx.$$

Since $\partial_N u_N$ lies in L^1, the right-hand side satisfies

$$\lim_{\substack{\alpha \to 0 \\ \alpha' \to 0}} \int_{\mathcal{A}_{\alpha'} \smallsetminus \mathcal{A}_\alpha} |\partial_N u_N(x)| \, dx = 0.$$

It follows that $\{g_\alpha\}$ is a Cauchy sequence in $L^1(\Sigma)$.

Let us set $\mathcal{B}_\alpha = \{(x', a_i(x') + \lambda) \mid \lambda \in [0, \alpha]\}$. By the above, the limit of $\{g_\alpha\}$, which we denote by g and which belongs to $L^1(\Sigma) = L^1(\partial\Omega \cap \Omega_i)$, satisfies

$$\int_\Sigma |g - g_\alpha| \, (x') d\sigma \leqslant C_1 \int_{\mathcal{B}_\alpha} |\partial_N u_N(x)| \, dx,$$

whence

$$\int_\Sigma |g| d\sigma \leqslant \int_\Sigma |g_\alpha| \, d\sigma + C_1 \int_{\mathcal{B}_\alpha} |\partial_N u_N(x)| \, dx.$$

By integrating this relation with respect to α over $[0, \alpha_0]$, where α_0 is bounded from above as a function of the compact support of u, we obtain

$$\alpha_0 \int_\Sigma |g| d\sigma \leqslant \int_0^{\alpha_0} \int_\Sigma |g_\alpha| \, d\sigma ds + C_1 \int_0^{\alpha_0} \int_{\mathcal{B}_\alpha} |\partial_N u_N(x)| \, dx \, ds$$

$$\leqslant \int_{\mathcal{B}_{\alpha_0}} |u_N(x)| \, dx + C_1 \int_0^{\alpha_0} \int_{\mathcal{B}_\alpha} |\partial_N u_N(x)| \, dx \, ds.$$

The first term on the right-hand side is bounded from above by $\|u_N\|_{L^1(\Omega)}$ and the second term by $\alpha_0 \|\partial_N u_N\|_{L^1(\Omega)}$. Consequently, the function g, which we now denote by $\gamma_0 u_N$, satisfies the inequality

$$\|\gamma_0 u_N\|_{L^1(\partial\Omega \cap \Omega_i)} \leqslant K \|u_N\|_{LD(\partial\Omega \cap \Omega_i)}.$$

This implies that the map that sends u_N to g, which is linear, is a continuous map from $LD(\partial\Omega \cap \Omega_i)$ to $L^1(\partial\Omega \cap \Omega_i)$.

This reasoning remains valid for every component u_i in the neighborhood of a boundary point x with $\nu_i(x) \neq 0$. If $\nu_i(x) = 0$, then there exists a j different from i, such that $\nu_j(x) \neq 0$. We then have $(\nu_i + \nu_j)(x) \neq 0$ and, by an argument we already used in the proof of Theorem 6.89, we can use the previous method to define the trace $\gamma_0(u_i + u_j)$ in a neighborhood of x. Moreover, since $\gamma_0 u_j$ is well defined, this leads to the trace of u_i in this neighborhood. As we have already stated, we construct the trace of each component in $L^1(\partial\Omega)$ and the resulting trace map is indeed linear and continuous.

Moreover, since the trace map γ_0 from $W^{1,1}(\Omega, \mathbb{R}^N)$ to $L^1(\partial\Omega, \mathbb{R}^N)$ is surjective, we see that the embedding $W^{1,1}(\Omega, \mathbb{R}^N) \subset BD(\Omega, \mathbb{R}^N)$ gives the surjectivity of the new trace map. $\qquad \square$

6.7.2 Embedding Results

Theorem 6.95. *Let Ω be a Lipschitz open subset of $\mathbb{R}^N$; then the space $LD(\Omega)$ is embedded in $L^{N/(N-1)}(\Omega, \mathbb{R}^N)$, and therefore in $L^q(\Omega, \mathbb{R}^N)$ for every q with $q \leqslant N/(N-1)$.*

Proof of Theorem 6.95.

We begin by establishing the critical property of the embedding, namely the inequality $\|u\|_{L^{N/(N-1)}(\Omega, \mathbb{R}^N)} \leqslant C(|\varepsilon(u)|_1)$ for C^∞ functions with compact support. The corresponding result for functions in $LD(\Omega)$ will follow by density. Let $u \in \mathcal{D}(\Omega, \mathbb{R}^N)$. We consider

$$\alpha = \sum_{i=1}^{i=N} \alpha_i e_i, \ |\alpha| = 1 \quad \text{and} \quad v_\alpha = \alpha \cdot u = \sum_1^N \alpha_i u_i.$$

Using the inequality $\left|\sum_{i \leqslant N, j \leqslant N} \alpha_i \alpha_j \varepsilon_{i,j}(u)\right| \leqslant N|\varepsilon(u)|$, we have

$$|v_\alpha(x)| = \left|\int_{-\infty}^0 \frac{d}{ds} v_\alpha(x + s\alpha) ds\right| \leqslant \int_{-\infty}^0 \left|\sum_{i,j=1}^N \alpha_i \alpha_j \partial_j u_i(x + s\alpha)\right| ds$$

$$= \int_{-\infty}^0 \left|\sum_{i,j=1}^N \alpha_i \alpha_j \varepsilon_{ij}(u)(x + s\alpha)\right| ds \leqslant N^2 I_\alpha,$$

where $I_\alpha = \int_{-\infty}^0 |\varepsilon(u)(x + s\alpha)| ds$.

Let us now consider vectors $h_k = \alpha - \alpha_k e_k$ for $k = 1, 2, \ldots, N - 1$. For $i \neq k$, we write

$$\cdot u_i(x) = \int_{-\infty}^0 \frac{d}{ds} u_i(x + sh_k) ds = \int_{-\infty}^0 \sum_{j \neq k} \alpha_j \partial_j u_i(x + sh_k) ds$$

and for $i = k$,

$$u_k(x) = \int_{-\infty}^0 \partial_k u_k(x + se_k) ds.$$

For a given k in $\{1, \ldots, N - 1\}$, we can then also write $v_\alpha(x)$ as

$$\sum_{i=1}^N \alpha_i u_i(x) = \int_{-\infty}^0 \sum_{i,j \neq k} \alpha_i \alpha_j \partial_j u_i(x + sh_k) ds + \int_{-\infty}^0 \alpha_k \partial_k u_k(x + se_k) ds$$

$$= 2\int_{-\infty}^0 \sum_{i,j \neq k} \alpha_i \alpha_j \varepsilon_{ij}(u)(x + sh_k) ds$$

$$+ \int_{-\infty}^0 \alpha_k \varepsilon_{kk}(u)(x + se_k) ds = I_k + J_k.$$

Let us consider the power $|v_\alpha(x)|^{N/(N-1)}$. We must show that this belongs to L^1_{loc}. We begin by using the definition of I_α given before to write the following inequality, which holds up to a multiplicative constant:

$$|v_\alpha(x)|^{N/(N-1)} \leqslant \left[I_\alpha |v_\alpha(x)|\right]^{1/(N-1)}.$$

Using the formula $|v_\alpha(x)|^{N-1} = \prod_1^{N-1}(I_k + J_k)$ and a classical inequality on norms in finite dimension, we deduce that $|v_\alpha(x)|^{N/(N-1)}$ is bounded from above by a linear combination of functions of the form

$$\left[I_\alpha H_1 H_2 \cdots H_{N-1}\right]^{1/(N-1)},$$

where H_i denotes either an integral I_i or an integral J_i. In the situations where we can apply Lemma 2.40 of Chapter 2, we will bound each term of such a product from above by a function in $N-1$ variables. Exercise 6.20 concerns the case $N = 3$, where we need a change of variables for which these products are all functions of two variables. That exercise can help motivate the following algebraic lemma, which we will use to determine the upper bounds. We state and prove the lemma in the general case.

Lemma 6.96. *Consider vectors $\alpha = \sum_i \alpha_i e_i$ with nonzero α_i and for every $i \in [1, N-1]$, let $h_i = \alpha - \alpha_i e_i$. For each index i, let E_i be a vector belonging to $\{h_i, e_i\}$. Then every sequence of the form $\alpha, E_1, E_2, \ldots, E_{N-1}$ is a basis for $\mathbb{R}^N$.*

Proof of Lemma 6.96.

We begin by supposing that $E_i = h_i$ for every i. In this case, the determinant of the system $\alpha, h_1, h_2 \cdots h_{N-1}$ equals $\alpha_1 \cdots \alpha_N \det(J)$, where J is the matrix whose elements all equal 1 except for those on the first superdiagonal, which are all 0. Consequently, the lemma holds since this determinant is nonzero.

To show the result in the other cases, we use an induction on the dimension of the space, where the initial step is obvious. We use vectors $\overline{\alpha}$ and $\overline{E_i}$ such that

$$\alpha = \overline{\alpha} + \alpha_N e_N \quad \text{and} \quad \forall i \leqslant N-2, \; E_i = \overline{E_i} + \varepsilon_i e_N,$$

where $\varepsilon_i = \alpha_N$ if $E_i = h_i$ and $\varepsilon_i = 0$ if $E_i = e_i$. The induction hypothesis applied to the $N-1$-dimensional space $[e_1, e_2, \ldots, e_{N-1}]$ ensures us that the vectors $\overline{\alpha}, \overline{E_1}, \ldots, \overline{E_{N-2}}$ form a basis of that space. Indeed, they are defined in the same manner as α, E_i, but without components over e_N. Since $E_{N-1} \in \{h_{N-1}, e_{N-1}\}$, we obtain the result of the lemma for dimension N by proving that the sequences

$$\overline{\alpha} + \alpha_N e_N, \; \overline{E_1} + \varepsilon_1 e_N, \ldots, \overline{E_{N-2}} + \varepsilon_{N-2} e_N, \; e_{N-1}$$
$$\overline{\alpha} + \alpha_N e_N, \; \overline{E_1} + \varepsilon_1 e_N, \ldots, \overline{E_{N-2}} + \varepsilon_{N-2} e_N, \; h_{N-1}$$

both form bases.

Consider the first sequence, and let λ_j, $j \in [0, N-1]$, satisfy

$$\lambda_0(\overline{\alpha} + \alpha_N e_N) + \sum_1^{N-2} \lambda_i(\overline{E_i} + \varepsilon_i e_N) + \lambda_{N-1} e_{N-1} = 0,$$

which implies that

$$(6.97) \qquad \lambda_0\overline{\alpha} + \sum_1^{N-2} \lambda_i \overline{E_i} + \lambda_{N-1} e_{N-1} = -\left(\lambda_0\alpha_N + \sum_1^{N-2} \lambda_i\varepsilon_i\right)e_N.$$

We deduce from this that $\lambda_0\alpha_N + \sum_1^{N-2} \lambda_i\varepsilon_i = 0$ or, by letting λ_i^* denote the λ_i for which ε_i is nonzero, that $\lambda_0\alpha_N + \sum_1^{N-2} \lambda_i^*\alpha_N = 0$. Consequently, since $\alpha_N \neq 0$, we obtain the relation $\lambda_0 + \sum_1^{N-2} \lambda_i^* = 0$. When $\varepsilon_i \neq 0$, that is, when $E_i = h_i$, the coefficient of $\overline{E_i}$ over e_{N-1} is α_{N-1}. Consequently, the coefficient of e_{N-1} on the left-hand side of (6.97) can be written as $\lambda_{N-1} + \lambda_0\alpha_{N-1} + \sum_1^{N-2} \lambda_i^*\alpha_{N-1}$ and therefore equals λ_{N-1}. By this result and the induction hypothesis, we see that when the left-hand side of (6.97) equals 0, we have $\lambda_{N-1} = 0$, $\lambda_0 = 0$, and $\lambda_i = 0$ for every $i \in [1, N-2]$.

Next, consider the second sequence. In this case, since $h_{N-1} = \overline{\alpha} + \alpha_N e_N - \alpha_{N-1} e_{N-1}$, the right-hand side of (6.97) is replaced by

$$-\left(\lambda_0\alpha_N + \sum_1^{N-2} \lambda_i^*\alpha_N + \lambda_{N-1}\alpha_N\right)e_N,$$

whence

$$(6.98) \qquad \lambda_0 + \sum_1^{N-2} \lambda_i^* + \lambda_{N-1} = 0.$$

The left-hand side of (6.97) is replaced by

$$(\lambda_0 + \lambda_{N-1})\overline{\alpha} - \lambda_{N-1} e_{N-1} + \sum_1^{N-2} \lambda_i \overline{E_i}.$$

Taking into account equality (6.98), we see that the coefficient of the left-hand side with index $N-1$ is $-\lambda_{N-1}$. We conclude, as in the first case, by using the induction hypothesis. $\square$

Let us return to the proof of the theorem. We consider a product $I_\alpha H_1 \cdots H_N$ where $H_i = \int_{\mathbb{R}^N} |\varepsilon(u)|(x + sE_i)ds$. Let ξ_j be the coefficient in the basis $\alpha, E_1, \ldots, E_{N-1}$, so that $x = \sum x_i e_i = \xi_0\alpha + \sum_1^{N-1} \xi_j E_j$. Then, through a change of variables that involves the determinant of the system of vectors $\alpha, E_1, \ldots, E_N$, we prove that H_i does not depend on the variable ξ_i. Consequently, we can apply Lemma 2.40 of Chapter 2, which tells us that v_α belongs to $L_{\text{loc}}^{N/(N-1)}(\Omega)$.

Moreover, the inequality concerning the norms in the lemma shows that there exists a constant C such that $\|v_\alpha\|_{L^{N/(N-1)}} \leqslant C\|u\|_{LD(\Omega)}$. Finally, since this is true for every α, we can deduce that for the functions in $\mathcal{D}(\Omega)$, the embedding is not surjective, and the existence of the embedding is proved, as stated at the beginning of the proof.   □

To obtain the regularity up to the boundary, we take up arguments already used in Theorem 6.74.

Theorem 6.99. *Let Ω be a Lipschitz bounded open subset of $\mathbb{R}^N$. The embeddings of $LD(\Omega)$ in $L^p(\Omega, \mathbb{R}^N)$ for $p < N/N - 1$ are compact.*

Proof of Theorem 6.99. By the previous theorem and Lemma 2.82 of Chapter 2, it suffices to show that the embedding of $LD(\Omega)$ in $L^1(\Omega)$ is compact. We will use the compactness criterion of Theorem 1.95. Let $\{u_n\}$ be a bounded sequence in $LD(\Omega)$. We want to show the following statement:

$$\forall \varepsilon > 0, \ \exists \delta > 0, \ \exists G \text{ compact}, \ \forall n \in \mathbb{N}, \ \forall h, \ |h| \leqslant \inf(\delta, d(G, \partial\Omega)) \Longrightarrow$$

$$(6.100) \qquad \int_{\Omega \smallsetminus G} |u_n(x)|dx \leqslant \varepsilon \quad \text{and} \quad \int_G |u_n(x+h) - u_n(x)|dx \leqslant \varepsilon.$$

The first inequality of (6.100) is obvious, because u_n is bounded, owing to the existence of the embedding of $BV(\Omega)$ into $L^{N/(N-1)}(\Omega)$

$$(6.101) \qquad \int_{\Omega \smallsetminus G} |u_n(x)|dx$$
$$\leqslant \left(\int_{\Omega \smallsetminus G} |u_n(x)|^{N/(N-1)}dx \right)^{N-1/N} \text{mes}(\Omega \smallsetminus G)^{1/N}.$$

Moreover, because Ω is bounded, this measure can be made arbitrarily small by a suitable choice of G.

Proving the second statement is more delicate. To begin, we can drop the index n and suppose that u has compact support in Ω. Namely, it suffices to replace u by φu, where φ is a C^1 function with compact support in Ω and value 1 on G. Let α be a vector of norm 1 in $\mathbb{R}^N$. We will show that for h sufficiently small,

$$\forall s \in \,]0, 1[, \ \exists c > 0, \quad \|\tau_h(\alpha \cdot u) - \alpha \cdot u\|_{L^1(\Omega)} \leqslant c|h|^s \|\varepsilon(u)\|_{L^1(\Omega, \mathbb{R}^{N^2})}.$$

We use the computations of Theorem 6.89. Let E_α be as defined in the proof of that theorem and satisfy

$$\Delta E_\alpha + \nabla(\text{div}(E_\alpha)) = \alpha\delta_0,$$

and let γ be a function in $\mathcal{D}(B(0,\eta))$. We recall the following result from Theorem 6.89:

$$\alpha \cdot u - u \overrightarrow{\star} \zeta = 2 \sum_{1 \leqslant i,j \leqslant N} \varepsilon_{ij}(u) \star \varepsilon_{ij}(\gamma E_\alpha),$$

in which ζ is a regular function with compact support in $\mathbb{R}^N$. Since translation commutes with convolution, it follows that

$$\tau_h(\alpha \cdot u) - \alpha \cdot u = 2\sum_{ij} \varepsilon_{ij}(\tau_h(\gamma E_\alpha) - (\gamma E_\alpha)) \star \varepsilon_{ij}(u) + (\tau_h\zeta - \zeta) \overrightarrow{\star} u.$$

To continue, we have $|(\tau_h\zeta - \zeta)\overrightarrow{\star} u| \leqslant C|h|$ and $\varepsilon_{ij}(E_\alpha)$ is a positively homogeneous function of degree $1 - N$, which allows us to apply the following lemma.

Lemma 6.102. *Let f be a function on $\mathbb{R}^N$ with values in $\mathbb{R}$ that is positively homogeneous of degree $1 - N$ and $\mathcal{C}^1$ outside of 0. Then for every $s \in [0,1[$, there exists a C such that for every h with $|h| \leqslant 1$, we have*

$$|f(x+h) - f(x)| \leqslant C|h|^s \left\{ \frac{1}{|x+h|^{N-1+s}} + \frac{1}{|x|^{N-1+s}} \right\}.$$

Proof of Lemma 6.102.

We reduce to showing the result for x of norm 1. Indeed, let us suppose the result proved for such x and for every h. Using the homogeneity, we then write

$$|f(x+h) - f(x)| = |x|^{-N+1}|f((x+h)/|x|) - f(x/|x|)|$$
$$\leqslant C|x|^{-N+1} (|h|/|x|)^s \left(\frac{1}{(1 + |h|/|x|)^{N-1+s}} + 1 \right)$$
$$= C|h|^s \left(\frac{1}{|x+h|^{N-1+s}} + \frac{1}{|x|^{N-1+s}} \right).$$

We therefore wish to prove the property for x of norm 1. Let us suppose that $|h| < 1/2$. We use the inequality of the mean value theorem at x. Since f is homogeneous of degree $1 - N$, its gradient is homogeneous of degree $-N$, whence

$$|f(x+h) - f(x)| \leqslant \sup_{|y|=1} |\nabla f(y)| \frac{|h|}{|x+\theta h|^N}.$$

Using $|h| < 1/2$, we have

$$|\theta h + x| \geqslant |x| - |h| \geqslant \frac{1}{2} \quad \text{and} \quad |\theta h + x| \leqslant \frac{3}{2} \leqslant 3|x+h|.$$

Hence

$$|h|^{1-s}\frac{1}{|x+\theta h|^N} \leqslant \frac{1+|x+h|^{1-s}}{|x+\theta h|^N} \leqslant 2^N + \frac{3^N}{|x+h|^{N-1+s}}$$

$$\leqslant C\Big(1+\frac{1}{|x+h|^{N-1+s}}\Big).$$

Consequently,

$$|f(x+h)-f(x)| \leqslant \frac{C'|h|}{|x+\theta h|^N} \leqslant C'|h|^s\Big(\frac{1}{|x|^{N-1+s}}+\frac{1}{|x+h|^{N-1+s}}\Big).$$

Let us now suppose that $|h| \geqslant 1/2$ and $|x| = 1$. We then have $|h|/|x+h| \geqslant 1/3$ and, by the homogeneity, $|f(x)| \leqslant |x|^{1-N}\sup_{|y|\leqslant 1}|f(y)|$. It follows that

$$|f(x+h)-f(x)| \leqslant C\Big(\frac{1}{|x+h|^{N-1}}+1\Big) \leqslant C'\Big(\frac{3^s|h|^s}{|x+h|^{N-1+s}}+1\Big)$$

$$\leqslant Ch^s\Big(\frac{1}{|x+h|^{N-1+s}}+1\Big)$$

because $h \geqslant 1/2$ implies $(3|h|)^{-s} \leqslant 1$.   □

We return to the proof of the theorem by applying the lemma to the $\varepsilon_{ij}(E_\alpha)$. Taking into account all components and the factor γ, up to the term concerning ζ, we can write

$$|\tau_h(\alpha \cdot u)-\alpha \cdot u|(x) \leqslant C|h|^s\Big\{\tau_h\big(\frac{\gamma(x)}{|x|^{N-1+s}}\big)+\frac{\gamma(x)}{|x|^{N-1+s}}\Big\} \star |\varepsilon(u)|,$$

or

$$|\tau_h(\alpha \cdot u)-\alpha \cdot u|(x) \leqslant C|h|^s\Big\{\frac{\gamma(x)}{|x|^{N-1+s}} \star (|\tau_h\varepsilon(u)|+|\varepsilon(u)|)\Big\}.$$

The Hausdorff–Young theorem (cf. Appendix to Chapter 4) implies that, since $x \mapsto \gamma(x)|x|^{-N+1-s}$ belongs to L^k for $k < N/(N-1+s)$, hence for $k = 1$ in the present situation, the convolution $\gamma 1/|x|^{N-1+s}\star(|\tau_h\varepsilon(u)|+|\varepsilon(u)|)$ belongs to $L^k(G)$ for the same values of k. For $k = 1$, we have the inequality

$$\Big\|\gamma\frac{1}{|x|^{N-1+s}} \star \big(|\tau_h\varepsilon(u)|+|\varepsilon(u)|\big)\Big\|_{L^1(G)} \leqslant \Big\|\gamma\frac{1}{|x|^{N-1+s}}\Big\|_1 |\varepsilon(u)|_{L^1(\Omega)}.$$

We deduce from this that

$$\|\tau_h(\alpha \cdot u)-\alpha \cdot u\|_{L^1(G)} \leqslant C|h|^s|\varepsilon(u)|_{L^1(\Omega)}$$

for every $s < 1$. Returning to the vector function u, this concludes the proof of the compactness of the embedding of $LD(\Omega)$ in $L^1(\Omega)$, and therefore in every $L^p(\Omega)$ with $1 < p < N/(N-1)$.   □

6.8 The Space of Functions with a Measure as Deformation

For an open subset Ω of $\mathbb{R}^N$ that need not be bounded, we let

$$BD(\Omega) = \left\{ u \in L^1(\Omega, \mathbb{R}^N) \mid \forall i, j \in [1, N], \ \varepsilon_{ij}(u) \in M^1(\Omega) \right\}$$

($BD(\Omega)$ means "with bounded deformations".) Taking the seminorm $\int_\Omega |\varepsilon(u)|$ defined by

$$\int_\Omega |\varepsilon(u)| = \sup_{\{\varphi_{ij} \in \mathcal{C}_c(\Omega), \sum_{1 \leqslant i, j \leqslant N} |\varphi_{ij}|_\infty^2 \leqslant 1\}} \int_\Omega \varepsilon_{ij}(u) \varphi_{ij} \, dx,$$

we can endow the space BD with the norm

$$\|u\|_{BD(\Omega)} = \|u\|_{L^1(\Omega, \mathbb{R}^N)} + \int_\Omega |\varepsilon(u)|$$

for which it is a Banach space.

6.8.1 Regularity and Density Results

Theorem 6.103. *Let $T \in \mathcal{D}'(\Omega, \mathbb{R}^N)$ be such that for every $(i, j) \in [1, N]^2$, $\varepsilon_{ij}(T) \in M^1(\Omega)$; then $T \in BD_{\mathrm{loc}}(\Omega)$. If Ω is moreover a bounded open set of class $\mathcal{C}^1$, then $T \in BD(\Omega)$.*

The proof of this theorem is similar to that for $LD(\Omega)$. We leave it to the reader.

Theorem 6.104. *The space $\mathcal{C}^\infty(\Omega) \cap W^{1,1}(\Omega)$ is dense for the tight topology on $BD(\Omega)$. In other words,*

$$\forall u \in BD(\Omega), \ \exists \{u_n\} \subset W^{1,1}(\Omega) \cap \mathcal{C}^\infty(\Omega),$$

$$\begin{cases} u_n \to u \text{ in } L^1(\Omega), \\ \varepsilon(u_n) \rightharpoonup \varepsilon(u) \text{ vaguely in } M^1(\Omega) \\ \int_\Omega |\varepsilon(u_n)| \to \int_\Omega |\varepsilon(u)|. \end{cases}$$

Proof of Theorem 6.104.

We will use the approximation *from the inside* of Theorem 6.56 and its notation. Moreover, we impose the following inequalities:

$$\left| \int_\Omega |\rho_{\eta_j} * (\varphi_j \varepsilon(u))| - \int_\Omega |\varphi_j \varepsilon(u)| \right| < \delta,$$

$$\int_\Omega |\rho_{\eta_j} * (\varphi_j u) - \varphi_j u| < \delta 2^{-j},$$

$$\int_\Omega |\rho_{\eta_j} * (\nabla \varphi_j \otimes u) - \nabla \varphi_j \otimes u| < \delta 2^{-j}.$$

We let

$$u_\delta = \sum_0^\infty \rho_{\eta_j} * (\varphi_j u).$$

We can easily verify that

$$\int_\Omega |u_\delta - u| < \delta \quad \text{and} \quad \left| \int_\Omega |\varepsilon(u_\delta)| - \int_\Omega |\varepsilon(u)| \right| < 2\delta,$$

concluding the proof.   □

Corollary 6.105. *Let Ω be a Lipschitz open subset of $\mathbb{R}^N$; we then have*

$$\forall p \leqslant \frac{N}{N-1}, \quad BD(\Omega) \hookrightarrow L^p(\Omega),$$

where the embedding is compact for $p < N/(N-1)$ if Ω is bounded.

Proof of Corollary 6.105.

Let $u \in BD(\Omega)$ and let $\{u_n\}$ be as in Theorem 6.104; then there exists a constant $C > 0$ depending only on Ω, such that

$$\|u_n\|_p \leqslant C(\|u_n\|_1 + \|\varepsilon(u_n)\|_1).$$

In particular, since the sequence $\{u_n\}$ is bounded in $LD(\Omega)$, it is bounded in every $L^p(\Omega)$ with $p \leqslant N/(N-1)$. We can therefore extract a subsequence that converges weakly in L^p for $p > 1$. Since $\{u_n\}$ also converges to u in L^1, we see that the lower semicontinuity of the norm in $L^p(\Omega)$ gives

$$\|u\|_p \leqslant \varliminf_{n \to \infty} \|u_n\|_p \leqslant \varliminf_{n \to \infty} C\left(\|u_n\|_1 + \|\varepsilon(u_n)\|_1\right)$$
$$= C(\|u\|_1 + \|\varepsilon(u)\|_1),$$

and therefore $u \in L^p(\Omega)$. To see that the embedding is compact in $L^1(\Omega)$ (for example) when Ω is bounded, we prove the following inequality, which holds for $G \Subset \Omega$ and $h > 0$ satisfying $G + B(0,h) \subset \Omega$:

$$\|\tau_h u - u\|_{L^1(G)} \leqslant h^s \int_\Omega |\varepsilon(u)|.$$

Here s is a real number in $[0, 1[$ that we obtain by using both the analogue of this inequality for functions in $LD(\Omega)$ and the previous density theorem.   □

Korn's inequality (cf. the remark after Definition 6.78) does not hold in $BD(\Omega)$. In other words, we have the following result.

Theorem 6.106.
$$BV(\Omega, \mathbb{R}^N) \neq BD(\Omega).$$

Proof of Theorem 6.106.

We will give a proof by contradiction. Let us therefore assume that $BV(\Omega, \mathbb{R}^N) = BD(\Omega)$. The open image theorem then tells us that there exists a constant $C > 0$ such that for every u in $BV(\Omega, \mathbb{R}^N)$, we have

$$(6.107) \qquad \|u\|_{L^1(\Omega)} + \int_\Omega |\nabla u| \leqslant C \Big(\|u\|_{L^1(\Omega)} + \int_\Omega |\varepsilon(u)| \Big).$$

Let $u \in LD(\Omega)$, $u \notin W^{1,1}(\Omega)$, and let $\{u_n\} \in C^\infty \cap LD(\Omega)$ converge to u in $LD(\Omega)$. Then the inequality applied to $\{u_p - u_q\}$ implies that $\{u_p\}$ is a Cauchy sequence in $W^{1,1}(\Omega)$, hence converges in this space. Now, $\{u_n\}$ converges to u in L^1. It follows by the uniqueness of the limit that $u \in W^{1,1}(\Omega)$, giving a contradiction. $\qquad \square$

6.8.2 Results on Traces

Theorem 6.108. *Let Ω be an open subset of $\mathbb{R}^N$ of class C^1. There exists a surjective linear map from $BD(\Omega)$ onto $L^1(\partial\Omega)$ that coincides with the trace map on $W^{1,1}(\Omega)$ defined earlier.*

Remark 6.109. This *trace map* is not continuous for the weak topology.

Proof of Theorem 6.108.

We follow the arguments used for $LD(\Omega)$. We begin by proving the existence of a trace for u_N in a neighborhood of a boundary point where there exists a system of coordinates that allows us to write

$$\Omega \cap \Omega_i \subset \{(x', x_N) \mid x' \in \mathcal{O}', \, x_N > a_i(x')\},$$
$$\partial\Omega \cap \Omega_i = \{(x', a_i(x')) \mid x' \in \mathcal{O}'\},$$

where $\mathcal{O}'$ is an open subset of $\mathbb{R}^{N-1}$ and a_i is a C^1 function on $\mathcal{O}'$. We moreover may, and do, assume that u_N has compact support in $\overline{\Omega} \cap \Omega_i$. Let α have the property that $\int_{\Sigma_\alpha} |\partial_N u_N| = 0$, that is, that $\partial_N u_N$ does not charge the hypersurface $\Sigma_\alpha = \{(x', a(x') + \alpha) \mid x' \in \mathcal{O}'\}$.

For α and α' chosen this way with $\alpha < \alpha'$, we write

$$u_N(x', a(x') + \alpha') - u_N(x', a(x') + \alpha) = \int_{a(x')+\alpha}^{a(x')+\alpha'} \frac{\partial u_N}{\partial x_N}(x', s) ds.$$

By integrating over $\Sigma = \{(x', a(x'), x' \in \mathcal{O}'\}$, using the notation g_α for the function $g_\alpha(x') = u_N(x', a(x') + \alpha)$ we obtain

$$\int_\Sigma |g_\alpha - g_{\alpha'}|(x') dx' \leqslant \int_{\mathcal{O}'} \int_{a(x')+\alpha}^{a(x')+\alpha'} \left| \frac{\partial u_N}{\partial x_N}(x', s) \right| \frac{ds dx'}{|\nu_N|(x', a(x'))},$$

with $\nu_N(x', a(x')) = -(1 + |\nabla a(x')|^2)^{-1/2}$. Consequently,

$$\int_\Sigma |g_\alpha - g_{\alpha'}| \leqslant C_1 \int_{\mathcal{A}_{\alpha'} \smallsetminus \overline{\mathcal{A}_\alpha}} \left|\frac{\partial u_N}{\partial x_N}\right| dx \leqslant C_1 \int_{(\Omega \cap \Omega_i) \smallsetminus \overline{\mathcal{A}_\alpha}} \left|\frac{\partial u_N}{\partial x_N}\right| dx,$$

where $\mathcal{A}_\alpha = \{(x', x_N) \in \Omega \mid x_N < a(x') + \alpha\}$. When α and α' tend to 0, the term on the right-hand side of this inequality tends to 0, because it is the integral of a measure that is bounded on the complement in $\Omega \cap \Omega_i$ of a sequence of compact sets $\overline{\mathcal{A}_\alpha}$ that tends to $\Omega \cap \Omega_i$. It follows that $\{g_\alpha\}$ is a Cauchy sequence in $L^1(\Sigma)$. Let g be its limit. By the above, we have

$$\int_\Sigma |g - g_\alpha| \leqslant C_1 \int_{\mathcal{A}_\alpha \smallsetminus \mathcal{A}_0} \left|\frac{\partial u_N}{\partial x_N}\right|,$$

whence

$$\int_\Sigma |g| \leqslant \int_\Sigma |g_\alpha| + C_1 \int_{\mathcal{A}_\alpha \smallsetminus \mathcal{A}_0} \left|\frac{\partial u_N}{\partial x_N}\right|.$$

Integrating with respect to $\alpha \in [0, \alpha_0[$, we obtain

$$\int_\Sigma |g| \leqslant \frac{1}{\alpha_0} \int_0^{\alpha_0} \int_\Sigma |g_\alpha|\, d\alpha + C_1 \frac{1}{\alpha_0} \int_0^{\alpha_0} \int_{\mathcal{A}_\alpha \smallsetminus \mathcal{A}_0} \left|\frac{\partial u_N}{\partial x_N}\right| d\alpha$$

$$\leqslant C \left(\int_\Omega |u_N| + \int_\Omega |\partial_N u_N| \right)$$

(in these inequalities, α_0 satisfies $u_N(x', a(x') + \alpha_0) = 0$). When $\nu(x) \cdot e_N = 0$, we use an i for which $\nu_i(x) \neq 0$. We then have $(\nu_i + \nu_N)(x) \neq 0$, so that we can define $u_i + u_N$, and therefore u_N since u_i is well defined. $\qquad\square$

The reader may also consult [67].

At this point, let us make an important remark concerning, for example, $BD(\Omega)$, which emphasizes the value of the interior and exterior traces of a function on a *hypersurface* in Ω.

Proposition 6.110. *Let Ω_1 and Ω_2 be two open subsets of $\mathbb{R}^N$ of class $\mathcal{C}^1$ and let Σ be a manifold of dimension $N - 1$ such that $\Omega = \Omega_1 \cup \Sigma \cup \Omega_2$, $\Omega_1 \cap \Omega_2 = \varnothing$, $\overline{\Omega_1} \cap \overline{\Omega_2} = \overline{\Sigma}$, and Ω is the interior of $\overline{\Omega_1 \cup \Omega_2}$.*

If $u \in BD(\Omega)$ and if u^+ and u^- are the traces of u on Σ seen as elements of $BD(\Omega_2)$ and $BD(\Omega_1)$, respectively, then for every $\varphi \in \mathcal{D}(\Omega)$, we have

$$\langle \varepsilon_{ij}(u), \varphi \rangle = \langle \varepsilon_{ij}(u), \varphi\chi_{\Omega_1} \rangle + \langle \varepsilon_{ij}(u), \varphi\chi_{\Omega_2} \rangle$$
$$- \int_\Sigma \varphi \frac{u_i^+ n_j + u_j^+ n_i - (u_i^- n_j + u_j^- n_i)}{2},$$

where $\vec{n}$ denotes the outward-pointing normal to Σ in the direction from Ω_1 to Ω_2.

Proof of Proposition 6.110.

Let $u \in BD(\Omega)$ with $u|_{\Omega_i} \in BD(\Omega_i)$. Let $\varphi \in \mathcal{D}(\Omega)$. We first apply Green's formula to $\varepsilon_{ij}(u)$ and to φ in the regular open set Ω_1, noting that the trace is reduced to the trace on Σ, that is, to u^-, and that the outward-pointing normal is $\overrightarrow{n}$, with components n_i:

$$2 \int_{\Omega_1} \varepsilon_{ij}(u)\varphi \, dx = - \int_{\Omega_1} \Big[u_i \partial_j \varphi + u_j \partial_i \varphi \Big] dx$$
$$+ \int_{\Sigma} \Big[(u_i)^-(x')(n_j) + (u_j)^-(x')(n_i) \Big] \varphi(x') dx'.$$

Likewise, in Ω_2, noting that for the function we are considering, the trace on the boundary of $\partial\Omega_2$ reduces to the trace on Σ, that is, to u^+, and that the outward-pointing normal is $-\overrightarrow{n}$ with components $-n_i$, we have

$$2 \int_{\Omega_2} \varepsilon_{ij}(u)\varphi \, dx = - \int_{\Omega_2} \Big[u_i \partial_j \varphi + u_j \partial_i \varphi \Big] dx$$
$$- \int_{\Sigma} \Big[(u_i)^+(x')(n_j) + (u_j)^+(x')(n_i) \Big] \varphi(x') dx'.$$

We obtain the desired formula by adding the last two equalities and using the definition of the derivative of a distribution in Ω. $\qquad\square$

As was the case for BV, we have a continuity result for the trace map for the intermediate topology.

Theorem 6.111. *Let Ω be an open subset of $\mathbb{R}^N$ of class $\mathcal{C}^1$ and let $\{u_n\}$ be a sequence in $BD(\Omega)$ that converges tightly to u in $BD(\Omega)$ in the following sense:*

$$u_n \longrightarrow u \text{ in } L^1(\Omega) \quad \text{and} \quad \int_{\Omega} |\varepsilon(u_n)| \longrightarrow \int_{\Omega} |\varepsilon(u)|;$$

then $\gamma_0(u_n) \to \gamma_0(u)$ in $L^1(\partial\Omega)$.

Proof of Theorem 6.111.

Let C be a constant such that for every $u \in BD(\Omega)$, we have

$$\|u\|_{L^1(\partial\Omega)} \leqslant C \left(\|u\|_1 + |\varepsilon(u)|_1 \right).$$

Let Ω_0 be a relatively compact subset of Ω with $\int_{\Omega \setminus \overline{\Omega_0}} |\varepsilon(u)| \leqslant \eta$. Let φ be a regular function with values between 0 and 1 and compact support in Ω that equals 1 on Ω_0. Moreover, let N_0 satisfy

$$\forall n \geqslant N_0, \quad \int_{\Omega} |u_n - u| \leqslant \frac{\eta}{1 + \|\nabla\varphi_0\|_\infty}$$

and
$$\int_{\Omega} |\varepsilon(u_n)|(1 - \varphi_0) \leqslant \int_{\Omega} |\varepsilon(u)(1 - \varphi_0)| + \eta \leqslant 2\eta.$$

Such an N_0 exists by the tight convergence of $|\varepsilon(u_n)|$ to $|\varepsilon(u)|$. Then, since $\varphi_0 = 1$ on $\partial\Omega$, we see that the integral $\int_{\partial\Omega} |\gamma_0(u_n - u)|$ is bounded from above as follows:

$$C\Big(\int_\Omega |(u_n - u)(1 - \varphi_0 + |\nabla\varphi_0|)| + \int_\Omega |\varepsilon(u_n)(1 - \varphi_0) - \varepsilon(u)(1 - \varphi_0)| \Big) \leqslant 4\eta. \quad \square$$

6.9 Generalized Green's Formulas

Using a simplified notation, we define the following space:

$$(6.112) \qquad W(\mathrm{div})(\Omega) = \big\{ \sigma \in L^\infty(\Omega, \mathbb{R}^N) \mid \mathrm{div}\, \sigma \in L^N(\Omega) \big\}.$$

We endow this with the norm

$$(6.113) \qquad \|\sigma\|_{W(\mathrm{div})(\Omega)} = \|\sigma\|_\infty + \|\mathrm{div}\, \sigma\|_{L^N(\Omega)}.$$

We also define the space

$$(6.114) \qquad L(\mathrm{div})(\Omega) = \big\{ \sigma \in L^\infty(\Omega, E) \mid \mathrm{div}\, \sigma \in L^N(\Omega, \mathbb{R}^N) \big\},$$

where E denotes the space of symmetric tensors of order 2 on $\mathbb{R}^N$, endowed with the same norm, adapted to the functions with values in $\mathbb{R}^N$. We then have the following generalized Green's formula (see also Exercise 3.6 of Chapter 3).

Theorem 6.115. *Let Ω be an open set of class C^1. There exists a continuous linear map from $W(\mathrm{div})(\Omega)$ to $L^\infty(\partial\Omega)$ that sends σ to $\sigma \cdot \vec{n}$ and for which the generalized Green's formula*

$$\int_\Omega \nabla u \cdot \sigma + \int_\Omega u \, \mathrm{div}\, \sigma = \int_{\partial\Omega} (\sigma \cdot \vec{n})\, u$$

holds for every $u \in W^{1,1}(\Omega)$ and every $\sigma \in W(\mathrm{div})(\Omega)$. The vector $\vec{n}$ in the formula denotes the unit outward-pointing normal to $\partial\Omega$. Moreover, $\sigma \cdot \vec{n}$ coincides with the restriction to the boundary when

$$\sigma \in C(\overline{\Omega}) \cap W(\mathrm{div})(\Omega).$$

The following is an extension of this formula to the functions in $BV(\Omega)$.

Theorem 6.116. *Let Ω be an open set of class C^1 and let $(u, \sigma) \in BV(\Omega) \times W(\mathrm{div})(\Omega)$. We consider the distribution $(\nabla u \cdot \sigma)$ defined by*

$$\forall \varphi \in \mathcal{D}(\Omega, \mathbb{R}), \quad \langle (\nabla u \cdot \sigma), \varphi \rangle = -\int_\Omega u \, \mathrm{div}\, \sigma \cdot \varphi - \int_\Omega u\, (\sigma \cdot \nabla\varphi).$$

Then $(\nabla u \cdot \sigma)$ *is a bounded measure on* Ω *that is absolutely continuous with respect to* $|\nabla u|$ *and coincides with the usual definition of* $\nabla u \cdot \sigma$ *when* $u \in W^{1,1}(\Omega)$ *and* $\sigma \in W(\mathrm{div})(\Omega)$. *More precisely,* $|\nabla u \cdot \sigma| \leqslant \|\sigma\|_\infty |\nabla u|$. *Moreover, the measure* ∇u^S *defined by* $(\nabla u^S \cdot \sigma) = (\nabla u \cdot \sigma) - (\nabla u^{\mathrm{ac}} \cdot \sigma)$ *is a singular measure that satisfies* $|(\nabla u^S \cdot \sigma)| \leqslant |(\nabla u)^S| \|\sigma\|_\infty$.

Finally, we obtain the following Green's formula. If $(u, \sigma) \in BV(\Omega) \times W(\mathrm{div})(\Omega)$ *and if* $\varphi \in \mathcal{C}(\overline{\Omega}) \cap \mathcal{C}^1(\Omega)$, *then*

$$\langle (\nabla u \cdot \sigma), \varphi \rangle = - \int_\Omega u \, \mathrm{div}\, \sigma \varphi - \int_\Omega u \sigma \cdot \nabla \varphi + \int_{\partial\Omega} u \sigma \cdot \vec{n}\, \varphi.$$

Proof of Theorem 6.115.

Let $\sigma \in W(\mathrm{div})(\Omega)$. By the surjectivity of the trace map from $W^{1,1}(\Omega)$ to $L^1(\partial\Omega)$, there exists a $C > 0$ with the following property. For every $v \in L^1(\partial\Omega)$, there exists a $V \in W^{1,1}(\Omega)$ such that $V|_{\partial\Omega} = v$ and

(6.117) $$\|V\|_{W^{1,1}(\Omega)} \leqslant C \|v\|_{L^1(\partial\Omega)}.$$

This defines a linear functional on $L^1(\partial\Omega)$. For $v \in L^1(\partial\Omega)$ and V as before, we set

$$\forall v \in L^1(\partial\Omega), \quad L_\sigma(v) = \int_\Omega \sigma \cdot \nabla V + \int_\Omega \mathrm{div}(\sigma) V.$$

To see that this does not depend on the choice of V, we must show that if $v = 0$ on $\partial\Omega$, then $L_\sigma(v) = 0$. We know that if $v = 0$, then $V \in W_0^{1,1}$. Since Ω is of class $\mathcal{C}^1$, there exists a sequence $\{V_n\}$ in $\mathcal{C}_c^\infty(\Omega)$ that converges to V in $W^{1,1}(\Omega)$. By the definition of $\mathrm{div}\,\sigma$ in the sense of distributions, we have

$$\int_\Omega \sigma \cdot \nabla V_n + \int_\Omega \mathrm{div}(\sigma) V_n = 0.$$

Taking its limit gives

$$\int_\Omega \sigma \cdot \nabla V + \int_\Omega \mathrm{div}(\sigma) V = 0.$$

This remark also shows the linearity of L. Indeed, for v_1 and $v_2 \in L^1(\partial\Omega)$, let V_1 and V_2 be elements of $W^{1,1}(\Omega)$ with $V_i = v_i$ on $\partial\Omega$. Let $\lambda \in \mathbb{R}$. Then $V_1 + \lambda V_2$ belongs to $W^{1,1}(\Omega)$ and equals $v_1 + \lambda v_2$ on $\partial\Omega$. Since $L_\sigma(v_1 + \lambda v_2)$ can be written as

$$\int_\Omega \sigma \cdot \nabla(V_1 + \lambda V_2) + \int_\Omega \mathrm{div}(\sigma)(V_1 + \lambda V_2),$$

which equals $L_\sigma(v_1) + \lambda L_\sigma(v_2)$, we have the linearity. The continuity follows from the following sequence of inequalities:

$$\|L_\sigma(v)\| \leq \|\sigma\|_\infty \int_\Omega |\nabla V| dx + \|V\|_{N/(N-1)} \|\operatorname{div}\sigma\|_N$$
$$\leq C\|V\|_{W^{1,1}(\Omega)}(\|\sigma\|_\infty + \|\operatorname{div}\sigma\|_N)$$
$$\leq C'\|v\|_{L^1(\partial\Omega)}(\|\sigma\|_\infty + \|\operatorname{div}\sigma\|_N),$$

with V as in (6.117). Since L_σ is a continuous linear functional on $L^1(\partial\Omega)$, there exists an element of $L^\infty(\partial\Omega)$, which we denote by $\sigma \cdot \vec{n}$, such that

$$\forall v \in L^1(\partial\Omega), \quad L_\sigma(v) = \int_{\partial\Omega} (\sigma \cdot \vec{n})\, v. \qquad \square$$

Proof of Theorem 6.116.

Consider the map defined by

$$\forall \varphi \in \mathcal{D}(\Omega), \quad \langle(\nabla u \cdot \sigma), \varphi\rangle = -\int_\Omega u \operatorname{div}\sigma \cdot \varphi - \int_\Omega u\sigma \cdot \nabla\varphi.$$

This is clearly a distribution. Let $\{u_n\}$ be a sequence in $W^{1,1}(\Omega)$ that converges to u in the sense of Theorem 6.56. The terms $-\int_\Omega u_n \operatorname{div}\sigma\varphi$ and $-\int_\Omega u_n\sigma \cdot \nabla\varphi$ converge to $-\int_\Omega u \operatorname{div}\sigma\varphi$ and $-\int_\Omega u\sigma \cdot \nabla\varphi$, respectively. Consequently, the distribution $\nabla u_n \cdot \sigma$ converges to $\nabla u \cdot \sigma$ in $\mathcal{D}'(\Omega)$.

We also have $\langle\nabla u_n \cdot \sigma, \varphi\rangle = \int_\Omega(\nabla u_n \cdot \sigma)\varphi$ by Green's formula. Since $\nabla u_n \in L^1$, it follows that

$$|\langle\nabla u_n \cdot \sigma, \varphi\rangle| \leq \|\nabla u_n\|_1 \|\sigma\|_\infty \|\varphi\|_\infty.$$

Consequently, the sequence of distributions $\{\nabla u_n \cdot \sigma\}$ is bounded in $M^1(\Omega)$. Since it converges to $\nabla u \cdot \sigma$ in $\mathcal{D}'(\Omega)$, this last distribution belongs to $M^1(\Omega)$ and satisfies

$$|\langle\nabla u \cdot \sigma, \varphi\rangle| \leq \lim_{n\to\infty}\left|\int_\Omega \nabla u_n \cdot \sigma\,\varphi\right| \leq \lim_{n\to\infty}\left(\int_\Omega |\nabla u_n|\,|\varphi|\right)\|\sigma\|_\infty$$
$$= \left(\int_\Omega |\nabla u|\,|\varphi|\right)\|\sigma\|_\infty \leq \left(\int_\Omega |\nabla u|\right)\|\varphi\|_\infty \|\sigma\|_\infty$$

for every $\varphi \in \mathcal{C}_c(\Omega)$. In particular, the before last inequality gives the absolute continuity of $\nabla u \cdot \sigma$ with respect to $|\nabla u|$ (cf. Definition 6.39 and Proposition 6.42).

To prove Green's formula, we use the generalized Green's formula from Theorem 6.115 for $\{u_n\}$, where $\{u_n\} \in W^{1,1}(\Omega)$ converges tightly to u in $BV(\Omega)$. We then have

$$\int_\Omega u_n \operatorname{div}(\sigma)\varphi \longrightarrow \int_\Omega u \operatorname{div}(\sigma)\,\varphi \quad \text{and} \quad \int_\Omega u_n\,\sigma \cdot \nabla\varphi \longrightarrow \int_\Omega u\sigma \cdot \nabla\varphi.$$

Finally, the sequence $\{u_n\}$ converges to u in $L^1(\partial\Omega)$, so that

$$\int_{\partial\Omega} (u_n - u)\, \sigma \cdot \vec{n}\, \varphi \longrightarrow 0.$$

We also know that the sequence $\{\nabla u_n \cdot \sigma\}$ converges tightly to $\nabla u \cdot \sigma$. Indeed, since we already have vague convergence, it suffices to verify that given $\varepsilon > 0$, there exists a compact subset K of Ω such that

$$\int_{\Omega \smallsetminus K} |\nabla u_n \cdot \sigma| \leqslant \varepsilon.$$

for every n. Let $\varepsilon > 0$ and let K be a compact subset of Ω such that for every n, we have $\int_{\Omega \smallsetminus K} |\nabla u_n| \leqslant \varepsilon$; then $\int_{\Omega \smallsetminus K} |\nabla u_n \cdot \sigma| \leqslant \int_{\Omega \smallsetminus K} |\nabla u_n|\, |\sigma|_\infty \leqslant \varepsilon \|\sigma\|_\infty$.

To conclude, the sequence $\{\nabla u_n \cdot \sigma\}$ converges tightly to $\nabla u \cdot \sigma$ and Green's formula holds.

We now wish to show that $\nabla u^S \cdot \sigma$ is a singular measure. We will use the remark following the approximation theorem (Theorem 6.56), which notes that the sequence $\{u_n\}$ may be chosen in such a way that $|\nabla u_n - (\nabla u)^{\mathrm{ac}}|$ converges tightly to $|(\nabla u)^S|$. By construction, we also have the vague convergence of the sequence $\{(\nabla u_n - \nabla u^{\mathrm{ac}}) \cdot \sigma\}$ to $(\nabla u)^S \cdot \sigma$. By the lower semicontinuity for the vague topology of an integral over an open set and by the vague convergence of $|\nabla u_n - (\nabla u)^{\mathrm{ac}}|$ to $|(\nabla u)^S|$, we can write, for every $\varphi \in \mathcal{D}(\Omega)$,

$$|\langle \nabla u^S \cdot \sigma\varphi \rangle| \leqslant \lim_{n \to \infty} \left| \int_\Omega (\nabla u_n - \nabla u^{\mathrm{ac}}) \cdot \sigma\varphi \right|$$

$$\leqslant \|\sigma\|_\infty \lim_{n \to \infty} \int_\Omega |\nabla u_n - \nabla u^{\mathrm{ac}}|\, |\varphi|dx$$

$$\leqslant \|\sigma\|_\infty \int_\Omega |\nabla u^S|\, |\varphi|dx.$$

This implies the following inequality in the sense of measures:

$$|\nabla u^S \cdot \sigma| \leqslant \|\sigma\|_\infty |\nabla u^S|$$

and concludes the proof (cf. Proposition 6.42) because $\nabla u^S \cdot \sigma$ is absolutely continuous with respect to $|\nabla u^S|$.   □

Theorem 6.118. *Let Ω be an open subset of $\mathbb{R}^N$ and let*

$$(u, \sigma) \in BD(\Omega) \times L(\mathrm{div})(\Omega).$$

Then there exists a measure, which we denote by $(\varepsilon(u) : \sigma)$, that is absolutely continuous with respect to $|\varepsilon(u)|$ and satisfies

$$\forall \varphi \in \mathcal{D}(\Omega, \mathbb{R}), \quad \langle (\varepsilon(u) : \sigma), \varphi \rangle = - \int_\Omega u \cdot \mathrm{div}\, \sigma\varphi dx - \int_\Omega u \otimes \nabla\varphi : \sigma dx$$

$$= - \int_\Omega u \cdot \mathrm{div}\, \sigma\varphi dx - \sum_{i,j} \int_\Omega u_i \partial_j \varphi \sigma_{ij} dx.$$

Moreover, this measure coincides with the function in $L^1(\Omega)$ defined by the product $(\varepsilon(u) : \sigma) = \sum_{i,j} \varepsilon_{ij}(u)\sigma_{ij}$ for $(u,\sigma) \in LD(\Omega) \times L(\mathrm{div})$. We also have

$$|(\varepsilon(u) : \sigma)| \leqslant \|\sigma\|_\infty |\varepsilon(u)|.$$

The measure $(\varepsilon(u)^S : \sigma) = (\varepsilon(u) : \sigma) - (\varepsilon(u)^{\mathrm{ac}} : \sigma)$ is singular and satisfies

$$|(\varepsilon(u)^S : \sigma)| \leqslant |\varepsilon(u)^S| \|\sigma\|_\infty.$$

To conclude, if Ω is of class $\mathcal{C}^1$, then we have Green's formula, which holds for every function $\varphi \in \mathcal{C}(\overline{\Omega}) \cap \mathcal{C}^1(\Omega)$:

$$\langle (\varepsilon(u) : \sigma), \varphi \rangle = - \int_\Omega u \cdot \mathrm{div}\,\sigma\,\varphi dx - \int_\Omega \sum_{ij} u_i \partial_j \varphi \sigma_{ij} dx$$

$$+ \int_{\partial\Omega} \sum_{ij} (u_i n_j + u_j n_i)\sigma_{ij}\varphi.$$

The proof is analogous to that of the previous theorem.

6.10 Functions of a Measure

In modeling problems for the mechanics of materials, as well as in problems coming from the calculus of variations, we use functionals $\int_\Omega f(\nabla u)$ where f is a convex function with linear growth at infinity. We gave an example of such a functional in Chapter 5 while treating minimal surfaces. Even if studying these functions can be of general interest to the reader, we will presently justify the techniques and results that we used to solve the variational problem in Section 5.10. We will need some preliminary results, in particular concerning conjugates in the sense of Fenchel. The reader may also consult [25] and [26].

6.10.1 Definitions and Properties

In the general case, the functions f that we consider are defined on a Banach space X and take on their values in $\overline{\mathbb{R}}$. The domain of f, which we denote by $\mathrm{dom}\,f$, is defined to be the set $\mathrm{dom}\,f = \{x \in X \mid f(x) < +\infty\}$. We say that f is proper if its domain is nonempty and if the function only takes on finite values in this domain.

Definition 6.119. Let f be a function defined on a Banach space X with values in $\overline{\mathbb{R}}$ and a nonempty domain. The conjugate of f, which we denote by f^*, is the function defined on the dual X^* by

$$\forall y \in X^*, \quad f^*(y) = \sup_{x \in X}\{\langle y, x \rangle - f(x)\}.$$

Proposition 6.120. *If f is convex and proper, then its conjugate is convex, lower semicontinuous for the weak topology on X, and does not take on the value $-\infty$.*

We also state the following result without proof.

Proposition 6.121. *Let f be convex on X with nonempty domain; then the four following properties concerning $u \in \operatorname{dom} f$ and $y \in X^*$ are equivalent:*

(1) $y \in \partial f(u)$,
(2) $f(u) + f^*(y) \leqslant \langle u, y \rangle$,
(3) $f(u) + f^*(y) = \langle u, y \rangle$,
(4) $\forall x \in X, \ f(x) \geqslant \langle x - u, y \rangle + f(u)$.

We define the biconjugate of f to be $f^{**} = (f^*)^*$. We have the following result.

Proposition 6.122.

(1) *If f is convex, then at every point x in the interior of $\operatorname{dom} f$, f is continuous, subdifferentiable, and $f(x) = f^{**}(x)$.*
(2) *If f is convex on $\mathbb{R}^N$ and everywhere finite, then it is everywhere subdifferentiable and $f = f^{**}$.*

The book [23] contains examples of computations of conjugates and biconjugates (see also further on in this section and in the exercises). That same book (cf. its Theorem 6.2) contains the proof of a result concerning the conjugate of a functional on the space $L^p(\Omega)$ ($p > 1$) defined by an integral. This result is related to the definition of a function of a measure. The argument we present in the preliminaries below gives a version of the result for $p = 1$.

Let us define the linear growth at infinity and the asymptotic function.

Definition 6.123. Let f be a convex proper function defined on $\mathbb{R}^N$. We say that it has linear growth at infinity if there exist constants $c_0 > 0$ and $c_1 > 0$ such that

$$(6.124) \qquad \forall x \in \mathbb{R}^N, \quad c_0(|x| - 1) \leqslant f(x) \leqslant c_1(|x| + 1).$$

The function f_∞, which we call the *asymptotic function* of f, is then defined to be

$$f_\infty(x) = \lim_{t \to +\infty} \frac{f(tx)}{t}.$$

The function f_∞ is everywhere finite, convex, and positively homogeneous of degree 1.

Moreover, when f has linear growth at infinity, we can show that the domain of its conjugate f^* is a bounded subset of $L^\infty(\mathbb{R}^N)$ that is contained in the ball $B(0, c_1)$ and itself contains the ball $B(0, c_0)$. If we also have $f \geqslant 0$ and $f(0) = 0$, then $f^*(0) = \sup -f(x) = 0$ and $f^* \geqslant 0$. Let us note that the inequality (6.124) also implies that $u \mapsto f \circ u$ is continuous from $L^1(\mathbb{R}^N, \mathbb{R}^N)$ to $L^1(\mathbb{R}^N)$, (cf. [13]).

6.10.2 Preliminaries to the Definition

We intend to use an example to show how the definition of the conjugate of f^* can be adapted to extend to measures. Since under conditions that are not very restrictive, this conjugate equals f, namely $f = f^{**}$, we see that we are led to define the function $f(\mu)$, where μ is a measure, using the conjugate f^*. To illustrate the ideas, let Ω be an open subset of $\mathbb{R}^N$ and let f be convex and nonnegative, satisfy the conditions of linear growth, and have $f(0) = 0$. Consider the measure $u(x)dx$, where $u \in L^1(\Omega, dx)$ and dx is the Lebesgue measure on Ω. Using linear growth, we see that $f \circ u \in L^1(\Omega, dx)$. By adapting the definition of f^{**}, we consider the functional $f(udx)$ on the cone of continuous nonnegative functions φ with compact support in Ω, defined by

$$\langle f(udx), \varphi \rangle = \sup_{v \in L^\infty(\Omega, \operatorname{dom} f^*)} \left\{ \int_\Omega u(x)v(x)\varphi(x)dx - \int_\Omega f^*(v)(x)\varphi(x)dx \right\}.$$

We now wish to show that under certain assumptions, this function satisfies the relation

$$(6.125) \qquad \langle f(udx), \varphi \rangle = \int_\Omega (f \circ u)(x)\varphi(x)dx.$$

In other words, we wish to prove that $f(udx)$ extends to the measure $(f \circ u)(x)dx$ defined previously.

In addition to the assumptions on f, which imply that $\operatorname{dom} f^*$ is bounded and that $f^*(0) = 0$, we will suppose that f^* is bounded on its domain.

Proof of formula (6.125).

Let us begin by proving that

$$(6.126) \quad \int_\Omega f(u)(x)\varphi(x)dx$$

$$\geqslant \sup_{v \in L^\infty(\Omega, \operatorname{dom} f^*)} \left\{ \int_\Omega u(x)v(x)\varphi(x)dx - \int_\Omega f^*(v)(x)\varphi(x)dx \right\}.$$

Indeed, by the definition of f^*, we have

$$\forall x \in \Omega, \ \forall v \in L^\infty, \quad f(u)(x) \geqslant u(x)v(x) - f^*(v)(x).$$

Multiplying by the nonnegative function φ and integrating over Ω gives inequality (6.126).

Let us now show the opposite inequality to (6.126). Let $\varepsilon > 0$ and let $u \in L^1(\Omega, dx)$ be fixed. We consider a simple function $w = \sum_i w_i \chi_{A_i}$, where the A_i are universally disjoint measurable sets whose union equals Ω. As said above, the map $u \mapsto f \circ u$ from L^1 to L^1 is continuous. Consequently, there exists a simple function w such that

$$(6.127) \qquad \|u - w\|_{L^1(\Omega, dx)} \leqslant \varepsilon \quad \text{and} \quad \|f(u) - f(w)\|_{L^1(\Omega)} \leqslant \varepsilon.$$

The second inequality implies that

$$\forall \varphi \in \mathcal{C}_c^+(\Omega), \quad \|(f(u) - f(w))\varphi\|_{L^1(\Omega)} \leqslant \varepsilon \|\varphi\|_\infty.$$

Let us now use the formula $f = f^{**}$, which holds because f is convex on $\mathbb{R}^N$ and therefore continuous (cf. [23] and Proposition 6.122). Therefore, for every i, there exists an element v_i of dom f^* such that

$$(6.128) \qquad f(w_i) \leqslant v_i w_i - f^*(v_i) + \varepsilon \cdot 2^{-i-1}/|A_i|.$$

By the assumptions $f(0) = 0$ and $f^*(0) = 0$, we have $f(w) = \sum_i f(w_i)\chi_{A_i}$ and $f^*(v) = \sum_i f^*(v_i)\chi_{A_i}$. Moreover, by taking the product of simple functions,

$$\int_\Omega v(x) w(x) \varphi(x) dx = \sum_i v_i w_i \int_{A_i} \varphi(x) dx.$$

Next by multiplying (6.128) by $\varphi \chi_{A_i}$, taking the sum over i, and integrating over Ω, we obtain

$$\int_\Omega f(w)\varphi dx = \sum_i f(w_i) \int_{A_i} \varphi dx$$

$$\leqslant \sum_i v_i w_i \int_{A_i} \varphi dx - \sum_i f^*(v_i) \int_{A_i} \varphi dx + \varepsilon \|\varphi\|_\infty$$

$$= \int_\Omega v(x) w(x) \varphi(x) dx - \int_\Omega f^*(v)(x)\varphi(x) dx + \varepsilon \|\varphi\|_\infty.$$

The relations (6.127) now give

$$\int_\Omega f(u)\varphi dx \leqslant \int_\Omega f(w)\varphi dx + \varepsilon \leqslant \int_\Omega vw\varphi dx - \int_\Omega f^*(v)\varphi dx + \varepsilon(1 + \|\varphi\|_\infty)$$

$$\leqslant \int_\Omega vu\varphi dx - \int_\Omega f^*(v)\varphi dx + \int_\Omega |v| |u - w|\varphi dx + \varepsilon(1 + \|\varphi\|_\infty).$$

Taking into account that since f^* is bounded on its domain, we have the upper bound $\int_\Omega |v||u - w|\varphi dx \leqslant \varepsilon \|\varphi\|_\infty \sup_{x \in \text{dom} f^*} |v(x)|$, we obtain the opposite inequality to (6.126), thus concluding the proof. $\qquad \square$

6.10.3 Definition of a Function of a Measure and First Properties

The computation we just carried out suggests the following general definition.

Definition 6.129. Let Ω be an open subset of $\mathbb{R}^N$. Let f be a nonnegative convex function from $\mathbb{R}^k$ to $\mathbb{R}$ with linear growth at infinity and $f(0) = 0$. Let μ be a bounded measure with values in $\mathbb{R}^k$. The function $f(\mu)$ sends a nonnegative function φ in $\mathcal{C}_c(\Omega)$ to the number

$$(6.130) \qquad \langle f(\mu), \varphi \rangle = \sup_{\{v \in \mathcal{C}_c(\Omega, \mathrm{dom}\, f^*)\}} \langle \mu, v\varphi \rangle - \int_\Omega (f^* \circ v)\varphi\, dx,$$

where $\langle \mu, v\varphi \rangle = \sum_1^k \langle \mu_i, v_i\varphi \rangle$.

Remark 6.131. In this definition, the upper bound is taken in the set $\mathcal{C}_c(\Omega, \mathrm{dom}\, f^*)$. It remains the same when taken over $L^\infty(\Omega, \mathrm{dom}\, f^*)$ or even over $L^1(\Omega, \mu + dx)$. It follows that when $\mu = u\, dx$ with $u \in L^1$, the measure $f(\mu)$ is identical to $(f \circ u)dx$.

These equalities of upper bounds over different sets are studied in Exercise 6.5.

Proposition 6.132. *Let Ω be an open subset of $\mathbb{R}^N$. We suppose that f is convex and satisfies (6.124), and that f^* is bounded on its domain. Let μ be a measure on Ω; then $f(\mu)$ is positively homogeneous and additive. Consequently, it extends to a measure on Ω. This measure is absolutely continuous with respect to $|\mu| + dx$.*

When the measure μ is moreover bounded on Ω, then the measure $f(\mu)$ is also bounded and formula (6.130) extends to functions $\varphi \in \mathcal{C}_b(\Omega)$.

Proof of Proposition 6.132.

The positive homogeneity is obvious. Let us show the additivity. Let $\varepsilon > 0$, let φ_i be a nonnegative function in $\mathcal{C}_c(\Omega)$ for $i = 1, 2$, and let $v \in \mathcal{C}_c(\Omega, \mathrm{dom}\, f^*)$ satisfy

$$\langle f(\mu), \varphi_1 + \varphi_2 \rangle \leqslant \langle \mu, v(\varphi_1 + \varphi_2) \rangle - \int_\Omega (f^* \circ v)(\varphi_1 + \varphi_2) + \varepsilon.$$

The right-hand side is then lesser than or equal to $\langle f(\mu), \varphi_1 \rangle + \langle f(\mu), \varphi_2 \rangle + \varepsilon$.
Conversely, let v_1 and v_2 in $\mathcal{C}_c(\Omega, \mathrm{dom}\, f^*)$ satisfy

$$\langle f(\mu), \varphi_i \rangle \leqslant \langle \mu, v_i\varphi_i \rangle - \int_\Omega (f^* \circ v_i)\varphi_i + \varepsilon$$

and let $v = \sum_i v_i \varphi_i / (\sum_i \varphi_i)$. This function has values in $\operatorname{dom} f^*$ because $\operatorname{dom} f^*$ is convex, and it is continuous. Moreover, by the convexity of f^*, we have

$$f^*(v)(\varphi_1 + \varphi_2) \leqslant \sum_i f^*(v_i)\varphi_i.$$

It follows that

$$\langle f(\mu), \textstyle\sum_{i=1,2} \varphi_i \rangle \geqslant \langle \mu, v \sum_i \varphi_i \rangle - \int_\Omega f^*(v) \sum_i \varphi_i$$

$$\geqslant \sum_i \left(\langle \mu, v_i \varphi_i \rangle - \int_\Omega (f^* \circ v_i) \varphi_i \right) \geqslant \sum_i \langle f(\mu), \varphi_i \rangle - 2\varepsilon,$$

completing the proof of the additivity.

The absolute continuity of $f(\mu)$ with respect to $|\mu| + dx$ follows from the inequality below, which holds for every v with values in the domain of f^*. Recall that we assumed f^* to be bounded on its domain. By Section 6.2, Proposition 6.42, we have

$$(6.133) \quad \left| \langle \mu, v\varphi \rangle - \int_\Omega f^*(v)\varphi \right| \leqslant C_1 \int_\Omega |\mu|\,|\varphi| + \sup_{x \in \operatorname{dom} f^*} |f^*(x)| \int_{\operatorname{dom} f^*} |\varphi|.$$

We now suppose that μ is a bounded measure. It is obvious that $f(\mu)$ is also bounded, since $f(\mu)$ is absolutely continuous with respect to $|\mu| + \chi_{\operatorname{dom} f^*} dx$. We wish to show that the formula defining $\langle f(\mu), \varphi \rangle$ extends to the bounded continuous functions φ. Let ψ be a nonnegative element of $\mathcal{C}_b(\Omega)$. Let $\varepsilon > 0$ and let $\varphi \in \mathcal{C}_c(\Omega)$ be nonnegative, such that

$$(6.134) \quad \int_\Omega f(\mu)\psi \leqslant \int_\Omega f(\mu)\varphi + \varepsilon \quad \text{and}$$

$$(6.135) \quad \int_\Omega |\psi - \varphi| + \int_\Omega |\mu|(|\psi - \varphi|) \leqslant \frac{\varepsilon}{C_1 + \sup_{x \in \operatorname{dom} f^*} f^*(x)}.$$

Moreover, let $v \in \mathcal{C}_c(\Omega, \operatorname{dom} f^*)$ satisfy

$$(6.136) \quad \int_\Omega f(\mu)\varphi \leqslant \int_\Omega \mu v \varphi - \int_\Omega f^*(v)\varphi + \varepsilon.$$

Owing to the relations (6.134) and (6.136), followed by (6.135) and (6.133), the expression $\langle f(\mu), \psi \rangle$ is bounded from above as follows:

$$\int_\Omega f(\mu)\varphi + \varepsilon \leqslant \int_\Omega \mu v \varphi - \int_\Omega f^*(v)\varphi + 2\varepsilon$$

$$\leqslant \int_\Omega \mu v \psi - \int_\Omega f^*(v)\psi + \int_\Omega \mu v(\varphi - \psi) - \int_\Omega f^*(v)(\varphi - \psi) + 2\varepsilon$$

$$\leqslant \sup_{v \in \mathcal{C}_c(\Omega, \operatorname{dom} f^*)} \int_\Omega \mu v \psi - \int_\Omega f^*(v)\psi + 3\varepsilon.$$

For the opposite inequality, let $v \in \mathcal{C}_c(\Omega, \mathrm{dom}\, f^*)$ satisfy

$$\sup_{v \in \mathcal{C}_c(\Omega, \mathrm{dom}\, f^*)} \int_\Omega \mu v \psi - \int f^*(v)\psi \leq \int_\Omega \mu v \psi - \int_\Omega f^*(v)\psi + \varepsilon$$

and let $\varphi = 1$ on $\mathrm{supp}\, v$ and have compact support in Ω. We have

$$\int_\Omega \mu v \psi - \int_\Omega f^*(v)\psi = \int_\Omega \mu v \psi \varphi - \int_\Omega f^*(v)\psi\varphi$$
$$\leq \langle f(\mu), \varphi\psi\rangle \leq \langle f(\mu), \psi\rangle,$$

giving the opposite inequality. We conclude that the formula defining $\langle f(\mu), \varphi\rangle$ extends to the functions $\varphi \in \mathcal{C}_b(\Omega)$. $\qquad\square$

Remark 6.137 (on the conditions of Proposition 6.132). When f does not satisfy the condition $f(0) = 0$, we can still make sure that the formula defining $f(\mu)$ holds (cf. Exercises 6.15 and 6.16). Indeed, we use the fact that f, which is defined on $\mathbb{R}^k$ and is convex and everywhere finite, is everywhere subdifferentiable (cf. 6.122) and therefore admits a continuous linear lower bound. By Subsection 5.2.2, $f(0) + \langle y, x\rangle$ is such a lower bound, where y is an element of $\partial f(0)$ (we just noted that $\partial f(0)$ is nonempty).

For example, in the case of the function used in Chapter 5 in the context of minimal surfaces, the function f defined by $f(x) = \sqrt{1 + |x|^2}$ satisfies $f(0) = 1$. We then use the function g defined by $g(x) = f(x) - f(0)$. We can verify that the assumptions of Definition 6.129 hold for g. We will see in Exercise 6.19 that the formula defining $f(\mu)$ can be extended to any f, not only the ones verifying $f(0) = 0$ and $f \geq 0$.

Theorem 6.138. *Let $\mu = g\,dx + \mu^S$ be the Lebesgue decomposition of μ with $g \in L^1(\Omega, dx)$ and μ^S singular. We suppose that f satisfies the conditions of Proposition 6.132. The Lebesgue decomposition of $f(\mu)$ is then*

$$f(\mu) = (f \circ g)dx + f_\infty(\mu^S).$$

Proof of Theorem 6.138.

We refer to Section 6.2 for the Lebesgue decomposition of a measure (cf. Theorem 6.46). We begin by showing that $f(\mu) \leq (f \circ g)dx + f_\infty(\mu^S)$. After noting that $f_\infty^* = \chi_{\mathrm{dom}\, f^*}$ (cf. Exercise 6.6), we have, for every $v \in \mathcal{C}_c(\Omega, \mathrm{dom}\, f^*)$ and every $\varphi \geq 0$,

$$\langle \mu, v\varphi\rangle - \int_\Omega f^*(v)\varphi dx = \int_\Omega g v \varphi dx + \langle \mu^S, v\varphi\rangle - \int_\Omega f^*(v)\varphi dx$$
$$\leq \sup_v \left(\int_\Omega g v \varphi dx - \int_\Omega f^*(v)\varphi \right) + \sup_v \langle \mu^S, v\varphi\rangle$$
$$\leq \int_\Omega (f \circ g)\varphi dx + \langle f_\infty(\mu^S), \varphi\rangle.$$

Indeed, in the previous inequalities, we have used on the one hand, the property of $f(g dx)$ given in 6.10.2 and on the other hand, the definition of $f_\infty(\mu^S)$ taken from the remark on $(f_\infty)^*$.

Conversely, let $\varphi \geqslant 0$, ε, and v_i in $\mathcal{C}_c(\Omega, \operatorname{dom} f^*)$ for $i = 1, 2$ be such that we have the following inequalities:

$$(6.139) \qquad \int_\Omega (f \circ g)\varphi\, dx \leqslant \int_\Omega g v_1 \varphi\, dx - \int_\Omega f^*(v_1)\varphi\, dx + \varepsilon,$$

$$(6.140) \qquad \langle f_\infty(\mu^S), \varphi \rangle \leqslant \int_\Omega \mu^S v_2 \varphi\, dx + \varepsilon.$$

Let K be a compact set that contains $\operatorname{supp} \mu^S$ and let Ω_1 be an open set containing K, with $\int_{\Omega_1}(|g| + 1)dx < \varepsilon$. This last property is a consequence of the mutual singularity of μ^S and dx. Next, let ψ be a function equal to 1 on K, with values in $[0, 1]$, and continuous and with compact support in Ω_1. We set $v = v_2\psi + v_1(1 - \psi)$ and $D = \int_\Omega \mu v \varphi dx - \int_\Omega g v_1 \varphi dx - \langle \mu^S, v_2\varphi \rangle$. We will show that there exists a C such that $|D| \leqslant C\varepsilon$.

Indeed, since $(v - v_2)\psi = (1 - \psi)(v_1 - v_2)$ is zero on the support of μ^S and ψ is zero outside of Ω_1, we have

$$|D| = \left| \int_\Omega g(v_2 - v_1)\psi\varphi \right| \leqslant \|\varphi\|_\infty \int_{\Omega_1} |g|\, |v_2 - v_1| dx \leqslant C\varepsilon.$$

Taking into account this definition of D and the definition of a conjugate, adding the inequalities (6.139) and (6.140) then gives

$$\int_\Omega (f \circ g)\varphi dx + \int_\Omega f_\infty(\mu^S)\varphi dx$$

$$\leqslant \int_\Omega g v_1 \varphi dx - \int_\Omega f^*(v_1)\varphi dx + \int_\Omega \mu^S v_2 \varphi dx + 2\varepsilon$$

$$\leqslant \int_\Omega \mu v \varphi dx - D - \int_\Omega f^*(v)\varphi dx + \int_\Omega (f^*(v) - f^*(v_1))\varphi dx + 2\varepsilon$$

$$\leqslant \int_\Omega \mu v \varphi dx - \int_\Omega f^*(v)\varphi dx + |D| + \int_\Omega (f^*(v_2) - f^*(v_1))\psi\varphi dx + 2\varepsilon$$

$$\leqslant \int_\Omega f(\mu)\varphi + C\varepsilon + 2\varepsilon + 2 \sup_{\operatorname{dom}(f^*)} |f^*| \int_\Omega \psi\varphi dx$$

$$\leqslant \int_\Omega f(\mu)\varphi + C''\varepsilon,$$

concluding the proof.   □

Remark 6.141. In fact, we can show, more generally, that if μ_1 and μ_2 are two mutually singular measures, then we also have

$$f(\mu_1 + \mu_2) = f(\mu_1) + f(\mu_2).$$

This property is the object of Exercise 6.17.

Because of its role in the problem of minimal surfaces (cf. Chapter 5), we choose to illustrate the definition using $x \mapsto \sqrt{1 + |x|^2} - 1$ as an example.

Example 6.142. We propose to give the formula defining $\sqrt{1 + |\mu|^2}$ explicitly, where μ is an arbitrary measure on the bounded open set Ω.

The function g defined on $\mathbb{R}^k$ by $g(x) = \sqrt{1 + |x|^2} - 1$ possesses the required properties, namely $g(0) = 0$, $g \geqslant 0$, and g has linear growth at infinity. We have $g^* = f^* + 1$. The function f^*, which is the conjugate of a radial function, is clearly also radial. This allows us to reduce to considering $\mathbb{R}$.

- For $|y| > 1$, the upper bound defining $f^*(y)$ is $+\infty$.
- For $|y| = 1$, this upper bound is 0.
- For $|y| < 1$, the derivative of $x \mapsto xy - \sqrt{1 + x^2}$ vanishes for $x_0 = y/\sqrt{1 - y^2}$ and the maximum equals $f(x_0)$. It follows that

$$\forall y \in \operatorname{dom} f^* = B(0,1), \quad f^*(y) = -\sqrt{1 - |y|^2} \quad \text{and} \quad g^*(y) = 1 - \sqrt{1 - |y|^2}.$$

We note that $\operatorname{dom} f^*$ is bounded and that the functions g^* and f^* are bounded and continuous on $\operatorname{dom} f^*$.

We also verify that $g^*(0) = 0$ and $g^* \geqslant 0$. The function g therefore satisfies all the conditions of Proposition 6.132. Moreover, $x \mapsto |x|$ is the asymptotic function of both f and g. Consequently, if we write $\mu = \mu^{\mathrm{ac}} + \mu^S$, then Theorem 6.138 allows us to write

$$\langle \sqrt{1 + \mu^2}, \varphi \rangle = \sup_{v \in \mathcal{C}_c(\Omega, \overline{B(0,1)})} \left\{ \int_\Omega v\varphi d(\mu^{\mathrm{ac}}) + \int_\Omega \sqrt{1 - |v(x)|^2}\varphi(x)dx \right\} + \langle |\mu^S|, \varphi \rangle.$$

6.10.4 Sequences of Measures and Density Results

We begin by showing that under the previous assumptions, the map $\mu \mapsto f(\mu)$ is l.s.c. for the topology of the vague convergence of measures.

Theorem 6.143. *Let f be convex and satisfy the conditions of Proposition 6.132. If $\{\mu_n\}$ is a sequence of bounded measures on a bounded open subset Ω of $\mathbb{R}^N$ that converges vaguely to a bounded measure μ on Ω, then there exists a subsequence of $\{f(\mu_n)\}$ that converges vaguely to a bounded measure ν on Ω with $f(\mu) \leqslant \nu$. As a consequence,*

$$f(\mu) = \varliminf_{n \to \infty} f(\mu_n).$$

Proof of Theorem 6.143.

The sequence of integrals $\int_\Omega f(\mu_n)$ is bounded because $f(\mu_n)$ is absolutely continuous with respect to $|\mu_n| + dx$. We can therefore extract a subsequence that converges vaguely to a bounded measure ν (cf. Proposition 6.20). It follows that there exists a sequence $\sigma(n)$ such that

$$\mu_{\sigma(n)} \longrightarrow \mu \quad \text{and} \quad \lim f(\mu_{\sigma(n)}) = \nu$$

for the vague convergence. Let $\varepsilon > 0$ and let $\varphi \in C_c(\Omega)$ with $\varphi \geqslant 0$. By the definition of $\langle f(\mu), \varphi \rangle$, there exists a $v \in C_c(\Omega, \operatorname{dom} f^*)$ such that

$$\langle f(\mu), \varphi \rangle \leqslant \int_\Omega \mu v \varphi - \int_\Omega f^*(v)\varphi + \varepsilon.$$

By the lower semicontinuity of the integral over an open set for the vague topology, the right-hand side can be bounded from above by

$$\varliminf \int_\Omega \mu_{\sigma(n)} v\varphi - \int_\Omega f^*(v)\varphi + \varepsilon$$

$$\leqslant \varliminf \sup_{v \in C_c(\Omega)} \left\{ \int_\Omega \mu_{\sigma(n)} v\varphi - \int_\Omega f^*(v)\varphi \right\} + \varepsilon$$

$$\leqslant \lim \{ \langle f(\mu_{\sigma(n)}), \varphi \rangle \} + \varepsilon \leqslant \langle \nu, \varphi \rangle + \varepsilon.$$

Since this is true for every ε, this concludes the proof of the desired property.

$\square$

The following is another important result, concerning the density of the regular functions for a topology intermediate between the norm topology and the vague convergence topology, which is close to the tight topology.

Theorem 6.144. *Let Ω be an open subset of $\mathbb{R}^k$, let μ be a measure in $M^1(\Omega, \mathbb{R}^k)$, and let f be a nonnegative convex function satisfying the conditions of Proposition 6.132 and the equality $f(0) = 0$. Then there exists a sequence $\{u_n\}$ of elements of $C^\infty(\Omega) \cap W^{1,1}(\Omega)$ such that*

$$u_n \longrightarrow \mu, \quad f(u_n) \longrightarrow f(\mu) \quad \text{and} \quad \int_\Omega f(u_n) \longrightarrow \int_\Omega f(\mu).$$

In particular, we can deduce that inequality (6.124) extends to measures, giving $c_0(|\mu| - 1) \leqslant f(\mu) \leqslant c_1(|\mu| + 1)$.

Proof of Theorem 6.144.

We begin by showing that if θ is continuous with compact support in Ω and values in $[0, 1]$, then, as when μ is a function, we have

$$f(\theta\mu) \leqslant \theta f(\mu).$$

Let φ be a nonnegative function in $C_c(\Omega)$ and let $v \in C_c(\Omega, \operatorname{dom} f^*)$. Since f^* and φ are nonnegative and $\theta \in [0, 1]$, we can write

$$\langle \mu, \theta v\varphi \rangle - \int_\Omega f^*(v)\varphi \leqslant \langle \mu v\theta, \varphi \rangle - \int_\Omega f^*(v)\theta\varphi \leqslant \langle \theta f(\mu), \varphi \rangle.$$

The desired result follows by taking the supremum in v. In particular, if $\{\theta_j\}$ is a sequence of continuous functions with compact support equal to 1 on a compact set K_j that for every j satisfies $d(K_j, \partial\Omega) \leqslant 1/j$, so that the sequence converges to 1_Ω, then the sequence $\{f(\theta_j\mu)\}$ converges tightly to $f(\mu)$. Indeed, since $f(\theta_j\mu) \leqslant \theta_j f(\mu)$ and $f(\mu)$ is a bounded measure, we see that the sequence $f(\theta_j\mu)$ is bounded. We can therefore extract a subsequence that converges vaguely to a positive and bounded measure (cf. Proposition 6.20). By the previous theorem, we have

$$f(\mu) \leqslant \nu = \lim_{j \to +\infty} f(\theta_j\mu) \leqslant \lim \theta_j f(\mu) \leqslant f(\mu).$$

Since, by the lower semicontinuity, we also have

$$\int_\Omega f(\mu) \leqslant \lim_{j \to +\infty} \int_\Omega f(\theta_j\mu) \leqslant \int_\Omega f(\mu),$$

we see that $f(\theta_j\mu)$ converges tightly to $f(\mu)$, that is, converges in $(\mathcal{C}_b(\Omega))'$.

We now suppose that μ has support in a fixed compact subset of $\mathbb{R}^N$ contained in Ω.

Let ρ be an element of $\mathcal{D}(\mathbb{R}^N)$ that is even and nonnegative, and which has integral equal to 1. We set $\rho_\varepsilon(x) = 1/\varepsilon^N \rho(x/\varepsilon)$ and $u_\varepsilon = \rho_\varepsilon * \mu$.

We first show that

$$\forall v \in \mathcal{C}_c(\mathbb{R}^N, \operatorname{dom} f^*), \quad \int_{\mathbb{R}^N} f^*(\rho_\varepsilon \star v) \leqslant \int_{\mathbb{R}^N} f^*(v).$$

This inequality comes from the properties of f^* (cf. Theorem 6.2 in [23]). Since the formula is also true for ρ, we will from now on denote both ρ and ρ_ε by ρ. We set $dm_t = \rho dt$, giving a measure that satisfies $\int_{\mathbb{R}^N} dm_t = 1$. Since the domain of f^* is bounded and f^* is bounded on its domain, we have $f^*(0) = 0$. Consequently, the composition $f^*(v \star \rho)$ is summable over $\mathbb{R}^N$ and since f^* is convex and $f^* \geqslant 0$, Jensen's inequality gives

$$\forall x \in \mathbb{R}^N, \quad f^*\left(\int_{\mathbb{R}^N} v(x-t)dm_t\right) \leqslant \int_{\mathbb{R}^N} f^*(v(x-t))dm_t.$$

By integrating and using Fubini's formula, we obtain the desired property

$$\int_{\mathbb{R}^N} f^*(v \star \rho)dx \leqslant \int_{\mathbb{R}^N} \int_{\mathbb{R}^N} f^*(v(t))\rho(x-t)dt$$

$$= \int_{\mathbb{R}^N} f^*(v(t)) \int_{\mathbb{R}^N} \rho(x-t)dx\,dt$$

$$= \int_{\mathbb{R}^N} f^*(v(t))dt \int_{\mathbb{R}^N} \rho(\xi)d\xi = \int_{\mathbb{R}^N} (f^* \circ v)(t)dt.$$

The definition of $f(\rho \star \mu)$, where $\rho \star \mu \in L^1(\mathbb{R}^N)$, gives

$$\int_{\mathbb{R}^N} f(\rho \star \mu) = \sup_{v \in \mathcal{C}_c(\mathbb{R}^N, \operatorname{dom} f^*)} \left(\int_{\mathbb{R}^N} [(\rho \star \mu)v - f^*(v)]dx \right).$$

Given a number $\delta > 0$, there exists a function $v \in \mathcal{C}_c(\mathbb{R}^N, \operatorname{dom} f^*)$ such that

$$\int_{\mathbb{R}^N} f(\rho \star \mu) \leqslant \int_{\mathbb{R}^N} [(\rho \star \mu)v - f^*(v)]dx + \delta.$$

Noting that by the parity of ρ, we have

$$\int_{\mathbb{R}^N} \rho \star v \, d\mu = \langle \mu, \langle \rho_y, v(\cdot + y) \rangle \rangle = \langle \mu, \langle \rho(-y), v(\cdot - y) \rangle \rangle,$$

which gives $\int_{\mathbb{R}^N} \rho \star v \, d\mu = \langle \mu, \rho \star v \rangle$, we can deduce that

$$\int_{\mathbb{R}^N} f(\rho \star \mu) \leqslant \langle \mu, (\rho \star v) \rangle - \int_{\mathbb{R}^N} f^*(\rho \star v) + \delta.$$

Let us recall that μ has compact support. Hence, by taking $\varphi = 1$ in a neighborhood of the support of μ, we can write the following inequality for the total variation of the measure $f(\mu)$:

$$\int_{\mathbb{R}^N} f(\mu) \geqslant \langle \mu, (\rho \star v) \rangle - \int_{\mathbb{R}^N} f^*(\rho \star v).$$

It follows that $\int_{\mathbb{R}^N} f(\rho \star \mu) \leqslant \int_{\mathbb{R}^N} f(\mu) + \delta$, and finally

$$\int_{\mathbb{R}^N} f(\rho \star \mu) \leqslant \int_{\mathbb{R}^N} f(\mu) \quad \text{and} \quad \int_{\mathbb{R}^N} f(\rho_\varepsilon \star \mu) \leqslant \int_{\mathbb{R}^N} f(\mu).$$

Owing to this property, we can choose sequences $\{\theta_j\}$ and $\{\varepsilon_j\}$ such that the sequence of integrals $\int_\Omega f(\rho_{\varepsilon_j} \star \theta_j \mu)$ converges to $\int_\Omega f(\mu)$. Let θ_j be as in the first part of the proof, and let $\varepsilon_j < d(\operatorname{supp} \theta_j, \partial \Omega)$. Since the sequence of positive measures $f(\rho_{\varepsilon_j} \star \theta_j \mu)$ is bounded, we can extract a subsequence that converges vaguely to a bounded measure ν with

$$f(\mu) \leqslant \nu = \varliminf f(\rho_{\varepsilon_{\sigma(j)}} \star \theta_{\sigma(j)} \mu),$$

whose integrals satisfy

$$\int_\Omega f(\mu) \leqslant \varliminf \int_\Omega f(\rho_{\varepsilon_{\sigma(j)}} \star \theta_{\sigma(j)} \mu) \leqslant \varliminf \int_\Omega f(\theta_{\sigma(j)} \mu) \leqslant \int_\Omega f(\mu).$$

We now deduce that the full sequence $\{\int_\Omega f(\rho_{\varepsilon_j} \star \theta_j \mu)\}$ converges to $\int_\Omega f(\mu)$.

Since inequality (6.124) is true for the functions $\rho_{\varepsilon_j} \star \mu$, it extends to the measure μ. □

Corollary 6.145. *Let θ be a function in $\mathcal{C}_c(\Omega)$ with values in $[0,1]$, let μ be a measure in M^1, and let ρ be a function in $\mathcal{D}$ with $\operatorname{supp}\rho + \operatorname{supp}(\theta\mu) \subset \Omega$. Then the inequality $f(\rho \star \theta u) \leqslant \rho \star (\theta f(u))$, which holds for functions u, extends to the measure μ, giving*

$$f(\rho \star \theta\mu) \leqslant \rho \star (\theta f(\mu)).$$

Proof of the corollary.

Indeed, let $\{u_j\}$ in $\mathcal{C}_c^\infty(\Omega)$ be as in the first part of the previous proof, with

$$u_j \longrightarrow \mu \quad \text{and} \quad f(u_j) \longrightarrow f(\mu).$$

The pointwise inequality gives

$$f(\rho \star (\theta u_j)) \leqslant \rho \star (\theta f(u_j)).$$

Moreover, since the sequence $f(u_j)$ converges vaguely to $f(\mu)$, we can use a simple argument to show that $\rho \star (\theta f(u_j))$ tends vaguely to $\rho \star (\theta f(\mu))$. Likewise, the sequence $\{\rho \star \theta u_j\}$ converges vaguely to $\rho \star \theta\mu$. Hence, using the lower semicontinuity property of Theorem 6.143, we obtain

$$f(\rho \star (\theta\mu)) \leqslant \varliminf f(\rho \star (\theta u_j)) \leqslant \rho \star (\theta f(\mu)). \qquad \square$$

The reader can consult [25] and [26] for more details and other results concerning functions of a measure.

Comments

This chapter gives us the first notions of spaces of functions with a measure as derivative. These spaces have been introduced to form models of problems coming from the computation of variations and from solid mechanics. On the subject of the space BV, the work of Giusti [35] is no doubt one of the most complete. The first important advances on the subject of the spaces BD are due to Suquet [67], Strang and Temam [71], and Kohn and Temam [42].

6.11 Exercises for Chapter 6

Exercise 6.1 (Vague and Tight Convergence).

Let $\{\mu_n\}$ be a sequence of positive measures that converges vaguely to μ on Ω. Prove that it converges tightly on every open set $\Omega_1 \subset \overline{\Omega_1} \subset \Omega$ with $\int_{\partial\Omega_1} \mu = 0$.

Hints. First, $\{\mu_n\}$ also converges vaguely to μ on Ω_1. Since Ω_1 is an open set, it follows that

$$\int_{\Omega_1} \mu \leqslant \varliminf \int_{\Omega_1} \mu_n \quad \text{and} \quad \int_{\overline{\Omega_1}} \mu \geqslant \varlimsup \int_{\overline{\Omega_1}} \mu_n.$$

Indeed, if we let F denote the set of φ with $\varphi = 1$ on $\overline{\Omega_1}$, then we have $\int_{\overline{\Omega_1}} \mu = \sup_{\varphi \in F} \int \mu \varphi \geqslant \overline{\lim} \int_{\overline{\Omega_1}} \mu_n$, whence

$$\int_{\Omega_1} \mu = \int_{\overline{\Omega_1}} \mu = \lim \int_{\overline{\Omega_1}} \mu_n.$$

Exercise 6.2 (Characterization of the Gradient Distributions).

Let $T \in \mathcal{D}'(\Omega, \mathbb{R}^N)$. Show that if $T = \nabla S$ with $S \in \mathcal{D}'$, then for every $(i,j) \in [1,N]^2$, $\partial_i T_j = \partial_j T_i$. Establish the converse. Deduce that $T = \nabla S$ if and only if for every $\varphi \in \mathcal{D}(\Omega, \mathbb{R}^N)$ with $\operatorname{div} \varphi = 0$, we have $\langle T, \varphi \rangle = 0$.

Hints. Use an induction argument for the converse, where the case $N = 1$ is the existence of a primitive of a distribution. For the second part, consider the functions of the form $\varphi = \partial_j v e_i - \partial_i v e_j$ for $v \in \mathcal{D}(\Omega)$.

Exercise 6.3 (On the Absolutely Continuous and Singular Parts of a Sequence ∇u_n that Tends to ∇u when $u \in BV(\Omega)$).

We use the notations of Theorem 6.56. Prove that

$$\int_\Omega |\nabla u_\delta - (\nabla u)^{\mathrm{ac}}| \longrightarrow \int_\Omega |\nabla u^S|,$$

where μ^{ac} and μ^S denote the absolutely continuous and singular parts of the measure μ, respectively (we refer to Section 6.2 for the definitions and for the Lebesgue decomposition). Use inequalities of the same type as (6.60) and (6.62).

Hints. Write

$$|\nabla u_\delta - (\nabla u)^{\mathrm{ac}}| = \left| \sum \left[\rho_{n_j} \star (\varphi_j \nabla u + u \nabla \varphi_j) - \varphi_j (\nabla u)^{\mathrm{ac}} \right] \right|$$
$$\leqslant \left| \sum \left[\rho_{n_j} \star (\varphi_j (\nabla u)^{\mathrm{ac}} - \varphi_j (\nabla u)^{\mathrm{ac}}) \right] \right| + \sum |\rho_{n_j} \star (\varphi_j (\nabla u)^S)|.$$

Through inequalities of the type used in the proof of the theorem, show that

$$\int_\Omega |\nabla u_\delta - (\nabla u)^{\mathrm{ac}}| \leqslant \int_\Omega |(\nabla u)^S| + 2\delta.$$

Exercise [**] 6.4 (Determining E_α in the Proof of Theorem 6.89).

Determine a solution of the following equation, taken in the sense of distributions:

$$(6.146) \qquad (\Delta + \nabla(\operatorname{div}))(E_\alpha) = \alpha \delta_0.$$

Use the fundamental solution of the Laplacian, that is, M with $\Delta M = \delta_0$. This solution equals

$$(6.147) \qquad M = \begin{cases} \dfrac{\ln r}{2\pi} & \text{if } N = 2, \\ k_N |x|^{2-N} & \text{if } N \geqslant 3. \end{cases}$$

Prove that

(6.148) $$E_\alpha = \frac{3\alpha}{4}M - \frac{x}{4}(\alpha \cdot \nabla M)$$

is indeed a solution of (6.146). Deduce from this the explicit formula

$$E_\alpha = \begin{cases} \dfrac{3\alpha}{8\pi}\ln r - x\dfrac{\alpha \cdot x}{8\pi} & \text{if } N = 2, \\ k_N \dfrac{3\alpha}{4r^{N-2}} + k_N\left(\dfrac{N-2}{4}\right)\dfrac{x(x \cdot \alpha)}{r^N} & \text{if } N > 2. \end{cases}$$

Exercise [**] 6.5 (Comparison of Upper Bounds in the Definition of $f(\mu)$).

We would like to justify Remark 6.131. In the formula defining $f(\mu)$, under the assumptions of Proposition 6.132, we consider the upper bounds α, β, and γ of $\{\langle \mu, v\varphi \rangle - \int_\Omega (f^* \circ v)\varphi dx\}$ when v belongs to $L^1(\Omega, \mu + dx)$, $L^\infty(\Omega, \mathrm{dom}\, f^*)$, and $\mathcal{C}_c(\Omega, \mathrm{dom}\, f^*)$, respectively.

First prove that $\alpha \geqslant \beta \geqslant \gamma$. Next, show that $\alpha \leqslant \gamma$.

Hints. To prove that $\alpha \leqslant \gamma$, show that given a v in $L^1(\Omega, \mu + dx)$, we can associate with it a function $\underline{v} \in \mathcal{D}(\Omega, \mathrm{dom}\, f^*)$ such that

$$\int_\Omega |\underline{v} - v|(d\mu + dx) \leqslant \varepsilon \quad \text{and} \quad \|f(\underline{v}) - f(v)\|_\infty \leqslant \varepsilon.$$

Exercise 6.6 (Determining the Conjugate of the Asymptotic Function).

Show that if f satisfies the conditions of the definition of a function of a measure $f(\mu)$, then $f_\infty^* = \chi_{\mathrm{dom}\, f^*}$.

Hints. Reduce to showing that $f_\infty(x) = \sup_{y \in \mathrm{dom}\, f^*}(\langle x, y \rangle)$. Show that $f_\infty(x) \geqslant \langle x, y \rangle$ using the definition of the conjugate, which when defining $f_\infty(x)$ involves the expression $\langle tx, y \rangle - f^*(y)$ for $y \in \mathrm{dom}\, f^*$.

Conversely, show that given ε, we can find $y_{t,\varepsilon} \in \mathrm{dom}\, f^*$ such that

$$f(tx) \leqslant \langle tx, y_{t,\varepsilon} \rangle - f^*(y_{t,\varepsilon}) + \varepsilon.$$

Exercise [*] 6.7 (Properties of the Functions in $L^2(\Omega)$ with Divergence in $L^2(\Omega)$).

Let Ω be an open subset of $\mathbb{R}^N$ and let $X(\Omega) = \{u \in L^2(\Omega, \mathbb{R}^N) \mid \mathrm{div}\, u \in L^2(\Omega)\}$.

(1) Prove that X endowed with the norm $\|.\|_X$ defined by

$$\|u\|_X = \left(\sum_{1 \leqslant i \leqslant N} |u_i|_2^2\right)^{1/2} + \left(\int_\Omega (\mathrm{div}\, u)^2 dx\right)^{1/2}$$

is a Banach space.

(2) Suppose that Ω is of class $\mathcal{C}^1$. Show, beginning with the case $\Omega = \mathbb{R}^N$, that the functions in $\mathcal{C}^1(\overline{\Omega}) \cap X(\Omega)$ are dense in $X(\Omega)$. In the general case, use the method of Proposition 3.57 of Chapter 3.

(3) Still supposing that Ω is of class $\mathcal{C}^1$, show that we can define a trace map that is continuous on $X(\Omega)$, has values in $H^{-1/2}(\partial\Omega)$, and for which the following Green's formula holds:

$$\forall u \in H^1(\Omega),\ \forall \sigma \in X(\Omega),\quad \int_\Omega \nabla u \cdot \sigma + \int_\Omega \operatorname{div}(\sigma)u = \langle \sigma \cdot \vec{n}, u \rangle.$$

Exercise 6.8 (Details of the Proof of Theorem 6.89).
In the proof of Theorem 6.89, we work in the open set $\Omega \cap \Omega_k$ and on a component u_i of u such that $\nu_i = \vec{\nu} \cdot e_i \neq 0$ almost everywhere along $\partial\Omega \cap \Omega_k$, where $\vec{\nu}$ is the unit outward-pointing normal. The argument remains the same on a different component u_j if $\vec{\nu} \cdot e_j \neq 0$ almost everywhere. Let us assume that this is not the case.

(1) Prove that in this case, we have $\vec{\nu} \cdot (\frac{e_i + e_j}{\sqrt{2}}) \neq 0$ almost everywhere, which suggests that we reduce to the function v defined by $v = u_i + u_j$.

(2) We change the basis by replacing (e_i, e_j) by $((e_i + e_j)/\sqrt{2}, (e_i - e_j)/\sqrt{2})$, and leaving e_k the same for $k \neq i, j$. Prove that the function v obtained from this base change belongs to $LD(\Omega)$. Next, use the argument of the proof of Theorem 6.89 to deduce that $u_j \in L^p(\Omega \cap \Omega_k)$.

Exercise [∗∗] 6.9 (Functions in $W^{1,1}(\Omega)$ with Hessian in $M^1(\Omega)$).
Let Ω be an open subset of $\mathbb{R}^N$ and let

$$HB(\Omega) = \{u \in L^1(\Omega) \mid \nabla u \in L^1(\Omega, \mathbb{R}^N),\ \nabla\nabla u \in M^1(\Omega, \mathbb{R}^{N^2})\}.$$

For $u \in HB(\Omega)$, we set

$$\int_\Omega |\nabla\nabla u|\,dx = \sup_{\substack{\varphi \in \mathcal{C}_c(\Omega, \mathbb{R}^{N^2}) \\ \sum_{ij} |\varphi_{ij}|^2 \leqslant 1}} \int_\Omega \sum_{ij} \varphi_{ij} \frac{\partial^2 u}{\partial x_i \partial x_j}\,dx.$$

(1) Show that $HB(\Omega)$ endowed with the norm

$$\|u\|_{HB(\Omega)} = \|u\|_1 + \|\nabla u\|_1 + \int_\Omega |\nabla\nabla u|(x)\,dx$$

is a Banach space.

(2) Show that if $u \in \mathcal{D}'(\Omega)$ satisfies $\nabla\nabla u \in M^1(\Omega)$, then $u \in HB_{\text{loc}}(\Omega)$. Show that if Ω is moreover Lipschitz and bounded, then $u \in HB(\Omega)$.

Exercise 6.10 (Continuation of the Previous Exercise: the Trace Map).
Prove that if Ω is of class $\mathcal{C}^2$, then we can define the trace map to be

$$HB(\Omega) \longrightarrow W^{1,1}(\partial\Omega) \times L^1(\partial\Omega)$$
$$u \longmapsto (u, \partial u/\partial\overrightarrow{n}).$$

In $HB(\Omega)$, we define the weak convergence $u_n \rightharpoonup u$ by

$$\|u_n - u\|_{W^{1,1}(\Omega)} \longrightarrow 0 \text{ and } \forall \varphi \in \mathcal{C}_c(\Omega, \mathbb{R}^{N^2}), \int \nabla\nabla u_n : \varphi \longrightarrow \int \nabla\nabla u : \varphi.$$

Prove that the trace map is not continuous for the weak topology.
   Prove that if

$$u_n \longrightarrow u \quad \text{and} \quad \int_\Omega |\nabla\nabla u_n| \longrightarrow \int_\Omega |\nabla\nabla u|,$$

then

$$\int_{\partial\Omega} \left| \frac{\partial u_n}{\partial\overrightarrow{n}} - \frac{\partial u}{\partial\overrightarrow{n}} \right| \longrightarrow 0.$$

Exercise [*] 6.11 (Embeddings of the Space $HB(\Omega)$).

(1) Show that if $N \geqslant 2$ and if Ω is an open set of class $\mathcal{C}^2$, then we have an embedding

$$HB(\Omega) \hookrightarrow W^{1,N/(N-1)}(\Omega).$$

(2) Suppose that $N = 2$. We want to show that $HB(\mathbb{R}^2) \hookrightarrow \mathcal{C}_b(\mathbb{R}^2)$. This follows once we show that if v is an element of HB with compact support in $\mathbb{R}^2$, then the function V defined by

$$V(x,y) = \int_{]-\infty,x[\times]-\infty,y[} \frac{\partial^2 v}{\partial x \partial y} dx \, dy$$

is continuous and, moreover, equals v almost everywhere. To do this, show that the measure $\partial^2 v / \partial x \partial y$ charges neither horizontal nor vertical lines.

Exercise [*] 6.12 (Restriction of a Function in $BV(\Omega)$ to Ω).
As in Proposition 6.110, let Ω_1 and Ω_2 be two open subsets of $\mathbb{R}^N$ of class $\mathcal{C}^1$ and let Σ be a manifold of dimension $N-1$ with $\Omega = \Omega_1 \cup \Sigma \cup \Omega_2$, $\Omega_1 \cap \Omega_2 = \varnothing$, and $\overline{\Omega_1} \cap \overline{\Omega_2} = \overline{\Sigma}$. Let $\overrightarrow{n}$ be the outward-pointing normal to $\partial\Omega_2$. Let $u \in BV(\Omega)$ and consider the restrictions $u_i = u|_{\Omega_i}$, $i = 1, 2$.
   First show that $u_i \in BV(\Omega_i)$ and then that for the uniform Dirac measure $\delta_{\partial\Omega_1}$ on $\partial\Omega_1$, we have

$$\nabla u = \sum_{i=1,2} \nabla u_i \chi_{\Omega_i} + (\gamma_0(u_2 - u_1))\overrightarrow{n}\,\delta_{\partial\Omega_1}.$$

Also show that

$$|\nabla u| = \sum_{i=1,2} |\nabla u_i| \chi_{\Omega_i} + |(\gamma_0(u_2 - u_1))| \delta_{\partial \Omega_1}.$$

Let $\sigma \in \mathcal{C}(\Omega, \mathbb{R}^N)$. Show that if $\sigma \cdot \nabla u = |\nabla u|$ in Ω, then

- for every $i \in \{1, 2\}$ and every $x \in \Omega_i$, we have $\sigma \cdot \nabla u_i(x) = |\nabla u_i|(x)$,
- for every $x \in \partial \Omega_1$, we have $\sigma \cdot \overrightarrow{n}(u_2 - u_1) = |u_2 - u_1|(x)$.

Show that this property extends to the case where $\sigma \in L^\infty$ with $\mathrm{div}(\sigma) \in L^N(\Omega)$, where we see $\sigma \cdot \nabla u$ as a measure.

Exercise 6.13 (Restriction of a Function in $BD(\Omega)$ to Open Subsets of Ω).
Let Ω, Ω_1, and Ω_2 be as in the previous exercise. Let $u \in BD(\Omega)$. Prove that the restriction of u to Ω_k, which we denote by u_k, belongs to $BD(\Omega_k)$ for $k = 1, 2$ and that

$$\varepsilon_{ij}(u) = \varepsilon_{ij}(u_k)\chi_{\Omega_k} + ((u_2 - u_1)_i n_j + (u_2 - u_1)_j n_i))\delta_{\partial \Omega_1}.$$

Let $\sigma \in L^\infty(\Omega, E)$, where E denotes the space of symmetric matrices over $\mathbb{R}^N$. We suppose that $\mathrm{div}(\sigma) \in L^N(\Omega, \mathbb{R}^N)$. Prove that if $u \in BD(\Omega)$, then

$$\sigma : \varepsilon(u) = \sum_i (\sigma : \varepsilon(u_i))\chi_{\Omega_i} + \sum_{ij}(u_2 - u_1)_i n_j \sigma_{ij}\delta_{\partial \Omega_1}.$$

Exercise [$\ast\ast$] 6.14 (The Space $X_m(\Omega) = \{u \in L^p(\Omega) \mid \nabla^m u \in L^p(\Omega)\}$ for $p \geqslant 2$).
We endow $X_m(\Omega)$ with the natural norm $\|u\|_{X_m} = \|u\|_p + \|\nabla^m u\|_p$, for which it is complete.

(1) Use Theorem 6.74 to show that $X_m(\Omega)$ is of local type, that is,

$$\forall \varphi \in \mathcal{D}(\Omega), \forall u \in X_m(\Omega), \quad \varphi u \in X_m(\Omega).$$

(2) Show that the space $\mathcal{D}(\mathbb{R}^N)$ is dense in $X_m(\mathbb{R}^N)$.
(3) Show the following inequality for every $m \geqslant 2$ and every $j \leqslant m$:

$$(6.149) \qquad \|\nabla^j u\|_{L^p(\mathbb{R}^N)} \leqslant C\|\nabla^m u\|_{L^p(\mathbb{R}^N)}^{j/m}\|u\|_{L^p(\mathbb{R}^N)}^{1-j/m}.$$

(4) Let Ω be an open set of class $\mathcal{C}^m$. Show that inequality (6.149) implies that

$$\|\nabla^j u\|_{L^p(\Omega)} \leqslant C(\|u\|_p + \|\nabla^m u\|_{L^p(\Omega)}).$$

Hints. (2) For a given $\delta > 0$, use a function $\varphi \in \mathcal{D}(\mathbb{R}^N)$ with

(6.150) $$\|\varphi u - u\|_p \leqslant \delta \quad \text{and} \quad \|\varphi \nabla^m u - \nabla^m u\|_p \leqslant \delta.$$

Next, take a regularizing function ρ_ε and set $u_\varepsilon = \rho_\varepsilon \star (\varphi u)$, so that

(6.151) $$\|\nabla^m u_\varepsilon - \nabla^m(\varphi u)\|_p \leqslant \delta \quad \text{and} \quad \|u_\varepsilon - (\varphi u)\|_p \leqslant \delta.$$

Deduce that $\|u_\varepsilon - (\varphi u)\|_{X_m} \leqslant k\delta$. Apply the generalized Hölder's inequality to the integral $\int_{\mathbb{R}^N} u_\varepsilon \operatorname{div}(|\nabla u_\varepsilon|^{p-2} \nabla u_\varepsilon)$ to prove that we have

$$\int_{\mathbb{R}^N} |\nabla u_\varepsilon|^p \leqslant C \int_{\mathbb{R}^N} |u_\varepsilon||\nabla u_\varepsilon|^{p-2}|\nabla \nabla u_\varepsilon| \leqslant C\|\nabla \nabla u_\varepsilon\|_{L^p}\|u_\varepsilon\|_{L^p}\|\nabla u_\varepsilon\|_{L^p}^{p-2}$$

and, consequently, inequality (6.149) for u_ε, $j = 1$, and $m = 2$. Pass to the limit to prove that $\{\nabla u_\varepsilon\}$ is a Cauchy sequence in $L^p(\mathbb{R}^N)$ and that its limit in this space is ∇u (use convergence in the sense of distributions). Use an induction on m to prove that

(6.152) $$\forall j \leqslant m, \quad \|\nabla^j u\|_p \leqslant c_{p,j,m}\|u\|_p^{1-j/m}\|\nabla^m u\|_p^{j/m}.$$

Indeed, apply the induction formula, first with ∇u and $j = m - 1$, and then with u and $j = 1$, to show that there exist constant such that we have the following upper bound for $D = \|\nabla^m u\|_p$:

$$D \leqslant C\|\nabla u\|_p^{1-(m-1)/m}\|\nabla^{m+1} u\|_p^{(m-1)/m}$$
$$\leqslant C\|u\|_p^{(1-1/m)1/m}\|\nabla^m u\|_p^{1/(m^2)}\|\nabla^{m+1} u\|_p^{(m-1)/m}.$$

It follows that

$$\|\nabla^m u\|_p^{(m-1)(m+1)/m^2} \leqslant C\|u\|_p^{((m-1)/m^2)}\|\nabla^{m+1} u\|_p^{m-1/m}.$$

To conclude,

$$\|\nabla^m u\|_p \leqslant C\|u\|_p^{1/(m+1)}\|\nabla^{m+1} u\|_p^{m/(m+1)}$$

and for every $j \leqslant m - 1$,

$$\|\nabla^j u\|_p \leqslant C\|u\|_p^{1-j/m}\|\nabla^m u\|_p^{j/m}$$
$$\leqslant C\|u\|_p^{1-j/m+j/(m+1)m}\|\nabla^{m+1} u\|^{(jm)/[m(m+1)]}$$
$$\leqslant C\|u\|_p^{1-j/(m+1)}\|\nabla^{m+1} u\|_p^{j/(m+1)}.$$

Use these inequalities to deduce that $\nabla^j u_\varepsilon$ is a Cauchy sequence in $L^p(\mathbb{R}^N)$ that converges to $\nabla^j u$, which therefore belongs to $L^p(\mathbb{R}^N)$. In this manner, all the inequalities given above extend to the functions in $X(\mathbb{R}^N)$. Moreover, the norms are equivalent (use the open image theorem).

Exercise 6.15 (Example of a Function of a Measure).

Consider the measure μ defined by

$$\forall \varphi \in \mathcal{C}_c(]0, 1[), \quad \langle \mu, \varphi \rangle = \int_0^1 \frac{\varphi(x)}{\sqrt{x}} dx + \varphi(0).$$

(1) Show that μ is bounded on $]0, 1[$.

(2) Let $f(x) = \sqrt{x^2 + 1}$. Compute $f(\mu)$.

Exercise 6.16 (Second Example of a Function of a Measure).

Let f be a function on $\mathbb{R}^2$ defined by $f(x_1, x_2) = \sqrt{2x_1^2 + x_2^2} + x_1 + 2$. Show that f is convex and has linear growth at infinity. Compute f_∞. Let μ be the measure on $\mathbb{R}$ defined by $\mu = (x\,dx + \delta_1, \delta_1)$. Show that $f(\mu) = \sqrt{3}\delta_1 + \sqrt{2x^2 + x + 2}\,dx$.

Exercise [*] 6.17 (Images of Two Mutually Singular Measures Under a Function).

Let f be a convex function with linear growth at infinity with $f(0) = 0$. Prove that if μ_1 is a measure that is singular to μ_2, which we denote by $\mu_1 \perp \mu_2$ (cf. Section 6.2, Definition 6.43), then

$$f(\mu_1) \perp f(\mu_2).$$

Exercise [*] 6.18 (Property of the Composition of a Convex Function and a Gradient).

Let f be a convex function with linear growth at infinity such that $f(0) = 0$ and the conjugate f^* of f is bounded on its domain. Let Ω, Ω_1, Ω_2, and σ be as in Proposition 6.110 and Exercises 6.12 and 6.13, and let $u \in BV(\Omega)$. Prove that

$$f(\nabla u) = f(\nabla u)\chi_{\Omega_1} + f(\nabla u)\chi_{\Omega_2} + f_\infty(u_2 - u_1)\delta_\Sigma.$$

Exercise [*] 6.19 (Function of a Measure where the Function Admits a Nonempty Subdifferential at 0).

Let f be a convex function that admits a nonempty subdifferential at 0. Let $g = f(x) - f(0) - \langle x^*, x \rangle$, where $x^* \in \partial f(0)$. Show that $\mathrm{dom}\, g^* = \mathrm{dom}(f^*) - \partial f(0)$ and that

$$g^*(x) = f(0) + f^*(x + x^*).$$

Deduce the following property: if f is a convex function with linear growth at infinity and with conjugate f^* that is bounded on its domain and if φ is a nonnegative function in $\mathcal{C}_c(\Omega)$, then the formula

$$\langle f(\mu), \varphi \rangle = \sup_{v \in \mathcal{C}_c(\Omega, \mathrm{dom}\, f^*)} \int_\Omega \mu\, v\varphi - \int_\Omega f^*(v)\varphi$$

still holds. Prove that $g(\mu) = f(\mu) - f(0) - x^* \cdot \mu$.

Exercise [*] 6.20 (Details for $N = 3$ in the Proof of Theorem 6.95).

We use the notation of the proof of Theorem 6.95 in the case $N = 3$. We set $\alpha = \alpha_1 e_1 + \alpha_2 e_2 + \alpha_3 e_3$ and suppose that $\alpha_i \neq 0$ for every $i \in \{1, 2, 3\}$. We begin by proving Lemma 6.96 in this situation.

(1) Consider the product $I_\alpha J_1 J_2$. Use the components (ξ_1, ξ_2, ξ_3) of x in the new basis α, e_1, e_2 to show that

$$I_\alpha(x) = \int_{-\infty}^0 \widetilde{f}(\xi_1 + s, \xi_2, \xi_3)ds = \int_{-\infty}^{\xi_1} \widetilde{f}(s, \xi_2, \xi_3)ds.$$

Deduce that there exists a $w_\alpha \in L^2(\mathbb{R}^2)$ such that $|I_\alpha(x)| \leqslant w_\alpha(\xi_2, \xi_3)$. Also show that $|J_2(x)| \leqslant w_2(\xi_1, \xi_3)$ and $|J_1(x)| \leqslant w_1(\xi_1, \xi_2)$. Apply Lemma 2.40 to prove that $w_\alpha w_2 w_1 \in L^1(\mathbb{R}^3)$ and conclude that $I_\alpha J_1 J_2 \in L^1(\mathbb{R}^3)$.

(2) Use a different basis to show that the same holds for a different product, for example $I_\alpha I_1 J_2$. Deduce that every linear combination of these products, each taken to the power $1/2$, therefore belongs to $L_{\mathrm{loc}}^{3/2}(\mathbb{R}^3)$. This concludes the proof of Theorem 6.95 in the case $N = 3$.

Hints. For the first question, we have, for example,

$$J_2(x) = \widetilde{J}_2(\xi_1, \xi_2, \xi_3) = \int_{-\infty}^0 \widetilde{f}(\xi_1, \xi_2 + s, \xi_3)ds = \int_{-\infty}^{\xi_2} \widetilde{f}(\xi_1, s, \xi_3)ds.$$

Use an integral w_2 over $\mathbb{R}$ to give an upper bound and conclude that $|J_2(x)| \leqslant w_2(\xi_1, \xi_3)$.

Exercise 6.21 (Linear Combinations of Dirac Masses, [50, 51]).

Let ν be a positive measure for which there exists a constant $C > 0$ such that for every measurable set A, we have

$$\text{either} \quad \nu(A) = 0 \quad \text{or} \quad \nu(A) \geqslant C.$$

Prove that ν is a linear combination of Dirac masses with mass $\geqslant C$.

Hints. If ν is not identically zero, then let $x_0 \in \mathrm{supp}\,\nu$. Suppose that $\nu(x_0) = 0$; then there exists a ball $B(x_0, r)$ with $r > 0$ such that $\nu(B(x_0, r)) = 0$. Indeed, if this were not the case, then there would exist a sequence r_n tending to 0, such that $\nu(B(x_0, r_n)) > 0$, and therefore $\geqslant C$. Consequently, by the definition of the measure of a compact set, we would have

$$\nu(\{x_0\}) \geqslant \overline{\lim}\, \nu(B'(x_0, r_n)) \geqslant C.$$

It follows that in this case, either we have $\nu(\{x\}) \geqslant C$ at every point, or the measure is identically zero. However, we also have $\nu(B(x_0, r)) \geqslant C$ for every $r > 0$, so that by using a countable finite open set in Ω with finite measure for ν, we would have

$$\nu(\Omega) \geqslant \nu\left(\sum_n x_n\right) \geqslant NC$$

for every N. It follows that if ν is a bounded measure, then it cannot consist of a finite number of Dirac masses.

Exercise 6.22 (Generalization of the Previous Result, [50, 51]).

Let μ and ν be two positive measures on $\mathbb{R}^N$ for which there exist a constant $C > 0$ and real numbers p and q satisfying $1 \leqslant p < q \leqslant \infty$ such that, for every universally measurable function φ, we have

$$\left(\int |\varphi|^q \nu \right)^{1/q} \leqslant C \left(\int |\varphi|^p \mu \right)^{1/p}.$$

Prove that there exist a countable set of points $\{x_j\}$ in $\mathbb{R}^N$ and a sequence of real numbers ν_j such that

$$\nu = \sum_j \nu_j \delta_{x_j} \quad \text{and} \quad \mu \geqslant \sum_j \nu_j^{p/q} \delta_{x_j}.$$

Hints. First note that the assumptions imply that ν is absolutely continuous with respect to μ, so that

$$\nu = f \mu.$$

Next, by the Lebesgue–Radon–Nikodym theorem, there exist $g \in L^1(\mathbb{R}^N, \nu)$ and a measure σ singular with respect to ν, such that

$$\mu = g\nu + \sigma.$$

Reduce to the case where $\sigma = 0$ and set $\nu_k = g^{q/(q-p)} 1_{\{x|\ g(x) \leqslant k\}} \nu = g^{p/(q-p)} 1_{\{x|\ g(x) \leqslant k\}} \mu$. Let ψ be a universally measurable function and let

$$\varphi = g^{1/(q-p)} 1_{g \leqslant k} \psi.$$

Write

$$\left(\int \varphi^q d\nu \right)^{1/q} \leqslant C \left(\int |\varphi|^p d\mu \right)^{1/p}.$$

We then have

$$\left(\int |\psi|^q d\nu_k \right)^{1/q} \leqslant C \left(\int |\psi|^p g^{p/(q-p)} g 1_{\{x|g(x) \leqslant k\}} d\nu \right)^{1/p}$$

$$= C \left(\int |\psi|^p d\nu_k \right)^{1/p}.$$

Taking $\psi = \chi_A$, deduce that ν_k satisfies the conditions of Exercise 6.21, and conclude.

Exercise 6.23 (Applications of the Previous Exercises, [50, 51]).

Let $p < N$ and let $p^* = Np/(N-p)$. Let $\{u_m\}$ be a sequence that converges weakly to 0 in $W^{1,p}(\mathbb{R}^N)$. Use the continuity inequality

$$C \left(\int_{\mathbb{R}^N} |\varphi u_m|^{p^*} \right)^{1/p^*} \leqslant \|\nabla(\varphi u_m)\|_p$$

for $\varphi \in \mathcal{D}(\mathbb{R}^N)$ and the previous exercise, after extracting a subsequence from $\{u_m\}$, to show that $\{|u_m|^{p^*}\}$ converges weakly to a linear combination of Dirac masses $\nu = \sum_i \nu_i \delta_{x_i}$. Also show that

$$|\nabla u_m|^p \longrightarrow \mu, \quad \text{with} \quad \mu \geqslant C \sum_i \nu_i^{p/p^*} \delta_{x_i}.$$

7

Korn's Inequality in L^p

This final chapter is devoted to the proof of *Korn's inequality*, which we have already used in Chapter 5. This inequality says that if Ω is a regular bounded open set, then

$$\exists\, C > 0,\ \forall u \in W_0^{1,p}(\Omega, \mathbb{R}^N),\quad |\nabla u|_p \leqslant C|\varepsilon(u)|_p,$$

where the last inequality can also be written as

$$(7.1)\qquad \int_\Omega \Big(\sum_{i,j} |\partial_j(u_i)(x)|^2\Big)^{p/2} dx \leqslant C^p \int_\Omega \Big(\sum_{i\leqslant j} \Big|\frac{\partial_j u_i + \partial_i u_j}{2}(x)\Big|^2\Big)^{p/2} dx.$$

Let us begin with an introductory remark.

When Korn's inequality is explained in the mathematical literature, it is, in general, in the case $p = 2$; see, in particular, the articles contained in [44], [45], [43], [32], [54], and [30]. In some works, it is just mentioned that the result extends to the case where $1 < p < \infty$, with counterexamples for the cases $p = 1$ and $p = \infty$. Most articles about these inequalities concern the case $p = 2$ and look to extend the result to quite general classes of open sets, for example open sets of class $\mathcal{C}^1$, open sets with the cone property, or certain unbounded open sets. In the case $p \neq 2$, P. Ciarlet gives a proof that uses rather difficult results on the regularity of solutions of elliptic equations over $W^{1,p}$, as in [2] (cf. [15]).

Because of the lack of simple proofs in the case $p \neq 2$, we have chosen to prove the result for those values of p, for a bounded open set Ω of class $\mathcal{C}^2$, using results from harmonic analysis, without worrying about generalizing to less regular open sets.

Let us return to inequality (7.1). To obtain it, we will show the property

$$\forall T \in \mathcal{D}'(\Omega),\quad \nabla T \in W^{-1,p'}(\Omega) \implies T \in L^{p'}(\Omega).$$

F. Demengel, G. Demengel, *Functional Spaces for the Theory
of Elliptic Partial Differential Equations*, Universitext,
DOI 10.1007/978-1-4471-2807-6_7,
© Springer-Verlag London Limited 2012

This can be proved using Riesz's inequality, where C is a constant depending on N and p:

$$\forall \varphi \in \mathcal{S}(\mathbb{R}^N), \quad \left\| \frac{\partial^2 \varphi}{\partial x_i \partial x_j} \right\|_p \leqslant C |\Delta \varphi|_p.$$

Namely, we will use arguments from distribution theory and characterizations of the images of the operators div and Δ on the space $\mathcal{S}(\mathbb{R}^N)$.

Riesz's inequality, which bounds the mixed partial derivatives from above using only the seminorm of the Laplacian in L^p, can be shown using the Fourier transform applied to convolutions of functions in L^p with Riesz kernels (*Riesz transforms*).

An important part of this chapter consists of studying Hardy's and Hilbert's maximal functions, leading to properties of the Riesz transforms. The arguments we give in these preliminaries mostly come from the book [64], after being ordered and adapted to suit our objectives.

7.1 Harmonicity, Mean values, Hardy Maximal Functions

7.1.1 Construction of Harmonic Functions using the Poisson Kernel

The homogeneous Dirichlet problem associated with the operator Δ and $\mathbb{R} \times]0, +\infty[$ with boundary condition defined by a continuous function admits a regular solution. Below we provide the means to give the solution explicitly. When the open set is a ball, such a solution is defined by the formula given in Remark 5.70.

Definition 7.2. A function f of class $\mathcal{C}^2$ on an open subset Ω of $\mathbb{R}^N$ is called harmonic if

$$\forall x \in \Omega, \quad \Delta f(x) = \sum_1^N \partial_{ii} f(x) = 0.$$

In the case $N = 2$, the real and imaginary parts of these functions are holomorphic functions. The same holds for the *Poisson kernel* P defined on $\mathbb{R} \times]0, +\infty[$ by

$$P(x, y) = \frac{1}{\pi} \frac{y}{x^2 + y^2} = \Re \left(-\frac{1}{i \pi z} \right).$$

Let f be a continuous function on $\mathbb{R}$. We wish to extend f to a function on $\mathbb{R} \times]0, +\infty[$ that coincides with f on $\mathbb{R} \times \{0\}$ and is harmonic on the upper half-plane. Note that if we let P_y be the function $x \mapsto P(x, y)$, then the combination of the differentiation of the convolution $h = (f \star P_y)$ in x and the differentiation with respect to y gives $\Delta h = 0$, at least formally for now. More precisely, we have the following result.

Proposition 7.3. *Let $f \in L^p(\mathbb{R})$ for p satisfying $1 \leqslant p \leqslant \infty$; then the function u defined by*

$$\forall y > 0, \ \forall x \in \mathbb{R} \quad u(x,y) = \int_{\mathbb{R}} P(x-t,y)f(t)dt$$

belongs to $L^p(\mathbb{R} \times \,]0,+\infty[)$ with $\|u(\cdot,y)\|_p \leqslant \|f\|_p$.
  Moreover, u is harmonic on the upper half-plane and

$$\lim_{y \to 0} \|u(\cdot,y) - f\|_p = 0.$$

If f is continuous and bounded on $\mathbb{R}$, then the convergence is uniform on every compact subset of $\mathbb{R}$.[1]

Remark 7.4. When we only have the inclusion of f in L^p, there exist regions where the convergence of $P(\cdot,y) \star f$ to f when $y \to 0$ is uniform. More precisely, let $x_0 \in \mathbb{R}$ and let $\alpha > 0$ be a real number. We let $\Gamma_\alpha(x_0)$ denote the open cone with top $x_0 \in \mathbb{R}$ lying in $\mathbb{R} \times \,]0,+\infty[$, defined by

$$\Gamma_\alpha(x_0) = \{(x,y) \in \mathbb{R} \times \,]0,+\infty[\mid |x-x_0|/y < \alpha\}.$$

This region is a cone with vertical axis, whose top lies on the horizontal axis, and whose top semi-angle is less than $\pi/2$. When (x,y) tends to $(x_0,0)$ while staying in the cone, the resulting limit of $P(\cdot,y) \star f$ is called nontangential. We will show further on that if x_0 is a Lebesgue point[2] of f, then this limit exists and, moreover, the convergence is uniform in the cone. This property will be useful when we study the Hilbert transform. Its proof is given in Exercise 7.15.

Proof of Proposition 7.3.
  We will use two important properties in the proof, namely the positivity of P in the upper half-plane and the relation $\int_{\mathbb{R}} P(x,y)dx = 1$ that holds for every $y > 0$.

---

[1] In the book [64] we mentioned above, the results concern the harmonicity in the half-plane $\mathbb{R}^N \times \,]0,+\infty[$.
[2] Given a locally integrable function f in $\mathbb{R}^N$, an element x of $\mathbb{R}^N$ is called a *Lebesgue point* of f if

$$\lim_{r \to 0} \frac{1}{|B(0,r)|} \int_{|t|<r} |f(x-t) - f(x)| \, dt = 0.$$

We can show that the set of these points has a complement with measure zero.

(1) To establish the harmonicity, we can use derivatives or the characterization of harmonic functions using the mean value property (cf. Exercise 7.3). Let $\mathcal{M}_{x,y,r}(f)$ denote the mean value of f on the ball $B((x,y),r)$. We use Fubini's formula and the fact that the function $(x,y) \mapsto P(x-t,y)$ is harmonic for every t to obtain that for every $y > 0$ and for every $r < y$,

$$\mathcal{M}_{x,y,r}(u) = \frac{1}{\pi r^2} \int_{B((x,y),r)} \left[\int_{\mathbb{R}} P(\zeta - t, \eta) f(t) dt \right] d\zeta d\eta$$

$$= \frac{1}{\pi r^2} \int_{\mathbb{R}} f(t) \left[\int_{B((x,y),r)} P(\zeta - t, \eta) d\zeta d\eta \right] dt$$

$$= \int_{\mathbb{R}} f(t) P(x-t,y) dt = u(x,y).$$

Since the function u is continuous, this shows that $\Delta u = 0$ (cf. Exercise 7.3).

(2) Let us now show the assertion concerning the uniform convergence of $P_y \star \varphi - \varphi$ to 0 when $y \to 0$ on a compact subset K of $\mathbb{R}^2$, provided that φ is continuous and bounded.

Let $\varepsilon > 0$ and $\delta > 0$ satisfy $\pi/2 - \arctan(1/\delta) \leqslant \varepsilon$ and for every $x \in K$,

$$|\varphi(x) - \varphi(x-t)| \leqslant \varepsilon$$

provided that $|t| \leqslant \delta$. Then for $y \leqslant \delta^2$, we can write

$$\pi |P_y \star \varphi(x) - \varphi(x)| \leqslant \int_{|t|<\delta} \frac{y}{y^2 + t^2} |\varphi(x-t) - \varphi(x)| dt$$

$$+ \int_{|t|>\delta} \frac{y}{y^2 + t^2} |\varphi(x-t) - \varphi(x)| dt$$

$$\leqslant \varepsilon \int_{|t|<\delta} \frac{y}{y^2 + t^2} dt + 2\|\varphi\|_\infty \int_{|t|>\delta} \frac{y}{t^2 + y^2} dt$$

$$\leqslant \varepsilon \pi + 2\|\varphi\|_\infty (\pi - 2\arctan(\delta/y))$$

$$\leqslant (\pi + 4\|\varphi\|_\infty)\varepsilon,$$

which concludes the proof of the uniform convergence.

(3) Let us now show the convergence of $\|P_y \star \varphi - \varphi\|_p$ in L^p when $\varphi \in \mathcal{C}_c(\mathbb{R})$. We use the equality

$$(P_y \star \varphi - \varphi)(x) = \frac{1}{\pi} \int_{\mathbb{R}} \frac{\varphi(x - yt) - \varphi(x)}{1 + t^2} dt,$$

which is obtained after a change of variables. We will then use the density of $\mathcal{C}_c(\mathbb{R})$ in $L^p(\mathbb{R})$ and the following property, which holds for f in L^p:

$$\|P_y \star f\|_p \leqslant C\|f\|_p.$$

This inequality is a consequence of Hölder's inequality together with Fubini's formula. Indeed, using $(1+t^2) = (1+t^2)^{1/p}(1+t^2)^{1/p'}$, we have

$$\pi^p \int_{\mathbb{R}} |P_y \star f|^p(x)dx \leqslant \int_{\mathbb{R}} \left| \int_{\mathbb{R}} \frac{f(x-yt)}{1+t^2} dt \right|^p dx$$

$$\leqslant \int_{\mathbb{R}} \left(\int_{\mathbb{R}} \frac{|f(x-yt)|^p}{1+t^2} dt \right) \left(\int_{\mathbb{R}} \frac{1}{1+t^2} dt \right)^{p/p'} dx$$

$$\leqslant \pi^{p/p'} \int_{\mathbb{R}} |f(x-yt)|^p \left(\int_{\mathbb{R}} \frac{dt}{1+t^2} \right) dx \leqslant c\|f\|_p^p.$$

We therefore suppose that φ is continuous and has compact support. Let $\varepsilon > 0$ and let $\delta < 1$ be such that by the uniform continuity on $\mathbb{R}$, $|x-x'| \leqslant \delta$ implies that

$$|\varphi(x) - \varphi(x')| \leqslant \frac{\varepsilon}{|\operatorname{supp}\varphi| + 1}.$$

Suppose that $y < 1$ and let D denote the order δ neighborhood of the support of φ, so that if $y|t| < \delta$ and $x \notin D$, then $\varphi(x - yt) - \varphi(x) = 0$. Computations similar to the previous ones give

$$\pi^p \int_{\mathbb{R}} |P_y \star \varphi - \varphi|^p dx \leqslant \int_{\mathbb{R}} \left| \int_{\mathbb{R}} \frac{\varphi(x-yt) - \varphi(x)}{1+t^2} dt \right|^p dx$$

$$\leqslant \int_{\mathbb{R}} \left(\int_{\mathbb{R}} \frac{|\varphi(x-yt) - \varphi(x)|^p}{1+t^2} dt \right) \left(\int_{\mathbb{R}} \frac{1}{1+t^2} dt \right)^{p/p'} dx$$

$$\leqslant \pi^{p/p'} \left[\int_D \left(\int_{t,|yt|\leqslant\delta} \frac{|\varphi(x-yt) - \varphi(x)|^p}{1+t^2} dt \right) dx \right.$$

$$\left. + \int_{\mathbb{R}} \left(\int_{\{t,|yt|>\delta\}} \frac{|\varphi(x-yt) - \varphi(x)|^p}{1+t^2} dt \right) dx \right]$$

$$\leqslant c\varepsilon^p \pi^{p/p'} \int_D dx + 2c \int_{\mathbb{R}} |\varphi|^p dx \int_{\{|yt|>\delta\}} \frac{dt}{1+t^2}$$

$$\leqslant c'\varepsilon^p + 4c\|\varphi\|_{L^p}^p \left(\pi/2 - \arctan(\delta/y) \right),$$

which concludes the proof by choosing $y \leqslant \delta^2$.

To conclude, we suppose that $f \in L^p(\mathbb{R})$. Let $\varepsilon > 0$ and $\varphi \in \mathcal{C}_c(\mathbb{R})$ satisfy

$$\|f - \varphi\|_p \leqslant \varepsilon.$$

Under the previous conditions, let δ be a number such that $y \leqslant \delta^2$ implies the inequality

$$\|P_y \star \varphi - \varphi\|_p \leqslant \varepsilon.$$

Then

$$\|P_y \star f - f\|_p \leqslant \|P_y \star (f - \varphi)\|_p + \|P_y \star \varphi - \varphi\|_p + \|\varphi - f\|_p$$

$$\leqslant C\|f - \varphi\|_p + \varepsilon + \varepsilon \leqslant c\varepsilon,$$

completing the proof. $\qquad\qquad\square$

Proposition 7.5. *If u is defined as before with $f \in L^p(\mathbb{R})$, then $|u(x, y)| \leqslant Cy^{-1/p}$ for every $y > 0$. In particular, the function u is bounded in the half-plane $\{y \geqslant y_0\}$, where y_0 is taken to be positive.*

Proof of Proposition 7.5.

For a fixed x in $\mathbb{R}$, we use Hölder's inequality. By the change of variable $t = yz$, we have

$$\pi|(P_y \star f)(x)| \leqslant \pi\|P_y\|_{p'}\|f\|_p = y\left[\int_{\mathbb{R}} \frac{y dz}{y^{2p'}(1 + z^2)^{p'}}\right]^{1/p'}\|f\|_p$$

$$= y^{-1+1/p'}\left[\int_{\mathbb{R}} \frac{1}{(1 + |z|^2)^{p'}} dz\right]^{1/p'}\|f\|_p \leqslant cy^{-1/p}\|f\|_p. \quad \square$$

Proposition 7.6. *Let u be a harmonic function on the half-plane $\{y > 0\}$ that is bounded on every half-space $\{y \geqslant y_0\}$ with $y_0 > 0$; then for every pair (y_1, y_2) of positive numbers, we have*

$$u(x, y_1 + y_2) = \int_{\mathbb{R}} u(x - t, y_1)P(t, y_2)dt.$$

Proof of Proposition 7.6.

We fix a $y_0 > 0$. By assumption, the function $(x, y) \mapsto v(x, y) = u(x, y + y_0)$ is harmonic in a neighborhood of the upper half-plane $\{y \geqslant 0\}$ and bounded in this half-plane. We let v_1 denote the function associated with the continuous function $t \mapsto u(t, y_0)$ on $\mathbb{R}$ as in Proposition 7.3, namely

$$\forall x \in \mathbb{R}, \ \forall y > 0, \quad v_1(x, y) = \int_{\mathbb{R}} P(x - t, y)u(t, y_0)dt.$$

This function v_1 is harmonic in the upper half-plane and extends continuously to the function $t \mapsto u(t, y_0)$ on the boundary $\{y = 0\}$. In other words, we have $v_1(x, 0) = u(x, y_0)$.

We will show that the functions v and v_1 coincide in the upper half-plane, which will prove the equality of Proposition 7.6.

Indeed, the two functions v and v_1 are harmonic in $\{y > 0\}$ and, since $v_1(x, 0) = v(x, 0)$, they coincide on $\{y = 0\}$. Moreover, they are bounded. For v, this follows from the conditions of the proposition, and for v_1, it follows from Proposition 7.3 in the case $p = \infty$ and also from Proposition 7.5 because the function $t \mapsto u(t, y_0)$ belongs to $L^\infty(\mathbb{R})$. The conclusion now follows using a symmetry argument. For this, we extend the difference $d(x, y) = v(x, y) - v_1(x, y)$ to the lower half-plane using the formula

$$\forall x \in \mathbb{R}, \ \forall y > 0, \quad d(x, -y) = -d(x, -y),$$

which, because of $\Delta d(x, y) = -\Delta d(x, -y)$, implies that the extended function is harmonic on $\mathbb{R}^2 \smallsetminus \{y = 0\}$. Moreover, by extending the function d by 0 on

$\{y = 0\}$, we obtain a continuous function on $\mathbb{R}^2$. Using the Poisson kernel, we can use, for example, the solution of a Dirichlet problem in a ball, with continuous boundary condition, to show that this function is harmonic in $\mathbb{R}^2$. Furthermore, the extended function d is bounded in $\mathbb{R}^2$. It follows, in the dimension 2 case, that it is the real part of an integral function that is holomorphic in the plane and bounded, and therefore constant by Liouville's theorem. Consequently, $v - v_1$ is a constant, which must be zero since it is zero on $\{y = 0\}$.   □

Remark 7.7. We must emphasize the importance of the boundedness in this argument. Since the domain is unbounded, we cannot use the uniqueness of the solutions of Dirichlet problems. Moreover, we can easily construct nonzero functions that are harmonic in the plane and zero on the horizontal axis.

7.1.2 Rearrangement Function

Definition 7.8. The rearrangement function λ_f of the function f is defined to be

$$\lambda_f(s) = |\{x \mid |f(x)| > s\}|.$$

We can easily see that the function λ_f is nonincreasing and right-continuous. This function will be useful when we study the maximal functions further on. For the moment, the inclusion of f in L^p gives the following result.

Proposition 7.9. *Let $f \in L^1(\mathbb{R}^N)$; then the function f belongs to $L^p(\mathbb{R}^N)$ if and only if $\int_0^\infty s^{p-1}\lambda_f(s)ds < \infty$. More precisely, we have*

$$(7.10) \qquad \int_0^\infty s^{p-1}\lambda_f(s)ds = \frac{1}{p}\|f\|_p^p.$$

Proof of Proposition 7.9.

We begin by proving relation (7.10) when f is simple. By considering the positive and negative parts of f and the relation $|f| = f^+ + f^-$, we see that we may assume that $f \geqslant 0$ and that f is simple, which we do. Then f can be written as

$$f = \sum_{j=1}^n c_j\chi_{E_j},$$

where $c_{n+1} = 0 < c_n < c_{n-1} < \cdots < c_1$ and the E_j are two-by-two disjoint measurable subsets of $\mathbb{R}^N$. For $j \in [1, n]$, we set $d_j = |E_1| + \cdots + |E_j|$. The function λ_f can then be written as

$$\lambda_f(s) = \begin{cases} d_j & \text{if } c_{j+1} \leqslant s < c_j, \\ 0 & \text{if } s > c_1. \end{cases}$$

(cf. Exercise 1.23). Consequently,

$$\int_0^\infty s^{p-1}\lambda_f(s)ds = \sum_1^n \int_{c_{j+1}}^{c_j} s^{p-1}dsd_j = \frac{1}{p}\sum_1^n (c_j^p - c_{j+1}^p)d_j$$

$$= \frac{1}{p}c_1^p|E_1| + \sum_2^n c_j^p(d_j - d_{j-1}) = \frac{1}{p}\Big(\sum_1^n c_j^p|E_j|\Big) = \frac{1}{p}\|f\|_p^p.$$

We continue with the general case, where we may, and do, still suppose that $f \geqslant 0$. Since $f \in L^1(\mathbb{R}^N)$, there exists a nondecreasing sequence of simple functions $\{f_n\}$ with $f_n \leqslant f$ and $\|f_n - f\|_1 \to 0$. In particular, after extracting a subsequence, if necessary, the sequence $\{f_n\}$ converges almost everywhere to f. The sequence $E_n(s)$ is nondecreasing, hence $E(s) = \{x \mid |f(x)| > s\} = \bigcup_n \{x \mid |f_n(x)| > s\} \equiv \bigcup_n E_n(s)$ by the monotone convergence theorem. Moreover, $\lambda_f(s) = \lim \lambda_{f_n}(s)$.

Let us assume that $\int_0^\infty s^{p-1}\lambda_f(s)ds < +\infty$; then the dominated convergence theorem gives

$$\int_0^\infty s^{p-1}\lambda_{f_n}(s)ds \longrightarrow \int_0^\infty s^{p-1}\lambda_f(s)ds.$$

We can also apply the monotone convergence theorem to the sequence $\{f_n^p\}$. Using the result already proved for the simple functions, this gives

$$\frac{1}{p}\|f\|_p^p = \frac{1}{p}\lim_{n\to\infty}\|f_n\|_p^p = \lim_{n\to\infty}\int_0^\infty \lambda_{f_n}(s)s^{p-1}ds = \int_0^\infty \lambda_f(s)s^{p-1}ds.$$

In particular, this implies that $f \in L^p(\mathbb{R}^N)$.

Let us now suppose that $f \in L^p$. The sequence $\{f_n\}$ of simple functions can be chosen such that $\|f_n - f\|_p \to 0$. One of the previous relations then implies the convergence of $\int_0^\infty s^{p-1}\lambda_{f_n}(s)ds$ and equality (7.10). $\square$

7.1.3 Hardy–Littlewood Maximal Functions

In this subsection, we take $f \in L^1_{\text{loc}}(\mathbb{R}^N)$ and define the mean value of f on the balls in $\mathbb{R}^N$ using the formula

$$\mathcal{M}_f(x)(r) = \frac{1}{|B(x,r)|}\int_{B(x,r)} |f(t)|dt = \frac{1}{|B(r)|}\int_{B(0,r)} |f(t+x)|dt,$$

where $r > 0$. We then study the existence of the Hardy–Littlewood maximal function (HLM function) defined below.

Definition 7.11. Let f be a function in $L^1_{\text{loc}}(\mathbb{R}^N)$. The maximal function m_f of f is the supremum of the mean values on the balls with center x:

$$m_f(x) = \sup_{r>0}\frac{1}{|B(0,r)|}\int_{B(0,r)} |f(x+t)|dt = \sup_{r>0}\frac{1}{|B(0,r)|}\int_{x+B(0,r)} |f(t)|dt.$$

The HLM Function When $f \in L^1$.

Example 7.12. Let f be the function on $\mathbb{R}$ defined by $f(t) = 1/(t^2 + 1)$. We study the existence of m_f and its possible inclusion in a space $L^p(\mathbb{R})$.

The change of variables $t = -\tau$ shows that m_f is an even function. Since the function $r \mapsto (\arctan r)/r$ is nonincreasing, setting $x = 0$, we obtain $m_f(0) = \lim_{r \to 0} (\arctan r)/r = 1$. We therefore need to study the following mean values when $x > 0$:

$$u(r, x) = \frac{1}{2r} \int_{x-r}^{x+r} \frac{dt}{t^2 + 1} = \frac{\arctan(x + r) - \arctan(x - r)}{2r}.$$

The function $U(r, x) = -2u_r'(r, x)r^2$ satisfies

$$U(r, x) = \arctan(x + r) - \arctan(x - r)) - r\Big(\frac{1}{(x + r)^2 + 1} + \frac{1}{(x - r)^2 + 1}\Big).$$

Setting $a = x + r$ and $b = x - r$, its derivative can be written as

$$U_r'(r, x) = 2r\Big[\frac{a}{(a^2 + 1)^2} - \frac{b}{(b^2 + 1)^2}\Big].$$

By expanding $a(b^2 + 1)^2 - b(a^2 + 1)^2$, we see that $U_r'(r, x)$ has the same sign as the trinomial $T(r^2)$ defined by

$$T(r^2) = r^4 + 2(1 + x^2)r^2 - 3x^4 - 2x^2 + 1 = r^4 + 2(1 + x^2)r^2 - (x^2 + 1)(3x^2 - 1).$$

We note that the discriminant of $T(r^2)$ equals $\Delta = 4x^2(1 + x^2)$. For $x \neq 0$, the trinomial therefore admits two distinct roots in the variable r^2. Moreover, when $x < 1/\sqrt{3}$, these two solutions are negative, so that the trinomial is positive for every r. When $x \geq 1/\sqrt{3}$, one of the solutions we just mentioned is positive, namely $r_1^2(x) = -(1 + x^2) + 2x\sqrt{1 + x^2}$.

In Exercise 7.4, we will study u when $x \leq 1/\sqrt{3}$ and show not only the existence of the function m_f on the interval $[0, 1/\sqrt{3}]$ but also the equality $m_f = f$ in this interval.

For $x > 1/\sqrt{3}$, we see that the function $r \mapsto U_r'(r, x)$ is positive on $[r_1, +\infty[$ and negative on $]0, r_1[$. Since $U(0, x) = 0$ and $\lim_{r \to +\infty} U(r, x) = \pi$, it follows that there exists an $r_2(x) > r_1(x)$ such that $U(r_2(x), x) < 0$ on $]0, r_2[$ and $U(r_2(x), x) > 0$ on $[r_2, +\infty[$. To conclude, $r \mapsto u(r, x)$ reaches its supremum for $r = r_2(x)$ and we have

$$\forall x > 1/\sqrt{3}, \quad m_f(x) = u(r_2(x), x).$$

In the exercise we mentioned above, we also prove the continuity of the function m_f in the interval $]1/\sqrt{3}, +\infty[$. Studying the inclusion of m_f in a space $L^p(\mathbb{R})$ therefore reduces to studying its behavior at $+\infty$.

To do this, we estimate $r_2(x)$ using the signs of the numbers $U(x, x)$ and $U(2x, x)$ when $x \to +\infty$. We have

$$U(x, x) = \arctan(2x) - x(4x^2 + 2)/(4x^2 + 1),$$

which tends to $-\infty$ when $x \to +\infty$ and

$$U(2x, x) = \arctan(3x) + \arctan x - 2x(10x^2 + 2)/[(9x^2 + 1)(x^2 + 1)],$$

which tends to π when $x \to +\infty$. We deduce from this that for a large positive x, we have $x < r_2(x) < 2x$. Let us return to $m_f(x) = u(r_2(x), x)$. For $x > 1/\sqrt{3}$, we have the following results:

$$2r_2(x)u(r_2(x), x) < \int_{-x}^{3x} \frac{dt}{1+t^2} \quad \text{and} \quad 2r_2(x)u(r_2(x), x) > \int_0^{2x} \frac{dt}{1+t^2}.$$

These inequalities lead to the bounds

$$\frac{1}{4x} \int_0^{2x} \frac{dt}{1+t^2} < u(r_2(x), x) < \frac{1}{2x} \int_{-x}^{3x} \frac{dt}{1+t^2}.$$

It follows that the function m_f is not summable on $\mathbb{R}$ while it does belong to $L^p(\mathbb{R})$ for every $p > 1$.

Example 7.13 (HLM Function of the Characteristic Function of $[a, b]$).

- If $x \in \,]a, b[$ then either $\mathcal{M}_f(r)(x) = 1$ or $\mathcal{M}_f(x) < 1$. We therefore have $m_f(x) = 1$.
- If $x = a$ or b, then the mean value is either $1/2$ or $< 1/2$. Consequently, $m_f(x) = 1/2$.
- Finally, let us consider $x \notin [a, b]$. If $x < a$, then the mean values are zero if $r < a - x$, equal to $(1/2r)(x + r - a)$ if $a < x + r < b$, and equal to $b - a/2r$ if $r > b - x$. It follows that $m_f(x) = (b - a)/[2(b - x)]$. For $x > b$, we obtain $m_f(x) = (b - a)/2(x - a)$. It again follows that $m_f \in L^p$ for $p > 1$.

Remark 7.14. We can also use other mean values to define an HLM function, for examples the mean values on open hypercubes with sides parallel to the coordinate axes. In this case, we can see on the one hand, that the subsets of $\mathbb{R}^N$ where the two associated maximal functions are finite coincide and on the other hand, that each of these functions can be bounded from above by the other function times a constant depending only on N.

Indeed, it suffices to use the fact that the Euclidean ball of radius r with center x is contained in an open hypercube with center x and edges of length $2r$ and itself contains a hypercube with center x and edges of length $r/\sqrt{N}$. By the inequalities on the integrals of nonnegative functions that we can associate with these two types of integration domains, we obtain upper and lower bounds, giving the result by taking the suprema. Therefore, in the following theorem the HLM function may be defined using the mean values on these hypercubes.

Theorem 7.15. *Let $f \in L^1(\mathbb{R}^N)$. We set*

$$\forall s > 0, \quad F_s = \{x \in \mathbb{R}^N \mid m_f(x) > s > 0\}.$$

Then the Lebesgue measure of F_s, that is, the value of the rearrangement function of m_f at the point s satisfies

$$|F_s| \leqslant \frac{c\|f\|_1}{s},$$

where $c = c(N)$ with $c = 2^N$ when we take the mean values on the hypercubes. In particular, we have $m_f(x) < \infty$ for almost every $x \in \mathbb{R}^N$.

Proof of Theorem 7.15.

Taking the above into account, we let $C(x, r)$ denote the open hypercube with center x and edge $2r$. For $s > 0$, we let

$$F_s = \left\{x \in \mathbb{R}^N \;\middle|\; \sup_{r>0} \frac{1}{(2r)^N} \int_{C(x,r)} |f(t)|\, dt > s\right\}.$$

If this set is empty, then the property we wish to prove is trivial. We therefore assume that $F_s \neq \varnothing$. Let S be a compact subset of F_s; then for every $x \in S$, there exists an $r_x > 0$ such that $1/((2r_x)^N) \int_{C(x,r_x)} |f(t)|\, dt > s$. The function $y \mapsto \int_{C(y,r_x)} |f(t)|\, dt$ is continuous because $f \in L^1$; hence there exists a ball B_x with center x such that

$$\forall y \in B_x, \quad \frac{1}{(2r_x)^N} \int_{C(y,r_x)} |f(t)|\, dt > s.$$

The compact set S is covered by these balls B_x. Therefore there exists a finite number B_{x_i} with $1 \leqslant i \leqslant n$ that cover S. We choose such a finite cover with hypercubes $C(x_i, r_{x_i})$.

Let C_i' denote the hypercube with center 0 and edge r_{x_i}, so that $C(x_i, r_{x_i}) = x_i + C_i'$. We may, and do, assume that the numbering is such that we have the inclusions

$$C_1' \subset C_2' \subset \cdots \subset C_n'.$$

Furthermore, for every y in S, we set

$$K(y) = \sup\left\{ i \in [1,n] \ \middle| \ \frac{1}{|C_i'|} \int_{y+C_i'} |f(t)|dt > s \right\},$$

thus defining a map from S to $[1,n]$. To simplify the ideas behind the reasoning below, we can first consider the case $N = 1$, which is dealt with in Exercise 7.7. The first question of the exercise consists of proving Lemma 7.78, stated there. That result is generalized in the following lemma, which we will use in the proof of Theorem 7.15.

Lemma 7.16. *We take the situation as above.*

(1) *There exists a finite set of points $\{s_j\}_{1 \leqslant j \leqslant k}$ such that the set S is contained in $\bigcup_{1 \leqslant j \leqslant k} \{s_j + C_{K(s_j)}'\}$ and each of the centers s_j of these hypercubes belongs only to the hypercube with index j.*
(2) *Every intersection of more than 2^N hypercubes with two-by-two distinct indexes among the $V_j = s_j + C_{K(s_j)}'$ is empty.*

Proof of Lemma 7.16.

For (1), we choose s_1 in S such that $K(s_1) \geqslant K(s)$ for every s, which is possible because the image of K is finite. We consider the set $S_1 = S \setminus \{s_1 + C_{K(s_1)}'\}$. If this difference of sets is empty, then $S \subset V_1 = s_1 + C_{K(s_1)}'$ and the first part of the lemma holds for $k = 1$ while the second part is trivial. If the difference is nonempty, then we choose a point s_2 in S_1 such that $K(s_2) \geqslant K(s)$ for every $s \in S_1$. If $S_2 = S_1 - V_2$ is empty, then we obtain the lemma with $k = 2$ by noting that because of the inequality $r_{K(s_2)} \leqslant r_{K(s_1)}$, the center s_1 of the first hypercube cannot belong to the second one, $s_2 + C_{K(s_2)}'$.

We can continue this construction using the same algorithm. The number of steps is necessarily finite. Indeed, by the previous property of the centers of these hypercubes, the distance between two centers is greater than $r_0 = \min_i \{r_{x_i}\}$. It follows that the balls of radius $r_0/2$ with center s_j are two-by-two disjoint. Since the set S is bounded, it cannot contain infinitely many such balls, thus proving the desired property and the first statement of the lemma.

For (2), consider an intersection point of hypercubes V_j and take this point as the origin. We consider the 2^N quadrants of $\mathbb{R}^N$ that are delimited by the coordinate hyperplanes through this origin. Let Q be such a quadrant; then for every i, the coordinates with index i of two arbitrary points of Q have the same sign. Let us show that the centers of two hypercubes in the intersection cannot belong to the same quadrant. To illustrate the ideas, let $C(s, a)$ and $C(t, b)$ with $a \geqslant b$ be two such hypercubes, where we leave out the indexes to simplify. Let s_i be the coordinates of s and let t_i be the coordinates of t. We will show that for $i \in [1, N]$, we cannot have $\operatorname{sign} s_i = \operatorname{sign} t_i$. We argue by contradiction and assume that we do have this relation and, moreover, that $s_i > 0$ and $t_i > 0$, for further simplification. Since the origin is in $C(s, a)$, we then have $s_i < a$ for every i, whence $|s_i - t_i| < a$ for every i. However, the point t must lie in the exterior of the hypercube $C(s, a)$, so that $|s_j - t_j| > a$ for every j, contradicting the previous inequality. We conclude that the centers of the hypercubes in the intersection we are considering lie in different quadrants, and therefore cannot be more than 2^N in number. $\Box$

Let us return to the proof of the theorem. The measure of S is lesser than that of the union of the V_j, hence lesser than the sum of the measures $\sum_1^k |V_j|$. It then follows from the definition of the V_j using the map K that

$$|S| \leqslant \frac{1}{s} \sum_1^k \int_{V_j} |f(t)| dt.$$

Let us consider the sum of the characteristic functions of the sets V_j. This sum has value $m > 1$ at a point $s \in S$ only if s belongs to the intersection of m sets V_j. Since m is at most 2^N, it follows that $\sum_1^k \chi(V_j) \leqslant 2^N \chi(\bigcup V_j)$. Consequently,

$$\sum_1^k \int_{V_j} |f(t)| dt \leqslant 2^N \int_{\bigcup V_j} |f(t)| dt \leqslant 2^N \int_{\mathbb{R}^N} |f(t)| dt,$$

and therefore

$$|S| \leqslant \frac{1}{s} \sum_1^k \int_{V_j} |f(t)| dt \leqslant \frac{2^N}{s} \|f\|_{L^1(\mathbb{R}^N)}.$$ $\Box$

Remark 7.17. We can obtain the following partial result more easily. We take balls instead of hypercubes and construct $B(s_i, K(s_i))$ in an analogous manner. We then have

$$|S| \leqslant \frac{2^N \|f\|_1}{s}$$

without having to use that the intersection of more than 2^N balls is empty.

Indeed, by construction,

$$|s_i - s_j| \geqslant \sup(r_{K(s_i)}, r_{K(s_j)}) \geqslant \frac{r_{K(s_i)} + r_{K(s_j)}}{2}$$

for $i \neq j$, which implies that $B(s_i, r_{K(s_i)}/2) \cap B(s_j, r_{K(s_j)}/2) = \varnothing$, and therefore

$$\sum_i |B(s_i, r_{K(s_i)}/2)| = |\cup B(s_i, r_{K(s_i)}/2)| \leqslant \frac{\|f\|_1}{s}$$

and

$$|S| \leqslant \sum_i |B(s_i, r_{K(s_i)})| = 2^N \sum_i |B(s_i, r_{K(s_i)}/2)| \leqslant \frac{2^N |f|_1}{s}.$$

This in turn implies that

$$|F_s| \leqslant \frac{2^N}{s} \|f\|_1,$$

thus justifying the remark.

Consequently,

$$\text{for almost all } x \in \mathbb{R}, \quad m_f(x) < \infty.$$

Indeed, if $m_f(x) = +\infty$, then we can apply the theorem with arbitrary s, which leads to $|F_s| = \infty$, giving a contradiction.

Using examples, we have seen that when $f \in L^1$, the HLM function m_f does not necessarily belong to L^1. The situation is different for L^p with $p > 1$.

The HLM Function for Functions in L^p with $p > 1$. Let us first give a property that will allow us to generalize the previous theorem.

Proposition 7.18. *Let $p \geqslant 1$ and let $f \in L^p(\mathbb{R}^N)$; then the function*

$$f^s(x) = \begin{cases} f(x) & \text{if } |f(x)| > s, \\ 0 & \text{otherwise,} \end{cases}$$

belongs to $L^1(\mathbb{R}^N)$.

Proof of Proposition 7.18.

For $|f(x)| > s$, we can write $|f(x)| = |f^p(x)| |f^{1-p}(x)| \leqslant s^{1-p} |f^p(x)|$. It follows by integration that

$$\int_{\mathbb{R}^N} |f^s(x)| dx = \int_{\{x | |f(x)| > s\}} |f(x)| dx \leqslant s^{1-p} \int_{\{x | |f(x)| > s\}} |f^p(x)| dx$$
$$\leqslant s^{1-p} \|f\|_p^p,$$

concluding the proof.   □

This property will allow us to generalize Theorem 7.15 to functions in $L^p(\mathbb{R}^N)$ when $p > 1$.

Theorem 7.19. *Let $f \in L^p(\mathbb{R}^N)$ with $p > 1$; then for almost all x, we have $m_f(x) < +\infty$. Moreover, there exists a constant $c(p, N)$ such that*

$$\forall f \in L^p(\mathbb{R}^N), \quad \|m_f\|_p \leqslant c(p, N) \|f\|_p.$$

Proof of Theorem 7.19.

Let $f \in L^p(\mathbb{R}^N)$. We denote the rearrangement functions of m_f and m_{f^s} by λ and λ^s, respectively. We set $f_s = f - f^s$. The subadditivity of $f \mapsto m_f$, which clearly follows from the definition that uses a supremum, gives $m_f \leqslant m_{f^s} + m_{f_s}$. Since $|f_s|$ is bounded by s, we deduce that it is an element of L^∞. Moreover, since the mean value of f_s is $\leqslant s$, we deduce that $m_{f_s} \leqslant s$. By the inclusion of the function f^s in L^1, this inequality proves the almost everywhere finiteness of m_f.

Let us now show that $\lambda(2s) \leqslant \lambda^s(s)$. We set $E_f(s) = \{x \mid |m_f(x)| > s\}$ and compare the measures of $E_f(2s)$ and of $E_{f^s}(s)$. If $x \in E_f(2s)$, then $2s < |m_f(x)| \leqslant m_{f^s}(x) + m_{f_s}(x)$, which implies that $m_{f^s}(x) > s$ because $m_{f_s}(x) \leqslant s$. The inclusion $x \in E_{f^s}(s)$ follows. Consequently, $E_f(2s) \subset E_{f^s}(s)$, and therefore

$$\lambda(2s) \leqslant \lambda^s(s).$$

We then apply relation (7.10) of Proposition 7.9 to the function m_f and to its rearrangement function λ, where the common value can be either finite or infinite. Using the integration variable $2s$ in this relation, applying Theorem 7.15 to the function f^s (cf. Proposition 7.18), and then Fubini's formula, we obtain

$$\|m_f\|_p^p \leqslant p2^p \int_0^\infty s^{p-1}\lambda(2s)ds \leqslant p2^p \int_0^\infty s^{p-1}\lambda^s(s)ds$$

$$\leqslant p2^p C \int_0^\infty s^{p-2} \int_{x,|f(x)|>s} |f(x)|dx$$

$$\leqslant p2^p C \int_{\mathbb{R}^N} |f(x)| \int_0^{|f(x)|} s^{p-2}dsdx \leqslant \frac{p2^p C}{p-1} \int_{\mathbb{R}^N} |f(x)|^p dx.$$

To conclude, this equality implies that $m_f \in L^p(\mathbb{R}^N)$ and proves the assertion of the theorem. $\square$

An important application of this property concerns the convolution of a function in L^p with a radial function.

Corollary 7.20. *Let $\varphi \in L^1(\mathbb{R}^N)$ satisfy $\varphi(t) = \varphi^*(|t|)$, where φ^* is a nonnegative nonincreasing function on $[0, +\infty[$. We set $\varphi_\varepsilon(t) = \varepsilon^{-N}\varphi(t/\varepsilon)$.*

Then for every $f \in L^p(\mathbb{R}^N)$, we have

$$\sup_{\varepsilon > 0} |f \star \varphi_\varepsilon|(x) \leqslant m_f(x)\|\varphi\|_1 \leqslant C\|f\|_p\|\varphi\|_1$$

for almost all $x \in \mathbb{R}^N$.

Proof of Corollary 7.20.

We may, and do, assume that $f \geqslant 0$. We begin by proving the property when φ^* is a linear combination of characteristic functions of intervals in $\mathbb{R}^+$, that is, $\varphi^* = \sum_0^m a_k \chi([t_k, t_{k+1}])$, where the sequence $\{t_k\}$ is increasing and $t_0 = 0$. Since $\{a_k\}$ is nonincreasing and nonnegative, we can write

$$\varphi^* = \sum_0^m b_k \chi_{[0, t_{k+1}]},$$

where the b_k are defined by

$$b_k = a_k - a_{k+1}, \quad a_m = b_m$$

and are therefore $\geqslant 0$. Since φ is radial, it follows that

$$\varphi = \sum_k b_k \chi_{B(0, t_{k+1})}.$$

Let us set $\chi_k = \chi_{B(0, t_k)}$. The convolution $\varepsilon^{-N} \chi_{k+1}(x/\varepsilon) \star f$ can be written as

$$\varepsilon^{-N} \int_{|t| \leqslant \varepsilon t_{k+1}} f(x - t) dt.$$

Denoting the volume of the unit ball by ω_N, we have

$$(\varphi_\varepsilon \star f)(x) = \sum_1^m b_k t_{k+1}^N \omega_N \left[\frac{1}{\varepsilon^N t_{k+1}^N \omega_N} \int_{|t| \leqslant \varepsilon t_{k+1}} f(x - t) dt \right]$$

$$\leqslant m_f(x) \sum_1^m b_k \left| B(0, t_{k+1}) \right| = m_f(x) \|\varphi\|_1.$$

The desired inequality follows for simple functions.

Let us now suppose φ^* to be an arbitrary nonincreasing and nonnegative function on $\mathbb{R}^+$. If $\varphi(t) = \varphi^*(|t|)$ belongs to L^1 and if $\{\varphi_n^*\}$ is a nonincreasing sequence of simple functions that converges to φ while $\varphi_n^* \leqslant \varphi^*$ converges almost everywhere to φ^*, then the dominated convergence theorem implies that

$$\int_{\mathbb{R}^N} \left| \varphi^*(|t|) - \varphi_n^*(|t|) \right| |t|^{N-1} dt \longrightarrow 0.$$

By the first part of the argument, we have

$$\sup |f \star \varphi_{\varepsilon, n}| \leqslant C \|f\|_p \|\varphi_n\|_1.$$

For fixed ε, since $\varphi_{\varepsilon, n}$ converges almost everywhere to φ_ε in L^1, we see that $f \star \varphi_{\varepsilon, n}$ converges in L^p to $f \star \varphi_\varepsilon$. In particular, after extracting a subsequence, if necessary, $f \star \varphi_{\varepsilon,n}(x) \to f \star \varphi_\varepsilon(x)$ for almost all x. It follows that for almost all x and for $\varepsilon > 0$, we have

$$|f \star \varphi_\varepsilon(x)| \leqslant \underline{\lim} |f \star \varphi_{\varepsilon,n}(x)| \leqslant C\|f\|_p \lim \|\varphi_n\|_1 = C\|f\|_p \|\varphi\|_1,$$

giving the result by taking the supremum in ε, because the right-hand side does not depend on ε. □

Example 7.21. Consider, for $y > 0$ and $1 \leqslant p \leqslant \infty$, the convolution $u(\cdot, y) = f \star P(\cdot, y)$ studied in Proposition 7.3, where $f \in L^p(\mathbb{R})$. For almost all x in $\mathbb{R}$, we have

$$|u(x, y)| \leqslant m_f(x) < +\infty.$$

It suffices to apply the above to the function φ defined by $\varphi(x) = 1/(|x|^2 + 1)$.

7.2 Hilbert Transform in $\mathbb{R}$

7.2.1 Preliminaries to the Definition

Let $f \in L^p(\mathbb{R})$ with $1 \leqslant p < +\infty$. We first consider the convolution $f \star g_y$, where $\pi g_y(t) = t/(t^2 + y^2)$. Since the latter belongs to $L^q(\mathbb{R})$ for every $q > 1$, the convolution exists almost everywhere on $\mathbb{R}$. When $p = 1$, we use $q = \infty$. When $p > 1$, we choose q with $q < p/(2p - 1)$, so that $f \star g_y \in L^r(\mathbb{R})$ (cf. Corollary 4.60) for a real number $r > 1$ satisfying $1/r = 1/p + 1/q - 1$. When $y \to 0$, the function g_y converges, outside of $t = 0$, to the function $t \mapsto 1/t$, which does not belong to any of the L^p. Meanwhile, the distribution associated with g_y converges to the "principal value" distribution defined in Chapter 1. This leads us to conjecture that the limit of $f \star g_y$ is the distribution, or function, $\frac{1}{\pi} \mathrm{Vp}(1/t) \star f$. Classically, this convolution is called the Hilbert transform of the function f. Further on, we will generalize it to the Riesz transforms for the dimensions $N \geqslant 2$.

7.2.2 Complements on Convolutions and the Fourier Transform

Let T be a tempered distribution and let φ be a function of $\mathcal{S}$. Their convolution can be seen as a generalized convolution (cf. the G-convolution [22]). In order to illustrate its use for the reader, we will now give a number of results that are well adapted to the cases we will be studying.

Proposition 7.22. Let $T \in \mathcal{S}'(\mathbb{R}^N)$ and let $\varphi \in \mathcal{S}(\mathbb{R}^N)$; then the convolution $T \star \varphi$ exists and is the slowly increasing C^∞ function f defined by

$$\forall x \in \mathbb{R}^N, \quad f(x) = \langle T, \tau_x(\check{\varphi}) \rangle,$$

where $\check{\varphi}$ is the function $t \mapsto \varphi(-t)$. Moreover, we have

$$(7.23) \qquad\qquad \langle T \star \varphi, \psi \rangle = \langle T, \check{\varphi} \star \psi \rangle.$$

Proof of Proposition 7.22.

We admit (cf. Exercise 7.8) that the function f defined in the proposition has the stated properties. It can therefore be identified with a tempered distribution. Let us verify the equality $T \star \varphi = [f]$.

To begin, $A = \langle [f], \psi \rangle$ is well defined for $\psi \in \mathcal{D}(\mathbb{R}^N)$, using the integral of the product. To show that the general definition using the tensor product is satisfied, we will consider ψ as a distribution (with compact support) and use the commutativity of the tensor product:

$$
\begin{aligned}
A &= \langle [\langle T_{[t]}, \tau_x(\check{\varphi}(t)) \rangle], \psi(x) \rangle = \langle [\psi]_{[x]}, [\langle T_{[t]}, \tau_x(\check{\varphi}(t)) \rangle] \rangle \\
&= \langle [\psi]_{[x]} \otimes T_{[t]}, \check{\varphi}(t-x) \rangle = \langle T_{[t]} \otimes [\psi]_{[x]}, \check{\varphi}(t-x) \rangle \\
&= \left\langle T_{[t]}, \int_{\mathbb{R}^N} \psi(x)\varphi(x-t)dx \right\rangle = \left\langle T_{[t]}, \int_{\mathbb{R}^N} \psi(t+y)\varphi(y)dy \right\rangle \\
&= \langle T_{[t]} \otimes [\varphi]_{[y]}, \psi(t+y) \rangle = \langle T \star \varphi, \psi \rangle.
\end{aligned}
$$

Inside these relations, we obtain equality (7.23) by noting in passing that $\check{\varphi} \star \psi$, the convolution of two functions in $\mathcal{S}(\mathbb{R}^N)$, is an element of $\mathcal{S}(\mathbb{R}^N)$. This moreover allows us to give a sense to the inequalities above. $\square$

We admit that the Fourier transform has the property of homomorphisms stated in the following proposition (cf. [22] or Exercise 7.9).

Proposition 7.24. *Let $T \in \mathcal{S}'(\mathbb{R}^N)$ and let $\varphi \in \mathcal{S}(\mathbb{R}^N)$; then the Fourier transform of the convolution $T \star \varphi$ equals the product of the Fourier transforms of T and φ.*

The other properties of convolutions, in particular those concerning differentiation, also hold. Moreover, we have the following result.

Proposition 7.25. *For a tempered distribution T, the map $\varphi \mapsto T \star \varphi$ from $\mathcal{S}(\mathbb{R}^N)$ to $\mathcal{S}'(\mathbb{R}^N)$ is continuous.*

Proof of Proposition 7.25.

Let $\{\varphi_n\}$ be a sequence of functions in $\mathcal{S}$ that converges to φ in $\mathcal{S}$. Let $\psi \in \mathcal{S}$. By the continuity of convolution in $\mathcal{S}$, the sequence of convolutions $\{\check{\varphi}_n \star \psi\}$ converges to $\check{\varphi} \star \psi$ in $\mathcal{S}$. Since the distribution T is tempered, we deduce that $\langle T, \check{\varphi}_n \star \psi \rangle$ converges to $\langle T, \check{\varphi} \star \psi \rangle$. Since this is true for every $\psi \in \mathcal{S}$, it now follows from relation (7.23) that $T \star \varphi_n \to T \star \varphi$ in $\mathcal{S}'$. $\square$

7.2.3 Definition of the Hilbert Operator $f \longmapsto \frac{1}{\pi} \mathrm{Vp}(1/x) \star f$

Explicit Definition When f Belongs to $\mathcal{S}(\mathbb{R})$. By the above, when $\varphi \in \mathcal{S}(\mathbb{R})$, the convolution $\mathrm{Vp}(1/t) \star \varphi$ is the function h such that

$$\forall x \in \mathbb{R}, \quad h(x) = \langle \mathrm{Vp}(1/t), \tau_x(\check{\varphi})(t)\rangle = \lim_{\varepsilon \to 0} \int_{|t| \geqslant \varepsilon} \frac{\varphi(x-t)}{t} dt.$$

Explicit Definition When f Belongs to $L^p(\mathbb{R})$. Since the space $\mathcal{S}(\mathbb{R})$ is dense in $L^p(\mathbb{R})$, we can approximate $f \in L^p(\mathbb{R})$ by a sequence of functions $\{\varphi_n\}$ in $\mathcal{S}$. We must then show that the limit of the function

$$x \longmapsto (\mathrm{Vp}(1/t) \star \varphi_n)(x)$$

exists almost everywhere and that this limit also equals

$$\lim_{\varepsilon \to 0} \int_{|t| \geqslant \varepsilon} \frac{f(x-t)}{t} dt.$$

In order to do this, we establish the existence almost everywhere of the limit of $f \star g_y$, where $\pi g_y(t) = t/(t^2 + y^2)$ (cf. Preliminaries 7.2.1), when $y \to 0$.

Let F be the function of the complex variable z such that

$$\forall z \in \mathbb{C}, \quad \Im m\, z > 0 \implies F(z) = \frac{1}{\pi} \int_{\mathbb{R}} \frac{f(t)}{z-t} dt.$$

Since $z \mapsto 1/(z-t)$ is holomorphic, the Lebesgue theorem on complex differentiability tells us that F is analytic on the open upper half-plane. The real part of F can be written as a convolution:

$$\Re e\, F(x+iy) = \frac{1}{\pi} \int_{\mathbb{R}} \frac{f(t)(x-t)}{(x-t)^2 + y^2} dt = \frac{1}{\pi} \int_{\mathbb{R}} \frac{f(x-t)t}{t^2 + y^2} dt = f \star g_y.$$

We propose to show that this real part admits a nontangential limit almost everywhere (cf. Remark 7.4) when $y \to 0_+$.

Remark 7.26. The imaginary part of $-F$ is none other than the function $u(x,y)$ introduced in Proposition 7.3 as the convolution $f \star P(\cdot, y)$, where P is the Poisson kernel relative to the upper half-plane.

Proposition 7.27. *At every Lebesgue point x_0 of f, the function $x \longmapsto v(x,y) = (f \star g_y)(x)$ admits a nontangential limit when $(x,y) \to (x_0, 0)$.*

Proof of Proposition 7.27.
We fix a positive real number y and set $F(z) = v(x,y) - iu(x,y)$. By writing f as the sum of its positive and negative parts, we may, and do, assume

that the function f, and therefore also the function $u(\cdot,y) = f \star P(\cdot,y)$, is $\geqslant 0$. Let $G(z) = \exp(-iF(z))$. This function is holomorphic in the upper half-plane and bounded because $\exp(-u) = |\exp(-iF(z))| \leqslant 1$. Our problem therefore reduces to proving that the nontangential limit $\lim_{y \to 0_+} G(z)$ exists almost everywhere and is nonzero.

Since $|G(z)| \leqslant 1$, we know that the sequence $\{x \mapsto G(x+iy_n)\}$, where $\{y_n\}$ is a sequence of positive real numbers tending to 0, is bounded in $L^\infty(\mathbb{R})$. Since the space $L^\infty(\mathbb{R})$ is the dual of $L^1(\mathbb{R})$, it follows that there exists a subsequence of $\{y_n\}$, which we also denote by $\{y_n\}$, such that $\{x \mapsto G(x+iy_n)\}$ is weakly star convergent to a function h in $L^\infty(\mathbb{R})$. This means that for every element g of $L^1(\mathbb{R})$, we have

$$\lim_{n \to +\infty} \Big[\langle g, G(x+iy_n) \rangle \Big] = \langle g, h \rangle.$$

Now, the function $t \mapsto P(x-t,y)$ belongs to L^1 for every $x \in \mathbb{R}$ and every $y > 0$. Consequently,

$$\forall (x,y), \quad \lim_{n \to +\infty} \int_{\mathbb{R}} P(x-t,y)G(x+iy_n)dt = \int_{\mathbb{R}} P(x-t,y)h(t)dt.$$

Let us now show that this last integral in fact equals $G(x+iy)$. We will use Proposition 7.6, which gives us $\int_{\mathbb{R}} P(x-t,y)G(x+iy_n)dt = G(x+i(y+y_n))$. Since the function G is continuous in the upper half-plane, it follows that for every $y > 0$, we have

$$G(x+iy) = \lim_{n \to +\infty} \int_{\mathbb{R}} P(x-t,y)G(t+iy_n)dt = \int_{\mathbb{R}} P(x-t,y)h(t)dt \equiv G_1(x,y).$$

The function $x \mapsto G_1(x,y)$ is a convolution of h, an element of L^∞, with the Poisson kernel. Consequently, almost everywhere on $\mathbb{R}$, it admits a limit when y converges nontangentially to 0 (cf. Proposition 7.3 and, more precisely, Remark 7.4).

This limit of $G(x+iy)$ is, furthermore, almost everywhere nonzero. Indeed, by Corollary 7.20 (or, more precisely, by Example 7.21), the function u satisfies

$$\text{for almost all } x \in \mathbb{R}, \ \forall y > 0, \quad |u(x,y)| \leqslant m_f(x) < +\infty.$$

Since u is nonnegative, this proves that e^{-u} cannot tend to 0 almost everywhere. Therefore there exists a nonzero function $x \mapsto G_0(x)$ such that

$$\text{for almost all } x_0 \in \mathbb{R}, \quad \lim_{\substack{y \to 0 \\ (x,y) \in \Gamma_\alpha(x_0)}} G(x+iy) = G_0(x_0).$$

Since $|G(x+iy)| \to |G_0(x_0)|$ for this type of convergence, we find that $e^{-iv(x,y)}$ converges nontangentially to the point $e^{i\theta(x_0)}$ of the unit circle, where $\theta(x_0)$ is the argument of $G_0(x_0)$ up to a constant times 2π. It follows that if L and L' are two nontangential limits of v at the point x_0, then their distance to each other is $2k\pi$ for an integer k. In order to obtain a contradiction, we assume that $k \neq 0$ and, to illustrate the ideas, that $L < L'$. Let $l \in {]}L, L'{[}$. We will show that l is also a nontangential limit of v at x_0, giving the contradiction.

Let $\varepsilon < \inf(l - L/2, L' - l/2)$. By assumption, there exist sequences $\{(x_n, y_n)\}$ and $\{(x'_n, y'_n)\}$ that tend to $(x_0, 0)$ while staying in the fixed cone $\Gamma_\alpha(x_0)$ and satisfy $v(x_n, y_n) \to L$ and $v(x'_n, y'_n) \to L'$. In particular, there exists an n_0 sufficiently large that $n \geqslant n_0$ implies

$$(7.28) \qquad v(x_n, y_n) \leqslant L + \varepsilon < l \quad \text{and} \quad v(x'_n, y'_n) > L' - \varepsilon > l.$$

Let us set $Y_n = \sup_{m \geqslant n}(y_m, y'_m)$ for $n \geqslant n_0$, and let us consider the truncated cone

$$\Gamma_\alpha^{Y_n}(x_0) = \{(x, y) \mid y \leqslant Y_n, \, |x - x_0| \leqslant \alpha y\}$$

in the upper half-plane $\mathbb{R} \times {]}0, \infty{[}$. Since the function v is continuous in $\mathbb{R} \times {]}0, \infty{[}$, the image of the truncated cone $v(\Gamma_\alpha^{Y_n}(x_0))$ is convex. Since $n \geqslant n_0$, it contains all the real numbers $v(x_n, y_n)$ and $v(x'_n, y'_n)$ satisfying the relations (7.28). This image therefore also contains l. It follows that there exists a point (x''_n, y''_n) in $\Gamma_\alpha^{Y_n}(x_0)$ such that $v(x''_n, y''_n) = l$. Now, when $n \to +\infty$, the sequence $\{(x''_n, y''_n)\}$ tends to $(x_0, 0)$ while staying inside the cone $\Gamma_\alpha(x_0)$. The number l is therefore also a nontangential limit of v, giving a contradiction.

We conclude that a nontangential limit $\lim_{y \to 0}(f \star g_y)$ exists almost everywhere on $\mathbb{R}$. $\qquad\square$

7.2.4 Definition of the Hilbert Transform

Let us state the theorem and definition.

Theorem 7.29 (and definition).
Consider $f \in L^p(\mathbb{R})$ and the family of functions

$$\left\{ x \longmapsto \frac{1}{\pi} \int_{|t| > \varepsilon} \frac{f(x - t)}{t} dt \right\}_\varepsilon.$$

When $\varepsilon \to 0$, this family converges almost everywhere on $\mathbb{R}$ to the function $x \mapsto 1/\pi \lim_{y \to 0}(f \star g_y)(x)$. Consequently, we can define the Hilbert transform of f to be the function defined almost everywhere by

$$Hf(x) = \frac{1}{\pi}\left(\mathrm{Vp}(1/x) \star f\right)(x) = \frac{1}{\pi} \lim_{y \to 0}(f \star g_y)(x) = \frac{1}{\pi} \lim_{\varepsilon \to 0} \int_{|t| > \varepsilon} \frac{f(x - t)}{t} dt.$$

Proof of Theorem 7.29.

For the sake of simplicity, we will ignore the factor $1/\pi$. Let us first prove that for every fixed x in the Lebesgue set of the function f (cf. Remark 7.4), that is, for almost every x since the complement of this set has measure zero, we have

$$\lim_{\varepsilon \to 0} \left[\int_{|t| > \varepsilon} \frac{f(x-t)}{t} dt - \int_{\mathbb{R}} \frac{t}{t^2 + \varepsilon^2} f(x-t) dt \right] = 0.$$

By writing the integrals over $\mathbb{R}$ as the sums of two integrals over $]0, +\infty[$ and setting $h(x,t) = f(x-t) - f(x+t)$ and

$$\psi_\varepsilon(t) = \begin{cases} \dfrac{-t}{t^2 + \varepsilon^2} & \text{if } 0 < t < \varepsilon, \\[2mm] \dfrac{\varepsilon^2}{t(t^2 + \varepsilon^2)} & \text{if } t \geqslant \varepsilon, \end{cases}$$

we reduce the problem to showing that

(7.30) $$\lim_{\varepsilon \to 0} \int_0^{+\infty} h(x,t) \psi_\varepsilon(t) dt = 0.$$

We note that this function ψ_ε is not continuous but that $|\psi_\varepsilon|$ is continuous and piecewise C^1. It moreover belongs to $L^\infty \cap L^1$.

By assumption, x satisfies $\lim_{r \to 0} 1/r \int_{-r}^r |f(x-t) - f(x)| dt = 0$ (cf. Part [3] of Remark 7.4). The same property holds when we replace t by $-t$. Hence, for every $\delta > 0$, there exists an $\eta > 0$ such that

$$\forall r > 0, \quad r \leqslant \eta \implies \frac{1}{r} \int_0^r |h(x,t)| dt \leqslant \delta.$$

It follows that if we set $H(x,t) = \left| \int_0^t h(x,u) du \right|$, then

$$0 < t < \eta \implies H(x,t) \leqslant \delta t.$$

To prove property (7.30), it now suffices to show that when $\varepsilon \to 0$, we have

$$I_1(\varepsilon) = \int_0^\eta \psi_\varepsilon(t) h(x,t) dt \longrightarrow 0 \quad \text{and} \quad I_2(\varepsilon) = \int_\eta^{+\infty} \psi_\varepsilon(t) h(x,t) dt \longrightarrow 0.$$

From now on, we will assume that $\varepsilon < \inf\{\eta, (\eta \delta^{3p'-1})^{1/2}\}$.

The Integral $I_1(\varepsilon)$. We carry out an integration by parts over $]0, \varepsilon[$ and over $]\varepsilon, \eta[$, noting that $\psi_\varepsilon(\eta) = \varepsilon^2/[\eta(\eta^2 + \varepsilon^2)] \leqslant 1/\eta$ and $\lim_{t \to \varepsilon \pm 0} \psi_\varepsilon(t) = \pm 1/2\varepsilon$. Moreover, we let $\{\psi_\varepsilon'\}$ denote the absolutely continuous part of the derivative of ψ_ε, that is, $\psi_\varepsilon' = \{\psi_\varepsilon'\} + (1/\varepsilon)\delta_{\{x=\varepsilon\}}$. The integral I_1 can then be written as

$$|I_1(\varepsilon)| \leqslant \frac{H(x,\eta)}{\eta} + \frac{H(x,\varepsilon)}{\varepsilon} + \int_0^\eta H(x,t) |\psi_\varepsilon'(t)| dt$$

$$\leqslant \delta \left[1 + 1 + \int_0^\eta t |\psi_\varepsilon'(t)| dt \right] \equiv \delta(2 + J(\varepsilon)).$$

After computing the derivatives, the last integral $J(\varepsilon)$ becomes

$$\int_0^\varepsilon t \frac{\varepsilon^2 - t^2}{(t^2 + \varepsilon^2)^2} dt + \int_\varepsilon^\eta t\varepsilon^2 \frac{3t^2 + \varepsilon^2}{t^2(t^2 + \varepsilon^2)^2} dt.$$

The upper bounds

$$\frac{\varepsilon^2 - t^2}{(t^2 + \varepsilon^2)^2} \leqslant \frac{1}{t^2 + \varepsilon^2}, \quad \text{and} \quad \frac{3t^2 + \varepsilon^2}{t^2(t^2 + \varepsilon^2)^2} \leqslant \frac{3}{t^2(t^2 + \varepsilon^2)}$$

lead to

$$J(\varepsilon) \leqslant \int_0^\varepsilon \frac{t}{t^2 + \varepsilon^2} dt + \int_\varepsilon^\eta \frac{3\varepsilon^2}{t(t^2 + \varepsilon^2)} dt = \frac{1}{2} \ln\left(\frac{2\varepsilon^2}{\varepsilon^2}\right) + \int_1^{\eta/\varepsilon} \frac{3}{u(1 + u^2)} du$$

$$\leqslant \ln\sqrt{2} + \int_1^{+\infty} \frac{3}{u(1 + u^2)} du = K.$$

It follows that $|I_1(\varepsilon)| \leqslant \delta(2 + K)$, whence $I_1(\varepsilon) \to 0$.

The Integral $I_2(\varepsilon)$. We use Hölder's inequality to bound the integral I_2:

$$|I_2(\varepsilon)| \leqslant \left[\int_\eta^{+\infty} |h(x,t)|^p dt\right]^{1/p} \left[\int_\eta^{+\infty} \left[\frac{\varepsilon^2}{t(t^2 + \varepsilon^2)}\right]^{p'} dt\right]^{1/p'}.$$

The first integral on the right-hand side is bounded from above by $2\|f\|_p$ and the second one is bounded by $\varepsilon^2 \int_\eta^{+\infty} t^{-3p'} dt$, which converges because $p' > 1$. It follows that $|I_2(\varepsilon)| \leqslant K'\delta \to 0$, concluding the proof of equality (7.30). □

Exercises 7.11 and 7.13 propose computations of Hilbert transforms.

7.2.5 Operators of Weak Type (p, p)

Definition 7.31. We say that an operator T is of weak type (p, p) if there exists a constant C such that every $f \in L^p(\mathbb{R}^N)$ satisfies

$$s^p \lambda_{Tf}(s) \leqslant C\|f\|_p^p.$$

It is clear that if T sends $L^p(\mathbb{R}^N)$ continuously into itself, then it is of weak type (p, p). Indeed,

$$s^p |\{x \mid |Tf(x)| > s\}| \leqslant \int_{\mathbb{R}^N} |T(f)(x)|^p dx \leqslant C\|f\|_p^p.$$

This is, for example, the case for the Hilbert transform when $p = 2$.

Proposition 7.32. *The Hilbert transform sends $L^2(\mathbb{R})$ into $L^2(\mathbb{R})$.*

First proof of Proposition 7.32.

We first assume that $f \in S$. Let us recall relation (7.24), that is, when $T \in S'$, we have $\mathcal{F}(T \star f) = \mathcal{F}(T)\mathcal{F}(f)$ (cf. [22]). Using the transform of $\mathrm{Vp}(1/x)$ and noting that $\mathcal{F}$ is an isometry of $L^2(\mathbb{R})$, we then have (cf. [22] or Exercise 7.10):

$$\|Hf\|_2 = \|\mathcal{F}(Hf)\|_2 = \frac{1}{\pi}\|\mathcal{F}(\mathrm{Vp}(1/x))\mathcal{F}(f)\|_2$$
$$= \frac{1}{\pi}\| - (i\pi \operatorname{sign}\xi)\mathcal{F}(f)(\xi)\|_2 = \|\mathcal{F}(f)\|_2.$$

Hence, by the density of S in L^2, H extends to an isometry on L^2.   □

Second proof of Proposition 7.32.

This time, we will only use the properties of convolution in L^2 and the Fourier transform of functions.

We are looking for the Fourier transform of $g_y(\cdot, y)$, which belongs to L^2. It can be seen as the semiconvergent integral

$$\int_{\mathbb{R}} \exp(-2i\pi\xi t)\frac{t}{(t^2 + y^2)}dt.$$

The details of the computation of this integral are given in Exercise 7.1. If $\xi > 0$, then the result is $-i\pi \exp(-2i\pi\xi y))$. Replacing t by $-t$ gives the result when $\xi < 0$. The convolution $g_y(\cdot, y) \star f$ then belongs to L^2, as does its Fourier transform. The latter is therefore $(-i \operatorname{sign}\xi) \exp(-2\pi|\xi|y)\widehat{f}(\xi)$ and we can apply the Plancherel–Parseval theorem:

$$\|g_y(\cdot, y) \star f\|_2^2 = \|\exp(-2\pi|\xi|y)\widehat{f}(\xi)\|_2^2.$$

Now, we know that $Hf = \lim_{y\to 0} g_y(\cdot, y) \star f$. Hence, since the functions are nonnegative, Fatou's lemma followed by the Plancherel–Parseval theorem gives

$$\|Hf\|_2^2 \leqslant \lim_{y\to 0} \int_{\mathbb{R}} |\exp(-2\pi|\xi|y)\widehat{f}(\xi)|^2 d\xi = \|\widehat{f}\|_2^2 = \|f\|_2^2.$$

It follows that $\|Hf\|_2 \leqslant \|f\|_2$, allowing us to conclude the proof.   □

Proposition 7.33. *The Hilbert transform is of weak type $(1,1)$.*

Proof of Proposition 7.33.

By considering the nonnegative and nonpositive parts of f separately, we reduce to the case where $f \geqslant 0$. Let $F(z) = u(x,y) + iv(x,y) = P_y \star f(x) + iQ_y \star f(x)$ for $(x,y) \in \mathbb{R} \times]0, +\infty[$. The functions Q and P are the real and imaginary parts of $i/[\pi(x + iy)]$. The function F is holomorphic in $\mathbb{R} \times]0, +\infty[$. The function $w(x,y) = \ln(|1 + sF(z)|)$ is harmonic in the upper half-plane for every $s > 0$. It is bounded in the half-plane $\{x + iy \mid y \geqslant y_0\}$. By Proposition 7.3 with $y_1 = y - \eta$ and $y_2 = \eta$, $0 < \eta < y$, we have

$$w(x, y) = \pi \ln|1 + sF(x + iy)| = \int_{\mathbb{R}} \frac{y - \eta}{(x - \xi)^2 + (y - \eta)^2} \ln(|1 + sF(\xi + i\eta)|) d\xi.$$

Fatou's lemma then gives

$$\int_{\mathbb{R}} \frac{y}{(x - \xi)^2 + y^2} \ln|1 + sF(\xi)| d\xi$$
$$\leqslant \lim_{\eta \to 0} \int_{\mathbb{R}} \frac{y - \eta}{(x - \xi)^2 + (y - \eta)^2} \ln(|1 + sF(\xi + i\eta)|) d\xi.$$

Multiplying by y, we obtain

$$\int_{\mathbb{R}} \frac{y^2}{(x - \xi)^2 + y^2} \ln|1 + sF(\xi)| d\xi \leqslant \pi y \ln|1 + sF(x + iy)|$$
$$\leqslant \pi y \ln(1 + s|F(x + iy)|)$$
$$\leqslant \pi y s|F(x + iy)|$$

by the properties of the function ln. Furthermore, by the dominated convergence theorem, we see that

$$\lim_{y \to +\infty} yF(x + iy)$$
$$= \lim_{y \to +\infty} \left[\int_{\mathbb{R}} f(t) \frac{y^2}{(x - t)^2 + y^2} dt + i \int_{\mathbb{R}} f(t) \frac{y(x - t)}{(x - t)^2 + y^2} dt \right]$$
$$= \int_{\mathbb{R}} f(t) dt.$$

Thus, by taking the limit when $y \to +\infty$ and once more applying the dominated convergence theorem, we have

$$\int_{\mathbb{R}} \ln|\sqrt{(1 + sf(\xi))^2 + (sHf(\xi))^2}| d\xi \leqslant \pi s \|f\|_1.$$

Setting $E_\tau = \{\xi, |Hf(\xi)| > \tau\}$, we deduce that

$$\ln(s\tau)|E_\tau| \leqslant \int_{E_\tau} \ln|sHf(\xi)| d\xi \leqslant \pi s \|f\|_1.$$

Next, setting $s = e/\tau$, we obtain

$$|E_\tau| \leqslant \frac{\pi e}{\tau} \|f\|_1,$$

which implies that the Hilbert transform is of weak type $(1, 1)$. $\square$

Proposition 7.34 (weak form of the Marcinkiewicz theorem). *Let T be an operator on $L^1(\mathbb{R}^N) + L^r(\mathbb{R}^N)$ for some real number $r > 1$, that is subadditive, of weak type $(1,1)$, and continuous from $L^r(\mathbb{R}^N)$ to $L^r(\mathbb{R}^N)$. Then T sends $L^p(\mathbb{R}^N)$ continuously into $L^p(\mathbb{R}^N)$ for every $p \in\,]1, r]$.*

Proof of Proposition 7.34.

By Proposition 7.9, we must show that for $1 < p < r$, there exists a constant C_p such that

$$\forall f \in L^p(\mathbb{R}^N), \quad \int_0^\infty \alpha^{p-1} \big|\{x \mid |Tf(x)| > \alpha\}\big| d\alpha \leqslant C_p \|f\|_p^p.$$

Fixing α, we write $f = f_1 + f_2$, where

$$f_1 = \begin{cases} f(x) & \text{if } |f(x)| > \alpha \\ 0 & \text{if } |f(x)| \leqslant \alpha \end{cases}, \qquad f_2 = \begin{cases} f(x) & \text{if } |f(x)| < \alpha \\ 0 & \text{if } |f(x)| \geqslant \alpha. \end{cases}$$

The function f_1 then belongs to L^1 by Proposition 7.18. The function f_2 belongs to L^r because integrating the inequality $|f_2(x)|^r \leqslant \alpha^{r-p} |f(x)|^p$ gives the finiteness of $\|f_2\|_r$. The subadditivity of T gives $|Tf| \leqslant |Tf_1| + |Tf_2|$. Hence, if $|Tf(x)| > \alpha$, one of the numbers $|Tf_i(x)|$ is greater than $\alpha/2$ (use contradiction), whence

$$\{x \mid |Tf(x)| > \alpha\} \subset \{x \mid |Tf_1(x)| > \alpha/2\} \cup \{x \mid |Tf_2(x)| > \alpha/2\}.$$

By assumption, T is of type $(1,1)$ and (r,r). Hence we have the inequalities $[\alpha/2]\lambda_{Tf_1}(\alpha/2) \leqslant C_1\|f_1\|_1$ and $[\alpha/2]^r \lambda_{Tf_2}(\alpha/2) \leqslant C_r\|f_2\|_r^r$. Consequently,

$$\big|\{x \mid |Tf(x)| > \alpha\}\big| \leqslant C_1 (2/\alpha) \int_{\mathbb{R}} |f_1| dt + C_r (2/\alpha)^r \int_{\mathbb{R}} |f_2(t)|^r dt$$

$$= C\Big((2/\alpha) \int_{|f(t)| > \alpha} |f(t)| dt + (2/\alpha)^r \int_{|f(t)| < \alpha} |f(t)|^r dt \Big).$$

The integral $I \doteq \int_0^\infty \alpha^{p-1} \big|\{x \mid |Tf(x)| > \alpha\}\big| d\alpha$ therefore satisfies

$$I \leqslant C \int_0^\infty \frac{\alpha^{p-1}}{\alpha} \int_{\{x \mid |f(x)| > \alpha\}} |f(x)| dx\, d\alpha$$

$$+ C \int_0^\infty \alpha^{p-1} \alpha^{-r} \int_{\{x \mid |f(x)| < \alpha\}} |f(x)|^r dx\, d\alpha$$

$$\leqslant C \int_0^\infty |f(x)| \int_0^{|f(x)|} \alpha^{p-2} d\alpha dx + C \int_0^\infty |f(x)|^r \int_{|f(x)|}^\infty \alpha^{p-r-1} d\alpha dx$$

$$\leqslant C \int_0^\infty \Big(|f(x)| |f(x)|^{p-1} dx + |f|^r(x) |f|^{p-r}(x) \Big) dx$$

$$\leqslant c_1 \|f\|_p^p,$$

where we have used Fubini's theorem for the last inequalities. This concludes the proof. □

Corollary 7.35. *The Hilbert transform on $\mathbb{R}$ sends $L^p(\mathbb{R})$ continuously into $L^p(\mathbb{R})$ for $p \in \,]1, \infty[$.*

Proof of Corollary 7.35.

Let us first consider $1 < p < 2$. By the two previous results, Marcinkiewicz's theorem can be applied with $r = 2$. We can therefore conclude that we have an inequality of the type $\|Hf\|_p \leqslant C_p \|f\|_p$ for every p with $1 < p < 2$.

Let us now take $p > 2$. Let H^* be the adjoint of the Hilbert transform H, which is defined by

$$\forall \varphi, \psi \in \mathcal{S}, \quad \langle H^*(\psi), \varphi \rangle = \langle H\varphi, \psi \rangle = \int_{\mathbb{R}} H(\varphi)(x)\psi(x)dx.$$

Since $p > 2$, we have $p' < 2$, whence, by the above, $\|H\varphi\|_{p'} \leqslant C_{p'} \|\varphi\|_{p'}$. By the definition and Hölder's inequality, it follows that

$$|\langle H^*(\psi), \varphi \rangle| \leqslant \|H(\varphi)\|_{p'} \|\psi\|_p \leqslant C_{p'} \|\varphi\|_{p'} \|\psi\|_p.$$

Hence, if $\psi \in \mathcal{S}$, then the linear functional associated with $H^*\psi$ is continuous on $\mathcal{S}$ for the topology of $L^{p'}$. By density, $H^*\psi$ extends to $L^{p'}$, whence it follows that this linear function is an element of L^p. Since we still have

$$\forall f \in L^{p'}, \quad |\langle H^*(\psi), f \rangle| \leqslant (C_{p'} \|\psi\|_p) \|f\|_{p'},$$

it follows that for every $\psi \in \mathcal{S}$, we have $\|H^*\psi\|_p \leqslant C_{p'} \|\psi\|_p$.

Let us now show that $H^*(\psi) = -\mathrm{Vp}(1/x) \star \psi$, which will prove that $\|H(\psi)\|_p \leqslant C_{p'} \|\psi\|_p$ and, by density, that the operator H is continuous from L^p into L^p. We use relation (7.23) and the oddness of the distribution $\mathrm{Vp}(1/x)$:

$$\langle H^*(\psi), \varphi \rangle = \langle \mathrm{Vp}(1/x), \check{\varphi} \star \psi \rangle = -\langle \mathrm{Vp}(1/x), (\check{\varphi} \star \psi)(-x) \rangle.$$

A direct computation gives

$$\int_{-\infty}^{+\infty} \check{\varphi}(-x - t)\psi(t)dt = \int_{-\infty}^{+\infty} \check{\psi}(x - t)\varphi(t)dt = (\check{\psi} \star \varphi)(x).$$

We therefore have

$$\forall \varphi, \psi \in \mathcal{S}, \quad \langle H^*(\psi), \varphi \rangle = -\langle \mathrm{Vp}(1/x), \check{\psi} \star \varphi \rangle = -\langle H\psi, \varphi \rangle. \quad □$$

7.2.6 Maximal Hilbert Function

Definition 7.36. The maximal Hilbert function of the function f, denoted by $H_m(f)$ or $H_m f$, is defined by

$$H_m(f)(x) = \sup_{\varepsilon > 0} \frac{1}{\pi} \left| \int_{|t| \geqslant \varepsilon} \frac{f(x-t)dt}{t} \right|.$$

Theorem 7.37. *Let $f \in L^p(\mathbb{R})$ with $1 < p < \infty$; then*

$$H_m(f)(x) \leqslant \frac{1 + \ln 2}{\pi} m_f(x) + m_{Hf}(x).$$

In particular, H_m acts on $L^p(\mathbb{R})$ and there exists a constant B_p such that

$$\forall f \in L^p(\mathbb{R}), \quad \|H_m(f)\|_p \leqslant B_p \|f\|_p.$$

Proof of Theorem 7.37.

We may, and do, assume that $f \geqslant 0$. Let φ_ε be defined by

$$\varphi_\varepsilon(t) = \begin{cases} \dfrac{t}{t^2 + \varepsilon^2} & \text{if } 0 < t < \varepsilon, \\[2mm] \dfrac{-\varepsilon^2}{t(t^2 + \varepsilon^2)} & \text{if } t \geqslant \varepsilon. \end{cases}$$

It allows us to write

$$\int_{|t| > \varepsilon} \frac{f(x-t)}{t} dt = \int_{\mathbb{R}} \frac{f(x-t)t}{t^2 + \varepsilon^2} dt - (f \star \varphi_\varepsilon)(x).$$

We can easily verify that $\varphi_\varepsilon = (1/\varepsilon)\varphi(x/\varepsilon)$, where φ is the function

$$\varphi(t) = \begin{cases} \dfrac{t}{t^2 + 1} & \text{if } |t| < 1, \\[2mm] -\dfrac{1}{t(t^2 + 1)} & \text{if } |t| \geqslant 1. \end{cases}$$

Since the function f is nonnegative, we can bound $|f \star \varphi_\varepsilon|$ from above by $f \star \psi_\varepsilon$ where ψ is defined by

$$\psi(t) = \begin{cases} \dfrac{1}{2} & \text{if } |t| < 1, \\[2mm] \dfrac{1}{|t|(t^2 + 1)} & \text{if } |t| \geqslant 1. \end{cases}$$

This element of $L^1(\mathbb{R})$ is a decreasing function of the absolute value and satisfies $\|\psi\|_1 = 1 + \ln 2$. We can therefore apply Corollary 7.20, giving

$$(7.38) \qquad \sup_{\varepsilon > 0} |f \star \varphi_\varepsilon(x)| \leqslant \|\psi\|_1 m_f(x) \leqslant (1 + \ln 2) m_f(x).$$

It remains to bound the integral $(1/\pi)f \star Q_\varepsilon$ from above, where $Q_\varepsilon(t) = t/(t^2 + \varepsilon^2)$ is the real part of $1/(t + i\varepsilon)$. We will use the following lemma.

Lemma 7.39. *Let $f \in L^p(\mathbb{R})$. We set $P_y(t) = y/(y^2 + t^2)$ (Poisson kernel) and $Q_y(t) = t/(t^2 + y^2)$; then*

$$\forall y > 0, \quad f \star Q_y = Hf \star P_y.$$

Proof of Lemma 7.39 when $f \in \mathcal{S}$.

It suffices to show the equality of the Fourier transforms with respect to the variable x. Using the results from the second proof of Proposition 7.32 or Exercise 7.1, we can write

$$\mathcal{F}(f \star Q_y)(\xi) = \mathcal{F}(f)(\xi)\mathcal{F}(Q_y)(\xi) = -i\pi \operatorname{sign} \xi \, e^{-2\pi |y\xi|} \mathcal{F}(f)(\xi).$$

Furthermore, using the Fourier transform of $\mathrm{Vp}(1/t)$, we also have

$$\mathcal{F}((Hf) \star P_y)(\xi) = \mathcal{F}(Hf)(\xi)\mathcal{F}(P_y)(\xi) = -i\pi \operatorname{sign} \xi \, e^{-2\pi |y\xi|} \mathcal{F}(f)(\xi).$$

Finally, applying the inverse Fourier transform gives the equality of the lemma when $f \in \mathcal{S}$. $\qquad\square$

Proof of Lemma 7.39 when $f \in L^p$.

We use the density by approximating f in L^p by a sequence $\{\varphi_n\}$ in $\mathcal{S}$. We note that P_y belongs to $L^{p'}$, as does Q_y. Hence $\varphi_n \star Q_y$ converges pointwise to $f \star Q_y$. Moreover, by Corollary 7.35, the Hilbert transform $H\varphi_n$ converges in L^p to Hf, from which it follows that $H\varphi_n \star P_y$ converges pointwise to $Hf \star P_y$. The equality we have proved in $\mathcal{S}$ gives the result by taking the limit in L^p. $\qquad\square$

Let us return to Theorem 7.37. With the help of Example 7.21, the equality of the lemma leads to the inequality

$$\|f \star Q(\cdot, y)\|_p = \|Hf \star P(\cdot, y)\|_p \leqslant m_{Hf}.$$

Together with the upper bound (7.38), this proves the theorem. $\qquad\square$

7.3 The Riesz Transforms on $\mathbb{R}^N$

7.3.1 Definition of the Riesz Transforms

We introduce generalizations of the Hilbert transform in dimension $N > 1$.

The functions $x \mapsto x_j(|x|)^{-(N+1)}$ are not locally summable. We will associate to them (cf. Chapter 1, Section 1.4) the finite parts $\mathrm{Pf}(x_j(|x|)^{-(N+1)})$, which are distributions in $\mathbb{R}^N$. Let us first define $\mathrm{Pf}(1/|x|^{N+1})$.

Classically, since the power we are considering is related to t^{-2} in $\mathbb{R}$, given a function φ in $\mathcal{D}(\mathbb{R}^N)$, we begin with the integral

$$\int_{|x|\geqslant\varepsilon}\frac{\varphi(x)-\theta_\varphi T_2(\varphi(x))}{(|x|^{N+1})}\,dx,$$

where $T_2(\varphi)$ is the Taylor expansion of φ at the point $x=0$ truncated at the order 2 and θ_φ is a function in $\mathcal{D}$ with value 1 on $\operatorname{supp}\varphi$, which we may assume to be an even function. We remove from this integral the terms whose limit when $\varepsilon\to0$ is not finite. By passing to polar coordinates, the first term $\theta_\varphi\varphi(0)$ of $T_2(\varphi)$ leads to the integral $\omega_{N-1}\int_\varepsilon^A\varphi(0)dr/r^2$ whose infinite part can be written as $\omega_{N-1}\varphi(0)/\varepsilon$, where ω_{N-1} denotes the $(N-1)$-dimensional surface area of the unit sphere $\mathbb{R}^N$. The other term of $T_2(\varphi)$, namely $x\cdot\nabla\varphi(0)\theta_\varphi$, leads to a combination of integrals that all vanish. Noting that the factor θ is redundant for the term $\varphi(0)$, we conclude with the following definition.

Definition 7.40. The finite part of $|x|^{-(N+1)}$ is the distribution such that for every function φ of $\mathcal{D}(\mathbb{R}^N)$, we have

$$\langle\operatorname{Pf}(1/|x|^{N+1}),\varphi\rangle=\lim_{\varepsilon\to0}\left[\int_{|x|\geqslant\varepsilon}\frac{\varphi(x)}{|x|^{N+1}}dx-\omega_{N-1}\frac{\varphi(0)}{\varepsilon}\right].$$

A similar process leads to the definition of $\operatorname{Pf}(x_j/|x|^{N+1})$.

Definition 7.41. The Riesz kernel K_j of index j is defined to be the finite part $\operatorname{Pf}(x_j/|x|^{N+1})$. This is the distribution such that for every $\varphi\in\mathcal{D}(\mathbb{R}^N)$ and for every even θ_φ in $\mathcal{D}(\mathbb{R}^N)$ with value 1 at 0, we have

$$\langle\operatorname{Pf}(K_j),\varphi\rangle=\lim_{\varepsilon\to0}\int_{|x|\geqslant\varepsilon}\frac{x_j(\varphi(x)-\theta_\varphi\varphi(0))}{|x|^{N+1}}\,dx=\int_{\mathbb{R}^N}\frac{x_j(\varphi(x)-\theta_\varphi\varphi(0))}{|x|^{N+1}}\,dx.$$

The last expression is justified by the fact that the absolute value of the integrant is bounded from above by $r^2|\nabla\varphi(0)|/r^{N+1}$, which shows the summability in $x=0$ when we take into account the Jacobian.

Remark 7.42. Since the integral concerning $x_j\varphi(0)|x|^{-(N+1)}$ vanishes, we could also define the distribution K_j using the integral of $x_j\varphi(x)/|x|^{N+1}$, as the sum of two absolutely convergent integrals, where the decomposition depends of the sign of x_j. The resulting expression is, however, less suited to our computations.

Remark 7.43. We can see that the finite part is the product of $\operatorname{Pf}(1/|x|^{N+1})$ and the monomial function $x\mapsto x_j$.

Indeed, by the previous remark, since the function $x_j\varphi$ vanishes in $x = 0$, we have

$$\langle x_j \operatorname{Pf}(1/|x|^{N+1}), \varphi \rangle = \langle \operatorname{Pf}(1/|x|^{N+1}), x_j\varphi \rangle$$
$$= \lim_{\varepsilon \to 0} \int_{|x| \geqslant \varepsilon} \frac{x_j\varphi(x)}{|x|^{N+1}} \, dx$$
$$= \int_{\mathbb{R}^N} \frac{x_j\varphi(x)}{|x|^{N+1}} \, dx$$
$$= \int_{\mathbb{R}^N} \frac{x_j(\varphi(x) - \theta_\varphi\varphi(0))}{|x|^{N+1}} \, dx.$$

Definition 7.44. We call Riesz transform of index j the map R_j that sends a function f in a space $L^p(\mathbb{R}^N)$ to the convolution $\operatorname{Pf}(K_j) \star f$, when this exists.

Noting that outside of $x = 0$, the derivative of the function $x \mapsto g(x) = |x|^{-(N-1)}$ with respect to x_j equals $-(N-1)K_j$, we begin by comparing this derivative to the finite part $\operatorname{Pf}(K_j)$.

Proposition 7.45. *Let $[g]$ be the distribution associated with the locally summable function $x \mapsto |x|^{-(N-1)}$. The derivative of this distribution with respect to x_j equals $-(N-1)\operatorname{Pf}(K_j)$.*

Proof of Proposition 7.45.

Let $X = \langle \partial_j[g], \varphi \rangle$. Using Fubini's formula, we reduce to integrating by parts with respect to x_j, where we use the function $\varphi_1 = \varphi - \theta_\varphi\varphi(0)$ that coincides with $\varphi - \varphi(0)$ on supp φ for the primitive of $\partial_j\varphi$:

$$X = -\langle [g], \partial_j\varphi \rangle = -\int_{\mathbb{R}^N} \frac{\partial_j\varphi(x)}{|x|^{N-1}} dx = -\int_{\mathbb{R}^{N-1}} d\widehat{x}_j \int_{\mathbb{R}} \frac{\partial_j\varphi(x)}{|x|^{N-1}} dx_j$$
$$= -\int_{\mathbb{R}^{N-1}} d\widehat{x}_j (N-1) \int_{\mathbb{R}} \varphi_1(x) K_j(x) dx_j$$
$$= -(N-1) \int_{\mathbb{R}^N} (\varphi(x) - \varphi(0)\theta_\varphi(x)) K_j(x) dx$$
$$= -(N-1)\langle \operatorname{Pf}(K_j), \varphi \rangle. \qquad \square$$

7.3.2 Fourier Transforms of the Riesz Kernels

Let us first note that by multiplying by the characteristic function of a compact set, we see that g is the sum of a summable function and a bounded function, both of which can be identified with tempered distributions. This function therefore admits a Fourier transform in the sense of distributions. Since its derivatives are tempered, it follows that the same holds for the finite parts $\operatorname{Pf}(K_j)$. We compute its transforms, beginning with that of $[g]$.

Since g is a radial function, its transform $\widehat{[g]}$ is also one (cf. Exercise 7.12). Moreover, using the properties of homogeneous tempered distributions and those of their Fourier transforms (cf. Exercise 4.4), we know that the transform $\widehat{[g]}$ is of the form $K|\xi|^m$. We can, moreover, compute the degree m using the dilation $[g]_k$ of the distribution $[g]$, which is defined by

$$\langle [g]_k, \varphi \rangle = \frac{1}{k^N} \langle [g], \varphi(x/k) \rangle.$$

On the one hand, we obviously have

$$\mathcal{F}([g]_k)(\xi) = K \frac{1}{k^{N-1}} |\xi|^m.$$

On the other hand, by the formula defining $[g]_k$,

$$\begin{aligned}
\langle \mathcal{F}([g]_k), \varphi \rangle &= \langle [g]_k, \widehat{\varphi} \rangle \\
&= k^{-N} \langle [g], \widehat{\varphi}(\xi/k) \rangle = k^{-N} \langle [g], k^N \widehat{\varphi(kx)} \rangle \\
&= \langle \widehat{[g]}, \varphi(kx) \rangle = K \int_{\mathbb{R}^N} |x|^m \varphi(kx) dx \\
&= Kk^{-N-m} \langle |\xi|^m, \varphi \rangle.
\end{aligned}$$

From these two equalities, we deduce that $N + m = N - 1$, whence $m = -1$.

To compute the constant K, we apply the definition of $\widehat{[g]}$ using the function $\varphi(x) = \exp(-\pi|x|^2)$, which is its own Fourier transform (cf. Exercise 4.1). We thus obtain the equality

$$\left\langle \frac{1}{|x|^{N-1}}, \exp(-\pi|x|^2) \right\rangle = \left\langle K \frac{1}{|\xi|}, \exp(-\pi|\xi|^2) \right\rangle.$$

Passing to integrals over $\mathbb{R}^N$ and polar coordinates, we have

$$\omega_{N-1} \int_0^{+\infty} \exp(-\pi r^2) dr = K \omega_{N-1} \int_0^{+\infty} r^{N-2} \exp(-\pi r^2) dr.$$

By the relation

$$\Gamma(t) = 2\pi^t \int_0^{+\infty} x^{2t-1} \exp(-\pi x^2) dr$$

(cf. Exercise 3.1 of Chapter 1), this becomes $\pi^{(N-1)/2} = K\Gamma((N-1)/2)$. The Fourier transform of $\text{Pf}(K_j)$ follows.

Proposition 7.46. *The Fourier transform of* $\text{Pf}(K_j)$ *is the function defined by*

$$\forall \xi \in \mathbb{R}^N, \quad \mathcal{F}(\text{Pf}(K_j))(\xi) = -iC_N \frac{\xi_j}{|\xi|}, \quad \text{where} \quad C_N = \frac{\pi^{(N+1)/2}}{\Gamma((N+1)/2)}.$$

Proof of Proposition 7.46.

This formula follows from Proposition 7.45 and the fact that on the Fourier transform, differentiation with respect to x_j becomes multiplication by $2i\pi\xi_j$.

□

7.3.3 Convolution of a Function and a Riesz Kernel

Convolution with a Function in $\mathcal{D}(\mathbb{R}^N)$. We use Proposition 7.22, which gives the formula

$$\mathrm{Pf}(K_j) \star \varphi = f \quad \text{with} \quad f(x) = \int_{\mathbb{R}^N} \frac{t_j(\varphi(x-t) - \varphi(x))}{|t|^{N+1}} \, dt.$$

Convolution with a Function in $\mathcal{S}$. We show that the previous formula still holds when $\varphi \in \mathcal{S}(\mathbb{R}^N)$. By the continuity of convolution (cf. Proposition 7.25) we know that if a sequence $\{\varphi_n\}$ in $\mathcal{D}$ converges in $\mathcal{S}$ to φ, then we have $\mathrm{Pf}(K_j) \star \varphi_n \to \mathrm{Pf}(K_j) \star \varphi$.

Let $\varphi \in \mathcal{S}$. Let $\eta \in \mathcal{D}$, with value 1 on the unit ball in $\mathbb{R}^N$, and let $\varphi_n(x) = \eta(x/n)\varphi(x)$. Then φ_n is an element of $\mathcal{D}(\mathbb{R}^N)$ and converges to φ in $\mathcal{S}$, and we have

$$\lim_{n \to +\infty} \int_{\mathbb{R}^N} \frac{t_j(\varphi_n(x-t) - \varphi_n(x))}{|t|^{N+1}} dt = \left[\mathrm{Pf}(K_j) \star \varphi\right](x).$$

Now, we can easily show that the integral of the left-hand side converges to the integral

$$\int_{\mathbb{R}^N} \frac{t_j(\varphi(x-t) - \varphi(x))}{|t|^{(N+1)}} \, dt,$$

so that

$$\forall \varphi \in \mathcal{S}, \quad \mathrm{Pf}(K_j) \star \varphi = f \quad \text{with} \quad f(x) = \int_{\mathbb{R}^N} \frac{t_j(\varphi(x-t) - \varphi(x))}{|t|^{(N+1)}} dt$$

for every x.

Convolution When φ Is an Element of a Space L^p. In the two previous cases, the formulas can be simplified to give the convolution in the form $\int_{\mathbb{R}^N} [t_j(\varphi(x-t))](|t|^{-(N+1)}) dt$. When $\varphi \in L^p$, density will give us the following formula, which holds for almost all $x \in \mathbb{R}^N$:

$$\forall f \in L^p, \quad \left[\mathrm{Pf}(K_j) \star f\right](x) = \lim_{\varepsilon \to 0} \int_{\varepsilon \leqslant |t|} \frac{t_j(\varphi(x-t))}{|t|^{N+1}} dt.$$

We will show not only that this limit exists almost everywhere, but also that it belongs to L^p, so that the operator R_j defines a continuous endomorphism of L^p.

7.3.4 Riesz Operator on $L^p(\mathbb{R}^N)$

We suppose that $1 < p < +\infty$ and $f \in L^p(\mathbb{R}^N)$. Using the formula from the previous subsection, we define

$$f_\varepsilon^j(x) = \int_{\varepsilon \leqslant |t|} \frac{t_j f(x-t)}{|t|^{N+1}} \, dt.$$

When $p > 1$, Hölder's inequalities show us that this integral exists for every $x \in \mathbb{R}^N$ and every $\varepsilon > 0$. Indeed, we have $Np' - (N-1) = N(p'-1)+1 > 1$, whence

$$\int_{\varepsilon \leqslant |t|} \left| \frac{t_j f(x-t)}{|t|^{N+1}} \right| dt \leqslant \left(\int_{\varepsilon \leqslant |t|} |f(x)|^p dx \right)^{1/p} \left(\int_{\varepsilon \leqslant |t|} \frac{1}{|t|^{Np'}} dt \right)^{1/p'} < +\infty.$$

Using the properties of the maximal functions defined before, we will show that the function $x \mapsto \sup_\varepsilon |f_\varepsilon^j(x)|$ is an element of $L^p(\mathbb{R}^N)$ whose norm is bounded from above by that of f. We will then show that this property implies, on the one hand, the existence almost everywhere of the limit when $\varepsilon \to 0$, and on the other hand, the continuity of the Riesz transform R_j in $L^p(\mathbb{R}^N)$. We begin with the following result.

Theorem 7.47. Let $f \in L^p(\mathbb{R}^N)$ with $1 < p < +\infty$; then the function $x \mapsto \sup_{\varepsilon>0} |f_\varepsilon^j(x)|$ belongs to $L^p(\mathbb{R}^N)$ for every integer j in $[1, N]$ and there exists a constant C depending only on p and N such that

$$\left\| \sup_{\varepsilon>0} |f_\varepsilon^j(x)| \right\|_{L^p(\mathbb{R}^N)} \leqslant C \|f\|_{L^p(\mathbb{R}^N)}.$$

Proof of Theorem 7.47.

Using the variables (r, θ) with $r = |t|$ and $\theta = t/|t|$ in $\mathbb{R}^N$, where the latter describes the unit sphere S_N in $\mathbb{R}^N$, we reduce to the integration over the unit sphere of a function that is, up to a factor depending on θ, a maximal Hilbert function, thus allowing us to apply Theorem 7.37.

Let $p_j(\theta)$ be the component of index j of the unit vector in $\mathbb{R}^N$ associated with $\theta \in S_N$, which we denote by $\vec{\theta}$. Using the oddness of p_j, that is, the property $p_j(-\theta) = -p_j(\theta)$, we have

$$
\begin{aligned}
f_\varepsilon^j(x) &= \int_\varepsilon^{+\infty} \Big[\int_{S_N} f(x - r\theta) p_j(\theta) d\theta \Big] \frac{dr}{r} \\
&= \int_{S_N} p_j(\theta) \Big[\int_\varepsilon^{+\infty} \frac{f(x - r\theta)}{r} dr \Big] d\theta \\
&= \int_{S_N} p_j(-\theta) \Big[- \int_\varepsilon^{+\infty} \frac{f(x - r\theta)}{r} dr \Big] d\theta \\
&= \int_{S_N} p_j(-\theta) \Big[\int_{-\infty}^{-\varepsilon} \frac{f(x + r\theta)}{r} dr \Big] d\theta \\
&= \int_{S_N} p_j(\theta) \Big[\int_{-\infty}^{-\varepsilon} \frac{f(x - r\theta)}{r} dr \Big] d\theta.
\end{aligned}
$$

From this, we deduce the equality

$$
f_\varepsilon^j(x) = \frac{1}{2} \int_{S_N} p_j(\theta) \Big[\int_{|s| \geqslant \varepsilon} \frac{f(x - s\theta)}{s} ds \Big] d\theta,
$$

and, by noting that $|p_j(\theta)| \leqslant 1$, we obtain

(7.48) $\qquad \forall \varepsilon > 0, \quad 2|f_\varepsilon^j(x)| \leqslant \int_{S_N} \sup_\varepsilon \Big| \int_{|s| \geqslant \varepsilon} \frac{f(x - s\theta)}{s} ds \Big| d\theta.$

Let us consider the function $x \mapsto \int_{|s| \geqslant \varepsilon} [f(x - s\theta)/s] \, ds$. Let e_1 be the first vector of the canonical basis of $\mathbb{R}^N$ and let σ_θ be an isometry of $SO(N)$, which we will simply denote by σ, such that $\sigma_\theta(e_1) = \theta$. Let $R_\sigma f$ be the function defined by $R_\sigma f(x) = f(\sigma x)$ for every $x \in \mathbb{R}^N$. We then have

$$
f(x - s\theta) = f(x - s\sigma e_1) = (R_\sigma f)(\sigma^{-1} x - s e_1).
$$

From this we deduce that the right-hand side of (7.48) satisfies

(7.49) $\qquad \displaystyle\int_{S_N} \sup_\varepsilon \Big| \int_{|s| \geqslant \varepsilon} \frac{f(x - s\theta)}{s} ds \Big| d\theta$

$$
= \int_{S_N} \sup_{\varepsilon > 0} \Big| \int_{|s| \geqslant \varepsilon} \frac{R_\sigma f(\sigma^{-1} x - s e_1)}{s} ds \Big| d\theta.
$$

Let $\xi = (\sigma^{-1} x)_1$ and let ξ' denote the $(N-1)$-tuple of the other coordinates of $\sigma^{-1} x$. We can write the previous integral as

$$
\int_{|s| > \varepsilon} \frac{R_\sigma f(\sigma^{-1} x - s e_1)}{s} ds = \int_{|s| > \varepsilon} \frac{R_\sigma f(\xi - s, \xi')}{s} ds.
$$

Let us therefore define, for a function h in $L^p(\mathbb{R}^N)$, the following HLM function:

$$\mathcal{M}_h^1(x) = \sup_{r>0} \frac{1}{2r} \int_{|s|<r} |h(x_1 - s, x_2, \ldots, x_N)| ds.$$

Using the one-dimensional model, we show that under the assumption that $h \in L^p(\mathbb{R}^N)$, the function $\mathcal{M}_h^1$ also belongs to $L^p(\mathbb{R}^N)$ and has norm in $L^p(\mathbb{R}^N)$ bounded from above, up to a constant, by the norm $\|h\|_p$. Indeed, by Theorem 7.19 for dimension 1, we have

$$\int_{\mathbb{R}^N} |\mathcal{M}_h^1(x)|^p dx = \int_{\mathbb{R}^{N-1}} \int_{\mathbb{R}} |\mathcal{M}_h^1(x_1, x')|^p dx_1 dx'$$

$$\leqslant c(p, 1)^p \int_{\mathbb{R}^{N-1}} \int_{\mathbb{R}} |h(x_1, x')|^p dx \, dx',$$

or

$$(*) \qquad \int_{\mathbb{R}^N} |\mathcal{M}_h^1(x)|^p dx \leqslant c(p, 1)^p \|h\|_{L^p(\mathbb{R}^N)}^p.$$

For almost all x' in $\mathbb{R}^{N-1}$, the function $h_{x'}$ defined by $x_1 \mapsto h(x_1, x')$ is an element of $L^p(\mathbb{R})$. We can therefore apply Theorem 7.37 concerning the maximal Hilbert function to it. Therefore, for almost all x in $\mathbb{R}^N$, we have

$$\sup_{\varepsilon > 0} \frac{1}{\pi} \left| \int_{|t| \geqslant \varepsilon} \frac{(R_\sigma f)(\sigma^{-1} x - s e_1) ds}{s} \right| \leqslant C_1 \mathcal{M}_{R_\sigma f}^1(\sigma^{-1} x) + \mathcal{M}_{H_m(R_\sigma f)}^1(\sigma^{-1} x).$$

By the properties of isometries, the maximal HLM functions and Hilbert transform of $x \mapsto R_\sigma f(\sigma^{-1} x)$ have norms in $L^p(\mathbb{R}^N)$ equal to those of these same functions associated with $x \mapsto R_\sigma f(x)$. By previous theorems, the norms of the latter are bounded from above by $\|R_\sigma f\|_p$. Moreover, by the invariance of the norm under σ, this equals $\|f\|_p$. We will use these properties further on.

Returning to inequality (7.48) and denoting by F_σ and G_σ the functions

$$x \longmapsto \mathcal{M}_{R_\sigma f}^1(\sigma^{-1} x) \quad \text{and} \quad x \longmapsto \mathcal{M}_{H_m(R_\sigma f)}^1(\sigma^{-1} x),$$

respectively, we can write

$$(7.50) \qquad 2 \sup_\varepsilon \left| \int_{|t| \geqslant \varepsilon} \frac{f(x - t) t_j}{|t|^{N+1}} dt \right| \leqslant \int_{S_N} [C_1 F_{\sigma_\theta}(x) + C_2 G_{\sigma_\theta}(x)] d\theta.$$

We take the pth power and integrate both sides of (7.48) over $\mathbb{R}^N$. By Hölder's inequality, the right-hand side is bounded from above by

$$\int_{\mathbb{R}^N} (\omega_{N-1})^{p/p'} \int_{S_N} |C_1 F_{\sigma_\theta}(x) + C_2 G_{\sigma_\theta}(x)|^p d\theta \, dx.$$

Using Fubini's formula and the inequality $|a + b|^p \leqslant 2^{p-1}(a^p + b^p)$, it follows that the right-hand side is bounded from above by

$$C(p, N) \int_{S_N} \left[\int_{\mathbb{R}^N} |F_\sigma(x)|^p dx + \int_{\mathbb{R}^N} |G_\sigma(x)|^p dx \right] d\theta.$$

Now, as we noted before, up to constants, these integrals over $\mathbb{R}^N$ are bounded from above by $\|f\|^p_{L^p(\mathbb{R}^N)}$. Consequently, we obtain the result

$$\| \sup_\varepsilon |f_\varepsilon^j| \|^p_p \leqslant C(p, N) \|f\|^p_p,$$

concluding the proof of Theorem 7.47. $\square$

Let us now establish the main result for R_j.

Theorem 7.51. *For every j and every p with $1 < p < \infty$, the operator R_j has the following property:*

$$\forall f \in L^p(\mathbb{R}^N), \quad R_j(f)(x) \text{ exists for almost all } x \in \mathbb{R}^N.$$

To a function f in $L^p(\mathbb{R}^N)$, this operator associates the function defined by

$$R_j(f)(x) = (K_j \star f)(x) = \lim_{\varepsilon \to 0} \int_{|t| > \varepsilon} \frac{t_j(f(x - t))}{|t|^{N+1}} dt.$$

Moreover, there exists a constant C depending only on p and N, such that

$$\forall f \in L^p(\mathbb{R}^N), \quad \|R_j(f)\|_p \leqslant C\|f\|_p.$$

Proof of Theorem 7.51.

Let $f \in L^p(\mathbb{R}^N)$. For every fixed integer j with $1 \leqslant j \leqslant N$, we set $f_\varepsilon^j(x) = \int_{\varepsilon \leqslant |t|} [t_j f(x - t)](|t|^{-(N+1)}) dt$. The space $\mathcal{S}$ is dense in L^p; hence, for every $\eta > 0$, we can find a $g \in \mathcal{S}$ such that $f - g = h$ with $\|h\|_p \leqslant \eta$.

We know (cf. Subsection 7.3.3) that the limit $\lim_{\varepsilon \to 0} g_\varepsilon^j(x)$ exists for every x. Let us consider, for every integer $k > 0$, the set $E_k(f)$ of $x \in \mathbb{R}^N$ such that we can find sequences $\{\varepsilon_n\}$ and $\{\varepsilon_n'\}$ tending to 0 and satisfying the inequality

$$|f_{\varepsilon_n}^j(x) - f_{\varepsilon_n'}^j(x)| > \frac{2}{k}.$$

Let us show that we have $|E_k(f)| \leqslant C\eta(2k)^p$ for some constant C. Indeed, by the above and Theorem 7.47, the map that sends the function h to the supremum

$$\sup_{\varepsilon > 0} |h_\varepsilon^j(x)| = \sup_{\varepsilon > 0} \left| \int_{\varepsilon \leqslant t} \frac{t_j h(x - t)}{|t|^{N+1}} dt \right|$$

is continuous from L^p to L^p, which implies that it is of weak type (p, p). It follows (cf. Definition 7.31) that $\lambda^* = \lambda_{\sup_\varepsilon |h_\varepsilon^j|}$ satisfies the inequality

$$(7.52) \qquad s^p \lambda^*(s) = s^p \left| \{ \sup_\varepsilon |h_\varepsilon^j(x)| > s \} \right| \leqslant \left\| \sup_\varepsilon |h_\varepsilon^j| \right\|_p^p .$$

Let $x \in E_k(f)$ and let $\varepsilon_n, \varepsilon_n'$ satisfy

$$|f_{\varepsilon_n}^j(x) - f_{\varepsilon_n'}^j(x)| > \frac{2}{k} .$$

Then for n sufficiently large, we have

$$|g_{\varepsilon_n}^j(x) - g_{\varepsilon_{n'}}^j(x)| < \frac{1}{k}$$

because the sequence $\{g_{\varepsilon_n}^j(x)\}$ tends to a finite limit.

It follows that for n sufficiently large, we have the lower bound

$$|h_{\varepsilon_n}^j(x) - h_{\varepsilon_n'}^j(x)| > \frac{1}{k} ,$$

whence $x \in E_{2k}(h)$. Consequently,

$$E_k(f) \subset E_{2k}(h).$$

Now, if $|h_{\varepsilon_n}^j(x) - h_{\varepsilon_n'}^j(x)| > 1/k$, then $\sup_\varepsilon |h_\varepsilon^j| > 1/2k$. Indeed, if the opposite inequality held, then the previous difference would be less than k^{-1}. The measure of $E_k(f)$ is therefore less than that of the set $\{\sup_\varepsilon |h_\varepsilon^j(x)| > 1/2k\}$. Now, by (7.52), we have

$$\left(\frac{1}{2k} \right)^p \left| \{ \sup_\varepsilon |h_\varepsilon^j| > 1/2k \} \right| \leqslant \| \sup_\varepsilon |h_\varepsilon^j| \|_p^p .$$

Since we have $\| \sup |h_\varepsilon^j| \|_p \leqslant C \|h\|_p$ by Theorem 7.47, it follows that $\left| \{ \sup_\varepsilon |h_\varepsilon^j(x)| > 1/2k \} \right| \leqslant C\eta(2k)^p$, and therefore $|E_k(f)| \leqslant C\eta(2k)^p$.

Since the number k is fixed and η is arbitrarily small, this proves that the set $E_k(f)$ has measure zero. The union $F = \bigcup_1^{+\infty} E_k(f)$ therefore also has measure zero, proving the first assertion of the theorem.

For the second assertion, we use Fatou's lemma, which gives us the inequality

$$\|R_j f\|_p^p \leqslant \varliminf_{\varepsilon \to 0} \|f_\varepsilon^j\|_p^p \leqslant \| \sup_\varepsilon |f_\varepsilon^j| \|_p^p .$$

Since the last norm is bounded from above by $C\|f\|_p$, (cf. Theorem 7.47), this concludes the proof.   □

7.4 Korn's Inequality in $W^{1,p}(\Omega)$ for Bounded Ω

The principal result of this section, which will imply Korn's inequality, is the following.

Theorem 7.53. *Let T be a distribution with compact support in a bounded domain Ω in $\mathbb{R}^N$. We suppose that for every $i \in [1, N]$, there exists a constant C such that the distribution $\partial_i T$ satisfies the property*

$$\forall \varphi \in \mathcal{C}^\infty(\mathbb{R}^N), \quad |\langle \partial_i T, \varphi \rangle| \leqslant C \|\nabla \varphi\|_{L^{p'}(\Omega)}.$$

The distribution T can then be identified with an element of $L^p(\Omega)$.

To prepare for the proof of this theorem, we first use the previous subsections to establish the Riesz inequalities that link the mixed derivatives of a function to the Laplacian of that function, after which we prove additional preliminary results.

7.4.1 Relation between $\Delta\varphi$ and a Mixed Derivative of φ in $\mathbb{R}^N$, Riesz's Inequalities

Let us consider the Riesz kernels $K_j(x) = \mathrm{Pf}[x_j |x|^{-(N+1)}]$. The finite parts K_j, which belong to $\mathcal{S}'(\mathbb{R}^N)$, have the functions defined by $\mathcal{F}(K_j)(\xi) = -iC_N \xi_j / |\xi|$ as Fourier transforms, with coefficients C_N computed in Proposition 7.46. We recall that the transform of a derivative ∂_j of a distribution is the product of the transform of the distribution and $2i\pi\xi_j$. It follows that if $\varphi \in \mathcal{S}(\mathbb{R}^N)$, then

$$\mathcal{F}(\Delta\varphi)(\xi) = -4\pi^2 |\xi|^2 \widehat{\varphi}(\xi).$$

Using Proposition 7.24, we can write $\widehat{A} = \mathcal{F}(\partial^2\varphi / \partial x_i \partial x_j)$ using the transform of $\Delta\varphi$:

$$\widehat{A} = -4\pi^2 \,\xi_j \xi_i \,\mathcal{F}(\varphi)(\xi) = -4\pi^2 \frac{\xi_j \xi_i}{|\xi|^2} |\xi|^2 \mathcal{F}(\varphi)(\xi)$$
$$= C_N^{-2} \mathcal{F}(K_i)\mathcal{F}(K_j)\mathcal{F}(\Delta\varphi)(\xi).$$

Now, by Proposition 7.24 or Theorem 7.51, the convolution $K_j \star \Delta\varphi$ exists and its Fourier transform is the product of the transforms. Moreover, this convolution is an element of $L^p(\mathbb{R}^N)$ for every $p > 1$. By Theorem 7.51, it now follows that the convolution $K_i \star (K_j \star \Delta\varphi)$ is well defined, and that

$$\widehat{A} = C_N^{-2} \mathcal{F}\big(K_i \star (K_j \star \Delta\varphi)\big).$$

Using the inverse Fourier transform in $\mathcal{S}'(\mathbb{R}^N)$, it follows that

$$\frac{\partial^2 \varphi}{\partial x_i \partial x_j} = C_N^2 K_i \star (K_j \star \Delta\varphi).$$

Using the results of the previous section, and in particular Theorem 7.51, we can deduce inequalities that will later lead to Theorem 7.53.

Theorem 7.54 (Riesz inequalities). *For every p with $1 < p < \infty$, there exists a constant $C(p, N)$ depending only on p and N, such that*

$$\forall \varphi \in \mathcal{S}(\mathbb{R}^N), \ \forall i, j \in [1, N], \quad \left\| \frac{\partial^2 \varphi}{\partial x_i \partial x_j} \right\|_p \leqslant C(p, N)\|\Delta\varphi\|_p.$$

This inequality, which holds in $\mathcal{S}(\mathbb{R}^N)$, extends by density to the closure of $\mathcal{S}(\mathbb{R}^N)$ for the norm $\varphi \mapsto \|\Delta\varphi\|_p$.

To attack the proof of Theorem 7.53, we need a number of lemmas allowing us to give, in *suitable spaces*, solutions u or σ of equations such as $\Delta u = f$ and $-\operatorname{div}\sigma = f$ for a regular function f.

Even when these lemmas establish properties that may be of interest outside of the present context, we have not tried to optimize these preliminary results, which are meant to be used in establishing Korn's inequality.

7.4.2 Preliminary Results

The proof of this first lemma is given in Exercise 7.16.

Lemma 7.55. *Let Ω_1 be a bounded open subset of $\mathbb{R}^N$; then there exist functions φ_i in $\mathcal{D}(\Omega_1)$ for $i \in [1, N]$ such that*

$$\forall i, j \in [1, N], \quad \int_{\Omega_1} \varphi_i(x)x_j dx = \delta_i^j \quad and \quad \forall i \in [1, N], \quad \int_{\Omega_1} \varphi_i(x)dx = 0$$

and a function φ in $\mathcal{D}(\Omega_1)$ such that

$$\int_{\Omega_1} \varphi = 1 \quad and \quad \forall i \in [1, N], \quad \int_{\Omega_1} \varphi(x)x_i dx = 0.$$

The second lemma gives the image of the Laplacian in the space $\mathcal{S}(\mathbb{R}^N)$ explicitly.

Lemma 7.56. *The image $\Delta(\mathcal{S}(\mathbb{R}^N))$ of $\mathcal{S}(\mathbb{R}^N)$ under the Laplacian is characterized by the equivalence of the following properties:*

(7.57) $g \in \mathcal{S}(\mathbb{R}^N)$ *   and $\exists u \in \mathcal{S}(\mathbb{R}^N)$ such that $\Delta u = g$.*

(7.58) $g \in \mathcal{S}(\mathbb{R}^N)$, $\displaystyle\int_{\mathbb{R}^N} g(x)dx = 0$, *   and $\forall i \in [1, N]$, $\displaystyle\int_{\mathbb{R}^N} g(x)x_i dx = 0$.*

Proof of Lemma 7.56.

Let us suppose that the element u of $\mathcal{S}(\mathbb{R}^N)$ is a solution of $\Delta u = g$. Using the Fourier transform, we obtain $4\pi^2 |\xi|^2 \, \widehat{u}(\xi) = \widehat{g}(\xi)$. Hence, if g satisfies (7.57), then it follows that $\xi \mapsto \widehat{g}(\xi)/|\xi|^2$ is in $\mathcal{S}(\mathbb{R}^N)$. In particular, this function is regular at the point $\xi = 0$. Using the Taylor expansion of g at the point 0, we necessarily have $\widehat{g}(0) = 0$ and, for every $i \in [1, N]$, $\partial_i \widehat{g}(0) = 0$. Using the inverse Fourier transform, these equalities are equivalent to

$$\int_{\mathbb{R}^N} g(x)dx = 0 \quad \text{and} \quad \forall i \in [1, N], \int_{\mathbb{R}^N} x_i g(x)dx = 0.$$

We have thus proved the implication (7.57) $\Rightarrow$ (7.58).

The converse is obvious. If g verifies (7.58), then

$$\frac{\widehat{g}(\xi)}{|\xi|^2} \in \mathcal{S}(\mathbb{R}^N) \quad \text{and} \quad \Delta u = g \quad \text{with} \quad \widehat{u}(\xi) = \frac{\widehat{g}(\xi)}{|\xi|^2} \in \mathcal{S}(\mathbb{R}^N). \qquad \square$$

Let us note, for later on, that the correspondence between u and g is linear. More precisely, under the given conditions, we can write $u = \Delta^{-1}g$. Indeed, using once again $\mathcal{F}$, we see that the operator Δ is injective into $\mathcal{S}(\mathbb{R}^N)$.

The third lemma is useful for proving the second part of Theorem 7.53. It is not essential for establishing the theorem, but by giving the image of the operator div on $\mathcal{S}(\mathbb{R}^N)$ explicitly, it allows us to better understand the problems linked to studying functions with given divergence.

Lemma 7.59. *Let $\varphi \in \mathcal{S}(\mathbb{R}^N)$. The following properties are equivalent:*

(7.60) $\exists \sigma = (\sigma_1, \ldots, \sigma_N) \in \mathcal{S}(\mathbb{R}^N, \mathbb{R}^N), \quad \text{div}\, \sigma = \varphi.$

(7.61) $\displaystyle\int_{\mathbb{R}^N} \varphi(x)dx = 0.$

Proof of Lemma 7.59.

We begin with the implication (7.60)$\Rightarrow$ (7.61).

If $\varphi = \text{div}(\sigma)$ with $\sigma \in \mathcal{S}(\mathbb{R}^N, \mathbb{R}^N)$, then

$$\left| \int_{\mathbb{R}^N} \varphi \right| = \lim_{R \to +\infty} \left| \int_{B(0,R)} \varphi \right| = \lim_{R \to 0} \left| \int_{\partial B(0,R)} (\sigma \cdot \overrightarrow{n})(s)ds \right|$$

$$\leqslant \lim_{R \to +\infty} \omega_{N-1} R^{N-1} \sup_{|x|=R} |\sigma(x)| = 0.$$

To show (7.61)$\Rightarrow$(7.60), we use an induction on the dimension of the space.

Let us begin with $N = 1$. It suffices to find a primitive for $\varphi \in \mathcal{S}(\mathbb{R})$ in $\mathcal{S}(\mathbb{R})$ when $\int_{\mathbb{R}} \varphi = 0$. Assuming that $\int_{\mathbb{R}} \varphi$ is arbitrary, we construct a primitive that will be useful for the induction in higher dimension. Let $\rho \in \mathcal{D}(\mathbb{R})$ have integral equal to 1. We set

$$\sigma(x) = \sigma_{\rho,\varphi}(x) = \int_{-\infty}^{x} \left(\varphi(t) - \rho(t)\int_{\mathbb{R}} \varphi(u)du\right)dt.$$

If we show that $\sigma_{\rho,\varphi}$ is strongly decreasing, then this will give the desired result when φ has integral zero in dimension 1. It is obvious that $\sigma_{\rho,\varphi}$ is $\mathcal{C}^\infty$ and that its derivatives are strongly decreasing. It therefore suffices to show that for every $k \in \mathbb{N}$,

$$\lim_{|x| \to +\infty} |x|^k |\sigma(x)| = 0.$$

Now, for large $|x|$ with $x < 0$, we have

$$|\sigma(x)| = \left| \int_{-\infty}^{x} \varphi(t)dt \right| \leqslant c \int_{-\infty}^{x} (-t)^{-k-2}\, dt \leqslant c|x|^{-k-1},$$

giving the desired result. When x is large and positive, we have the same:

$$\sigma(x) = \int_{-\infty}^{x} \varphi(t)dt - \int_{\mathbb{R}} \varphi(t)dt = \int_{x}^{+\infty} \varphi(t)dt,$$

giving

$$|\sigma(x)| \leqslant cx^{-k-1}.$$

The result follows for $N = 1$.

Let us continue with arbitrary dimension N. We suppose the result proved in dimension $N - 1$ for the variables $(x_2, \ldots, x_N)$. Let φ be an element of $\mathcal{S}(\mathbb{R}^N)$ with integral zero. We associate to it the function φ_1 defined by

$$\varphi_1(x_1, x_2, \ldots, x_N) = \sigma_{\rho,\varphi(.,x_2,\ldots,x_N)}(x_1)$$
$$= \int_{-\infty}^{x_1} \left(\varphi(t, x_2, \ldots, x_N) - \rho(t)\int_{\mathbb{R}} \varphi(u, x_2, \ldots, x_N)du\right)dt.$$

It follows from the computations in dimension 1 that this function is rapidly decreasing in x_1. Moreover, we can easily verify that this holds for all variables. Let us therefore consider the function

$$\psi(x_2, \ldots, x_N) = \int_{\mathbb{R}} \varphi(t, x_2, \ldots, x_N)dt.$$

Since, by assumption, $\int_{\mathbb{R}^N} \varphi(x_1, x_2, \ldots, x_N)dx = 0$, we have

$$\int \psi(x_2, \ldots, x_N)dx_2 \cdots dx_N = 0.$$

By the induction hypothesis, it follows that there exists an $(N-1)$-tuple $(\psi_2, \ldots, \psi_N)$ in $\mathcal{S}(\mathbb{R}^{N-1})$ such that

$$\sum_{2}^{N} \partial_i \psi_i = \int_{\mathbb{R}} \varphi(t, x_2, \ldots, x_N) dt.$$

Next, let φ_i be defined for $i \in [2, N]$ by

$$\varphi_i(x_1, x_2, \ldots, x_N) = \rho(x_1)\psi_i(x_2, x_3, \ldots, x_N).$$

These functions are rapidly decreasing and

$$\sum_{2}^{N} \partial_i \varphi_i + \partial_1 \varphi_1 = \varphi,$$

concluding the proof. $\qquad \square$

These lemmas lead to the following result.

Proposition 7.62. *Let Ω be a bounded open subset of $\mathbb{R}^N$; then there exists a constant C such that for every function $f \in \mathcal{D}(\Omega)$, there is a $\sigma \in \mathcal{C}^\infty(\mathbb{R}^N, \mathbb{R}^N)$ satisfying the following conditions:*

(7.63) $-\operatorname{div}\sigma = f,$

(7.64) $\|\nabla\sigma\|_{L^{p'}(\Omega)} \leqslant C\Big(\|f\|_{L^{p'}(\Omega)} + \Big|\int_{\Omega} f(x)dx\Big| + \sum_{1}^{N}\Big|\int_{\Omega} fx_i dx\Big|\Big)$

$$\leqslant C'\|f\|_{L^{p'}(\Omega)}.$$

If moreover f has integral zero, then the function σ associated with f is an element of $\mathcal{S}(\mathbb{R}^N, \mathbb{R}^N)$.

Proof of Proposition 7.62.

Let us consider the functions φ and φ_i introduced in Lemma 7.55. We can deduce from them functions $\vec{\psi}$ and $\vec{\psi_i}$ for $i \in [1, N]$ with values in $\mathbb{R}^N$, each belonging to $\mathcal{C}^\infty(\mathbb{R}^N, \mathbb{R}^N) \cap W^{1,\infty}(\mathbb{R}^N, \mathbb{R}^N)$, such that

$$\operatorname{div}\vec{\psi} = \varphi \quad \text{and} \quad \forall i \in [1, N], \operatorname{div}\vec{\psi_i} = \varphi_i.$$

To see this, we can, for example, set $\psi = \int_{-\infty}^{x_1} \varphi(t, x_2, \ldots, x_N)dt$ and $\vec{\psi} = \psi e_1$, and define the $\vec{\psi_i}$ analogously.

Let us note that for $i \in [1, N]$, the functions φ_i satisfy $\int \varphi_i = 0$. Moreover, since we can identify these functions with functions in $\mathcal{S}(\mathbb{R}^N)$ with zero integral, we can apply the more precise construction of Lemma 7.59 to them, which gives functions $\vec{\psi_i}$ belonging to $\mathcal{S}(\mathbb{R}^N, \mathbb{R}^N)$.

Consider the function $g = f - (\int_\Omega f(x)dx)\varphi - \sum_1^N (\int_\Omega f x_i dx)\varphi_i$. This is an element of $\mathcal{D}(\mathbb{R}^N)$ that satisfies the equalities (7.58). Lemma 7.56 therefore gives the existence and uniqueness of a u in $\mathcal{S}(\mathbb{R}^N)$ such that

$$(7.65) \qquad -\Delta u = f - \left(\int_\Omega f(x)dx\right)\varphi - \sum_1^N \left(\int_\Omega f x_i dx\right)\varphi_i.$$

We then define

$$\sigma = \nabla u - \left(\int_\Omega f(x)dx\right)\vec{\psi} - \sum_1^N \left(\int_\Omega f x_i dx\right)\vec{\psi_i}.$$

By the definitions of u, div $\vec{\psi}$, and div $\vec{\psi_i}$, we see that $\sigma \in \mathcal{C}^\infty(\mathbb{R}^N, \mathbb{R}^N) \cap W^{1,\infty}(\mathbb{R}^N, \mathbb{R}^N)$. A fortiori, its restriction to Ω belongs to $W^{1,p'}(\Omega)$. This vector function satisfies

$$-\operatorname{div}\sigma = f,$$

and, setting $a = \int_\Omega f(x)dx$ and $a_i = \int_\Omega x_i f(x)dx$, its gradient satisfies the inequality

$$(7.66) \quad \|\nabla\sigma\|_{L^{p'}(\Omega)} \leqslant \|\nabla\nabla u\|_{L^{p'}(\Omega)} + |a|\,\|\nabla\vec{\psi}\|_{L^{p'}(\Omega)} + \sum_1^N |a_i|\,\|\nabla\vec{\psi_i}\|_{L^{p'}(\Omega)}.$$

Since u is an element of $\mathcal{S}(\mathbb{R}^N)$, we can use Riesz's inequality, which leads to $\|\nabla\nabla u\|_{L^{p'}(\Omega)} \leqslant \|\nabla\nabla u\|_{L^{p'}(\mathbb{R}^N)} \leqslant C_N \|\Delta u\|_{L^{p'}(\mathbb{R}^N)}$. Since the function Δu has compact support in Ω, we also have

$$\|\nabla\nabla u\|_{L^{p'}(\Omega)} \leqslant C_N \|\Delta u\|_{L^{p'}(\Omega)}.$$

Letting K and K_i denote constants fixed by the choice of the functions φ and φ_i, respectively, we obtain

$$\|\nabla\sigma\|_{L^{p'}(\Omega)} \leqslant C_N \|\Delta u\|_{L^{p'}(\Omega)} + K\left|\int_\Omega f dx\right| + K_i \left|\int_\Omega f(x)x_i dx\right|.$$

This gives the first upper bound of the proposition. Bounding the integrals $|a|$ and $|a_i|$ from above using Hölder's inequality, we finally obtain

$$\|\nabla\sigma\|_{L^{p'}(\Omega)} \leqslant C(\Omega, p', N)\|f\|_{L^{p'}(\Omega)},$$

which concludes the proof of the first part of Proposition 7.62.

For the second part, we keep the same formula to define g. Since the function f has zero integral, as well as the φ_i, the same holds for g. Lemma 7.59 therefore tells us that the function σ defined above is an element of $\mathcal{S}(\mathbb{R}^N, \mathbb{R}^N)$. $\square$

7.4.3 Local Korn's Inequality

Theorem 7.67. *Let T be a distribution with compact support in a bounded domain Ω in $\mathbb{R}^N$. We suppose that for every $i \in [1, N]$ there exists a constant C such that the distribution $\partial_i T$ satisfies the property*

$$\forall \varphi \in \mathcal{C}^\infty(\mathbb{R}^N), \quad |\langle \partial_i T, \varphi \rangle| \leqslant C \|\nabla \varphi\|_{L^{p'}(\Omega)}.$$

The distribution T can then be identified with an element of $L^p(\Omega)$.

Proof of Theorems 7.67 and 7.53.

We begin by defining a distribution T_1 on Ω. Let f be an element of $\mathcal{D}(\Omega)$ with zero integral. The distribution T_1 acts on f by

$$\langle T_1, f \rangle = \langle \nabla T, \sigma \rangle,$$

where σ is an element of $\mathcal{C}^\infty(\mathbb{R}^N, \mathbb{R}^N)$ satisfying $- \operatorname{div} \sigma = f$ (cf. Lemma 7.59). For a fixed σ, the right-hand side is well defined because T has compact support. Moreover, this definition does not depend on the choice of σ. Indeed, let $\sigma_1, \sigma_2 \in \mathcal{C}^\infty$ satisfy $\operatorname{div} \sigma_1 = \operatorname{div} \sigma_2$; then we have the relation

$$\langle \nabla T, \sigma_1 - \sigma_2 \rangle = -\langle T, \operatorname{div}(\sigma_1 - \sigma_2) \rangle = 0.$$

Next, we define T_1 on the functions $f \in \mathcal{D}(\Omega)$. Setting

$$f = f - \left(\int_\Omega f \right) \zeta + \left(\int_\Omega f \right) \zeta$$

where ζ is an element of $\mathcal{D}(\Omega)$ with integral equal to 1, we let

$$(*) \qquad \langle T_1, f \rangle = \left\langle T_1, f - \left(\int_\Omega f \right) \zeta \right\rangle + \left(\int_\Omega f(x) dx \right) \langle T, \zeta \rangle,$$

where we use the earlier definition of T_1 on the function $f - \left(\int_\Omega f \right) \zeta$, whose integral is zero. It is obvious that T_1 is linear and is a distribution on Ω. We still need to show that T_1 belongs to $L^p(\Omega)$. Now, because of the independence of the choice of σ, we can choose one provided by Proposition 7.62, so that there exists a constant C such that for every $f \in \mathcal{D}(\Omega)$,

$$|\langle T_1, f \rangle| \leqslant C \|f\|_{L^{p'}(\Omega)}.$$

The desired conclusion, namely the extension of T_1 to the space $L^p(\Omega)$, follows.

Let us now show that the distributions T and T_1 have the same gradient. Let us consider a derivative $\partial_i T_1$. Let σ satisfy $- \operatorname{div} \sigma = f$, so that $- \operatorname{div} \partial_i \sigma = \partial_i f$. Since $\int_\Omega \partial_i f = 0$, it follows that we can take $\partial_i \sigma$ to be the function σ associated with $\partial_i f$. By definition $(*)$, we then have

$$\langle \partial_i T_1, f \rangle = -\langle T_1, \partial_i f \rangle = -\langle \nabla T, \partial_i \sigma \rangle.$$

Moreover,

$$\langle \partial_i T, f \rangle = -\langle T, \partial_i f \rangle = \langle T, \operatorname{div} \partial_i \sigma \rangle = -\langle \nabla T, \partial_i \sigma \rangle.$$

We therefore have $\partial_i T = \partial_i T_1$ for every $i \in [1, N]$. Using the connectedness of Ω, we conclude that there exists a constant C such that $T = T_1 + C$ in Ω. Since we moreover have $\langle T, \zeta \rangle = \langle T_1, \zeta \rangle$, it follows that $C \int_\Omega \zeta dx = 0$, whence $C = 0$ and $T = T_1$.   □

Applications to the so-called Korn's Inequality.

Proposition 7.68. *Let $1 < p < \infty$ and let $u \in L^p(\Omega, \mathbb{R}^N)$ satisfy $\varepsilon(u) \in L^p_{\mathrm{loc}}(\mathbb{R}^N)$. Then for every function φ in $\mathcal{D}(\mathbb{R}^N)$, the functions $\partial_j((u\varphi)_i)$ belong to $L^p(\Omega)$; in other words, $\nabla(u\varphi) \in L^p(\Omega, \mathbb{R}^{2N})$.*

Proof of Proposition 7.68 when $p = 2$.

This case is elementary and does not need the previous theorem. We show that for every $u \in Y_2(\mathbb{R}^N)$,

$$\|\varepsilon(u)\|_2 \geqslant C \|\nabla u\|_2.$$

We begin by noting that for every $i, j \in [1, N]$ with $i \neq j$ and for u in $\mathcal{C}_c^2(\mathbb{R}^N)$, we have

$$(7.69) \quad \int_{\mathbb{R}^N} |\partial_j u_i|^2 dx + \int_{\mathbb{R}^N} |\partial_i u_j|^2 dx$$

$$\leqslant 4 \int_{\mathbb{R}^N} |\varepsilon_{ij}(u)|^2 dx + \int_{\mathbb{R}^N} [\varepsilon_{ii}^2(u) + \varepsilon_{jj}(u)^2] dx.$$

To prove identity (7.69), we write the integral $\int_{\mathbb{R}^N} (\partial_j u_i + \partial_i u_j)^2 dx$ for any pair (i, j) as follows, by applying two integrations by parts on the term $\int_{\mathbb{R}^N} \partial_j u_i \partial_i u_j dx$:

$$\int_{\mathbb{R}^N} (\partial_j u_i + \partial_i u_j)^2 dx = \int_{\mathbb{R}^N} (\partial_j u_i)^2 dx + \int_{\mathbb{R}^N} (\partial_i u_j)^2 dx + 2 \int_{\mathbb{R}^N} \partial_j u_i \, \partial_i u_j dx$$

$$= \int_{\mathbb{R}^N} (\partial_j u_i)^2 dx + \int_{\mathbb{R}^N} (\partial_i u_j)^2 dx + 2 \int_{\mathbb{R}^N} \partial_i u_i \, \partial_j u_j dx.$$

Let $Y_2(\mathbb{R}^N)$ be the space of vector functions v with the property that both v and the deformation tensor $\varepsilon(v)$ belong to $L^2(\mathbb{R}^N, \mathbb{R}^N)$. Let $u \in Y_2(\mathbb{R}^N)$ have compact support and let $\{u_n\}$ be a sequence in $\mathcal{C}_c^2(\mathbb{R}^N, \mathbb{R}^N)$ obtained by convolution with a regularizing kernel, that converges to u in the space $Y_2(\mathbb{R}^N)$. The identity (7.69) shows that $\{\nabla u_n\}$ is a Cauchy sequence in L^2. Consequently, $\nabla u \in L^2(\mathbb{R}^N, \mathbb{R}^N)$. It follows that if $\varepsilon(u) \in L^2(\mathbb{R}^N, \mathbb{R}^N)$, then $\nabla u \in L^2(\mathbb{R}^N, \mathbb{R}^{2N})$.

Finally, let $u \in L^2$ with $\varepsilon(u) \in L^2$. Then for every $\varphi \in \mathcal{D}(\Omega)$, we have $u\varphi \in Y_2(\mathbb{R}^N)$, whence $u\varphi \in H^1(\mathbb{R}^N)$. It follows that $\nabla(u) \in L^2_{\mathrm{loc}}(\Omega)$, thus concluding the proof in the case $p = 2$. $\square$

Proof of Proposition 7.68 when $p > 2$.

Let $v = u\varphi$. We first demonstrate a relation expressing a distributional mixed derivative of u in terms of the tensor $\varepsilon(u)$:

$$(7.70) \qquad \partial_{ik}(v_j) = \partial_k(\varepsilon_{ij}(v)) + \partial_i(\varepsilon_{jk}(v)) - \partial_j(\varepsilon_{ik}(v)).$$

Since $\varepsilon(u\varphi) \in L^p$, we see that the derivatives of $\varepsilon(v)$ are distributions T with compact support that satisfy the conditions of the previous propositions. Hence, for fixed j and k, the distribution $\partial_k v_j$ has compact support and satisfies the conditions of Theorem 7.67. Consequently, $\partial_k v_j \in L^p$, giving the desired result because j and k are arbitrary. $\square$

To conclude, we prove the following result.

Theorem 7.71 (Korn's inequality in $L^p(\Omega)$, $1 < p < \infty$). *Let Ω be a domain in $\mathbb{R}^N$. We consider the space*

$$Y_p(\Omega) = \{u \in L^p(\Omega) \mid \forall (i,j) \in [1, N],\ \varepsilon_{ij}(u) = (\partial_j u_i + \partial_i u_j)/2 \in L^p(\Omega)\}.$$

If $u \in Y_p(\Omega)$, then $u \in W^{1,p}_{\mathrm{loc}}(\Omega)$. If, moreover, Ω is bounded and of class $\mathcal{C}^2$, then the space $Y_p(\Omega)$ can be identified with $W^{1,p}(\Omega)$. More precisely, there exists a constant C such that every $u \in W^{1,p}(\Omega)$ satisfies

$$\|\nabla u\|_{L^p(\Omega)} \leqslant C\Big(\|u\|_p^p + \int_\Omega |\varepsilon(u)(x)|^p dx\Big)^{1/p}.$$

The idea of the proof of the inclusion $u \in W^{1,p}(\Omega)$ consists in extending a function u in $Y_p(\Omega)$, when Ω is bounded, to a function with compact support in $Y_p(\mathbb{R}^N)$. We then apply Theorem 7.68. We begin by extending u in the case $\Omega = \mathbb{R}^{N-1} \times]0, \infty[$, giving a general idea of the proof, after which we proceed with the general case.

Proof of Theorem 7.71 around a point where $\partial\Omega$ is locally straight.

We wish to extend the vector function u, which is an element of $Y_p(\mathbb{R}^{N-1} \times]0, \infty[)$ with compact support in $\mathbb{R}^{N-1} \times [0, \infty[$, to a vector function $\widetilde{u}$ in $Y_p(\mathbb{R}^N)$.

For $x_N < 0$ and $i \in [1, N-1]$, we set

$$(7.72) \qquad u_i(x', x_N) = 2u_i(x', -x_N) - u_i(x', -3x_N)$$

and for $x_N < 0$ and $i = N$, we set

$$(7.73) \qquad u_N(x', x_N) = -2u_N(x', -x_N) + 3u_N(x', -3x_N).$$

We thus obtain a function $\widetilde{u}$ on $\mathbb{R}^N$ with compact support. We can easily verify that $\widetilde{u} \in Y_p(\mathbb{R}^N)$. Indeed, for $x_N < 0$ and i and $j \in [1, N-1]$, we have

$$(7.74) \qquad 2\partial_j u_i(x', x_N) = 2\partial_j u_i(x', -x_N) - \partial_j u_i(x', -3x_N),$$

whence

$$(7.75) \qquad 2\varepsilon_{ij}(u)(x', x_N) = 2\varepsilon_{ij}(u)(x', -x_N) - \varepsilon_{ij}(u)(x', -3x_N).$$

Furthermore, if one of the indexes is N, then we have

$$\begin{aligned} 2\varepsilon_{iN}(u)(x', x_N) &= -2\partial_N u_i(x', -x_N) + 3\partial_N u_i(x', -3x_N) \\ &\quad - 2\partial_i u_N(x', -x_N) + 3\partial_i u_N(x', -3x_N) \\ &= -4\varepsilon_{iN}(u)(x', -x_N) + 6\varepsilon_{iN}(u)(x', -3x_N) \end{aligned}$$

and $\quad \varepsilon_{N,N}(u)(x', x_N) = 2\partial_N u_N(x', -x_N) - 9\partial_N u_N(x', -3x_N).$

We thus see that the function $\widetilde{u}$ belongs to $Y_p(\mathbb{R}^N)$. It follows that $\widetilde{u} \in W^{1,p}(\mathbb{R}^N)$ and that $u \in W^{1,p}(\mathbb{R}^{N-1} \times \mathbb{R}^+)$. $\qquad\square$

Proof of Theorem 7.71 when Ω is a bounded open set of class C^2.

Let us recall our motivation, which is presented in the introduction of this chapter. Readers interested in other arguments in the case $p = 2$ or for much more general open spaces than those we consider may consult, for example, the article by Nitsche [54]. The proof given by Nitsche concerns open sets with only the cone property. The methods used for $p = 2$ for such open sets can no doubt be adapted to arbitrary p. We will not address this research. Consequently, we will only be interested in the extension of the local Korn inequality when the open set is of class C^2. We begin by noting that it suffices to prove the result in the neighborhood of a boundary point x_0, where the normal to $\partial\Omega$ has a nonzero scalar product with e_N. Locally, the open set Ω lies on one side of its boundary in the neighborhood of this point, and there exists an open subset Ω_i of $\mathbb{R}^N$ containing x_0 such that

$$\begin{aligned} \Omega_i \cap \Omega &\subset \{(x', x_N) \mid x' \in \mathcal{O}', a_i(x') < x_N\}, \\ \Omega_i \cap \partial\Omega &= \{(x', a_i(x')) \mid x' \in \mathcal{O}'\}, \end{aligned}$$

where $\mathcal{O}'$ is an open subset of $\mathbb{R}^{N-1}$ and a_i is a class C^2 function on $\mathcal{O}'$. The set Ω can be covered with such open sets Ω_i. Consequently, using a partition of unity $\{\varphi_i\}$ subordinate to this cover of Ω, it suffices to show that if $u \in Y_p(\Omega \cap \Omega_i)$, then $\varphi_i u \in W^{1,p}(\Omega \cap \Omega_i)$. For the sake of simplicity, we will omit the factor φ_i. In other words, we assume that u belongs to $Y_p(\Omega \cap \Omega_i)$ and that u has compact support in $\overline{\Omega} \cap \Omega_i$. We will also omit the index i. We can reduce to the case of a straight boundary, that is, to the case of functions on $\mathbb{R}^{N-1} \times]0, +\infty[$, which we have already studied.

We use the function v with components v_i defined by

$$v_i(x', t) = (u_i + (\partial_i a) \, u_N)(x', a(x') + t)$$

for $i \leqslant N - 1$ and by

$$v_N(x', t) = u_N(x', a(x') + t)$$

for $i = N$. The function v is defined on $\mathcal{O}' \times \mathbb{R}^+$. Let us show that $v \in Y_p(\mathcal{O}' \times]0, +\infty[)$. To do this, we compute the derivatives $\partial_j v_i$ and $\partial_i v_j$ for i and j in $[1, N-1]$ plus the derivatives $\partial_N v_i$ and $\partial_i v_N$, where we use the assumption that the function a is $\mathcal{C}^2$ on the open set $\mathcal{O}'$:

$$\partial_j v_i = \big(\partial_j u_i + \partial_N u_i \partial_j a + \partial_i a \partial_j u_N + \partial_i a \partial_j a \partial_N u_N + \partial_{ij} a u_N\big)(x', a(x') + t)$$
$$\partial_i v_j = \big(\partial_i u_j + \partial_N u_j \partial_i a + \partial_j a \partial_i u_N + \partial_i a \partial_j a \partial_N u_N + \partial_{ij} a u_N\big)(x', a(x') + t)$$
$$\partial_N v_N = \partial_N u_N(x', a(x') + t)$$
$$\partial_N v_i = \big(\partial_N u_i + \partial_i a \partial_N u_N\big)(x', a(x') + t)$$
$$\partial_i v_N = \big(\partial_i u_N + \partial_i a \partial_N u_N\big)(x', a(x') + t).$$

It follows that the components of $\varepsilon(v)$ with i and j in $[1, N-1]$ satisfy

$$\varepsilon_{ij}(v) = \big(\varepsilon_{ij}(u) + \partial_j a \varepsilon_{iN}(u) + \partial_i a \varepsilon_{jN}(u) + \partial_i a \partial_j a \partial_N u_N + \partial_{ij} a u_N\big)(x', a(x') + t).$$

Moreover, for $(i, j) = (i, N)$, we have

$$\varepsilon_{iN}(v) = (\varepsilon_{iN}(u) + (\partial_i a)\partial_N u_N)(x', a(x') + t).$$

These formulas clearly show that v belongs to $Y_p(\mathbb{R}^{N-1} \times]0, +\infty[)$ and has compact support in $\mathbb{R}^{N-1} \times [0, +\infty[$. Keeping the results for a straight boundary in mind, we obtain

$$v \in W^{1,p}(\mathcal{O}' \times]0, +\infty[).$$

In particular, the component v_N, that is, u_N, belongs to $W^{1,p}(\Omega_i \cap \Omega)$. Finally, by noting that

$$u_i(x', x_N) = v_i(x', x_N - a(x')) - (\partial_i a)v_N(x', x_N - a(x')),$$

we obtain the inclusion of u_i in the space $W^{1,p}(\Omega_i \cap \Omega)$, concluding the proof.

$\square$

Comments

Since we are not specialists in harmonic analysis, we have used the book of
Stein and Weiss [64] as our principal source. We recommend that the reader
who wishes to learn more consult the following books and articles for more
details: Stein and Weiss [64], Stein and Weiss [65], Stein [63], and Zygmund
[77].

7.5 Exercises for Chapter 7

Exercise 7.1 (Fourier Transform of a Function in $L^2(\mathbb{R})$).
Let f be defined by $f(t) = t/(t^2 + y^2)$, where $y > 0$.

(1) Show that $f \in L^2(\mathbb{R})$ and that its Fourier transform in the sense of
    tempered distributions is defined by a semiconvergent integral, namely
    $\widehat{f}(\xi) = \int_{\mathbb{R}} t \exp(-2i\pi\xi t)(t^2 + y^2)^{-1} dt$.
(2) Use the residue theorem applied to the contour consisting of a segment
    $[-R, R]$ and a semicircle (C_R or C'_R) and a suitable holomorphic function
    to compute $\widehat{f}(\xi)$ when $\xi < 0$ and when $\xi > 0$. You can also use one of the
    contours and the reflexion $\xi \mapsto -\xi$.

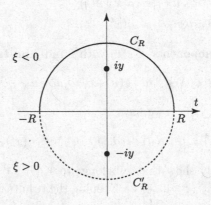

Fig. 7.1. A computation using the residue theorem.

Hints. For (2), use the function $F(z) = z \exp(-2i\pi\xi z)/(z^2 + y^2)$. When $\xi > 0$,
you must show that $\lim_{R \to +\infty} \int_{C'_R} F(z) dz = 0$. Reduce to bounding the integral
$\int_0^{\pi/2} \exp(-a \sin\theta) d\theta$ when a is a positive real number by using a lower bound for
$\sin\theta$, and conclude that this integral is lesser than K/R. Conclude that

$$\forall \xi \in \mathbb{R}, \quad \widehat{f}(\xi) = -i\pi \operatorname{sign}(\xi) \exp(-2\pi|\xi y|).$$

Exercise 7.2 (Mean Value Property for Harmonic Functions).
Let $N > 2$. We recall that the fundamental solution of the Laplacian is
$E(x) = k_N|x|^{-(N-2)}$, where k_N is a constant. Let u be a harmonic function in a domain Ω in $\mathbb{R}^N$. Consider a ball $B(a, r)$ whose closure lies inside Ω.
Generalize the case $N = 2$ by showing that $u(a)$ equals the mean value of u on the sphere $\partial B(a, r)$. Use Green's formula for class $\mathcal{C}^2$ functions in the following form:

$$\int_\Omega \left(g(x)\Delta f(x) - f(x)\Delta g(x)\right)dx = \int_{\partial\Omega} \left(g(x)\partial_{\vec{n}}f(x) - f(x)\partial_{\vec{n}}g(x)\right)d\sigma(x).$$

Apply this formula to the functions u and 1 to determine a property of the normal derivative of u on the spheres inside Ω. Next, apply this formula to E and u in the region between the sphere $\partial B(a, r)$ and the sphere of radius ε with center a to show that the mean value on $\partial B(a, r)$ equals the mean value on $\partial B(a, \varepsilon)$. Conclude.

Hints. We may, and do, assume that $a = 0$. By Green's formula, we have

$$0 = \int_{B(0,r)} \Delta u(x)dx = \int_{\partial B(0,r)} \partial_{\vec{n}}u(x)dx$$

for every r such that $B(0, r) \subset \Omega$. We then apply Green's formula to the functions E and u in the region $\Omega_{\varepsilon, r}$ delimited by the spheres $S_\varepsilon = \partial B(0, \varepsilon)$ and $S_r = \partial B(0, r)$.
By the harmonicity of the two functions, we have

$$\int_{\Omega_{\varepsilon,r}} \left(u\Delta E - E\Delta u\right)dx = 0.$$

Moreover, the normal differentiation of E on the spheres gives the expressions $-(N-2)|x|^{-N+1}$, which are constant on each of the spheres. This leaves

$$-(N-2)\int_{S_\varepsilon} \varepsilon^{-N+1}u(s)ds + (N-2)\int_{S_r} r^{-N+1}u(s)ds$$

$$-\int_{S_\varepsilon} E(s)\partial_{\vec{n}}u(s)ds + \int_{S_r} E(s)\partial_{\vec{n}}u(s)ds = 0$$

in Green's formula. By the previous result, since the function E is constant on the spheres, the sum of the last two integrals is zero. Consequently, we have

$$\frac{1}{\omega_{N-1}r^{N-1}}\int_{S_r} u(s)ds = \frac{1}{\omega_{N-1}\varepsilon^{N-1}}\int_{S_\varepsilon} u(s)ds.$$

Since the mean value of u on the sphere S_r equals its mean value on the sphere S_ε, which by the continuity of u is arbitrarily close to $u(0)$ when ε is sufficiently small, the result follows.

Exercise 7.3 (Converse of the Previous Exercise's Property).
Consider a continuous function u on a domain Ω in $\mathbb{R}^N$ that has the mean value property on this open set. In other words, for every $a \in \Omega$, the mean value $M_u(a, r)$ of u on a sphere with boundary $B(a, r)$ and closure contained in Ω equals $u(a)$. Prove that the function u is harmonic in Ω.

(1) To begin, assume that u is a C^2 function. Establish the result by showing that the limit of the second derivative of $r \mapsto M_u(a, r)$ at the point a is proportional to $\Delta u(a)$.

(2) In the general case, where the function u is only continuous, use a regularization of u and show that, locally, u coincides with its regularization, which allows us to reduce to the first case.

Hints.

(1) The second derivative of $r \mapsto \int_{\partial B(0,1)} u(a + rs)ds$ gives

$$\frac{d^2}{dr^2}[M_u(a, r)] = \frac{1}{\omega_{N-1}} \int_{\partial B(0,1)} \frac{d^2}{dr^2} u(a + rs)ds.$$

Up to ω_{N-1}, the limit of this derivative at a equals the sum

$$\sum_{ij} \partial_{ij} u(a) \int_{\partial B(0,1)} s_i s_j ds.$$

We note that if $i \neq j$, then $\int_{\partial B(0,1)} s_i s_j ds = 0$ and, moreover, that $\int_{\partial B(0,1)} s_i^2 ds = \int_{\partial B(0,1)} s_j^2 ds$. It follows that the limit of this derivative at a is proportional to $\Delta u(a)$, giving the result since by assumption, the mean value function is constant for $r > 0$.

(2) Consider a ball $B_0 = B(x_0, r_0)$ with closure inside Ω and let u_0 be the restriction of u to this ball extended by 0 outside of the ball. We use the convolution $U_\varepsilon = u_0 \star \rho_\varepsilon$ where, as usual, $\rho_\varepsilon(x) = \varepsilon^{-N} \rho(x/\varepsilon)$ with ρ a positive function in $\mathcal{D}(\mathbb{R}^N)$ with support in $B(0, 1)$ and integral equal to 1. We may, and do, moreover assume ρ to be radial. Let $x \in B_0$. By definition, for $\varepsilon < r_0 - |x_0 - x|$, we have

$$U_\varepsilon(x) = \int_{\mathbb{R}^N} \rho_\varepsilon(t) u_0(x - t) dt = \int_{B(0,\varepsilon)} \rho_\varepsilon(t) u(x - t) dt.$$

Using the spherical coordinates of the variable t and Fubini's formula, and letting σ be the variable on the unit sphere such that $t = |t|\sigma$, we can write

$$U_\varepsilon(x) = \int_0^\varepsilon \varepsilon^{-N} \rho(r/\varepsilon) \left[\int_{\partial B(0,1)} u(x - r\sigma) d\sigma \right] r^{N-1} dr.$$

Now, the mean value of u at the point x is defined by

$$M_u(x, r) = \frac{1}{\omega_{N-1}} \int_{\partial B(0,1)} u(x + rs) ds = \frac{1}{\omega_{N-1}} \int_{\partial B(0,1)} u(x - r\sigma) d\sigma.$$

It follows that

$$U_\varepsilon(x) = \omega_{N-1} \int_0^\varepsilon \varepsilon^{-N} \rho(r/\varepsilon) M_u(x, r) r^{N-1} dr,$$

so that, using the assumption, which holds because of the condition on ε, we obtain

$$U_\varepsilon(x) = \omega_{N-1} u(x) \int_0^1 \rho(\lambda) \lambda^{N-1} d\lambda.$$

Finally, since

$$\omega_{N-1} \int_0^1 \rho(\lambda) \lambda^{N-1} \, d\lambda = \int_{B(0,1)} \rho(y) dy = 1,$$

we deduce that $u(x) = U_\varepsilon(x)$.

Taking x in $B(x_0, r_0/2)$, we can then fix $\varepsilon_0 = r_0/2$ and the function u coincides with the function U_{ε_0} in the entire ball $B(x_0, r_0/2)$. The function u is therefore of class C^∞ in Ω. We have thus reduced to case (1).

Exercise 7.4 (Complement to Example 7.12).

Consider the function f on $\mathbb{R}$ defined by $f(t) = (t^2 + 1)^{-1}$. For $0 < x < 1/\sqrt{3}$, we study the mean values defined by

$$u(r, x) = \frac{1}{2r} \int_{x-r}^{x+r} \frac{dt}{t^2 + 1} = \frac{\arctan(x + r) - \arctan(x - r)}{2r}.$$

The function $U(r, x) = -2u_r'(r, x)r^2$ can be written as

$$U(r, x) = \arctan(x + r) - \arctan(x - r)) - r\Big(\frac{1}{(x+r)^2 + 1} + \frac{1}{(x-r)^2 + 1}\Big).$$

Setting $a = x + r$ and $b = x - r$, its derivative equals

$$U_r'(r, x) = 2r\Big[\frac{a}{(a^2 + 1)^2} - \frac{b}{(b^2 + 1)^2}\Big].$$

Expanding $a(b^2 + 1)^2 - b(a^2 + 1)^2$, we see that $U_r'(r, x)$ has the same sign as the trinomial $T(r^2)$ defined by

$$T(r^2) = r^4 + 2(1 + x^2)r^2 - 3x^4 - 2x^2 + 1 = r^4 + 2(1 + x^2)r^2 - (x^2 + 1)(3x^2 - 1).$$

(1) Let $x \leqslant 1/\sqrt{3}$. Determine the sign of the derivative of $r \mapsto u(r, x)$ by first studying the sign of $T(r^2)$ and then using the formulas above. Prove that

$$\forall x \leqslant \frac{1}{\sqrt{3}}, \quad m_f(x) = \frac{1}{1 + x^2} = f(x).$$

(2) Next, assume that $x > 1/\sqrt{3}$ (use the results of Example 7.12). Prove that the function $x \mapsto U(r, x)$ is nondecreasing and that $x \mapsto r_2(x)$ is therefore nonincreasing in $]1/\sqrt{3}, +\infty[$. Deduce that the function $x \mapsto r_2(x)$ is continuous on this interval, and consequently that m_f is a continuous function on $]1/\sqrt{3}, +\infty[$. Finally, examine the behavior of $m_f(x)$ as x tends to $1/\sqrt{3}$ from above.

Exercise 7.5 (Solution for the Dirichlet Problem on the Sphere using the Poisson Integral).

Let B be the open unit ball in $\mathbb{R}^N$ and let ∂B be the unit sphere. We set (Poisson kernel):

$$\forall x \in B, \forall s \in \partial B, \quad p(s, x) = K_N \frac{1 - |x|^2}{|x - s|^N},$$

where the constant K_N is the reciprocal of the $(N-1)$-dimensional surface area of the unit sphere in $\mathbb{R}^N$. Note that the function p is nonnegative.

(1) Show that the function $x \mapsto p(s,x)$ is harmonic in B for every s in ∂B.
(2) Show that we have $\int_{\partial B} p(s,x)ds = 1$ for every x in B.
(3) We set $x = ry$ with $r < 1$ and $|y| = 1$. Show that for every $\eta > 0$, when $r \to 1$, the function $x \mapsto \int_{s \in \partial B, |s-y| > \eta} p(s,ry)ds$ converges uniformly to 0 at y.
(4) (Poisson formula) Let f be a continuous function on ∂B. Let u be the function on $\overline{B}$ defined by

$$(7.76) \qquad u(x) = \begin{cases} \int_{\partial B} f(s)p(s,x)ds & \text{if } x \in B, \\ f(x) & \text{if } x \in \partial B. \end{cases}$$

Show that the function u is harmonic in B and continuous on $\overline{B}$.

Hints.

(1) Compute the Laplacian of a product using the function $y \mapsto \left(1 - |y+s|^2\right)|y|^{-N}$.
(2) Let $r < 1$. Since the function p is harmonic in B for s fixed in ∂B, the mean value property (cf. Exercise 7.2) implies that

$$p(s,0) = \frac{1}{\omega_{N-1}} = \frac{1}{\omega_{N-1}r^{N-1}} \int_{\partial B(0,r)} p(s,x)dx,$$

whence, by setting $x = ry$, which allows us to reduce to the unit sphere,

$$p(s,0) = \frac{1}{\omega_{N-1}} \int_{\partial B(0,1)} p(s,ry)dy.$$

Show the inequality $|ry - s| = |rs - y|$ using, for example, the symmetry axis for the two rays $[0,s]$ and $[0,y]$ or a direct computation. It follows that

$$\omega_{N-1}p(s,ry) = \frac{1-r^2}{|s-ry|^N} = \frac{1-r^2|s|^2}{|rs-y|^N} = \frac{1-|rs|^2}{|rs-y|^N} = \omega_{N-1}p(y,rs).$$

We therefore have

$$1 = \omega_{N-1}p(s,0) = \int_{\partial B(0,1)} p(s,ry)dy = \int_{\partial B(0,1)} p(y,rs)dy.$$

This relation holds for arbitrary s of norm 1 in $\mathbb{R}^N$ and arbitrary real numbers r with $0 \leqslant r < 1$. Let x be a given element of B, so that $|x| < 1$; we can then choose the elements s and r in the relation in such a way that $rs = x$. We then obtain

$$1 = \int_{\partial B(0,1)} p(s,x)ds,$$

giving the result.

(3) We again set $x = ry$, where y lies on the sphere. We assume that $|s - y| > \eta$. Using a lower bound, we find

$$|ry - s| \geqslant |s - y| - (1 - r) \geqslant \frac{\eta}{2}$$

for $1 - r$ sufficiently small. From this, we deduce the uniform upper bound $C(1 - r^2)$ for $p(s, ry)$, giving the result.

(4) We use the first question and carry out a differentiation under the integral sign with respect to x when $|x| < 1$. It suffices to show the continuity at a point $z \in \partial B$. Let $\varepsilon > 0$ be given. We wish to show that for $x \in B$ sufficiently close to z, we have $|u(z) - u(x)| \leqslant \varepsilon$. We may, and do, assume that $x \neq 0$ and we use a y such that $x = ry$ and $|y| = 1$, which allows us to fall back on the previous results. Decomposing the integral into two parts, one on the set A_η of points of ∂B for which $|s - y| \geqslant \eta$, we have

$$|u(x) - u(y)| = \left| \int_{\partial B} [f(s) - f(y)] p(s, ry) ds \right|$$

$$\leqslant \int_{A_\eta} |f(s) - f(y)| p(s, ry) ds + \int_{\partial B \smallsetminus A_\eta} |f(s) - f(y)| p(s, ry) ds.$$

Since the integral of p on the boundary equals 1, we can bound the second integral on the right-hand side as follows:

$$\int_{\partial B \smallsetminus A_\eta} |f(s) - f(y)| p(s, ry) ds \leqslant \sup\{|f(s) - f(y)| \mid |s - y| \leqslant \eta\}.$$

By the continuity of f on ∂B, this integral can be bounded from above by $\varepsilon/2$ for $\eta \leqslant \eta_0$. Choosing $\eta = \eta_0$, we obtain

$$|u(x) - u(y)| \leqslant \frac{\varepsilon}{2} + 2 \sup_{t \in \partial B} |f(t)| \int_{A_\eta} p(s, ry) ds.$$

Now, by question (3), this last integral tends to 0 uniformly with respect to y when $r \to 1$. It follows that there exists an η_1 such that $|x - y| < \eta_1$ implies $|u(x) - u(y)| < \varepsilon$. Returning to z, we then write

$$|u(z) - u(x)| \leqslant |u(z) - u(y)| + |u(y) - u(x)|.$$

By the continuity of f on the boundary, the difference $|u(z) - u(y)|$, which equals $|f(z) - f(y)|$, can be made $< \varepsilon$ provided that $|z - y| \leqslant \eta_2$. Let $x \in B(z, 1/2 \inf(\eta_1, \eta_2))$; then $|x - y| < \eta_1$ and, consequently, the previous inequality implies that $|u(z) - u(x)| < 2\varepsilon$, giving the desired result.

Exercise 7.6 (Application of the Poisson Formula Given Above).

Consider a continuous function $(x, y) \mapsto u(x, y)$ on $\mathbb{R}^N \times \mathbb{R}$ with the following symmetry property:

$$\forall x \in \mathbb{R}^N, \forall y > 0, \quad u(x, -y) = -u(x, y).$$

We suppose that u is harmonic in $\mathbb{R}^N \times]0, +\infty[$. Show that the function u is then harmonic in $\mathbb{R}^N \times \mathbb{R}$. To do this, first show that u is harmonic in $\mathbb{R}^N \times]-\infty, 0[$ and then prove that it is harmonic in the entire ball with center $(x_0, 0)$ in $\mathbb{R}^{N+1}$. For that property, compare the function u in the ball to the harmonic function defined by the Poisson integral of Exercise 7.5 (cf. formula (7.76)).

Hints. Use formula (7.76) on the ball $B_0 = B((x_0, 0), r)$; this defines a function v that is harmonic inside B_0 and can be identified with u on ∂B_0. The Poisson kernel $p(s, x)$ of this formula has an analogue in dimension $N + 1$, where the point x is replaced by $(x_0 + r\xi, 0 + r\eta)$ for (ξ, η) on the unit sphere $\partial B(0, 1)$ in $\mathbb{R}^{N+1}$. Letting ω_N denote the surface area of the sphere and $d\sigma$ its Lebesgue measure, we obtain

$$v(x, y) = \frac{1}{\omega_{N-1} r^{1-N}} \int_{\partial B(0,1)} u(x_0 + r\xi, r\eta) p^*(x, y, \xi, \eta) d\sigma,$$

where p^* is defined by

$$p^*(x, y, \xi, \eta) = \frac{r^2 - [(x - x_0)^2 + y^2]}{\left((x - x_0) - r\xi)^2 + r^2\eta^2\right)^{(N+1)/2}}.$$

By the symmetry assumption on u, we have $v(x, 0) = 0$ when $y = 0$. In the bounded domain consisting of the interior of the hemisphere $B_0 \cap (\mathbb{R}^N \times]0, +\infty[)$, the functions v and u are therefore solutions of a same Dirichlet problem. Since the open set is not of class C^1, we do not have uniqueness. However, applying the maximum principle to the difference, as in Remark 5.69, nonetheless gives the equality $u = v$ in the open set. The same reasoning holds for the lower hemisphere. It follows that the function u is harmonic in B_0 and, consequently, everywhere in $\mathbb{R}^{N+1}$.

Exercise [**] 7.7 (Proof of Theorem 7.15 when $N = 1$).

Let us take the statement of Theorem 7.15. By translating the neighborhoods J_{x_i, r_i}, which in this case are intervals, so that their centers x_i become 0, we obtain intervals J_i with center 0 that we can order as follows:

$$J_1 \subset J_2 \subset \cdots \subset J_n,$$

where $J_i =] - r_i, r_i[$, with the property that

$$\forall y \in S, \; \exists i \in [1, n], \quad \frac{1}{2r_i} \int_{y + J_i} |f(t)| dt > s.$$

For every $y \in S$, we can set

$$K(y) = \sup \left\{ j \in [1, n] \; \Big| \; \frac{1}{2r_j} \int_{y + J_j} |f(t)| dt > s \right\},$$

thus defining a map K from S to $[1, n]$. We wish to estimate the measure of S using its cover by these intervals of length $2r_i$, which satisfy

$$(7.77) \qquad i = K(y) \implies 2r_i < \frac{1}{s} \int_{J_i} |f(t + y)| dt.$$

We will bound the measure $|S|$ from above by a sum of the lengths of the intervals in a suitable cover of S, so that we can use relation (7.77), allowing us to estimate this measure using the integral of $|f|$ over $\mathbb{R}$.

(1) More precisely, show that

Lemma 7.78. *There exist a finite number of points s_j, $1 \leqslant j \leqslant k$, of S such that*

a) *The set S is contained in $\bigcup_{1 \leqslant j \leqslant k} \{s_j + J_{K(s_j)}\}$ and a center s_j is contained only in the interval with index j.*

b) *Setting $V_i = s_i + J_{K(s_i)}$, we have*

$$\sum_{1}^{k} \int_{V_j} |f(t)| dt \leqslant 2 \int_{\mathbb{R}} |f(t)| dt = 2\|f\|_{L^1(\mathbb{R})}.$$

(2) After proving the lemma, finish the proof of Theorem 7.15 in the case $N = 1$ using relation (7.77):

$$|F_s| \leqslant \sum_{1}^{k} |V_j| \leqslant 2 \sum_{1}^{k} r_j \leqslant \frac{1}{s} \sum_{1}^{k} \int_{V_j} |f(t+y)| dt \leqslant \frac{2}{s}\|f\|_1.$$

Hints. Choose a point s_1 in S such that $K(s_1) \geqslant K(s) \; \forall s \in S$. Such a point exists because of the inverse image $K^{-1}(\{n\})$. Consider the set $S_1 = S \smallsetminus \{s_1 + J_{K(s_1)}\}$. If it is empty, then $S \subset V_1 = s_1 + J_{K(s_1)}$ and the first part of the lemma is verified with $k = 1$, while the second part is trivial. If the difference of the sets is nonempty, then we choose a point s_2 in S_1 such that $K(s_2) \geqslant K(s)$ for every $s \in S_1$. If $S_2 = S_1 \smallsetminus V_2$ is empty, then we obtain the lemma with $k = 2$ by noting, moreover, that the inequality $r_{K(s_2)} \leqslant r_{K(s_1)}$ implies that the center s_1 of the first interval does not lie in the second one, $s_2 + J_{K(s_2)}$.

The second part of the lemma then follows from

$$\int_{V_1} |f(t)| dt + \int_{V_2} |f(t)| dt = \int_{V_1 \cup V_2} |f(t)| dt + \int_{V_1 \cap V_2} |f(t)| dt \leqslant 2 \int_{\mathbb{R}} |f(t)| dt.$$

This construction can be extended using the given algorithm. The number of steps is necessarily finite, giving the first statement of the lemma. By the above, the center s_j does not belong to $s_{j'} + J_{K(s_{j'})}$ for $j' = j \pm 1$. By the assumption that the dimension is one, it follows that the same holds for every other index. The first part of the lemma follows.

For the second part of the lemma, we first note that any three V_j with two-by-two distinct indexes have an empty intersection. Indeed, let a belong to the intersection of two of the V_j. We may, and do, assume that i and j are the two smallest indexes for which $a \in V_i \cap V_j$. Then, if $a \in V_k$ for k other than i and j, we have $|s_k - a| < r_k \leqslant \inf(r_i, r_j)$, which implies that the center s_k belongs to one of the intervals V_i, V_j, giving a contradiction. Under these conditions, we can generalize an earlier equality by using the sum of the characteristic functions of the V_j. We will show that this sum is lesser than $2\chi(\cup V_j)$, from which it follows that

$$\sum_{1}^{k} \int_{V_j} |f(t)| dt \leqslant 2 \int_{\mathbb{R}} |f(t)| dt.$$

Consequently, Theorem 7.15 in dimension 1 follows from

$$\left|\{x \in \mathbb{R} \mid m_f(x) > s > 0\}\right| \leqslant \frac{2\|f\|_{L^1(\mathbb{R})}}{s}.$$

We could also formulate the reasoning given above in a way that makes general-ization easier. Namely, let τ_h be a translation such that $S \cap \tau_h(S) = \varnothing$ and consider two-by-two disjoint semi-open intervals $\{W_\alpha\}$ that are each contained in a V_j and that form a cover of S. To every point ζ belonging to two intervals V_i, we associate $\tau_h(\zeta)$. We denote the set of these translated points by S'. We then have

$$\sum_1^k \int_{V_j} |f(t)| dt = \int_{\cup W_\alpha} |f(t)| dt + \int_{S'} |f(t)| dt \leqslant 2 \int_S |f(t)| dt.$$

Exercise 7.8 (Convolution of $T \in \mathcal{S}'(\mathbb{R}^N)$ with $\varphi \in \mathcal{S}(\mathbb{R}^N)$).

In this chapter, we have seen that this convolution is a function f defined by

$$\forall x \in \mathbb{R}^N, \quad f(x) = \langle T, \tau_x(\check{\varphi}) \rangle,$$

where $\check{\varphi}$ is the function $t \mapsto \varphi(-t)$.

Prove that f is a $\mathcal{C}^\infty$ function and that there exist a multi-index k and a constant $C(k)$ such that

$$\forall x \in \mathbb{R}^N, \quad |f(x)| \leqslant C(k) |x|^k.$$

In other words, prove that f is a slowly increasing function.

Hints. Show that

$$\forall j, \quad \left\langle T_{(t)}, \frac{1}{h} \left[[\varphi(x + he_j - t) - \varphi(x + h - t) - h \partial_j \varphi(x - t)] \right\rangle \longrightarrow 0 \right.$$

when $h \to 0$. Deduce that $\partial_j f(x) = \langle T, \tau_x \partial_j^{\vee} \varphi \rangle$. Use iteration to obtain the result for an arbitrary order of differentiation.

For the slow growth, use the continuity of T and the family of seminorms defining the topology of $\mathcal{S}$. We have

$$|f(x)| \leqslant \sum_{\substack{|\alpha| \leqslant k \\ |\beta| \leqslant m}} \sup_X |X|^\alpha |D^\beta \varphi(X - x)|.$$

Use the Taylor expansion of φ to bound $|f|$ from above by a polynomial.

Exercise 7.9 (Fourier Transform of the Convolution $T \star \varphi$).

Let $T \in \mathcal{S}'$ and let $\varphi \in \mathcal{S}$. Show that the Fourier transform of the convolution $T \star \varphi$ is the product of the individual transforms.

Hints. Use the expression for $A = T \star \varphi$ given in Proposition 7.22 for the computation of $\langle \widehat{A}, \psi \rangle$, which makes use of the commutativity of the tensor product:

$$\langle \widehat{A}, \psi \rangle = \langle A, \widehat{\psi} \rangle = \langle \langle T, \tau_\lambda(\check{\varphi}) \rangle, \widehat{\psi}(\lambda) \rangle = \langle \widehat{\psi}_{[\lambda]} \otimes T_{[t]}, \tau_\lambda(\check{\varphi}) \rangle$$

$$= \langle T_{[t]} \otimes \widehat{\psi}_{[\lambda]}, \check{\varphi}(t - \lambda) \rangle = \left\langle T_{[t]}, \int_{\mathbb{R}^N} \widehat{\psi}(\lambda) \check{\varphi}(t - \lambda) d\lambda \right\rangle$$

$$= \langle T_{[t]}, (\widehat{\psi} \star \check{\varphi})(t) \rangle.$$

Show that the product $\widehat{\varphi} \psi$ is the convolution of the transforms, that is, $\check{\varphi} \star \widehat{\psi}$. Conclude.

Exercise 7.10 (Determining the Fourier Transform of $Vp(1/x)$).

(1) Prove that $v(\xi) = Vp(\int_{\mathbb{R}} \exp(-2i\pi\xi t)/t\,dt)$ exists for every real ξ. Decompose it into two integrals and show that computing it traditionally corresponds to computing $\int_0^{+\infty} \sin(2\pi\xi t)/t\,dt$. Deduce that $v(\xi) = -i\pi \, \text{sign}(\xi)$. Next, prove that the distributions $T_{\varepsilon,A}$ associated with the truncations of $1/t$ on $[-A, -\varepsilon] \cup [\varepsilon, A]$, which are tempered, converge in $\mathcal{S}'$ to $Vp(1/t)$. Finally, prove that the Fourier transforms of $T_{\varepsilon,A}$ converges to the function v.

(2) Use a different method: show that the desired transform is an odd function, and that $t\,Vp(1/t) = 1$. The result then follows using a property of the Fourier transform.

Exercise 7.11 (Computation of a Hilbert Transform).
Use the definition of the Fourier transform to compute the convolution of $Vp(1/t)$ and the function f defined by $f(t) = (t^2 + 1)/(t^2 + t + 1)^2$.

Exercise 7.12 (Fourier Transform of a Radial Function).
Use isometries to show that if f is a function in $L^1(\mathbb{R}^N)$ satisfying $f(x) = g(|x|)$, then the Fourier transform of f is a function of $\rho = \sqrt{\sum_1^N \xi_j^2}$.

Exercise 7.13 (Computation of a Hilbert Transform).
Consider the function f on $\mathbb{R} \setminus \{0\}$ defined by $f(t) = \left(\sqrt{|t|}(1 + |t|)\right)^{-1}$. We will use two different methods to compute its Hilbert transform Hf.

By way of this example, we will be able to illustrate certain results, namely Theorem 7.29, which gives two definitions of the Hilbert transform, the proposition concerning the weak type $(1, 1)$ of the transform, and Corollary 7.35, which states that the Hilbert transform maps L^p to itself for $p > 1$.

Let us therefore first note that the function f belongs to $L^p(\mathbb{R})$ for $1 \leqslant p < 2$.

(1) *First computation method.* Let F be the function on $\mathbb{R}$ defined by $F = f \star g_y$, where $g_y(t) = t/(t^2 + y^2)$ with $y > 0$. By one of the definitions in this book, the transform of f is

$$Hf(x) = \frac{1}{\pi} \lim_{y \to 0_+} F(x, y),$$

where

$$\forall x \in \mathbb{R}, \ \forall y > 0, \quad F(x, y) = \int_{\mathbb{R}} \frac{1}{\sqrt{|t|}(1 + |t|)} \frac{x - t}{[(x - t)^2 + y^2]} \, dt.$$

Replacing x by $-x$, we obtain, up to the sign, the same integral transformed by the change of variables $t \mapsto -t$. It follows that $x \mapsto F(x, y)$ is an odd function, allowing us to restrict our computation to $x > 0$.

Using changes of variables and, for example, the residue theorem, we reduce to computing two integrals of rational functions over $\mathbb{R}$.

(2) *Second computation method.* We use the formula

$$Hf(x) = 1/\pi \lim_{\varepsilon \to 0} \int_{|t|>\varepsilon} f(x-t)/t\,dt.$$

We therefore compute

$$\int_{|t|>\varepsilon} \frac{1}{\sqrt{|x-t|}\,(1+|x-t|)t}\,dt.$$

We can, for example, write this integral as the sum of three integrals, one of which concerns a rational function and can be computed using the residue theorem.

In the hints, we show how our results illustrate Theorem 7.29 and Corollary 7.35.

Hints.

(1) *First computation method.* Write $F(x,y)$ as the sum of two integrals over $]0,+\infty[$, namely:

$$I(x,y) = 2\int_0^{+\infty} \frac{x+u^2}{(1+u^2)(x+u^2)^2+y^2}\,du$$

and

$$J(x,y) = 2\int_0^{+\infty} \frac{x-u^2}{(1+u^2)(x-u^2)^2+y^2}\,du.$$

Since these are even functions, we have

$$I(x,y) = \int_{\mathbb{R}} \frac{x+u^2}{(1+u^2)(x+u^2)^2+y^2}\,du$$

$$J(x,y) = \int_{\mathbb{R}} \frac{x-u^2}{(1+u^2)(x-u^2)^2+y^2}\,du.$$

• Computation of $I(x,y)$ for $x>0$.

Use the residue theorem. Let $\theta = \arctan(y/x)$, which is an element of $]-\pi/2, \pi/2[$ and let $\rho = \sqrt{x^2+y^2}$. Consider the function G of the complex variable z defined by

$$G(z) = \frac{x+z^2}{(1+z^2)(z^2+x+iy)(z^2+x-iy)}.$$

When $x>0$, the square root of z^2+x+iy in the upper half-plane equals $z_1 = i\sqrt{\rho}\exp(i\theta/2)$. For z^2+x-iy, the square root z_2 is obtained by replacing θ by $-\theta$ in z_1.

The residue theorem now gives

$$I(x,y) = 2i\pi\left[\,\text{Rés}(G,i) + \text{Rés}(G,z_1) + \text{Rés}(G,z_2)\right].$$

For the simple poles, the classical formula gives

$$\text{Rés}(G, i) = \frac{x-1}{2i(\rho^2 + 1 - 2x)},$$

$$\text{Rés}(G, z_1) = \frac{-iy}{2i\sqrt{\rho}e^{i\theta/2}(1 - x - iy)(-2iy)} = \frac{e^{-i\theta/2}}{4i\sqrt{\rho}(1 - x - iy)},$$

$$\text{Rés}(G, z_2) = \frac{iy}{2i\sqrt{\rho}e^{-i\theta/2}(1 - x + iy)(2iy)} = \frac{e^{i\theta/2}}{4i\sqrt{\rho}(1 - x + iy)}$$

when $x > 0$. It follows that in this case,

$$I(x, y) = \pi\Big[\frac{x-1}{\rho^2 + 1 - 2x} + \frac{e^{-i\theta/2}}{2\sqrt{\rho}(1 - x - iy)} + \frac{e^{+i\theta/2}}{2\sqrt{\rho}(1 - x + iy)}\Big].$$

• Computation of $J(x, y)$ for $x > 0$.
Continue with similar computations, which give

$$J(x, y) = \pi\Big[\frac{x+1}{(x+1)^2 + y^2} + \frac{e^{i\theta/2}}{2\sqrt{\rho}(1 + x - iy)} - \frac{e^{-i\theta/2}}{2\sqrt{\rho}(1 + x + iy)}\Big].$$

We thus obtain the function F:

$$F(x, y) = \pi\Big[\frac{x-1}{\rho^2 + 1 - 2x} + \frac{x+1}{\rho^2 + 1 + 2x} + \frac{e^{-i\theta/2}}{2\sqrt{\rho}(1 - x - iy)}$$
$$+ \frac{e^{+i\theta/2}}{2\sqrt{\rho}(1 - x + iy)} + \frac{e^{+i\theta/2}}{2\sqrt{\rho}(1 + x - iy)} - \frac{e^{-i\theta/2}}{2\sqrt{\rho}(1 + x + iy)}\Big].$$

• Taking the limit for $y \to 0+$.
The result is obvious, because it suffices to replace y and θ by 0, ρ by x, and $\sqrt{\rho}$ by $\sqrt{x}$, because $x > 0$. We thus obtain the Hilbert transform of f:

$$\forall x > 0, \quad H(f)(x) = \frac{1}{x-1} + \frac{1}{x+1} + \frac{1}{\sqrt{x}(1-x)}$$

or

$$\forall x > 0, \quad H(f)(x) = \frac{1}{\sqrt{x}(1 + \sqrt{x})} + \frac{1}{(1+x)}.$$

Using the oddness noted above, we see that the function we obtain is defined everywhere except at $x = 0$, thus illustrating the existence almost everywhere of the Hilbert transform (cf. Proposition 7.26). Moreover, using this formula, we see that the Hilbert transform belongs to the space L^p for $1 < p < 2$, as stated in Corollary 7.35 on the interval $]1, 2[$.

(2) *Second computation method.* Let us compute

$$\int_{|t|>\varepsilon} \frac{1}{\sqrt{|x-t|}(1 + |x - t|)t}\, dt.$$

Assuming that $x > 0$ and $\varepsilon < x$, this integral can be written as the sum of three terms I_1, I_2, and I_3 by integrating over the intervals $]-\infty, -\varepsilon[$, $]\varepsilon, x[$, and

$]x, +\infty[$. Using changes of variables, we obtain

$$I_1 = \int_{-\infty}^{-\varepsilon} \frac{dt}{\sqrt{x-t}(1+x-t)t} = -2 \int_{\sqrt{x+\varepsilon}}^{+\infty} \frac{du}{(1+u^2)(u^2-x)}$$

$$I_2 = \int_{\varepsilon}^{x} \frac{dt}{\sqrt{x-t}(1+x-t)t} = -2 \int_0^{\sqrt{x-\varepsilon}} \frac{du}{(1+u^2)(u^2-x)}$$

$$I_3 = \int_x^{+\infty} \frac{dt}{\sqrt{t-x}(1+t-x)t} = 2 \int_0^{+\infty} \frac{du}{(1+u^2)(x+u^2)}.$$

The computations of I_1 and I_2 are rather elementary, while we can use the residue theorem to compute I_3. The result is

$$I_1 = \frac{2}{1+x} \left[\arctan u - \frac{1}{2\sqrt{x}} \ln \left| \frac{u-\sqrt{x}}{u+\sqrt{x}} \right| \right]_{\sqrt{x+\varepsilon}}^{+\infty}$$

$$= \frac{1}{1+x} \left[\pi - 2 \arctan \sqrt{x+\varepsilon} + \frac{1}{\sqrt{x}} \ln \left| \frac{\sqrt{x+\varepsilon}-\sqrt{x}}{\sqrt{x+\varepsilon}+\sqrt{x}} \right| \right],$$

$$I_2 = \frac{2}{1+x} \left[\arctan u - \frac{1}{2\sqrt{x}} \ln \left| \frac{u-\sqrt{x}}{u+\sqrt{x}} \right| \right]_0^{\sqrt{x-\varepsilon}}$$

$$= \frac{1}{1+x} \left[2 \arctan \sqrt{x-\varepsilon} - \frac{1}{\sqrt{x}} \ln \left| \frac{\sqrt{x-\varepsilon}-\sqrt{x}}{\sqrt{x-\varepsilon}+\sqrt{x}} \right| \right],$$

$$I_3 = 2i\pi \left[\text{Rés}(g; i) + \text{Rés}(g; i\sqrt{x}) \right] = \pi \left[\frac{1}{x-1} + \frac{1}{(1-x)\sqrt{x}} \right],$$

where g is the complex function $z \mapsto \dfrac{1}{(1+z^2)(x+z^2)}$ (the formulas we give still hold when we pass to the limit when the pole is of order 2, namely for $x=1$). It remains to take the limit of the sum of the three integrals for $\varepsilon \to 0$. Since $\lim_{\varepsilon \to 0} \left(\dfrac{\sqrt{x+\varepsilon}-\sqrt{x}}{\sqrt{x}-\sqrt{x-\varepsilon}} \right) = 0$ by an obvious equivalence, we find that for $x > 0$, we have

$$Hf(x) = \frac{1}{1+x} + \left[\frac{1}{x-1} + \frac{1}{(1-x)\sqrt{x}} \right] = \frac{1}{1+x} + \frac{1}{\sqrt{x}(1+\sqrt{x})}.$$

Since the function Hf is odd, this concludes the computation, and we note that this result equals that found using the first method, as was announced in Theorem 7.29.

Exercise [**] 7.14 (Computation of a Riesz transform in $\mathbb{R}^2$).

Let $f(x,y) = 1/(x^2+y^2+1)$ and let $\rho^2 = \xi^2 + \eta^2$. Prove that

$$R_1(f)(\xi,\eta) = f_1(\rho) = \lim_{\varepsilon \to 0, A \to +\infty} \int_0^{2\pi} \int_\varepsilon^A \frac{\cos u}{r(\rho^2+r^2+1-2\rho r \cos u)} dr\, du.$$

By decomposing a rational fraction to reduce to a simple trigonometric integral, show that

$$f_1(\rho) = \frac{\rho}{\rho^2+1} \int_0^\pi \frac{\cos^2 u}{\sqrt{1+\rho^2 \sin^2 u}} du,$$

which can therefore be expressed using a Legendre function.

Exercise 7.15 (Nontangential Uniform Convergence of $P(\cdot, y) \star f$ when $y \to 0$).

Recall that the Poisson kernel can be written as $P(t, y) = y/(t^2 + y^2)$. Let $x_0 \in \mathbb{R}$ and let $\alpha > 0$ be a real number. We let $\Gamma_\alpha(x_0)$ denote the open cone in $\mathbb{R} \times]0, +\infty[$ with top $x_0 \in \mathbb{R}$, which is defined by

$$\Gamma_\alpha(x_0) = \{(x, y) \in \mathbb{R} \times]0, +\infty[\mid |x - x_0|/y < \alpha\}.$$

Show that if $f \in L^p$ and if x_0 is a Lebesgue point, then

(7.79)
$$\lim_{y \to 0} \sup_{x \in \Gamma_\alpha(x_0)} \left| P(\cdot, y) \star f(x) - f(x) \right| = 0.$$

(1) First prove that if there exists a constant $d_\alpha > 0$ such that

$$\forall (x, y) \in \Gamma_\alpha(x_0), \ \forall t \in \mathbb{R}, \quad P(x - t, y) \leqslant d_\alpha P(x_0 - t, y),$$

then (7.79) holds.

(2) Proving the existence of d_α corresponds to proving that the function φ on $\mathbb{R}$ defined by $\varphi(t) = (y^2 + (x - t)^2)/(y^2 + (x_0 - t)^2)$ for fixed x_0 and y admits a positive minimum.

   a) First suppose that $x > x_0$ and determine the sign of the derivative of the function, which is the sign of a degree two trinomial. Deduce the lower bound

$$\forall t \in \mathbb{R}, \quad \varphi(t) \geqslant \frac{\left(x_0 - x + \sqrt{(x - x_0)^2 + 4y^2}\right)^2 + y^2}{\left(x - x_0 + \sqrt{(x - x_0)^2 + 4y^2}\right)^2 + y^2}$$

   for $x > x_0$. Deduce a similar lower bound for $x < x_0$ and prove that

$$\forall t \in \mathbb{R}, \quad \varphi(t) \geqslant \frac{\left(|x_0 - x| - \sqrt{(x - x_0)^2 + 4y^2}\right)^2 + y^2}{\left(|x - x_0| + \sqrt{(x - x_0)^2 + 4y^2}\right)^2 + y^2}.$$

   b) Study the sign of the derivative of this minimum using the variable $u = |x - x_0|/y$. Deduce the existence of the number d_α.

Hints.

(1) By the property $\int_{\mathbb{R}} P(x, y)dx = 1$, we have

$$|(P(\cdot, y) \star f)(x) - f(x_0)| = \left| \int_{\mathbb{R}} (P(x - t, y)(f(t) - f(x_0)dt \right|$$

$$\leqslant d_\alpha \int_{\mathbb{R}} (P(x - t, y)|f(t) - f(x_0)|dt.$$

The last term tends to 0 because x_0 is a Lebesgue point of f (cf. Proposition 7.3 and Remark 7.4), giving uniform convergence in the cone $\Gamma_\alpha(x_0)$ when y tends to 0.

(2) The sign of the derivative φ' is the same as that of the trinomial $T = t^2 - (x + x_0)t + xx_0 - y^2$ whose discriminant $\Delta = (x - x_0)^2 + 4y^2$ is > 0. The two roots are $t_j = x + x_0 \pm \sqrt{\Delta}/2$ with $j \in \{1, 2\}$. We have $T(x_0) = -y^2 < 0$, which implies that $x_0 \in]t_1, t_2[$. The function φ is therefore nonincreasing on $[t_1, t_2]$ and nondecreasing outside of this interval. Since $x > x_0$, we have

$$\varphi(t_2) = \frac{4y^2 + (\sqrt{\Delta} + (x_0 - x))^2}{4y^2 + (\sqrt{\Delta} - (x_0 - x))^2} < 1.$$

Moreover, the limit of φ at $-\infty$ equals 1. It follows that

$$\min \varphi = \varphi(t_2) = \frac{4y^2 + (\sqrt{\Delta} + (x_0 - x))^2}{4y^2 + (\sqrt{\Delta} - (x_0 - x))^2}.$$

When $x < x_0$, the function is replaced by its inverse and we obtain the same result by using the root t_1 instead of t_2. This corresponds to replacing $x - x_0$ by its absolute value in the formula giving the minimum.
(b) The derivative of the function

$$m(u) = \left[1 + (u - \sqrt{u^2 + 4})^2\right]/\left[1 + (u + \sqrt{u^2 + 4})^2\right],$$

where u is nonnegative, has the same sign as

$$-(u - \sqrt{u^2 + 4})^2 (1 + (u + \sqrt{u^2 + 4})^2) - (u + \sqrt{u^2 + 4})^2 (1 + (u + \sqrt{u^2 + 4})^2),$$

and therefore is nonpositive. The minimum of m is therefore $m(\alpha)$, concluding the proof.

Exercise 7.16 (Details of the Constructions of the Functions φ_i of Lemma 7.55).

Prove the following result corresponding to Lemma 7.55. Let Ω be a bounded open subset of $\mathbb{R}^N$. Then there exist functions φ_i for $i \in [1, N]$ in $\mathcal{D}(\Omega)$ such that

$$\forall i, j \in [1, N], \quad \int_\Omega \varphi_i(x)x_j dx = \delta_{ij} \quad \text{and} \quad \int_\Omega \varphi_i(x)dx = 0$$

and a function φ in $\mathcal{D}(\Omega)$ such that

$$\int_\Omega \varphi = 1 \quad \text{and} \quad \forall i \in [1, N], \quad \int_\Omega \varphi(x)x_i dx = 0.$$

Hints. Since the open set Ω is bounded in $L^2(\Omega)$, we see that the $N + 1$ functions x_0, x_i, where x_0 is the function $x \mapsto 1$ and the others are the coordinate functions, are linearly independent in $L^2(\Omega)$. Deduce that there exist functions $\zeta_i \in L^2(\Omega)$ such that the determinant

$$\det\left(\int \zeta_i(x)x_j dx\right)_{i,j \in [1, N+1]} \neq 0.$$

Next, use the density of $\mathcal{D}(\Omega)$ in $L^2(\Omega)$. Finally, look for functions of the form $\varphi_i = \sum_{k=0}^N a_{i,k}\zeta_k$.

Erratum

Erratum to: F. Demengel, G. Demengel,
*Functional Spaces for the Theory of Elliptic
Partial Differential Equations*, Universitext,
DOI 10.1007/978-1-4471-2807-6,
© Springer-Verlag London Limited 2012

In error, the title of this book was not correctly translated from the original French title. It should read as follows:

*Function Spaces for the Theory of Elliptic
Partial Differential Equations*

F. Demengel, G. Demengel, *Functional Spaces for the Theory
of Elliptic Partial Differential Equations*, Universitext,
DOI 10.1007/978-1-4471-2807-6_8,
© Springer-Verlag London Limited 2012

Appendix on Regularity

In this appendix, we will expand on results on the regularity of the solutions of certain elliptic PDEs that we studied in Chapter 5. We will, in particular, consider the solutions of the p-Laplacian equation.

Let us recall a result we used in Chapter 5 to show Vázquez's strong maximum principle. Let Ω be a bounded open subset of $\mathbb{R}^N$. Given a real number $p > 1$, let g be an element of $W^{1-1/p,p}(\Omega)$. The solution of the problem

$$(\text{A.1}) \qquad [\mathcal{L}ap]_0^p : \begin{cases} -\operatorname{div}(|\nabla u|^{p-2}\nabla u) = 0 & \text{in } \Omega, \\ u = g & \text{on } \partial\Omega, \end{cases}$$

is of class $\mathcal{C}^1$ inside Ω. This result is equivalent to the following one:

A solution u of $-\Delta_p u = 0$ in an open subset of $\mathbb{R}^N$ is of class $\mathcal{C}^1$ in that open set.

The steps needed to prove this general result are very long and rather difficult. They follow from different articles in the cases $p \leqslant 2$ and $p \geqslant 2$. The main part can be found in the articles by Evans [31], Moser [52], Tolksdorff [72], Lewis [46], and Di Benedetto [27].

Our aim is not to obtain the result that p-harmonic functions are $\mathcal{C}^1$ by adapting these proofs to the contents of this book. Taking into account earlier remarks, we have rather chosen to give a partial presentation of the arguments used by the authors mentioned above, insisting on *a priori* estimate and *fractional differentiation* arguments that can be used for those types of equations.

This appendix is therefore devoted to giving estimates for the typical problem of the so-called *p-harmonic* functions, that is, the solutions of $-\Delta_p u = 0$. We begin by giving L^∞ estimates, for which we need truncation methods and an iteration method by Moser, both of which can be followed quite easily.

F. Demengel, G. Demengel, *Functional Spaces for the Theory of Elliptic Partial Differential Equations*, Universitext, DOI 10.1007/978-1-4471-2807-6,

We then give $W^{1,k}$ estimates followed by $W^{1,\infty}$ estimates when $p \geqslant 2$, which are easier to deal with than the case $p \leqslant 2$. The latter requires additional precautions because of the singularity of the operator Δ_p.

A.1 L^∞ Estimate

A.1.1 Inclusion in $L^\infty(\Omega)$

We begin by showing that if the function giving the boundary condition is bounded, then the solution of the problem $[\mathcal{L}ap]_0^p$ (cf. Chapter 5) on a bounded open subset Ω of $\mathbb{R}^N$ of class $\mathcal{C}^1$ is also bounded.

Proposition A.2. *Let Ω be a bounded open subset of $\mathbb{R}^N$ of class $\mathcal{C}^1$. Let u be the solution in $W^{1,p}(\Omega)$ of the problem*

$$-\operatorname{div}(|\nabla u|^{p-2}\nabla u) = 0, \quad u = g \text{ on } \partial\Omega.$$

If g is a function in $L^\infty(\partial\Omega) \cap W^{1-1/p,p}(\partial\Omega)$, then the solution u belongs to $L^\infty(\Omega)$ and satisfies the inequalities

$$\min g \leqslant u \leqslant \max g.$$

Proof of Proposition A.2.
    We multiply the PDE by $(u - \max g)^+$, which is an element of $W_0^{1,p}(\Omega)$, and we use the generalized Green's formula to obtain

$$\int_\Omega \left(|\nabla u|^{p-2}\nabla u\right) \cdot \left(\nabla((u - \max g)^+)\right)dx = 0.$$

This implies the equality $\nabla((u - \max g)^+) = 0$ in Ω, whence $(u - \max g)^+ = C$ for some constant C. Since this function vanishes on the boundary, we deduce that $(u - \max g)^+ = 0$ in Ω, so that $u \leqslant \max g$. Multiplying the PDE by $(\min g - u)^+$, we obtain $u \geqslant \min g$ in the same manner. $\qquad\square$

A.1.2 Locally L^∞ Estimate

Proposition A.3. *Without conditions on the boundary, the solution of the problem $[\mathcal{L}ap]_0^p$, namely the p-harmonic u, satisfies*

$$u \in L_{\text{loc}}^\infty(\Omega) \quad \text{with} \quad \sup_{x \in B(x_0, R/2)} |u(x)| \leqslant C\|\nabla u\|_{L^p(B(x_0,R))}.$$

Proof of Proposition A.3.

- When $p > N$, the Sobolev embedding theorem tells us that $u \in L^\infty(\Omega)$, giving the first statement of the proposition.
- When $p = N$, the same theorem gives the inclusion $u \in L^q_{\mathrm{loc}}(\Omega)$ for every q with $p < q < +\infty$ (cf. proof of step E).
- When $p < N$, we first show that the p-harmonic function u belongs to $L^q_{\mathrm{loc}}(\Omega)$ for every $q > p$.

We use truncation. For $M > 1$, let

$$u_M = \sup(-M, \inf(u, M)).$$

It is obvious that $u_M \in W^{1,p}_0(\Omega) \cap L^\infty(\Omega)$ for every M.

Let us now consider the sequence of nonnegative real numbers $\{l_m\}_{n\in\mathbb{N}}$ with $l_0 = 0$ and $(2l_m + p)N/(N - p) = 2l_{m+1} + p$ for every $m \in \mathbb{N}^+$. This sequence is increasing and converges to $+\infty$. To show that $u \in L^q_{\mathrm{loc}}$ for every $q > p$, it therefore suffices to show that $u \in L^{l_m}_{\mathrm{loc}}$ for every integer m. This leads us to do an induction on the following property:

$$u \in L^{2l_m+p}_{\mathrm{loc}} \implies u \in L^{(2l_m+p)N/(N-p)}_{\mathrm{loc}}.$$

The initial step, for $m = 0$, follows from the Sobolev embedding theorem 2.31. For the sake of simplicity, we omit the index m in the rest of the proof; for example, l_m becomes l.

Let us consider $v_M = |u_M|^{2l}u_M$. On the one hand, since $|u_M|^{2l}$ is bounded and $u_M \in L^p(\Omega)$, we have $v_M \in L^p(\Omega)$. On the other hand, since the gradient $\nabla(u_M)$ is an element of L^p, which we see by differentiating in the sense of distributions, $\nabla(v_M)$ is the product of a bounded function with $\nabla(u_M)$, which belongs to $L^p(\Omega)$. We can deduce the inclusion $v_M \in W^{1,p}(\Omega)$ from these two results.

Let us multiply the equation of the p-Laplacian by $v_M\zeta^p$, where ζ is a regular function with values between 0 and 1. By the remark we made above on gradients, which implies that we should, in general, replace $|\nabla u|$ by the absolute value $|\nabla(u_M)|$ of the gradient in the products, Green's formula on Ω applied to the product

$$\mathrm{div}(|\nabla u_M|^{p-2}\nabla u_M)|u_M|^{2l}u_M\zeta^p$$

gives the inequality

$$(A.4) \quad (2l+1)\int_\Omega |\nabla u_M(x)|^p|u_M(x)|^{2l}\zeta^p dx$$
$$\leqslant p\int_\Omega \zeta^{p-1}|\nabla\zeta||\nabla u_M|^{p-1}|u_M(x)|^{2l+1}dx.$$

Applying Hölder's inequality to the right-hand side pB of (A.4), we find that for an arbitrary nonnegative real number a, we have

$$pB \leqslant p\Big(a \int_\Omega |\nabla u_M|^p |u_M|^{2l} \zeta^p dx\Big)^{1/p} \Big(a^{-p'/p} \int_\Omega |u_M|^{2l+p} |\nabla\zeta|^p dx\Big)^{1/p'}.$$

Next, for $a = 1/2$, we use a mean value inequality, giving a constant c depending only on p and on universal data, such that

$$pB \leqslant \frac{1}{2}\Big[\int_\Omega |\nabla u_M|^p |u_M|^{2l} \zeta^p dx\Big] + c\Big[\int_\Omega |u_M|^{2l+p} |\nabla\zeta|^p dx\Big].$$

The inequality (A.4) can then be written as

$$(\mathrm{A}.5) \quad (2l + 1/2) \int_\Omega |\nabla u_M(x)|^p |u_M(x)|^{2l} \zeta^p dx \leqslant c\Big[\int_\Omega |u_M|^{2l+p} |\nabla\zeta|^p dx\Big].$$

We note that $|\nabla u_M|^p u_M^{2l}$ can be written as $(p/(2l + p))^p |\nabla(|u_M|^{2l/p} u_M)|^p$. The function $w = |u_M|^{2l/p} u_M \zeta$ belongs to $W^{1,p}$ and its gradient satisfies $\nabla w = \zeta \nabla(|u_M|^{2l/p} u_M) + |u_M|^{2l/p} u_M \nabla\zeta$. Using Minkowski's inequality and the discrete Hölder inequality, it follows that

$$\|\nabla w\|_p^p \leqslant 2^{p/p'} \Big[\big\|\zeta\nabla(|u_M|^{2l/p} u_M)\big\|_p^p + \big\||u_M|^{2l/p} u_M \nabla\zeta\big\|_p^p\Big].$$

Noting that $(4l + 1)(p/(2l + p))^p$ is bounded from above by a constant depending only on p, equation (A.5) gives

$$\frac{(2l + 1/2)p^p}{(2l + p)^p} \int_{\mathbb{R}^N} |\nabla(|u_M|^{2l/p} u_M \zeta)|^p \leqslant C \int_{\mathbb{R}^N} |u_M|^{2l+p} |\nabla\zeta|^p.$$

Let us now use reasoning that combines the Sobolev inequality and that of Poincaré: since $w \in W^{1,p}(\Omega)$ and $p < N$, we can use the Sobolev embedding theorem to deduce the inequality $\|w\|_{L^{pN/(N-p)}} \leqslant C\|w\|_{W^{1,p}}$. Moreover, since ζ has compact support, the Poincaré inequality gives $\|w\|_{W^{1,p}} \leqslant C'\|\nabla w\|_{L^p}$. Combining these inequalities to obtain a lower bound for the left-hand side of (A.5), we find

$$(\mathrm{A}.6) \quad \frac{(2l + 1/2)p^p}{(2l + p)^p} \Big(\int_{\mathbb{R}^N} \big(|u_M|^{(2l/p)+1} \zeta\big)^{Np/N-p} dx\Big)^{(N-p)/N}$$
$$\leqslant K \int_{\mathbb{R}^N} |u_M|^{2l+p} |\nabla\zeta|^p dx.$$

Next, we use the induction hypothesis, namely that $u \in L_{\mathrm{loc}}^{2l+p}$. Since $0 \leqslant \zeta \leqslant 1$, we have $\zeta^{(2l+p)N/(N-p)} \leqslant \zeta^{Np/(N-p)}$. Consequently, we can take the right-limit of the previous inequality for $M \to +\infty$. Setting $C_{l,p} = (2l + 1/2)p^p/(2l + p)^p$, we obtain the relation

$$C_{l,p} \varlimsup_{M \to +\infty} \|u_M \zeta\|_{(2l+p)N/(N-p)}^{2l+p} \leqslant K \int_\Omega |u|^{p+2l} |\nabla\zeta|^p dx.$$

Both Fatou's lemma and the monotone convergence theorem ensure us that $u \in L_{\text{loc}}^{(2l+p)N/(N-p)}(\Omega)$, concluding the induction argument.

We have thus proved that for every $q > p$, the function u is an element of $L_{\text{loc}}^q(\Omega)$.

Next, we wish to show that u is an element of L_{loc}^∞. We will work the case $p < N$ out in detail. A remark at the end of the proof will make it possible to easily adapt the proof to the case $p = N$.

During the proof we will use uniform upper bounds for the gradients of regular functions with values between 0 and 1 whose supports form a nondecreasing sequence of compact sets. We have the following result.

Lemma A.7. *Let R and σ be two positive numbers. There exists a function ζ in $\mathcal{D}(B(0, R + \sigma))$ equal to 1 on $B(0, R)$, with values between 0 and 1, and such that*

$$|\nabla \zeta| \leqslant \frac{C}{\sigma}$$

for a universal constant C.

Proof of Lemma A.7.

Let φ be an even function on $\mathbb{R}$ with support in $\{|t| \leqslant 2\}$ that equals 1 on $\{|t| \leqslant 1\}$. We define the following radial function:

$$\zeta(x) = \varphi\big(|x|/\sigma + (1 - R/\sigma)\big).$$

The function ζ clearly has support in $B(0, R + \sigma)$ and equals 1 on $B(0, R)$. Moreover, we have

$$|\nabla\zeta(x)| = \left| \frac{x}{|x|\sigma} \varphi'\big(|x|/\sigma + (1 - R/\sigma)\big) \right| \leqslant \frac{1}{\sigma}\|\varphi'\|_\infty,$$

which concludes the proof. $\qquad\square$

Let us return to the estimate of Proposition A.3. We suppose that $x_0 \in \Omega$ and that R satisfies $B(x_0, R) \Subset \Omega$. We will show that $u \in L^\infty(B(x_0, R/2))$. To do this, we define sequences $\{k_m\}$, $\{R_m\}$, and $\{l_m\}$ (the latter has already been defined above):

$$k_m = \left(\frac{N}{N-p}\right)^m p, \ 2l_m + p = k_m = \frac{N}{N-p}(p + 2l_{m-1}), \ R_m = \frac{R}{2}(1 + 1/2^m).$$

We also define a regular function ζ_m with values between 0 and 1 that equals 1 on $B(x_0, R_{m+1})$, has support in $B(x_0, R_m)$, and whose gradient satisfies $|\nabla\zeta_m| \leqslant C/(R_m - R_{m+1}) \leqslant 2^m C'/R$ by the previous lemma.

Finally, let

$$\alpha_m = \left(\int_{B(x_0, R_m)} |u|^{k_m} \zeta_m^{Np/(N-p)} dx \right)^{1/k_m}.$$

From the previous inequalities, we deduce that there exists a constant K^* such that

(A.8) $$\alpha_{m+1} \leqslant \left(K^* \frac{k_m^p}{k_m + 1/2 - p}\right)^{1/k_m} \alpha_m.$$

Indeed, let

$$B_m = B(x_0, R_m) \quad \text{and} \quad I_m = \int_{B(x_0, R_m)} |u|^{k_m} (\zeta_m)^{Np/(N-p)} dx,$$

whence

$$I_{m+1} = \int_{B_{m+1}} \left(|u|^{1+2l_m/p} \zeta_{m+1}\right)^{Np/(N-p)} dx.$$

By taking the $(N-p)/N$th power and replacing ζ by the function ζ_{m+1}, which has the same properties as ζ, inequality (A.6) gives

$$(I_{m+1})^{(N-p)/N} \leqslant \frac{K}{C_{l_m,p}} \left(\int_{B_{m+1}} |u|^{k_m} |\nabla \zeta_{m+1}|^p \, dx\right)$$

and even, by using the upper bound for the gradient,

$$(I_{m+1})^{(N-p)/N} \leqslant \frac{K}{C_{l_m,p}} C'^p \frac{2^{(m+1)p}}{R^p} \left(\int_{B_{m+1}} |u|^{k_m} \, dx\right).$$

Since $\zeta_m = 1$ on B_{m+1}, the last integral may be replaced by the integral $\int_{B_{m+1}} |u|^{k_m} \zeta_m^{N/(N-p)} dx$. Finally, since $B_{m+1} \subset B_m$, we can bound this from above by the integral of the same function over B_m. It follows that

$$(I_{m+1})^{(N-p)/N} \leqslant \frac{K}{C_{l_m,p}} C'^p \frac{2^{(m+1)p}}{R^p} \left(\int_{B_m} |u|^{k_m} \zeta_m^{N/(N-p)} dx\right).$$

Note that $1/k_{m+1} = [(N-p)/N] \cdot [1/k_m]$, so that this inequality taken to the power $1/k_m$ leads to the relation

$$\alpha_{m+1} = [I_{m+1}]^{1/k_m} \leqslant K_m \alpha_m$$

in which

$$K_m = \left[\frac{K}{C_{l_m,p}} C'^p \frac{2^{(m+1)p}}{R^p}\right]^{1/k_m}.$$

Since $\left[KC'^p 2^{(m+1)p}/R^p\right]^{1/k_m}$ is bounded by K^*, which is independent of l, and

$$[C_{l_m,p}]^{1/k_m} = \left(\frac{k_m^p}{(k_m - p + 1/2)p^p}\right)^{1/k_m},$$

we obtain (A.8).

By iterating this relation, we obtain

$$\alpha_{m+1} \leqslant \alpha_0 \exp\Big[\sum_0^m \frac{\ln(K^*) + p\ln(k_j) - \ln(k_j - p + 1/2)}{k_j}\Big].$$

Since $\{k_j\}$ is a geometric progression with common ratio > 1, the sequence with general term $(\ln(K^*) + p\ln(k_j) - \ln(k_j - p + 1/2))k_j^{-1}$ converges. Consequently, we have $\alpha_m \leqslant K'\alpha_0$ for every m. By taking the limit for $m \to +\infty$, we obtain

$$\|u\|_{L^\infty(B(x_0,R/2))} \leqslant K \|u\|_{L^p(B(x_0,R))}. \qquad \square$$

Remark A.9. When $p = N$, we multiply by $|u|^{2l}u\zeta^p$ and use the Sobolev embedding of $W^{1,N}$ in L^q for a fixed $q > p$. The sequence k_m is then defined to be $(q/p)^m p$ and $2l_m + p = k_m = q/p(p + 2l_{m-1})$.

Remark A.10. Let β be a nondecreasing function with $\beta(0) = 0$ and $|\beta(x)| \leqslant C|x|^{p-1}$. The previous estimate then also holds for a solution $u \in W^{1,p}(\Omega)$ of

$$-\Delta_p u + \beta(u) = 0$$

in Ω.

It suffices to disregard the term $\int_\Omega \beta(u)|u_M|^{2l}u_M\zeta^p dx$, which is nonnegative, when multiplying the equation by $|u_M|^{2l}u_M\zeta^p$.

A.2 $W^{1,k}$ and $W^{1,\infty}$ Estimates When $p \geqslant 2$

In this section, we assume that $p \geqslant 2$. We first differentiate the equation of the p-Laplacian formally with respect to the variable x_i. This corresponds to considering u as a regular function. This technique will be justified by using the discrete derivative, that is, by replacing the expression $-\partial_i(\Delta_p u)$ by $(-\Delta_p u^h + \Delta_p u)/h$, where $h = he_i$, and a generalization of this for all derivatives.

We begin with estimates for $\|\nabla u\|_k$, for arbitrary $k > p$.

A.2.1 Estimates for ∇u in $W^{1,k}$

In the following computations, the symbol C denotes constants that can differ from one line to the next. These different values depend only on N, p, Ω and on universal data. Moreover, we may, and do, suppose that $N \geqslant 3$, in which case we pass to the next step of the induction we are using by considering the qth power of $\|\nabla u\|_p^p$ for $q = N/(N-2)$. When $N = 2$, we will replace this exponent by an arbitrary real number $q > 1$. In a first step, we multiply the equation $\partial_i(-\Delta_p u) = 0$ by $\zeta^2 \partial_i u$, where ζ is a regular function with values between 0 and 1, giving a first local estimate for the gradient in $W^{1,k}$ with $k = pN/(N-2)$ (this is the aim of Proposition A.11). In the next step, we take the analogous inequalities obtained by multiplying the same differential equation by $\zeta^2 |\partial_i u|^{2l} \partial_i u$. By induction, we thus obtain Proposition A.11, which gives a local estimate for the gradient in $W^{1,k}$ for arbitrary k.

Proposition A.11. *Let u be a regular solution of $-\Delta_p u = 0$ in Ω. Then for every $\rho > 0$ and every $\sigma > 0$, we have the following local estimate for u in $W^{1,k}$ with $k = pN/(N-2)$:*

$$\text{(A.12)} \qquad \left(\int_{B(0,\rho)} |\nabla u|^{pN/(N-2)} \, dx \right)^{(N-2)/N} \leqslant \frac{C}{\sigma^2} \int_{B(0,\rho+\sigma)} |\nabla u|^p dx,$$

which can also be written as

$$\text{(A.13)} \qquad \|\nabla u\|_{L^k(B(0,\rho))} \leqslant C(p,\rho,\sigma) \|\nabla u\|_{L^p(B(0,\rho+\sigma))}.$$

Proof of Proposition A.11. Let us first note that by exchanging the derivatives, expressing the identity $\partial_i(-\Delta_p u) = 0$ leads to

$$0 = \partial_i \partial_j (|\nabla u|^{p-2} u_{,j}) = \partial_j(|\nabla u|^{p-2} u_{,ij} + (p-2)|\nabla u|^{p-4} u_{,ki} u_{,k} u_{,j}).$$

As above, we multiply this relation by $(\partial_i u)\zeta^2$. Integrating over $\mathbb{R}^N$ and applying Green's formula, we obtain

$$\int_{\mathbb{R}^N} |\nabla u|^{p-2} |\partial_i \nabla u|^2 \zeta^2 + (p-2) \int_{\mathbb{R}^N} |\nabla u|^{p-4} (\partial_i \nabla u \cdot \nabla u)^2 \zeta^2$$
$$\leqslant 2p \int_{\mathbb{R}^N} |\nabla u|^{p-2} (|\partial_i \nabla u \cdot \nabla u|)\zeta |\partial_i \zeta|.$$

By taking the absolute values and disregarding the second term of the left-hand side, which is nonnegative because $p \geqslant 2$, we see that

$$\text{(A.14)} \qquad \int_{\mathbb{R}^N} |\nabla u|^{p-2} |\partial_i \nabla u|^2 \zeta^2 \leqslant 2p \int_{\mathbb{R}^N} |\nabla u|^{p-2} |\partial_i \nabla u| \, |\nabla u| \, |\zeta| \, |\partial_i \zeta|.$$

We apply Schwarz's inequality to the right-hand side:

$$\left[\int_{\mathbb{R}^N} |\nabla u|^{(p-2)/2} |\partial_i \nabla u| \, |\nabla u|^{p/2} |\partial_i \zeta| \, |\zeta| \, dx \right]^2$$
$$\leqslant \left(\int_{\mathbb{R}^N} |\nabla u|^{p-2} |\partial_i \nabla u|^2 |\zeta|^2 \, dx \right) \left(\int_{\mathbb{R}^N} |\nabla u|^p |\partial_i \zeta|^2 \, dx \right).$$

Applying the *Young type* inequality, which we will use several times, for a suitable choice of ε, we find

$$\text{(*)} \qquad \forall \varepsilon > 0, \quad |ab| \leqslant \varepsilon \frac{a^2}{4} + \frac{1}{\varepsilon} b^2,$$

so that relation (A.14) becomes

$$\int_{\mathbb{R}^N} |\nabla u|^{p-2} |\partial_i \nabla u|^2 \zeta^2 \leqslant \frac{1}{2} \int_{\mathbb{R}^N} |\nabla u|^{p-2} |\partial_i \nabla u|^2 \zeta^2 + c \int_{\mathbb{R}^N} |\nabla u|^p |\partial_i \zeta|^2.$$

Consequently, for a constant $C > 0$, we have

$$(A.15) \qquad \int_{\mathbb{R}^N} |\nabla u|^{p-2} |\partial_i \nabla u|^2 \zeta^2 \leqslant C \int_{\mathbb{R}^N} |\nabla u|^p |\partial_i \zeta|^2.$$

We note that the left-hand side of (A.15) equals the expression

$$\frac{4}{p^2} \int_{\mathbb{R}^N} \zeta^2 \big(\partial_i (|\nabla u|^{(p-2)/2} \nabla u) \big)^2 dx.$$

Given the formula for the derivative of a product, this last integral can be written as

$$\int_{\mathbb{R}^N} \big[\partial_i (|\nabla u|^{(p-2)/2} \nabla u \zeta) - (|\nabla u|^{(p-2)/2} \nabla u \partial_i \zeta) \big]^2 dx.$$

Expanding this square of a difference and applying inequality (∗) to the corresponding double product, for a suitable ε, we obtain a lower bound for the left-hand side of (A.15) that gives us the inequality

$$(A.16) \qquad \int_{\mathbb{R}^N} \big| \partial_i (|\nabla u|^{(p-2)/2} \nabla u \zeta) \big|^2 dx \leqslant C \int_{\mathbb{R}^N} |\nabla u|^p |\partial_i \zeta|^2 dx.$$

Taking the sum of this inequality over i then leads to

$$(A.17) \qquad \int_{\mathbb{R}^N} \big[\nabla (|\nabla u|^{(p-2)/2} \nabla u \zeta) \big]^2 \leqslant C \int_{\mathbb{R}^N} |\nabla u|^p |\nabla \zeta|^2 dx.$$

Let us now consider the function $\zeta |\nabla u|^{(p-2)/2} \nabla u$. Since $N > 2$, the Sobolev embedding theorem allows us to write the following inequality at the critical exponent $2N/(N-2)$:

$$\big\| \zeta |\nabla u|^{(p-2)/2} \nabla u \big\|_{2N/(N-2)} \leqslant C \big\| \zeta |\nabla u|^{(p-2)/2} \nabla u \big\|_{H^1(\mathbb{R}^N)}.$$

Moreover, since the function ζ has compact support, we can use the Poincaré inequality to determine the upper bound, giving

$$(A.18) \qquad \big\| \zeta |\nabla u|^{(p-2)/2} \nabla u \big\|_{2N/(N-2)} \leqslant C \big\| \nabla (\zeta |\nabla u|^{(p-2)/2} \nabla u) \big\|_2.$$

Applying inequality (A.17), we find

$$(A.19) \qquad \left(\int_{\mathbb{R}^N} (|\nabla u|^p \zeta^2)^{N/(N-2)} dx \right)^{(N-2)/N} \leqslant C \int_{\mathbb{R}^N} |\nabla u|^p |\nabla \zeta|^2 dx.$$

Let us now assume that the regular function ζ takes on its values between 0 and 1, has support in $B(0, \rho + \sigma)$, and equals 1 in $B(0, \rho)$. Then, using the usual upper bound for the gradient $\nabla \zeta$ (cf. Lemma A.7), the above implies the desired result:

$$(A.20) \quad \left(\int_{B(0,\rho)} |\nabla u|^{pN/(N-2)} dx \right)^{(N-2)/N} \leq \frac{C}{\sigma^2} \int_{B(0,\rho+\sigma)} |\nabla u|^p dx. \qquad \square$$

Proposition A.21. *Let u be a regular solution of $-\Delta_p u = 0$. Then for every $\rho > 0$ and for every $\sigma > 0$, there exists a constant C depending only on ρ, σ, p, and l, such that*

$$(A.22) \quad \|\nabla u\|_{L^{(p+2l)N/(N-2)}(B(0,\rho))} \leq \frac{C}{\sigma^2} \|\nabla u\|_{L^{p+2l}(B(0,\rho+\sigma))}.$$

Proof of Proposition A.21.

This time, we multiply the derivative with respect to x_i of the equation of the p-Laplacian by $\zeta^2 |\partial_i u|^{2l} \partial_i u$. By computations similar to the preceding ones, generalizing to the case related to $l = 0$, in particular the passage from (A.15) to (A.17), we obtain

$$\frac{4(2l+1)}{(2l+p)^2} \int_{\mathbb{R}^N} \left| \nabla(|\nabla u|^{p/2+l-1} \nabla u \zeta) \right|^2 dx \leq C \int_{\mathbb{R}^N} |\nabla u|^{p+2l} |\nabla \zeta|^2.$$

Once more using the combination of the Poincaré and Sobolev inequalities, the previous inequalities remain valid when we replace p by $p + 2l$ in each of the integrals. Setting $C_{l,p}^* = 4(2l+1)/(2l+p)^2$, we then obtain inequality (A.23), which, up to a coefficient, equals inequality (A.19) with p replaced by $p + 2l$, namely:

$$(A.23) \quad C_{l,p}^* \left(\int_{\mathbb{R}^N} \left(|\nabla u|^{(p+2l)} \zeta^2 \right)^{N/(N-2)} dx \right)^{N-2/N}$$
$$\leq C \int_{\mathbb{R}^N} |\nabla u|^{(p+2l)} |\nabla \zeta|^2 dx.$$

Using a regular function ζ equal 1 in $B(0, \rho)$ and with support in $B(0, \rho + \sigma)$, we deduce an upper bound analogous to (A.20):

$$(A.24) \quad C_{l,p}^* \left(\int_{B(0,\rho)} |\nabla u|^{(p+2l)N/(N-2)} dx \right)^{(N-2)/N}$$
$$\leq \frac{C}{\sigma^2} \int_{B(0,\rho+\sigma)} |\nabla u|^{(p+2l)} dx. \qquad \square$$

For an arbitrary integer l, these inequalities allow us to bound ∇u in L^q_{loc} for $q = (p+2l)N/N - 2$, from above by its norm in L^{p+2l}_{loc}. They will allow us to determine local estimates for the gradient in L^∞.

A.2.2 Estimate for the Gradient in L^∞_{loc}

Proposition A.25. *Let u be a p-harmonic function on $\mathbb{R}^N$. Then for every point x_0 and every $R > 0$, the gradient of u, which belongs to L^∞_{loc}, satisfies the inequality*

$$\sup\{|\nabla u(x)|^p \mid x \in B(x_0, R/2)\} \leqslant C \int_{B(x_0, R)} |\nabla u|^p dx.$$

Proof of Proposition A.25.

We use formula (A.24). To do this, as in Subsection A.1.2, we define the sequence $k_m = (2l_m + p) = (2l_{m-1} + p)N/(N-2)$ whose first term k_0 corresponds to $l_0 = 0$. This is a geometric progression with common ratio $N/(N-2) > 1$. One can assume that $x_0 = 0$. We also define the sequence $\{R_m\}$ by setting $R_m = (R/2)(1 + 2^{-m})$. We set

$$\alpha_m = \left(\int_{B(0, R_m)} |\nabla u|^{k_m} dx\right)^{1/k_m},$$

whence, by a computation analogous to that leading to (A.8),

$$\alpha_{m+1} \leqslant \left(\frac{Ck_m^2}{(k_m + 1 - p)4}\right)^{1/k_m} \alpha_m.$$

Using the infinite product $\prod_{m=0}^\infty \left(\frac{Ck_m^2}{(k_m + 1 - p)4}\right)^{1/k_m}$, which is convergent because $\{k_m\}$ is a geometric progression with common ratio > 1, we obtain

$$\varlimsup_{m \to +\infty} \left(\int_{B(0, R/2)} |\nabla u|^{k_m} dx\right)^{1/k_m} \leqslant \varlimsup_{m \to +\infty} \alpha_m \leqslant C\alpha_0,$$

giving the desired inequality. $\square$

A.2.3 Justification of the Formal Derivative for a Nonregular Function

Instead of differentiating with respect to x_i, we use a discrete differentiation with translation step $\vec{h} = he_i$. Instead of the equation, we write

(A.26)
$$\frac{-\Delta_p u^h + \Delta_p u}{h} = 0,$$

where u^h denotes the translation of u in the direction $\vec{h}$.

Outline of the Method. It is analogous to those used previously.

We first multiply equation (A.26) by $((u^h - u)/h)\zeta^2$ and integrate over the open set Ω. We can easily see that

$$(|\nabla u^h|^{p-2}\nabla u^h - |\nabla u|^{p-2}\nabla u) \cdot ((\nabla u^h - \nabla u)\zeta^2) \geqslant 0.$$

We thus obtain the inequality

$$(A.27) \quad \int_{\mathbb{R}^N} (|\nabla u^h|^{p-2}\nabla u^h - |\nabla u|^{p-2}\nabla u) \cdot ((\nabla u^h - \nabla u)\zeta^2) dx$$
$$\leqslant 2 \int_{\mathbb{R}^N} \left| (|\nabla u^h|^{p-2}\nabla u^h - |\nabla u|^{p-2}\nabla u) \cdot ((u^h - u)\zeta\nabla\zeta) \right| dx.$$

From this inequality, we deduce the formula

$$(A.28) \quad \left(\int_{\mathbb{R}^N} |\nabla u|^{pN/(N-2)}\zeta^{2N/(N-2)} \right)^{(N-2)/N} \leqslant C \int_{\mathbb{R}^N} |\nabla u|^p |\nabla\zeta|^2.$$

In a second step, we multiply equality (A.26) by the function $\zeta^2 |(u^h - u)/h|^{2l}(u^h - u)/h$. We set

$$D_h(u) = (|\nabla u^h|^{p-2}\nabla u^h - |\nabla u|^{p-2}\nabla u).$$

As in the previous step, we note that

$$|u^h - u|^{2l} D_h(u) \cdot (\nabla u_h - \nabla u)\zeta^2$$

is nonnegative. Consequently, Green's formula gives the inequality

$$(A.29) \quad (2l+1) \int_{\Omega} |u^h - u|^{2l} D_h(u) \cdot (\nabla u_h - \nabla u)\zeta^2 dx$$
$$\leqslant 2 \int_{\Omega} |D_h(u)| |u^h - u|^{2l+1}\zeta|\nabla\zeta| dx.$$

From this, computations similar to those of the first step allow us to establish on the one hand, that if $\nabla u \in L^{(p+2l)/2}$, then this gradient belongs to $L^{(p+2l)N/(N-2)}$ and on the other hand, that the corresponding norm satisfies

$$(A.30) \quad \frac{4(2l+1)}{(p+2l)^2} \left(\int_{\mathbb{R}^N} |\nabla u|^{(p+2l)N/N-2}\zeta^{2N/(N-2)} dx \right)^{(N-2)/N}$$
$$\leqslant C \int_{\mathbb{R}^N} |\nabla u|^{p+2l}|\nabla\zeta|^2 dx,$$

which generalizes equation (A.28). This establishes an induction, with initial step (A.28).

First Step. In order to bound the right-hand side of (A.27) from above, we use the vector function $|t|^{1-2/p}t$. By applying the mean value theorem to it for the vectors t and t', we can write

$$\left||t|^{1-2/p}t - |t'|^{1-2/p}t'\right| \leqslant (2-2/p)\left(|t| + |t'|\right)^{1-2/p}|t - t'|.$$

By taking $t = |x|^{(p-2)/2}x$ and $t' = |y|^{(p-2)/2}y$ for two given vectors x and y in $\mathbb{R}^N$, we obtain the inequality

(A.31) $\left||x|^{p-2}x - |y|^{p-2}y\right|$

$$= \left|\left||x|^{p/2-1}x\right|^{(p-2)/p}|x|^{p/2-1}x - \left||y|^{p/2-1}y\right|^{(p-2)/p}|y|^{p/2-1}y\right|$$

$$\leqslant (2-2/p)\left(|x|^{p/2} + |y|^{p/2}\right)^{(p-2)/p}\left||x|^{p/2-1}x - |y|^{p/2-1}y\right|.$$

We set

$$A_h(u) = \int_{\mathbb{R}^N} \left(|\nabla u^h|^{p-2}\nabla u^h - |\nabla u|^{p-2}\nabla u\right) \cdot \left((\nabla u^h - \nabla u)\zeta^2\right) dx$$

and

$$A_h'(u) = 2\int_{\mathbb{R}^N} \left(|\nabla u^h|^{p-2}\nabla u^h - |\nabla u|^{p-2}\nabla u\right) \cdot \left((u^h - u)\zeta\nabla\zeta\right) dx.$$

We wish to bound $A_h'(u)$ from above and $A_h(u)$ from below.

Using inequality (A.30) with vectors $x = \nabla u$ and $y = \nabla u^h$ and the inequality $(4 - 4/p)ab \leqslant \varepsilon a^2 + C_\varepsilon b^2$, where $\varepsilon > 0$ will be chosen later on depending on the upper bounds we have found, we can write the right-hand side $A_h'(u)$ of (A.27) as

$$A_h'(u) \leqslant 2\int_\Omega |D_h(u)|\,|u^h - u|\,\zeta\,|\nabla\zeta|\,dx$$

$$\leqslant (4 - 4/p)\left[\int_{\mathbb{R}^N} \left(|\nabla u|^{p/2} + |\nabla u^h|^{p/2}\right)^{(p-2)/p}\right.$$

$$\left.\left||\nabla u^h|^{(p-2)/2}\nabla u^h - |\nabla u|^{(p-2)/2}\nabla u\right|\,|u^h - u|\,|\zeta|\,|\nabla\zeta|dx\right],$$

whence

$$A_h'(u) \leqslant \varepsilon\int_{\mathbb{R}^N} \left||\nabla u^h|^{(p-2)/2}\nabla u^h - |\nabla u|^{(p-2)/2}\nabla u\right|^2 |\zeta|^2\,dx$$

$$+ C_\varepsilon\int_{\mathbb{R}^N} \left(|\nabla u|^{p/2} + |\nabla u^h|^{p/2}\right)^{2(1-2/p)}|u^h - u|^2\,|\nabla\zeta|^2\,dx.$$

Next, using the inequality

(A.32) $$\left(a^{p/2} + b^{p/2}\right)^{2/p} \leqslant C\left(a^{p-2} + b^{p-2}\right)^{1/(p-2)},$$

we obtain

$$(A.33) \quad A'_h(u) \leqslant \varepsilon \int_{\mathbb{R}^N} \left| |\nabla u^h|^{(p-2)/2} \nabla u^h - |\nabla u|^{(p-2)/2} \nabla u \right|^2 |\zeta|^2 \, dx$$

$$+ C_\varepsilon \int_{\mathbb{R}^N} \left(|\nabla u|^{p-2} + |\nabla u^h|^{p-2} \right) |u^h - u|^2 |\nabla \zeta|^2 \, dx.$$

For the sake of simplicity, we will, from now on, keep the notation $x = \nabla u$ and $y = \nabla u^h$. Moreover, we set

$$B_h(u) = \int_{\mathbb{R}^N} \left| |x|^{(p-2)/2} x - |y|^{(p-2)/2} y \right|^2 \zeta^2 \, dx,$$

$$C_h(u) = \int_{\mathbb{R}^N} \left[|x|^{p-2} + |y|^{p-2} \right] |u^h - u|^2 |\nabla \zeta|^2 \, dx.$$

Inequality (A.27) then becomes

$$|A_h(u)| \leqslant 2\varepsilon B_h(u) + 2C_\varepsilon C_h(u).$$

Let us continue by bounding $A_h(u)$ from below by an expression that is proportional to $B_h(u)$. This will then allow us to bound $B_h(u)$ from above by $C_h(u)$, up to a multiplicative constant. We use the following result for the lower bound.

Lemma A.34. *Let p be a real number $\geqslant 2$. There exists a constant $c_p > 0$ depending only on p, such that for every pair (x, y) of elements of $\mathbb{R}^N$, we have*

$$(A.35) \qquad (|x|^{p-2}x - |y|^{p-2}y) \cdot (x - y) \geqslant c_p \left| |x|^{(p-2)/2}x - |y|^{(p-2)/2}y \right|^2,$$

which in turn implies that $A_h(u) \geqslant c_p B_h(u)$.

Proof of Lemma A.34.

After dividing by $|x|^p$, if necessary, we may, and do, assume that x has norm 1.

Case Where $|x - y| \geqslant 1/2$. Let us use a contradiction argument. We suppose that there exist sequences $\{x_n\}$ and $\{y_n\}$ with $|x_n| = 1$, $|x_n - y_n| \geqslant 1/2$, and the following inequality, which implies that $\{y_n\}$ is bounded:

$$(1 + |y_n|^p - (x_n \cdot y_n)(1 + |y_n|^{p-2}) \leqslant \frac{1}{n} \left(1 + |y_n|^p - 2(x_n \cdot y_n)|y_n|^{(p-2)/2} \right).$$

We can then extract subsequences from x_n and y_n such that $x_n \to x$ with $|x| = 1$ and $y_n \to y$. By taking the limit in the inequality above, we obtain

$$(1 + |y|^p - (x \cdot y)(1 + |y|^{p-2})) \leqslant 0,$$

which can also be written as

$$(|x|^{p-2}x - |y|^{p-2}y) \cdot (x - y) \leqslant 0.$$

Now, by using the strict convexity of the function $x \mapsto |x|^p$, this inequality implies that $y = x$, giving a contradiction with $|x - y| > 1/2$. Inequality (A.35) follows.

Case Where $|x - y| < 1/2$. In this case, $|y| > 1/2$. We begin by showing (A.35) in the scalar case. If $x = 1$, then $y \in [1/2, 3/2]$ and if $x = -1$, then the situation is symmetric with respect to 0. In the scalar case, we reduce to proving that

$$(A.36) \qquad \forall y \in [1/2, 1], \quad (1 - y^{p-1})(1 - y) \geqslant \frac{(p-1)2^{4-p}}{p^2}(1 - y^{p/2})^2.$$

Indeed, by replacing y by $1/y$, this inequality remains true when $y \in [1, 2]$, and in particular when $y \in [1, 3/2]$.

In order to prove (A.36), we use the mean value theorem for the function $y \mapsto y^{p-1}$, and then for the function $y \mapsto y^{p/2}$. This leads to

$$(1 - |y|^{p-1})(1 - y) = (p - 1)(1 + \theta(y - 1))^{p-2}(1 - y)^2$$
$$\geqslant (p - 1)(1/2)^{p-2}(1 - y)^2$$

and $\qquad (1 - |y|^{p/2})^2 = (p/2)^2(1 + \theta'(y - 1))^{p-2}(1 - y)^2 \leqslant \frac{p^2}{4}(1 - y)^2,$

for real numbers θ and θ' in $]0, 1[$, and consequently (A.36).

Let us now prove inequality (A.35) in the vectorial case, again for $|x| = 1$ and $|y| > 1/2$, where the constant c_p is defined by $c_p = [(p - 1)/p^2]2^{4-p}$. By using, in particular, inequality (A.36) applied to the scalar function $Y = (1 - |y|^{p-1})(1 - |y|)$, we obtain

$$(|x|^{p-2}x - |y|^{p-2}y) \cdot (x - y) = Y + (|y| - x \cdot y)(1 + |y|^{p-2})$$
$$\geqslant c_p(1 - |y|^{p/2})^2 + (|y| - x \cdot y)(1 + |y|^{p-2})$$
$$= c_p\left||x|^{(p-2)/2}x - |y|^{(p-2)/2}y\right|^2 + 2c_p|y|^{(p-2)/2}(x \cdot y - |y|)$$
$$+ (|y| - x \cdot y)(1 + |y|^{p-2})$$
$$= c_p\left||x|^{(p-2)/2}x - |y|^{(p-2)/2}y\right|^2$$
$$+ (|y| - x \cdot y)(1 + |y|^{p-2} - 2c_p|y|^{(p-2)/2})$$
$$\geqslant c_p\left||x|^{(p-2)/2}x - |y|^{(p-2)/2}y\right|^2,$$

since we have, on the one hand, the inequality $|x \cdot y| \leqslant |y|$ and on the other hand, the inequality $2c_p|y|^{(p-2)/2} \leqslant 1 + |y|^{p-2}$ because c_p is less than 1. This concludes the proof of the lemma. $\square$

Let us return to Proposition A.25. Recall that the notation h in fact denotes he_i. By the lemma, the inequality $A_h(u) \leqslant 2\varepsilon B_h(u) + 2C_\varepsilon C_h(u)$ becomes $(c_p - 2\varepsilon)B_h(u) \leqslant 2C_\varepsilon C_h(u)$. In other words, since ε may be chosen $< c_p/2$, we may conclude that there exists a constant C such that $B_h(u) \leqslant CC_h(u)$. Dividing by h^2 then gives

$$\frac{B_h(u)}{h^2} = \int_{\mathbb{R}^N} \left| \frac{|\nabla u^h|^{(p-2)/2}\nabla u^h - |\nabla u|^{(p-2)/2}\nabla u}{h} \right|^2 \zeta^2$$

$$\leqslant C \int_{\mathbb{R}^N} (|\nabla u|^{p-2} + |\nabla u^h|^{p-2}) \left| \frac{u^h - u}{h} \right|^2 |\nabla\zeta|^2,$$

which can also be written as

$$(*) \quad \frac{B_h(u)}{h^2} \leqslant C \int_{\mathbb{R}^N} |\nabla u|^{p-2} \left| \frac{u^h - u}{h} \right|^2 |\nabla\zeta|^2 + C \int_{\mathbb{R}^N} |\nabla u^h|^{p-2} \left| \frac{u^h - u}{h} \right|^2 |\nabla\zeta|^2.$$

In the first integral on the right-hand side, the function $(u^h - u)/h$ converges almost everywhere to $\partial_i u$. Since the function u belongs to $W^{1,p}$, the continuity of the translation τ_h in L^p and the convergence of $(u^h - u)/h$ to $\partial_i u$ also give the convergence of the second integral on the right-hand side, to

$$C \int_{\mathbb{R}^N} |\nabla u|^{p-2} |\partial_i u|^2 |\nabla\zeta|^2.$$

It follows that when $he_i \to 0$, the right-hand side of $(*)$ converges to

$$2C \int_{\mathbb{R}^N} |\nabla u|^{p-2} |\partial_i u|^2 |\nabla\zeta|^2 dx.$$

The first integral in $(*)$ is therefore bounded. We also note that, up to a factor ζ^2, its integrand can be written as the quotient

$$\frac{1}{|h|} \left| |\nabla u|^{(p-2)/2}\nabla u - |\nabla u^h|^{(p-2)/2}\nabla u^h \right|,$$

which converges, almost everywhere, to the absolute value of the partial derivative

$$\frac{2}{p} \partial_i \left(|\nabla u|^{(p-2)/2}\nabla u \right).$$

From this result, the limits we found earlier, Fatou's lemma, and inequality $(*)$, we deduce

$$(A.37) \quad \int_{\mathbb{R}^N} \left| \partial_i(|\nabla u|^{(p-2)/2}\nabla u)\zeta \right|^2 dx \leqslant C \int_{\mathbb{R}^N} |\nabla u|^{p-2} |\partial_i u|^2 |\nabla\zeta|^2 dx.$$

Taking the sum of these inequalities from $i = 1$ to $i = N$, we obtain

$$(A.38) \quad \int_{\mathbb{R}^N} \left| \nabla(|\nabla u|^{(p-2)/2}\nabla u)\zeta \right|^2 dx \leqslant C \int_{\mathbb{R}^N} |\nabla u|^{p-2} |\nabla u|^2 |\nabla\zeta|^2 dx.$$

In the integral on the left-hand side of (A.38), we write

$$\nabla\big(|\nabla u|^{(p-2)/2}\nabla u\big)\zeta = \nabla\big(|\nabla u|^{(p-2)/2}\nabla u\,\zeta\big) - |\nabla u|^{(p-2)/2}\nabla u\,\nabla\zeta.$$

Taking the square of the absolute value and applying an inequality of the type $ab \leqslant \varepsilon a^2 + b^2/\varepsilon$, as we have done before, we deduce that

$$(A.39) \qquad \int_{\mathbb{R}^N} \big|\nabla(\zeta\,|\nabla u|^{(p-2)/2}\nabla u)\big|^2 dx \leqslant C \int_{\mathbb{R}^N} |\nabla u|^p |\nabla\zeta|^2 dx.$$

The absolute value of the part between parentheses on the left, whose gradient we take, is the pth power of $|\nabla u|\zeta^{2/p}$. Hence, since $|\nabla u|^{p/2}\zeta$ is an element of L^2 and the gradient of this function also belongs to L^2 by (A.39), we find that

$$\zeta\,|\nabla u|^{p/2} \in H^1(\mathbb{R}^N).$$

Let us apply a reasoning we have used before. First, by Sobolev's embedding theorem, we have

$$\zeta\,|\nabla u|^{(p-2)/2}\nabla u \in L^{2N/(N-2)}$$

and $\qquad \big\|\zeta\,|\nabla u|^{(p-2)/2}\nabla u\big\|_{2N/(N-2)} \leqslant \big\|\zeta\,|\nabla u|^{(p-2)/2}\nabla u\big\|_{H^1}.$

By the Poincaré inequality, which allows us to bound the H^1 norm from above by the norm of the gradient in L^2, we finally obtain the inequality

$$(A.40) \qquad \left(\int_{\mathbb{R}^N} |\nabla u|^{pN/(N-2)}\zeta^{2N/(N-2)} dx\right)^{(N-2)/N} \leqslant C \int_{\mathbb{R}^N} |\nabla u|^p |\nabla\zeta|^2 dx,$$

which is the bound (A.28). This completes the first step of our proof.

Second Step. Using a process similar to the previous one, we will now deduce from the upper bound (A.40) that, step by step, we can obtain estimates for the gradient in the spaces L_{loc}^k for arbitrary k.

We replace the assumption of the first step, namely $\nabla u \in L_{\text{loc}}^p$, by $\nabla u \in L_{\text{loc}}^{p+2l}$. Let us multiply the difference $\Delta_p u^h - \Delta_p u$ by

$$\left|\frac{(u^h - u)}{h}\right|^{2l}\left(\frac{u^h - u}{h}\right)\zeta^2,$$

where ζ is a regular function with values between 0 and 1. Using Green's formula, we have seen that we obtain inequality (A.29):

$$A_{h,l}(u) \leqslant 2A'_{h,l}(u),$$

where

$$A_{h,l}(u) = (2l + 1) \int_\Omega \left|\frac{u^h - u}{h}\right|^{2l} \frac{D_h(u)}{h} \cdot \frac{(\nabla u_h - \nabla u)}{h}\zeta^2 dx$$

$$A'_{h,l}(u) = \int_\Omega \left|\frac{D_h(u)}{h}\right| \left|\frac{u^h - u}{h}\right|^{2l+1} \zeta|\nabla\zeta| dx.$$

We first consider the right-hand side, using inequality (A.30):

$$
A'_{h,l}(u) \leqslant (2 - 2/p)\left[\int_{\mathbb{R}^N} \left|\frac{u^h - u}{h}\right|^l \left|\frac{|\nabla u^h|^{(p-2)/2}\nabla u^h - |\nabla u|^{(p-2)/2}\nabla u}{h}\right| \zeta |\nabla \zeta| \right.
$$
$$
\left. \left|\frac{u^h - u}{h}\right|^{l+1}\left(|\nabla u^h|^{p/2} + |\nabla u|^{p/2}\right)^{(p-2)/2} dx\right].
$$

By a classical inequality, this becomes

$$
A'_{h,l}(u)
$$
$$
\leqslant \varepsilon \int_{\mathbb{R}^N} \left|\frac{u^h - u}{h}\right|^{2l} \left|\frac{|\nabla u^h|^{(p-2)/2}\nabla u^h - |\nabla u|^{(p-2)/2}\nabla u}{h}\right|^2 \zeta^2 dx
$$
$$
+ C_\varepsilon \int_{\mathbb{R}^N} |\nabla \zeta|^2 \left|\frac{u^h - u}{h}\right|^{2(l+1)} \left(|\nabla u^h|^{p/2} + |\nabla u|^{p/2}\right)^{2(p-2)/2}
$$

for an ε that we will choose further on. We then use the lower bound for $A_{h,l}(u)$, taking into account the definition of $D_h(u)$, and using the result (A.35) of Lemma A.34:

$$
A_{h,l}(u) \geqslant (2l + 1)c_p \int_{\mathbb{R}^N} \left|\frac{u^h - u}{h}\right|^{2l} \zeta^2 \left|\frac{|\nabla u^h|^{(p-2)/2}\nabla u^h - |\nabla u|^{(p-2)/2}\nabla u}{h}\right|^2.
$$

Without going into the details of the computations, which are analogous to those that lead from (A.31) to (A.37), in particular concerning the choice of a suitable ε and the application of (A.32), we obtain

$$
\text{(A.41)} \quad \int_{\mathbb{R}^N} \left|\frac{u^h - u}{h}\right|^{2l} \zeta^2 \left|\frac{|\nabla u^h|^{(p-2)/2}\nabla u^h - |\nabla u|^{(p-2)/2}\nabla u}{h}\right|^2
$$
$$
\leqslant C \int_{\mathbb{R}^N} \left(|\nabla u^h|^{p-2} + |\nabla u|^{p-2}\right)\left|\frac{u^h - u}{h}\right|^{2l+2} |\nabla \zeta|^2 dx.
$$

Keeping in mind the assumption that $\nabla u \in L^{p+2l}_{\text{loc}}$ and using Hölder's inequality with exponents $(p+2l)/(2l+2)$ for $|(u^h - u)/h|^{2l+2}|\nabla \zeta|^{2(2l+2)/(p+2l)}$ and $(p+2l)/(p-2)$ for $(|\nabla u^h|^{p-2} + |\nabla u|^{p-2}|\nabla \zeta|^{2(p-2)/(p+2l)}$, we can repeat earlier arguments to show that the right-hand side of (A.41) is bounded from above by

$$
C\left(\int_{\mathbb{R}^N} |\nabla u^h|^{p+2l}|\nabla \zeta|^2 + \int_{\mathbb{R}^N} |\nabla u|^{p+2l}|\nabla \zeta|^2 + \int_{\mathbb{R}^N} \left|\frac{u^h - u}{h}\right|^{p+2l}|\nabla \zeta|^2\right).
$$

Consequently, by (A.41), the sequence

$$
\left\{\left|\frac{u^h - u}{h}\right|^l D_i(u)\right\}
$$

is bounded in L^2.

Since $\nabla(|\nabla u|^{p/2})\zeta$ is an element of L^2 and h is colinear with e_i, the sequence $\{D_h(u)\}$ converges strongly to $\partial_i(|\nabla u|^{(p-2)/2}\nabla u)$ in $L^2(\mathrm{supp}(\zeta))$ and there exists a subsequence that converges almost everywhere. Likewise, $|(u^h - u)/h|^l$ converges in L^2 to $|\partial_i u|^l$ and there exists a subsequence that also converges almost everywhere.

By Fatou's lemma, we therefore have

$$\int_{\mathbb{R}^N} \zeta^2 |\nabla u|^{2l} |\partial_i(|\nabla u|^{p/2})|^2 dx$$

$$\leqslant \lim \int_{\mathbb{R}^N} \zeta^2 \left|\frac{u^h - u}{h}\right|^{2l} \left|\frac{|\nabla u^h|^{(p-2)/2}\nabla u^h - |\nabla u|^{(p-2)/2}\nabla u}{h}\right|^2,$$

where the last sequence is bounded by

$$C \int |\nabla u|^{p+2l} |\nabla\zeta|^2.$$

By taking the sum of these results over the indexes i from 1 to N, we obtain

$$(A.42) \qquad \int_{\mathbb{R}^N} \zeta^2 |\nabla u|^{2l} |\nabla(|\nabla u|^{p/2})|^2 dx \leqslant C \int_{\mathbb{R}^N} |\nabla u|^{p+2l} |\nabla\zeta|^2 dx.$$

The results of Chapter 2 allow us to write

$$|\nabla u|^l |\nabla(|\nabla u|^{p/2})| = \frac{p}{(2l+p)}|\nabla(|\nabla u|^{p/2+l})|,$$

giving the inclusion of $|\nabla u|^{p/2+l}$ in L^2_{loc}.

From this, we deduce the following upper bound:

$$(A.43) \qquad \frac{(2l+1)4}{(p+2l)^2} \int_{\mathbb{R}^N} \zeta^2 |\nabla(|\nabla u|^{p+2l/2})|^2 \leqslant C \int_{\mathbb{R}^N} |\nabla u|^{p+2l} |\nabla\zeta|^2.$$

Differentiation of the product of ζ and $|\nabla u|^{(2l+p)/2}$ leads us to write the left-hand side as the integral associated with the square of

$$\nabla(|\nabla u|^{(p+2l)/2}\zeta) - |\nabla u|^{(p+2l)/2}\nabla\zeta.$$

We conclude as in the step $l = 0$, which gives us the existence of a constant C that is independent of l, such that

$$(A.44) \qquad \frac{4(2l+1)}{(p+2l)^2} \int_{\mathbb{R}^N} |\nabla(|\nabla u|^{(p+2l)/2}\zeta)|^2 dx \leqslant C \int_{\mathbb{R}^N} |\nabla u|^{p+2l} |\nabla\zeta|^2 dx.$$

By assumption, the function $|\nabla u|^{p/2+l}\zeta$ belongs to L^2_{loc}. The upper bound (A.44) proves that the gradient of this function also belongs to L^2_{loc}. It follows that $|\nabla u|^{p/2+l}\zeta \in H^1_{\mathrm{loc}}$, so that the Sobolev embedding theorem gives

$$(A.45) \qquad \||\nabla u|^{p/2+l}\zeta\|_{L^{2N/(N-2)}} \leqslant \||\nabla u|^{p/2+l}\zeta\|_{H^1}.$$

To conclude, we apply the Poincaré inequality, which gives

$$\big\| \, |\nabla u|^{p/2+l}\zeta \big\|_{L^{2N/(N-2)}} \leqslant \big\| \nabla(|\nabla u|^{(p+2l)/2}\zeta) \big\|_{L^2}.$$

Consequently, taking into account inequality (A.45), we obtain the inclusion of ∇u in $L^{(p+2l)N/(N-2)}$. Moreover, because of the upper bound (A.44), we can deduce the inequality announced in (A.30), namely

$$\frac{4(2l+1)}{(p+2l)^2}\Big(\int_{\mathbb{R}^N} |\nabla u|^{(p+2l)N/(N-2)}\zeta^{2N/(N-2)}dx\Big)^{(N-2)/N}$$
$$\leqslant C\int_{\mathbb{R}^N} |\nabla u|^{p+2l}|\nabla\zeta|^2 dx.$$

This concludes the second step.

Let us finish the proof. From this last upper bound, which allows us to pass from $\nabla u \in L^{(p+2l)/2}$ to $\nabla u \in L^{(p+2l)N/(N-2)}$, we deduce step by step that $\nabla u \in L^k$ for every k. Finally, by following the process described several times in this chapter and using once more the sequences $\{\zeta_m\}$, $\{k_m\}$, and $\{R_m\}$, we obtain, by induction, an estimate for the L^∞ norm of $|\nabla u|$. $\square$

References

1. R.A. ADAMS – *Sobolev spaces*, Pure and Applied Mathematics, vol. 65, Academic Press, New York-London, 1975.
2. C. AMROUCHE and V. GIRAULT – Decomposition of vector spaces and application to the Stokes problem in arbitrary dimension, *Czechoslovak Math. J.* **44**(119) (1994), no. 1, p. 109–140.
3. G. BARLES – *Solutions de viscosité des équations de Hamilton-Jacobi*, Mathématiques & Applications, vol. 17, Springer-Verlag, Paris, 1994.
4. H. BERESTYCKI, I. CAPUZZO-DOLCETTA and L. NIRENBERG – Variational methods for indefinite superlinear homogeneous elliptic problems, *NoDEA Nonlinear Differential Equations Appl.* **2** (1995), no. 4, p. 553–572.
5. F. BETHUEL, H. BREZIS and J.-M. CORON – Relaxed energies for harmonic maps, in *Variational methods (Paris, 1988)*, Progr. Nonlinear Differential Equations Appl., vol. 4, Birkhäuser, Boston, MA, 1990, p. 37–52.
6. F. BETHUEL – The approximation problem for Sobolev maps between two manifolds, *Acta Math.* **167** (1991), no. 3-4, p. 153–206.
7. I. BIRINDELLI and F. DEMENGEL – Comparison principle and Liouville type results for singular fully nonlinear operators, *Ann. Fac. Sci. Toulouse Math. (6)* **13** (2004), no. 2, p. 261–287.
8. N. BOURBAKI – *Éléments de mathématique. Fasc. XXI. Livre VI: Intégration. Chapitre V: Intégration des mesures*, 2nd ed., Actualités Scientifiques et Industrielles, vol. 1244, Hermann, Paris, 1967.
9. N. BOURBAKI – *Espaces vectoriels topologiques. Chapitres 1 à 5*, Éléments de mathématique, Masson, Paris, 1981.
10. H. BREZIS – *Analyse fonctionnelle*, Collection Mathématiques Appliquées pour la Maîtrise, Masson, Paris, 1983.
11. J. BUSCA, M.J. ESTEBAN and A. QUAAS – Nonlinear eigenvalues and bifurcation problems for Pucci's operators, *Ann. Inst. H. Poincaré Anal. Non Linéaire* **22** (2005), no. 2, p. 187–206.
12. L.A. CAFFARELLI and X. CABRÉ – *Fully nonlinear elliptic equations*, American Mathematical Society Colloquium Publications, vol. 43, American Mathematical Society, Providence, RI, 1995.
13. C. CARATHÉODORY – *Calculus of variations and partial differential equations of the first order. Part I: Partial differential equations of the first order*, Holden-Day Inc., San Francisco, Ca., 1965.

F. Demengel, G. Demengel, *Functional Spaces for the Theory of Elliptic Partial Differential Equations*, Universitext, DOI 10.1007/978-1-4471-2807-6,
© Springer-Verlag London Limited 2012

14. J. CASADO-DÍAZ, F. MURAT and A. PORRETTA – Uniqueness results for pseu-domonotone problems with $p > 2$, *C. R. Math. Acad. Sci. Paris* **344** (2007), no. 8, p. 487–492.

15. P.G. CIARLET – *Élasticité tridimensionnelle*, Recherches en Mathématiques Appliquées, vol. 1, 2, 3, Masson, Paris, 1986.

16. J.A. CLARKSON – Uniformly convex spaces, *Trans. Amer. Math. Soc.* **40** (1936), p. 396–414.

17. M. CUESTA and P. TAKÁČ – A strong comparison principle for positive solutions of degenerate elliptic equations, *Differential Integral Equations* **13** (2000), no. 4-6, p. 721–746.

18. F. DEMENGEL – Problèmes variationnels en plasticité parfaite des plaques, *Numer. Funct. Anal. Optim.* **6** (1983), no. 1, p. 73–119.

19. _____, Fonctions à hessien borné, *Ann. Inst. Fourier (Grenoble)* **34** (1984), no. 2, p. 155–190.

20. _____, Espaces de fonctions à dérivées mesure et applications à l'analyse limite en plasticité, *C. R. Acad. Sci. Paris Sér. I Math.* **302** (1986), no. 5, p. 179–182.

21. _____, Espaces de fonctions à dérivées mesure et théorème de compacité, *C. R. Acad. Sci. Paris Sér. I Math.* **302** (1986), no. 4, p. 143–145.

22. F. DEMENGEL and G. DEMENGEL – *Mesures et distributions. Théorie et illustration par les exemples*, collection Universités, Ellipses, Paris, 2000.

23. _____, *Convexité sur des espaces fonctionnels*, collection Universités, Ellipses, Paris, 2004.

24. F. DEMENGEL and E. HEBEY – On some nonlinear equations involving the p-Laplacian with critical Sobolev growth, *Adv. Differential Equations* **3** (1998), no. 4, p. 533–574.

25. F. DEMENGEL and R. TEMAM – Convex functions of a measure and applications, *Indiana Univ. Math. J.* **33** (1984), no. 5, p. 673–709.

26. _____, Convex function of a measure: the unbounded case, in *FERMAT days 85: mathematics for optimization (Toulouse, 1985)*, North-Holland Math. Stud., vol. 129, North-Holland, Amsterdam, 1986, p. 103–134.

27. E. DIBENEDETTO – $C^{1+\alpha}$ local regularity of weak solutions of degenerate elliptic equations, *Nonlinear Anal.* **7** (1983), no. 8, p. 827–850.

28. J. DIEUDONNÉ – *Éléments d'analyse. Tome I*, 3rd ed., Cahiers Scientifiques, vol. XXVIII, Gauthier-Villars, Paris, 1981.

29. _____, *Éléments d'analyse. Tome II*, Cahiers Scientifiques, vol. XXXI, Gauthier-Villars, Paris, 1968.

30. G. DUVAUT and J.-L. LIONS – *Les inéquations en mécanique et en physique*, Travaux et Recherches Mathématiques, vol. 21, Dunod, Paris, 1972.

31. L.C. EVANS – A new proof of local $C^{1,\alpha}$ regularity for solutions of certain degenerate elliptic p.d.e., *J. Differential Equations* **45** (1982), no. 3, p. 356–373.

32. K.O. FRIEDRICHS – On the boundary-value problems of the theory of elasticity and Korn's inequality, *Ann. of Math. (2)* **48** (1947), p. 441–471.

33. M. GIAQUINTA, G. MODICA and J. SOUČEK – Variational problems for maps of bounded variation with values in S^1, *Calc. Var. Partial Differential Equations* **1** (1993), no. 1, p. 87–121.

34. D. GILBARG and N.S. TRUDINGER – *Elliptic partial differential equations of second order*, Classics in Mathematics, Springer-Verlag, Berlin, 2001, Reprint of the 1998 edition.

35. E. GIUSTI – *Minimal surfaces and functions of bounded variation*, Monographs in Mathematics, vol. 80, Birkhäuser Verlag, Basel, 1984.

36. N. Grenon, F. Murat and A. Porretta – Existence and a priori estimate for elliptic problems with subquadratic gradient dependent terms, *C. R. Math. Acad. Sci. Paris* **342** (2006), no. 1, p. 23–28.

37. E. Hebey – *Nonlinear analysis on manifolds: Sobolev spaces and inequalities*, Courant Lecture Notes in Mathematics, vol. 5, New York University Courant Institute of Mathematical Sciences, New York, 1999.

38. F. Hélein – *Harmonic maps, conservation laws and moving frames*, second ed., Cambridge Tracts in Mathematics, vol. 150, Cambridge University Press, Cambridge, 2002, Translated from the 1996 French original.

39. H. Ishii – Viscosity solutions of nonlinear partial differential equations, *Sugaku Expositions* **9** (1996), no. 2, p. 135–152.

40. H. Ishii and P.-L. Lions – Viscosity solutions of fully nonlinear second-order elliptic partial differential equations, *J. Differential Equations* **83** (1990), no. 1, p. 26–78.

41. O. Kavian – *Introduction à la théorie des points critiques et applications aux problèmes elliptiques*, Mathématiques & Applications, vol. 13, Springer-Verlag, Paris, 1993.

42. R. Kohn and R. Temam – Dual spaces of stresses and strains, with applications to Hencky plasticity, *Appl. Math. Optim.* **10** (1983), no. 1, p. 1–35.

43. V.A. Kondratiev and O.A. Oleĭnik – On Korn's inequalities, *C. R. Acad. Sci. Paris Sér. I Math.* **308** (1980), p. 483–487.

44. _____, Hardy's and Korn's type inequalities and their applications, *Rend. Mat. Appl. (7)* **10** (1990), no. 3, p. 641–666.

45. _____, Korn's type inequalities for a class of unbounded domains and applications to boundary-value problems in elasticity, in *Elasticity. Mathematical methods and applications, The Ian N. Sneddon 70th Birthday Vol.* (G. Eason and R. Ogden, eds.), Ellis Horword Limited, West Sussex, England, 1990.

46. J.L. Lewis – Regularity of the derivatives of solutions to certain degenerate elliptic equations, *Indiana Univ. Math. J.* **32** (1983), no. 6, p. 849–858.

47. J.-L. Lions – *Problèmes aux limites dans les équations aux dérivées partielles*, Séminaire de Mathématiques Supérieures, vol. 1962, Les Presses de l'Université de Montréal, Montreal, Que., 1965.

48. _____, *Lectures on elliptic partial differential equations*, T.I.F.R. Lectures on Mathematics, vol. 10, Tata Institute of Fundamental Research, Bombay, 1967.

49. J.-L. Lions and J. Peetre – Sur une classe d'espaces d'interpolation, *Publ. Math. Inst. Hautes Études Sci.* (1964), no. 19, p. 5–68.

50. P.-L. Lions – The concentration-compactness principle in the calculus of variations. The locally compact case. I, *Ann. Inst. H. Poincaré Anal. Non Linéaire* **1** (1984), no. 2, p. 109–145.

51. _____, The concentration-compactness principle in the calculus of variations. The limit case. II, *Rev. Mat. Iberoamericana* **1** (1985), no. 2, p. 45–121.

52. J. Moser – A new proof of De Giorgi's theorem concerning the regularity problem for elliptic differential equations, *Comm. Pure Appl. Math.* **13** (1960), p. 457–468.

53. S.M. Nikol'skij and S.L. Sobolev – Imbedding theorems, in *Sixteen papers on Differential and Difference Equations, Functional Analysis, Games and Control*, Amer. Math. Soc. Transl. Ser. 2, vol. 87, American Mathematical Society, 1970, p. 147–173; Russian original: 1961.

54. J.A. Nitsche – On Korn's second inequality, *RAIRO Anal. Numér.* **15** (1981), no. 3, p. 237–248.

55. D. ORNSTEIN – A non-equality for differential operators in the L^1 norm, *Arch. Rational Mech. Anal.* **11** (1962), p. 40–49.

56. J. PEETRE – Espaces d'interpolation et théorème de Soboleff, *Ann. Inst. Fourier (Grenoble)* **16** (1966), no. fasc. 1, p. 279–317.

57. M.H. PROTTER and H.F. WEINBERGER – *Maximum principles in differential equations*, Prentice-Hall Inc., Englewood Cliffs, N.J., 1967.

58. W. RUDIN – *Functional analysis*, Series in Higher Mathematics, McGraw-Hill, New York, 1973.

59. L. SCHWARTZ – *Théorie des distributions*, Publications de l'Institut de Mathématique de l'Université de Strasbourg, No. IX & X, Hermann, Paris, 1966.

60. ———, *Analyse. Deuxième partie: Topologie générale et analyse fonctionnelle*, Collection Enseignement des Sciences, vol. 11, Hermann, Paris, 1970.

61. L. SIMON – Boundary regularity for solutions of the non-parametric least area problem, *Ann. of Math. (2)* **103** (1976), no. 3, p. 429–455.

62. S.L. SOBOLEV – On a theorem of functional analysis, *Mat. Sb., N. Ser.* **4 46** (1938), p. 471–497, English transl.: in *Ten papers in topology*, Amer. Math. Soc. Transl. Ser. 2, vol. 34, 1963, p. 39–68.

63. E.M. STEIN – *Singular integrals and differentiability properties of functions*, Princeton Mathematical Series, No. 30, Princeton University Press, Princeton, N.J., 1970.

64. E.M. STEIN and G. WEISS – *Introduction to Fourier analysis on Euclidean spaces*, Princeton Mathematical Series, vol. 32, Princeton University Press, Princeton, N.J., 1971.

65. E.M. STEIN and N.J. WEISS – On the convergence of Poisson integrals, *Trans. Amer. Math. Soc.* **140** (1969), p. 35–54.

66. M. STRUWE – *Variational methods*, fourth ed., Ergebnisse der Mathematik und ihrer Grenzgebiete, vol. 34, Springer-Verlag, Berlin, 2008, Applications to nonlinear partial differential equations and Hamiltonian systems.

67. P.-M. SUQUET – Sur les équations de la plasticité: existence et régularité des solutions, *J. Mécanique* **20** (1981), no. 1, p. 3–39.

68. L. TARTAR – Imbedding theorems of Sobolev spaces into Lorentz spaces, *Boll. Unione Mat. Ital. Sez. B Artic. Ric. Mat. (8)* **1** (1998), no. 3, p. 479–500.

69. M.E. TAYLOR – *Partial differential equations. Basic theory*, Texts in Applied Mathematics, vol. 23, Springer-Verlag, New York, 1996.

70. R. TEMAM – *Problèmes mathématiques en plasticité*, Méthodes Mathématiques de l'Informatique, vol. 12, Gauthier-Villars, Paris, 1983.

71. R. TEMAM and G. STRANG – Duality and relaxation in the variational problems of plasticity, *J. Mécanique* **19** (1980), no. 3, p. 493–527.

72. P. TOLKSDORF – Regularity for a more general class of quasilinear elliptic equations, *J. Differential Equations* **51** (1984), no. 1, p. 126–150.

73. S.V. USPENSKIĬ – An imbedding theorem for S.L. Sobolev's classes of fractional order W_{p^r}, *Soviet Math. Dokl.* **1** (1960), p. 132–133.

74. J.L. VÁZQUEZ – A strong maximum principle for some quasilinear elliptic equations, *Appl. Math. Optim.* **12** (1984), no. 3, p. 191–202.

75. VO-KHAC KHOAN – *Distributions. Analyse de Fourier*, Vuibert, Paris, 1972.

76. K. YOSIDA – *Functional analysis*, Classics in Mathematics, Springer-Verlag, Berlin, 1995, Reprint of the sixth (1980) edition.

77. A. ZYGMUND – On a theorem of Marcinkiewicz concerning interpolation of operations, *J. Math. Pures Appl. (9)* **35** (1956), p. 223–248.

Notation

Spaces
$(\mathbb{R}^N)^+$, 85
$X_m(\Omega)$, 325
$Y_p(\Omega)$, 326

Distribution spaces
$\mathcal{D}'(\Omega)$, 27
$\mathcal{D}'^k(\Omega)$, 27
$\mathcal{E}'(\mathbb{R}^N)$, 181
$H^{s-1/2}(\mathbb{R}^{N-1})$, 185
$H^{-s}(\mathbb{R}^N)$, 183
$\mathcal{S}'(\mathbb{R}^N)$, 180
$W^{s,p}(\Omega)$, 219

Function spaces
$\mathcal{C}_b^{0,\lambda}(\Omega)$, 21
$\mathcal{C}^\infty(\overline{\Omega})$, 94
$\mathcal{C}^m(\Omega)$, 20
$\mathcal{C}_b^m(\Omega)$, 20
$\mathcal{C}_b^{m,\lambda}(\Omega)$, 21
$C^{m-j,\lambda}(\overline{\Omega})$, 98
$\mathcal{C}_c^+(\Omega)$, 307
$\mathcal{D}(\Omega)$, 20
$\mathcal{D}(]0,+\infty[, B)$, 190
$\mathcal{D}^k(\Omega)$, 25
$\mathcal{D}_{K_j}^k(\Omega)$, 25
$\mathcal{E}^\infty(\Omega)$, 25
$\mathcal{L}(X,Y)$, 4
$L^p(\Omega,\mathbb{C})$, 34
$L^p(]0,+\infty[, B)$, 189

$\mathcal{S}(\mathbb{R}^N)$, 179
$T(p,\nu,\Omega)$ (trace space), 190
$T(p, 1-1/p-s,\Omega)$, 197
$W^{p'}(\mathrm{div})$, 140
$W_1^{p'}(\mathrm{div})$, 140
$W_\varepsilon^{p'}(\mathrm{div})$, 140
$W_{q'}^{p'}(\mathrm{div})$, 140
$LD(\Omega)$, 328

Spaces of functions with measures as derivatives
$BD(\Omega)$, 339
$BV(\Omega)$, 281, 299, 314
$BV_0(\Omega)$, 281

Measure spaces
$M(\Omega)$, 300
$M^1(\Omega)$, 300

Sobolev spaces
$H^m(\mathbb{R}^N)$, 58, 182
$H^s(\mathbb{R}^N)$, 181
$H^{1/2}(\partial B)$, 272
$W^{1-1/p,p}(\mathbb{R}^{N-1})$, 115
$W^{k-1/p,p}(\partial\Omega)$, 150
$W^{m,p}(\Omega)$, 57, 84, 94
$W^{s,p}(\Omega)$, 189, 192
$W_0^{m,p}(\Omega)$, 68
$W_{\mathrm{loc}}^{1,p}(\Omega)$, 63

F. Demengel, G. Demengel, *Functional Spaces for the Theory
of Elliptic Partial Differential Equations*, Universitext,
DOI 10.1007/978-1-4471-2807-6,
© Springer-Verlag London Limited 2012

Index

A
absolute continuity, 57, 64
absolutely continuous, 310

B
base, filter, 2
basis
  canonical –, 405
  dual –, 8
  of open subsets for a topology, 10
  of tangent vectors, 146
  orthonormal –, 146
best constant, 296

C
coercivity, 234, 242, 281, 283
compactness, 11
comparison of solutions, 268
computation of variations, 280
conjugate exponent, 63, 140, 141
constant
  Lipschitz –, 65
  universal –, 439
convergence
  almost everywhere –, 197, 227
  dominated –, 42, 48, 264, 386
  in the sense of distributions, 366
  monotone –, 378, 439
  nontangential –, 373, 389, 391, 433
  norm –, 50
  tight –, 303, 322, 360
  uniform –, 35, 301
  vague –, 284, 303, 347, 356, 357, 360
  weak –, 10, 227
  weak sequential –, 10
  weak-$*$ –, 390
convolution, 26, 49, 82, 147, 306, 324, 389, 394, 403
cover, 11, 23, 38, 60, 61, 104, 165

D
deformation tensor, 107, 176, 259, 416
density
  of a measure, 311
  of a subspace, 38, 172, 183, 271, 281, 314, 316, 333, 339
  superficial – on $\partial\Omega$, 130, 135
derivative
  A-normal –, 250
  directional –, 232, 235
  fractional –, 113, 114, 123, 169
  in the sense of distributions, 32, 139, 156, 241
  normal –, XV, 146, 176, 250, 274, 421
  tangential –, 95, 149, 176
  with respect to a vector, 145
differentiability
  in the sense of Fréchet, 232, 237
  in the sense of Gâteaux, 232–234, 239
displacement, 259
distribution
  associated with a locally summable function, 29, 225, 401
  deformation –, 326
  Dirac –, 29, 33, 123, 137
  finite part –, 399, 400
  finite subsets –, 52
  gradient –, 361

F. Demengel, G. Demengel, *Functional Spaces for the Theory
of Elliptic Partial Differential Equations*, Universitext,
DOI 10.1007/978-1-4471-2807-6,
© Springer-Verlag London Limited 2012

461